MOMENTUM, HEAT, AND MASS TRANSFER

BUILDING THE LITERATURE OF A PROFESSION

Fifteen prominent chemical engineers first met in New York more than 30 years ago to plan a continuing literature for their rapidly growing profession. From industry came such pioneer practitioners as Leo H. Baekeland, Arthur D. Little, Charles L. Reese, John V. N. Dorr, M. C. Whitaker, and R. S. McBride. From the universities came such eminent educators as William H. Walker, Alfred H. White, D. D. Jackson, J. H. James, Warren K. Lewis, and Harry A. Curtis. H. C. Parmelee, then editor of *Chemical & Metallurgical Engineering*, served as chairman and was joined subsequently by S. D. Kirkpatrick as consulting editor.

After several meetings, this first Editorial Advisory Board submitted its report to the McGraw-Hill Book Company in September, 1925. In it were detailed specifications for a correlated series of more than a dozen texts and reference books which have since become the McGraw-Hill Series in Chemical Engineering.

Since its origin the Editorial Advisory Board has been benefited by the guidance and continuing interest of such other distinguished chemical engineers as Manson Benedict, John R. Callaham, Arthur W. Hixson, H. Fraser Johnstone, Webster N. Jones, Paul D. V. Manning, Albert E. Marshall, Charles M. A. Stine, Edward R. Weidlein, and Walter G. Whitman. No small measure of credit is due not only to the pioneering members of the original board but also to those engineering educators and industrialists who have succeeded them in the task of building a permanent literature for the chemical engineering profession.

THE SERIES

MOMENTUM, HEAT,

C. O. BENNETT, MANAGER, PROCESS RESEARCH AND
DEVELOPMENT, THE LUMMUS COMPANY

NEW YORK   SAN FRANCISCO   TORONTO   LONDON

AND MASS TRANSFER

J. E. MYERS, PROFESSOR OF CHEMICAL ENGINEERING
PURDUE UNIVERSITY

McGraw-Hill Book Company, Inc.   *1962*

PREFACE

This book is written as an undergraduate textbook for the study of momentum, heat, and mass transfer. The work is not a complete treatise, and we make no claim to cover all aspects, either theoretical or practical, of the broad subjects discussed. Instead, we have attempted to present the most important parts of the theory and applications in a manner at once rigorous and uncluttered by excessive detail.

A book covering such a wide range of subjects can serve only as an introduction. A student who wishes to learn more will go on to the specialized texts in fluid dynamics, heat transfer, mass transfer, and the unit operations. However, the engineering student is now required to study so many topics that it seems to us essential to provide a unified introduction to the transport processes which can be covered in a year's study. We have attempted to discuss most of the important parts of the transport processes and yet provide enough detail to permit the reader to use the material given for the solution of typical problems.

The chemical engineer who studies this book should obtain a much better understanding of the transport processes basic to the unit operations than his predecessor of a few years ago. Too often the fundamental concepts and laws have been slighted in the haste to teach applications. The result has frequently been that a practicing engineer or graduate student, faced with problems for which his empirical training has not prepared him, has first had to learn the fundamental principles of the transport processes before he could proceed. This shortcoming has been evident to teachers of graduate courses for many years. It is no less serious a deficiency for the engineer in industry who has not gone to graduate school.

It is our belief that this shortcoming is best overcome by a direct study by the undergraduate of the fundamentals of momentum, heat, and mass transfer which underlie unit operations and other engineering applications.

We introduce the unit operations in this book as applications of the theory and show the bases of the correlations which the engineer has used in the past in the hope that he, himself, can provide new correlations in the future as he needs them.   The book is not written for only the best students or for only the students who will go to graduate school.   It is written for all students who will ultimately do work in which there can be no substitute for a fundamental understanding of the transport processes.   In spite of the organization of the subject matter on the basis of theory, we shall expect the student using our book to be able to apply scientific principles to concrete situations, to be able to find data in a handbook, to understand engineering terminology, and to be able to obtain the numerical solution of a problem.

There are already in existence many volumes containing long descriptions and numerous pictures of filters, evaporators, and other process equipment.   Although we have used sufficient drawings and pictures to illustrate our subject matter, we refer the reader to Perry's "Chemical Engineers' Handbook" for details of equipment and empirical correlations. We have not seen fit to increase the size of this book by the inclusion of tables of pipe sizes or physical properties which are contained in this readily available handbook and in other easily accessible sources.

As the various fields of engineering become better understood, the differences between the disciplines diminish.   Although the authors' professional experience has been in chemical engineering, we hope this book will be studied in courses intended to introduce engineers in all fields to momentum, heat, and mass transfer.   The treatment of fluid dynamics and heat transfer presents the fundamental concepts and laws which all engineers should know.   The study of mass transfer has, in the past, been limited almost entirely to chemical engineers.   Recently, however, engineers in other fields have shown greatly increased interest in mass transfer. It is our opinion that these engineers will profit from a presentation which gives mass transfer equal standing with momentum and heat transfer.

It is assumed that our readers have a basic knowledge of thermodynamics, calculus, and ordinary differential equations.   We have not used vector or tensor notation in the belief that it would obscure the physical principles behind symbols which are unfamiliar to most undergraduate students.   Perhaps in another few years a proficiency in vector analysis and functions of a complex variable can be assumed, just as we now assume proficiency in ordinary differential equations.

The entire subject matter and a selection of the problems of this book can be covered in about 125 class hours, i.e., two four-semester-hour courses.   These courses can extend over the junior year if sufficient thermodynamics and physical chemistry courses are available beforehand. If the subject matter is to be covered in two three-hour courses, as has been done at Purdue University, a number of chapters can either be treated qualitatively or omitted without loss of continuity; for instance, in Part 1, on Fluid Dynamics, those chapters on the differential balances and turbulent velocity distributions. Various choices of subject matter will occur to the qualified teacher, and we do not presume to advise him at length on the topics which will be most appropriate for his students.

It is a pleasure to acknowledge the assistance of a number of persons who helped us prepare this book for publication. Valuable reviews were written by Professors Max Peters and T..J. Hanratty of the University of Illinois, R. J. Grosh of Purdue University, J. R. Ferron of the University of Delaware, D. B. Spalding of the Imperial College of Science and Technology (London), and R. S. Brodkey of Ohio State University. We received many excellent suggestions from colleagues in the School of Chemical Engineering at Purdue University, particularly Professors L. C. Case, T. C. Doody, and A. H. Emery, Jr., who used the manuscript in their undergraduate classes. Much valuable help was received from graduate and undergraduate students at Purdue, especially from O. T. Hanna, D. W. Savage, and T. R. Slack. We also acknowledge the assistance of colleagues whose problems we may have used. Although we believe most of the problems to be original, some have been in our files so long that the authors can no longer be specified. Finally, we wish to acknowledge the very substantial assistance provided by the School of Chemical Engineering of Purdue University and by the Purdue Research Foundation, which provided a grant to one of the authors to assist him while writing part of the book; the cooperation of the Lummus Company is also gratefully acknowledged.

C. O. Bennett
J. E. Myers

CONTENTS

MOMENTUM, HEAT, AND MASS TRANSFER

INTRODUCTION
1

Engineers are employed in many industries in which raw materials are converted to products by chemical reactions and physical changes. Some industries depending upon chemical changes are the manufacture of sulfuric acid from sulfide ores, the production of ammonia, and the conversion of petroleum into a variety of petrochemicals. In other industries, such as the production of sugar from sugar beets or the extraction of oil from corn, physical changes predominate. Most industrial operations consist of a sequence of physical and chemical transformations, and this sequence is called a process.

The work of many engineers in industry involves the development of processes and the design and operation of plants. Process development is a term used by engineers to describe the search for optimum equipment and conditions for the process. The steps constituting the process are usually known; combining these steps so that the process is profitable when carried out in large-scale equipment is called "developing" a process. The job of the chemical engineer in design is usually to determine certain general characteristics and dimensions of the equipment. For example, he might specify the height, diameter, number of plates, and method of control of a distillation column. The thickness of the column walls and the dimensions of the foundation are likely to be specified by mechanical engineers, and the details of the control systems are normally in the hands of electrical engineers. The function of the engineer in plant operation is not only to supervise routine production, but to improve plant efficiency by changes within the existing process. Each engineer can perform his function best if he understands the principles behind the chemical and physical changes of the process.

Chemical industries operated long before the profession of chemical engineering was recognized. The technology of each industry was regarded as a special branch of knowledge, and the people who did the jobs now done by chemical engineers were trained as chemists, mechanical engineers,

1

and technologists.   Early courses in chemical engineering were based on the study of industrial technology.   These courses were greatly changed by the introduction of the concept of the unit operations.   The similarity of the physical changes occurring in widely differing industries led to the study of the many steps common to the industries; these became known as the unit operations.   For example, it was recognized that the evaporation of a liquid from a solution followed the same principles whether it occurred in a process for manufacturing sugar or fertilizer.   Thus evaporation became one of the earliest recognized unit operations.   Many other steps achieved the status of unit operations, including fluid flow, heat transfer, humidification, drying, distillation, gas absorption, extraction, crushing and grinding, crystallization, filtration, and mixing.

As the unit operations became better understood, it was apparent that they were not distinct entities.   Filtration was obviously a special case of fluid flow; evaporation was a form of heat transfer; extraction and gas absorption involved mass transfer.   Drying and distillation were recognized as operations in which both heat and mass transfer were important. The unit operations came to be regarded, therefore, as special cases or combinations of heat transfer, mass transfer, and fluid flow.   The latter are referred to by engineers as the transport processes and are the basis of the unit operations.   Any fundamental study of unit operations becomes ultimately a study of these transport processes.

Most of the important unit operations are concerned with the behavior of fluids in process equipment.   The chemical reactor is usually at the heart of the process, and here the engineer may utilize simultaneously the principles of fluid mechanics, heat transfer, and mass transfer, as well as chemical kinetics and thermodynamics.   In the preparation of reactants and in the separation of products, the unit operations of filtration, leaching, absorption, extraction, and distillation are important.   Underlying every step of the process are the principles of fluid flow and heat transfer; the fluid must be transported, and its temperature must be controlled.   In a chemical process, where composition is a variable, the principles of mass transfer are essential for the design of separation or reaction equipment.

The transport processes, which are basic in the study of the unit operations, also underlie the problems in fluid flow and heat transfer which are solved by mechanical and aeronautical engineers.   These problems traditionally have not been complicated by chemical reactions and have involved relatively simple geometry, such as flow in a pipe or around a body of revolution.   Because of the complications which arise from simultaneous heat and mass transfer in a chemically reacting system and from the complicated geometry of interphase contacting devices, the empirical approach has been fruitful for chemical engineers.   Until recently the basic theory of fluid dynamics and heat transfer has been studied mostly by physicists and mechanical and aeronautical engineers.   On the other hand, chemical engineers have made significant contributions in mass transfer.   However, in recent years other engineers have become more interested in mass transfer, and chemical engineers have found many applications of the theory of fluid dynamics and heat transfer.   The practical importance of theory has been greatly enhanced by high-speed electronic computers.   These devices have made possible the application of theory to complicated situations for which it was formerly necessary to be satisfied with empirical methods.

From the above discussion it is clear that as various types of engineers advance in the study of their fields, the differences which have caused the traditional specialization diminish.   The study of the principles of the transport processes becomes a central topic for every engineer, no matter what his field of specialization.   Although many of the examples which illustrate the principles presented in this book are taken from applications in chemical engineering, only Chap. 16, Filtration and Fluidization, and Chap. 41, Distillation of Binary Mixtures, concern topics which may be considered special to the chemical engineer.

The more fundamental approach to problems in the transport processes and unit operations means that the mathematical analysis of these problems has recently taken on added importance.   In addition to its use in design calculations, the computer is now being used to control the operating variables in a plant.   In order to put the computer into this application and to give it instructions to run the process so that it operates at an economic optimum, a mathematical model of the process is usually necessary.   This model depends on a more detailed understanding and on a more mathematical analysis of the process than was formerly necessary.

In a computer-controlled plant the operating conditions may be changed rather frequently in response to changes in raw materials, catalyst activity, equipment scaling, weather conditions, or market demand.   It is therefore necessary for the engineer to understand the unsteady-state behavior of a process, and the mathematics is made even more difficult.   This subject is usually called process dynamics.

For the reasons given above, the reader will find that the analytical, mathematical approach is stressed in this book in the hope of furnishing a firm foundation for subsequent work in more advanced engineering problems.

Notation and Units

The following table gives an explanation of most of the symbols in this book. Certain symbols may be explained more fully in the text, and some symbols used only a few times are omitted from the table.

The units given are consistent with American custom, using as basic units the pound mass (lb), the pound force (lb force), the foot (ft), the second or hour (sec or hr), and the degree Fahrenheit (°F). In this system the pound force is defined as an invariant quantity equal to the force necessary to give to one pound mass an acceleration of 32.17 ft/sec². This statement is in contrast to the definition used in some countries for the kilogram force: the force exerted by a mass of one kilogram at rest in the earth's gravitational field at the point. A pound weight can be defined in an analogous manner.

The symbols V, H, etc., refer to intensive properties, i.e., cu ft/lb or Btu/lb. The extensive properties are designated by a superscript, $\check{V} = MV$, $\check{H} = MH$, total volume or total enthalpy. We also use a superscript to denote molal quantities: $\tilde{V}$ or $\tilde{H}$, molal volume, in cu ft/lb mole, or molal enthalpy, in Btu/lb mole. The superscript is also used to distinguish between G, mass flux, in lb/(hr)(sq ft), and $\tilde{G}$, molal flux, in lb moles/(hr)(sq ft); x_A, mass fraction, and $\tilde{x}_A$, mole fraction; and a number of similar symbols.

Although English units are used in the examples of this book, unless otherwise noted all equations given can be used in another system of units. We have no desire to force our readers to use the English system, and we give quantities in these units only by way of illustration. Also, the time unit may be changed in various applications from sec to hr or min. Since the mechanical equivalent of heat is not included explicitly in the equations of this book, a number of symbols, such as H and other thermodynamic properties, can be expressed as Btu/lb or as (ft)(lb force)/lb.

Table of Notation

Symbol	Explanation	Typical units
A	Area; cross-sectional area	sq ft
α	Absorption factor, $\tilde{L}/m\tilde{G}$	dimensionless
A_i	Interfacial area	sq ft
B	Bottom product or raffinate flow rate	lb/hr
C	Sonic velocity	ft/sec
C_c	Contraction coefficient defined by Eq. (6-16)	dimensionless
C_D	Drag coefficient	dimensionless
C_D^o	Value of C_D in absence of bulk flow	dimensionless
C_o	Orifice coefficient defined by Eq. (6-15)	dimensionless
	Sonic velocity at upstream conditions	ft/sec
C_p	Specific heat at constant pressure	Btu/(lb)(°F)
C_{pH}	Humid heat defined by Eq. (38-46)	Btu/(lb)(°F)
C_r	Rotameter coefficient defined by Eq. (6-27)	dimensionless
C_t	Sonic velocity at throat conditions	ft/sec
C_v	Specific heat at constant volume	Btu/(lb)(°F)
	Venturi coefficient defined by Eq. (6-11)	dimensionless
D	Diameter	ft
	Distillate or extract flow rate	lb/hr
D_{AB}	Diffusivity of A through B	sq ft/hr
D_{ABe}	Eddy diffusivity	sq ft/hr
D_{ABT}	Thermal diffusivity	lb/(hr)(ft)
D'_{AB}	Diffusivity defined by Eq. (31-2)	sq ft/hr
$D/D\theta$	Substantial derivative operator	sec^{-1}
E	Total energy defined by Eq. (4-2)	(ft)(lb force)/lb
E_G	Murphree V-phase stage efficiency	dimensionless
E_{GP}	Murphree V-phase point efficiency	dimensionless
E_o	Over-all efficiency	dimensionless
Eu	Euler number, $g_c p/u^2\rho$	dimensionless
F	Feed rate	lb/hr
	Force	lb force
F_d	Drag force	lb force
F_g	Force of gravity	lb force
F_{xd}	Force in x direction due to drag at control surface	lb force
F_{xp}	Force in x direction due to pressure difference	lb force
F_x, F_y, F_z	Components of force vector	lb force
$F_{12}, \overline{F}_{12}, \mathfrak{F}_{12}$	View factors for radiant-heat transfer	dimensionless
Fr	Froude number, u^2/gL	dimensionless
G	Mass velocity of V phase	lb/(hr)(sq ft)
G_B	Mass velocity of component B	lb/(hr)(sq ft)
Gr	Grashof number, $gL^3\beta\,\Delta t/\nu^2$	dimensionless
H	Enthalpy	Btu/lb
H_A, H_x, H_y	Enthalpy of component A, L phase, or V phase	Btu/lb
H_G, H_L	Height of individual transfer unit	ft

Table of Notation (*Continued*)

Symbol	Explanation	Typical units
H_{OG}, H_{OL}	Height of over-all transfer unit	ft
H_{tx}, H_{ty}	Height of transfer unit for heat transfer	ft
I	Intensity of turbulence	dimensionless
	Intensity of radiant energy	Btu/(hr)(sq ft)
$\tilde{I}_A$	Flux of A with respect to $\tilde{u}$	lb moles/(hr)(sq ft)
J	Mechanical equivalent of heat, 778	(ft)(lb force)/Btu
J_A	Flux of A with respect to u	lb/(hr)(sq ft)
K	Consistency index	$[(\text{lb})(\text{ft})/\text{sec}^2]\,\text{sec}^n$
	Constant in Eq. (13-40)	dimensionless
K_A	Equilibrium vaporization ratio, $\tilde{y}_A/\tilde{x}_A$	dimensionless
K_{ABT}	Thermal-diffusion ratio	dimensionless
K_ρ, K_x, K_y, $K_{\tilde{x}}$, $K_{\tilde{y}}$	Over-all mass-transfer coefficients	
L	Mass velocity of L phase	lb/(hr)(sq ft)
	Length; thickness; scale of turbulence	ft
L_C	Mass velocity of C	lb/(hr)(sq ft)
L_e	Entrance length	ft
L_f	Cake thickness	ft
Le	Lewis number, $\mathbf{Sc}/\mathbf{Pr} = k/\rho D_{AB} C_p$	dimensionless
M	Mass	lb
M_c	Mass of filter cake	lb
M_A, M_B, M_m	Molecular weight	lb/lb mole
Ma	Mach number, u/C	dimensionless
N	Number of stages; number of tubes	dimensionless
	Flux with respect to fixed axes	lb/(hr)(sq ft)
N_A	Flux of A with respect to fixed axes	lb/(hr)(sq ft)
N_p	Number of particles	dimensionless
N_1	Number of tube rows	dimensionless
Nu	Nusselt number, hL/k	dimensionless
Nu$_a$	Nusselt number, $h_a L/k$	dimensionless
Nu$_m$	Mean Nusselt number $h_m L/k$	dimensionless
Nu$_x$	Local Nusselt number $h_x x/k$	dimensionless
O	Flow rate of L phase	lb/hr
O_C	Flow rate of component C	lb/hr
P	Upstream pressure	lb force/sq ft
	Power	(ft)(lb force)/sec
P_x, P_y, P_z	Components of momentum vector	(lb)(ft)/sec
Pe	Peclet number, $\mathbf{Re}\,\mathbf{Pr} = C_p \rho u L/k$	dimensionless
Pr	Prandtl number, $C_p \mu/k$	dimensionless
Q	Heat absorbed per unit mass	Btu/lb
R	Drying rate	lb/(hr)(sq ft)
	Heat-transfer resistance	(°F)(hr)/Btu
	Fractional recovery of pressure loss	dimensionless
R_i	Rate of generation of i	lb/hr
R_m	Resistance to flow of filter medium	ft^{-1}
R_x, R_y, R_z	Components of resultant force vector	lb force
$R(y)$	Correlation coefficient	dimensionless
Re	Reynolds number, $D u_b \rho/\mu$	dimensionless
Re$_L$	Reynolds number, $L u_o \rho/\mu$	dimensionless

Table of Notation (*Continued*)

Symbol	Explanation	Typical units
$\mathbf{Re}_p$	Reynolds number, $Du_{bs}\rho/\mu(1-\epsilon)$	dimensionless
$\mathbf{Re}_x$	Reynolds number, $xu_o\rho/\mu$	dimensionless
S	Entropy	Btu/(lb)(°R)
$\mathcal{S}$	Stripping factor, $m\tilde{G}/\tilde{L}$	dimensionless
S_p	Surface area of a particle	sq ft
S_v	Specific surface, S_p/v_p	ft^{-1}
$\mathbf{Sc}$	Schmidt number, $\mu/\rho D_{AB}$	dimensionless
$\mathbf{Sh}$	Sherwood number, $k_p L/D_{AB}$	dimensionless
$\mathbf{St}$	Stanton number, $h/C_p u\rho$	dimensionless
T	Absolute temperature	°R
T_o	Stagnation temperature	°R
U	Internal energy	Btu/lb
	Over-all heat-transfer coefficient	Btu/(hr)(sq ft)(°F)
V	Specific volume	cu ft/lb
	Flow rate of V phase	lb/hr
V_B	Flow rate of component B	lb/hr
V_f	Filtrate volume	cu ft
$\check{V}_f$	Rotameter float volume	cu ft
W	Work done by unit mass	(ft)(lb force)/lb
	Flux of radiant energy	Btu/(hr)(sq ft)
$W_{B\lambda}$	Flux of radiant energy in interval λ to $\lambda + d\lambda$ divided by $d\lambda$	Btu/(hr)(cu ft)
W_s	Shaft work per unit mass	(ft)(lb force)/lb
$\dot{W}$	Rate of work done	(ft)(lb force)/hr
$\dot{W}_s$	Rate of shaft work	(ft)(lb force)/hr
$\mathbf{We}$	Weber number, $\rho u^2 L/\sigma$	dimensionless
X, Y, Z	Components of body force	lb force
X_A	Mass ratio of A in L phase	dimensionless
X_c	Critical moisture content	dimensionless
X_e	Equilibrium moisture content	dimensionless
Y	Correction to Δt_{lm}	dimensionless
Y_A	Mass ratio of A in V phase	dimensionless
a	Interfacial area per unit volume	sq ft/cu ft
a_A	Activity of component A	dimensionless
a_x, a_y, a_z	Components of acceleration a	ft/sec^2
e	Effective height of roughness	ft
f	Friction factor, $g_c Dlw_f/2Lu_b^2$	dimensionless
f_p	Friction factor defined by Eq. (15-21)	dimensionless
g	Acceleration of gravity	ft/sec^2
g_c	Constant, 32.17	(lb)(ft)/(lb force)(sec^2)
h	Individual heat-transfer coefficient	Btu/(hr)(sq ft)(°F)
h_a	Value of h based on arithmetic mean Δt	Btu/(hr)(sq ft)(°F)
h_d	Fouling coefficient	Btu/(hr)(sq ft)(°F)
h_{lm}	Value of h based on logarithmic mean Δt	Btu/(hr)(sq ft)(°F)
h_m	Mean value of h (constant t_s)	Btu/(hr)(sq ft)(°F)
h_r	Radiant-heat-transfer coefficient	Btu/(hr)(sq ft)(°F)
h_x	Local value of h	Btu/(hr)(sq ft)(°F)
h^o	Value of h in absence of bulk flow	Btu/(hr)(sq ft)(°F)

Table of Notation *(Continued)*

Symbol	Explanation	Typical units
$\tilde{h}_R, \tilde{h}_n$	Enthalpy	Btu/lb mole
j_H	Colburn j factor for heat transfer	dimensionless
j_M	Colburn j factor for mass transfer	dimensionless
k	Thermal conductivity	Btu/(hr)(ft)(°F)
	Ratio of specific heats, C_p/C_v	dimensionless
k_x, k_y	Individual mass-transfer coefficient based on Δx_A or Δy_A	lb/(hr)(sq ft)
$k_{\tilde{x}}, k_{\tilde{y}}$	Individual mass-transfer coefficient based on $\Delta \tilde{x}_A$ or $\Delta \tilde{y}_A$	lb moles/(hr)(sq ft)
k_ρ	Individual mass-transfer coefficient based on $\Delta \rho_A$	ft/hr
k_x^o, k_y^o	Value of k_x or k_y in absence of bulk flow	lb/(hr)(sq ft)
k_ρ^o	Value of k_ρ in absence of bulk flow	ft/hr
k_ρ'	Mass-transfer coefficient defined by Eq. (38-7)	ft/hr
k_ρ''	Mass-transfer coefficient defined by Eq. (43-5)	ft/hr
ℓ	Prandtl mixing length	ft
lw	Friction, or lost work	(ft)(lb force)/lb
lw_f	lw due to pipe friction alone	(ft)(lb force)/lb
m	Mass ratio of wet to dry filter cake; stage number; constant in equilibrium relation $\tilde{y}_A = m\tilde{x}_A$	dimensionless
n	Flow-behavior index; stage number	dimensionless
n_G, n_L, n_{OG}, n_{OL}	Number of transfer units	dimensionless
p	Total pressure	lb force/sq ft
p_A	Vapor pressure of A	lb force/sq ft
$\bar{p}_A$	Partial pressure of A	lb force/sq ft
p_i	Pressure at filter medium	lb force/sq ft
p_o	Stagnation pressure; free-stream pressure	lb force/sq ft
p_s	Mechanical stress on filter cake	lb force/sq ft
q	Rate of heat transfer	Btu/hr
	Volumetric rate of flow	cu ft/hr
	Moles of liquid produced on feed plate per mole of feed	dimensionless
r	Radius	ft
r_H	Hydraulic radius	ft
r_A, r_i	Rate of generation of A or i	lb/(hr)(cu ft)
s	Mass-fraction solid in slurry	dimensionless
	Fractional rate of surface renewal	sec^{-1}
t	Temperature	°F
t_{as}	Adiabatic saturation temperature	°F
t_b	Bulk, or mixing-cup, temperature	°F
t_m	Temperature of fluid medium	°F
t_o, t_∞	Temperature outside boundary layer	°F
t_s	Surface temperature	°F
t_{sv}	Temperature of saturated vapor	°F

Table of Notation (*Continued*)

Symbol	Explanation	Typical units
$t_{s\ell}$	Temperature of saturated liquid	°F
t_{wb}	Wet-bulb temperature	°F
u	Velocity; magnitude of velocity vector	ft/sec
u_b	Bulk velocity	ft/sec
u_{br}	Bulk velocity at rotameter annulus	ft/sec
u_{bs}	Superficial velocity	ft/sec
u_{mf}	Minimum-fluidization velocity	ft/sec
u_o	Velocity outside boundary layer	ft/sec
u_t	Terminal velocity; throat velocity	ft/sec
u_x, u_y, u_z	Components of velocity vector	ft/sec
u_{ys}	Velocity normal to surface at surface	ft/sec
u_x', u_y', u_z'	Components of fluctuating velocity	ft/sec
$\bar{u}_x, \bar{u}_y, \bar{u}_z$	Components of time mean velocity	ft/sec
u^*	Friction velocity	ft/sec
u^+	u/u^*	dimensionless
v_p	Volume of a particle	cu ft
w	Mass-flow rate	lb/hr
x, y, z	Cartesian-coordinate distances	ft
x	Distance from leading edge	ft
x_A	Mass fraction A, especially in L phase	dimensionless
x_e	Condensate film thickness	ft
y	Distance from surface	ft
y_A	Mass fraction A, especially in V phase	dimensionless
y^+	yu^*/ν	dimensionless
z	Height of tower; height of manometer fluid	ft
α	Angle between velocity vector and outward normal to control surface; Mach angle	radians
	Thermal diffusivity, $k/\rho C_p$	sq ft/hr
	Specific cake resistance	ft/lb
	Absorptivity; relative volatility	dimensionless
α_{AB}	Relative volatility of A to B	dimensionless
α_e	Eddy thermal diffusivity	sq ft/hr
β	Angle between x direction and downward-directed vertical	radians
	Ratio of diameters	dimensionless
	Coefficient of thermal expansion	(°F)$^{-1}$
Γ	Mass flow per unit of perimeter	lb/(hr)(ft)
γ	Rate of change of angle ϕ	radians/sec
γ_A	Activity coefficient of component A	dimensionless
Δ	Operator indicating final minus initial or outlet minus inlet, for example, $\Delta w = w_2 - w_1$	dimensionless
	Net flow toward end of cascade	lb/hr
δ	Boundary-layer thickness	ft
δ_c	Concentration boundary-layer thickness	ft
δ_m	Film thickness	ft

Table of Notation (*Continued*)

Symbol	Explanation	Typical units
δ_{th}	Thermal boundary-layer thickness	ft
ϵ	Void fraction; emissivity	dimensionless
η	Dimensionless distance, $y\sqrt{u_o/\nu x}$	dimensionless
η_f	Fin efficiency	dimensionless
η_p, η_t	Efficiency of pump or turbine	dimensionless
θ	Time	sec
	Angle in polar coordinates	radians
Λ	Kármán number, **Re** $\sqrt{f}$	dimensionless
λ	Latent heat	Btu/lb
	Wavelength	ft
μ	Viscosity	lb/(ft)(hr)
μ_A	Chemical potential of A	Btu/lb
ν	Kinematic viscosity	sq ft/hr
ν_e	Eddy kinematic viscosity	sq ft/hr
ρ	Density	lb/cu ft
	Reflectivity	dimensionless
ρ_A	Concentration of A	lb/cu ft
ρ_{Am}	Concentration of A in fluid medium	lb/cu ft
ρ_{Ao}	Concentration of A outside boundary layer	lb/cu ft
ρ_{As}	Concentration of A at surface	lb/cu ft
ρ_s	Density of solid	lb/cu ft
σ	Surface tension	lb force/ft
	Stefan-Boltzmann constant	Btu/(hr)(sq ft)(°R)^4
τ	Transmissivity	dimensionless
	Shear stress	lb force/sq ft
τ_s	Shear stress at surface	lb force/sq ft
$\bar{\tau}^t$	Total stress	lb force/sq ft
$\bar{\tau}^r$	Reynolds stress	lb force/sq ft
Φ	Dissipation function	Btu/cu ft
ϕ	Angle defined in Fig. 11-4; angular variable in cylindrical coordinates	radians
	Potential function	sq ft/sec
ψ	Stream function	sq ft/sec
Ω	Potential energy	(ft)(lb force)/lb
ω	Angular velocity	radians/sec

PART
1

FLUID DYNAMICS

THE OVER-ALL BALANCES;
INTRODUCTION TO FLUID BEHAVIOR

Many problems which arise in the consideration of processes can be solved by viewing the process figuratively from outside its physical enclosure. The changes within the enclosure are measured in terms of the properties of the inlet and outlet streams and the exchanges of energy, in the form of heat and work, between the enclosure and its surroundings. This approach immediately calls to mind the idea of a system in thermodynamics and the application of the first law of thermodynamics thereto. What we shall call the over-all energy balance is merely the first law of thermodynamics applied to a general situation.

The same remarks can be made about the simpler case—the over-all mass balance—and its relation to the usual ideas of a material balance encountered in the study of stoichiometry. The over-all force balance, involving fluxes of momentum rather than energy or mass, is perhaps less familiar to the student.

We use the term over-all to describe these balances because of our viewpoint outside the enclosure; the details of what happens inside do not enter into the analysis. However, in many situations we do wish to consider the details of the process occurring inside the enclosure, and to achieve this end it is useful to write similar balances for a small or differential element of volume. These differential balances may then be integrated for situations where we know some of the characteristic properties of a fluid, such as the viscosity of a newtonian liquid. By this method of analysis we obtain a detailed picture of what happens inside the process enclosure. For example, the velocity distribution may be determined by a differential analysis, whereas average inlet and outlet velocities are all that can be considered in an over-all balance.

The over-all balances can, in general, be obtained by the integration of the differential balances; conversely, the latter can be obtained by the re-

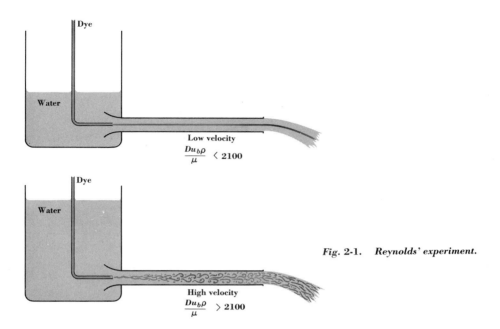

Fig. 2-1.   Reynolds' experiment.

duction of the enclosure considered to a differential volume.   For the sake of clarity, and to avoid certain mathematical complications, the two types of balance will be derived independently in this book; we shall start with the over-all balance because of its relative simplicity and its value in the solution of many important problems.

The Nature of Fluid Flow

In spite of the fact that the over-all mass, energy, and momentum balances can be derived and used without the extensive consideration of the details of fluid behavior, we shall find it useful to have a few preliminary ideas about the nature of a fluid and how it flows.

It is an empirical fact that a fluid flowing in a small tube or at low velocity does so by the mechanism of laminar flow, also called viscous, or streamline, flow.   The layers of fluid slide over each other with no macroscopic mixing, and the velocity in macroscopic steady flow is constant at any point.   At higher velocities flow becomes turbulent; there is mixing by eddy motion between the layers, and even in over-all steady flow the velocity at a point fluctuates about some mean value.   The existence of these two types of flow was demonstrated by Reynolds,[1] who performed the experiment illustrated in Fig. 2-1.

If different sizes of circular pipe and different fluids are used, it is found that laminar flow generally exists when the dimensionless ratio $Du_b\rho/\mu$ is less than 2100. This ratio, which is called the Reynolds number, is extremely useful and will often be encountered in our analyses; it will be explained further in the discussion of dimensional analysis in Chap. 14. The magnitude of the Reynolds number is independent of the system of units employed. Laminar flow can exist at Reynolds numbers above 2100 in very smooth pipes, but the flow is unstable, and small disturbances may cause a transition to turbulent flow. It will also be found useful to characterize other kinds of fluid behavior by dimensionless groups; for instance, calculations for heat transfer in fluids often involve the Prandtl number, $C_p\mu/k$, and those for mass transfer, the Schmidt number, $\mu/\rho D_{AB}$.

A remark on the structure of fluids should also be made here before writing expressions involving a differential volume of a fluid. The element really contains an assembly of individual molecules. We shall choose, however, to regard the fluid as a continuum, so that the differential volume will be treated as a homogeneous sample rather than as a collection of molecules and empty spaces between the molecules. This simplification permits us to write differential equations to characterize and analyze fluid behavior.

[1] O. Reynolds, *Trans. Roy. Soc. London,* **A174:**935 (1883).

THE 3 OVER-ALL MASS BALANCE

We shall begin the quantitative study of the over-all balances by applying the principle of conservation of mass to a hypothetical enclosure fixed in space; we call the space enclosed the control volume and its boundary the control surface. Since the rate of accumulation of mass within the volume is equal to the rate of mass flow in minus the rate of mass flow out, the equation expressing the principle can be written almost immediately. Defining α as the angle between a line normal to the surface and directed outward and a line representing the direction of the velocity at the point considered, the net outward flow across the surface becomes

$$\iint_A u\rho \cos \alpha \, dA \tag{3-1}$$

Figure 3-1 illustrates this assertion.

Where the velocity u is parallel to the surface, $\cos \alpha$ is zero; where u is directed inward, α is greater than $\pi/2$ and $\cos \alpha$ is negative. Hence it can be seen that the integration over the whole surface does indeed give the net outflow of mass. The quantity $u\rho$ has the units of lb/(hr)(sq ft) and is called a flux. It is also called the mass velocity G.

The integral (3-1), the units of which are lb/hr, must equal the negative of the rate of accumulation of mass in the control volume. This statement is true at any instant, even for the unsteady-state process. Since in gen-

Fig. 3-1. Flow through differential area on control surface.

Fig. 3-2. *Simplified control volume.*

eral the density is a function of position within the volume, we write the total accumulation rate as

$$\frac{d}{d\theta} \iiint\limits_{\check{V}} \rho \, d\check{V} = \frac{dM}{d\theta} \tag{3-2}$$

These two expressions (3-1) and (3-2) are then combined to give the over-all mass balance in general form

$$\iint\limits_{A} u\rho \cos \alpha \, dA + \frac{d}{d\theta} \iiint\limits_{\check{V}} \rho \, d\check{V} = 0 \tag{3-3}$$

The application of Eq. (3-3) is clarified if it is written for the most usual situation encountered, for which all the flow inward is normal to an area A_1 and all the flow out is normal to an area A_2, as shown in Fig. 3-2. The flow is parallel to the other parts of the control surface. For these conditions

$$u_{b2}\rho_2 A_2 - u_{b1}\rho_1 A_1 + \frac{dM}{d\theta} = 0 \tag{3-4}$$

The quantity u_b is called the bulk, or average, velocity and is defined by

$$u_b = \frac{1}{A} \iint\limits_{A} u \, dA \tag{3-5}$$

for a surface over which u is normal to A. The density is assumed constant over the area of integration. We define w, the mass rate of flow, by

$$w = u_b \rho A \tag{3-6}$$

so that

$$\Delta w + \frac{dM}{d\theta} = 0 \tag{3-7}$$

Equation (3-7) can be integrated immediately if w_1 and w_2 are given as functions of θ. Often one or more of the flow rates is constant; if both flow rates are equal and constant, the process is at steady state and we have

$$\frac{dM}{d\theta} = 0 \tag{3-8}$$

These equations are readily extended to apply to a component, i, in a multicomponent system. For the case illustrated by Fig. 3-2, we have

$$\Delta w_i - R_i + \frac{dM_i}{d\theta} = 0 \tag{3-9}$$

where R_i is the rate of generation of i by chemical reaction within the volume in pounds per hour, and there are no significant fluxes by diffusion at the inlet or outlet [diffusion terms could easily be added to Eq. (3-9)]. Equation (3-9) can be written for each constituent; the sum of these equations will give Eq. (3-7), because

$$\sum_{i=1}^{n} R_i = 0 \tag{3-10}$$

for n components in a system.

Although some of the equations which have been presented here may seem rather obvious, the method of reasoning used will be helpful in the derivations of the energy and momentum balances, where the results are not so easy to obtain.

Example 3-1

In order to show how the variation of velocity across a part of the control surface is taken into account, let us calculate the rate of flow of 98 per cent sulfuric acid at 32°F in a 2-in., schedule-40 pipe. The velocity is measured at the center of the pipe by a pitot tube and is 3.00 ft/sec. The flow is laminar, and the variation of the velocity across the pipe radius is given for laminar flow by

$$u = u_{\max} \left(1 - \frac{r^2}{r_i^2} \right) \tag{1}$$

where $u_{\max}$ = maximum velocity
r_i = inside radius of pipe

The velocity increases from zero at $r = r_i$ to its maximum value at $r = 0$. For all fluids except gases at very low pressure there is no slip between the fluid and a solid boundary. Equation (1) will be derived later by using the differential momentum balance; this is the type of result which cannot be obtained by using the over-all balances.

Since $w = u_b \rho A$, the problem is to find u_b from

$$u_b = \frac{1}{A} \iint_A u \, dA \tag{3-5}$$

In cartesian coordinates dA would be expressed by $dx \, dy$, but for flow through a circular pipe polar coordinates are more appropriate, so we use $dA = r \, dr \, d\theta$ (θ is of course the angle in polar coordinates, not the time). Equation (1) is substituted into Eq. (3-5) to get

$$u_b = \frac{u_{\max}}{\pi r_i^2} \int_0^{2\pi} \int_0^{r_i} \left(1 - \frac{r^2}{r_i^2} \right) r \, dr \, d\theta \tag{2}$$

The variable θ does not appear in Eq. (1) because there is axial symmetry. The evaluation of the integral of Eq. (2) gives the simple result

$$u_b = \frac{u_{\max}}{2} \tag{3}$$

and so we obtain

$$w = \frac{u_{\max}\rho\pi r_i^2}{2} = \frac{u_{\max}\rho\pi D^2}{8} \tag{4}$$

The inside diameter of the pipe D is found from the table in Perry's Handbook,[1] p. 415, as 2.067 in.; the density of 98 per cent sulfuric acid at 32°F is 1.8567 g/cu cm (Perry, p. 185). Therefore

$$w = \frac{(3.00)(62.3)(1.86)(3.14)(2.067)^2}{(8)(144)}$$

$$= 4.07 \text{ lb/sec (or 14,600 lb/hr)}$$

The calculation could have been shortened by reading the inside sectional area from the table in Perry as 0.0233 sq ft.

Let us also calculate the Reynolds number; the bulk velocity should be used.

$$\mathbf{Re} = \frac{Du_b\rho}{\mu} = \frac{(2.067/12)(1.50)(62.3)(1.86)}{(47.0)(6.72 \times 10^{-4})}$$

$$= 950$$

The viscosity (47.0 cp) is found in Perry, p. 373, and is multiplied by 6.72×10^{-4} to convert to the required units of lb/(ft)(sec). One should always check calculations for dimensional consistency; in the calculations being illustrated, only ft, lb, lb force, and sec should appear.

Since the Reynolds number is less than 2100, it is verified that the flow is laminar.

Example 3-2

Water is flowing into a well-stirred tank at 150 lb/hr, and salt (NaCl) is being added at 30 lb/hr. The resulting solution is leaving the tank at 120 lb/hr; because of the effective stirring, the concentration of the outlet solution is the same as that within the tank. There is 100 lb of fresh water in the tank at the start of the operation, and the rates of input and output remain constant thereafter. Calculate the outlet concentration (mass fraction salt) after 1 hr.

Equations (3-7) and (3-9) must be solved simultaneously. Consider first a balance on the salt (component A).

$$w_{A2} - w_{A1} + \frac{dM_A}{d\theta} = 0 \tag{1}$$

Let x_A represent the mass fraction salt in the solution leaving the tank. Then we have

$$w_2 x_A - w_{A1} + \frac{d(Mx_A)}{d\theta} = 0 \tag{2}$$

and

$$120x_A - 30 + M\frac{dx_A}{d\theta} + x_A\frac{dM}{d\theta} = 0 \tag{3}$$

[1] John H. Perry (ed.), "Chemical Engineers' Handbook," 3d ed., McGraw-Hill Book Company, Inc., New York, 1950. Future references will be made informally to Perry's Handbook without footnotes.

This equation is simplified, using the balance on the total streams,

$$w_2 - w_1 + \frac{dM}{d\theta} = 0 \tag{4}$$

and we get

$$120 - (150 + 30) + \frac{dM}{d\theta} = 0 \tag{5}$$

This gives the rate of accumulation $dM/d\theta$ as 60 lb/hr. The inlet is made up of two streams, the water and the salt, so $w_1 = 150 + 30$. Equation (5) can also be integrated to give

$$M = 60\theta + M_o \tag{6}$$

where M_o is 100 lb for this problem. These results are substituted into Eq. (3) so that it contains only θ and x_A as variables.

$$120x_A - 30 + (60\theta + 100) \frac{dx_A}{d\theta} + 60x_A = 0 \tag{7}$$

The variables are separated, resulting in

$$\int_0^\theta \frac{d\theta}{60\theta + 100} = -\int_0^{x_A} \frac{dx_A}{180x_A - 30} \tag{8}$$

which, upon integration and rearrangement, yields

$$x_A = \frac{1}{6}\left[1 - \left(\frac{10}{60\theta + 10}\right)^3\right] \tag{9}$$

For $\theta = 1$ hr, $x_A = 0.126$ mass fraction NaCl. Equation (9) shows that as θ becomes very large, x_A tends toward $\frac{1}{6}$, as common sense would indicate.

PROBLEMS

3-1. Write the analogs of Eqs. (3-7) and (3-9) if the quantities are expressed in molal units: $\tilde{w}_i = $ moles/hr, etc.

3-2. One hundred pound moles per hour of a mixture containing 0.35 mole fraction toluene and 0.65 mole fraction benzene is fed continuously to a distillation process. Two product streams are obtained, one containing 0.99 mole fraction benzene and one containing 5 per cent of the entering benzene. Find the rates of flow (pound moles per hour) of both streams and the composition of the toluene-rich stream. There is no accumulation within the system.

3-3. A batch distillation unit is charged with 150 lb moles of a liquid mixture containing 60 mole per cent benzene and 40 mole per cent toluene. The composition of the vapor leaving the still is related to the composition of the liquid remaining by the equation $\tilde{y}_A = \tilde{x}_A/[1 + (\alpha - 1)\tilde{x}_A]$, in which $\tilde{y}_A$ and $\tilde{x}_A$ represent the mole fraction of benzene in the vapor and liquid, respectively, and α, the relative volatility, is a constant, 2.57. If the distillation is continued until only 30 moles of liquid remains in the still, what is the composition of the collected distillate?

3-4. At a Reynolds number of 110,000, the velocity profile is given by

$$u = u_{max}\left(\frac{r_i - r}{r_i}\right)^{1/7}$$

for turbulent flow in a smooth, circular tube. Find the value of u_b/u_{max} for this situation. If a variable y is substituted for $r_i - r$, the integration will be simplified.

3-5. The velocity profile developed in a layer of liquid flowing in laminar flow down a vertical surface can be represented by the equation

$$u_y = \frac{\rho g}{\mu} \left(Lx - \frac{x^2}{2} \right)$$

where L = thickness of liquid layer

u_y = downward velocity at a distance x from wall

(a) Prove that the average velocity of the liquid is two-thirds the velocity at the free surface.

(b) Find the thickness of a layer of water at 60°F flowing down a vertical surface 3 ft wide at the rate of 100 gal/min.

3-6. Steam enters a long section of 3-in., schedule-40 steel pipe at 200 psia, 600°F, and a bulk velocity of 10 ft/sec.   At a point downstream the pressure is 140 psia and the temperature is 590°F; what is the bulk velocity at this point?   Calculate also the Reynolds numbers at both the upstream and the downstream. points.   Use data from steam tables.

3-7. In an agitated tank in a part of a simplified process for making H_3PO_4, 10,000 lb/hr of $Ca_3(PO_4)_2$ in a suspension in water is reacted continuously with a stoichiometric amount of 94 mass per cent H_2SO_4.   Sufficient water is added with the ground phosphate rock to give 40 mass per cent phosphoric acid when the process operates at steady state. The phosphoric acid solution and the $CaSO_4 \cdot 2H_2O$ (gypsum) formed are removed from the agitator at a constant rate, so that the total mass in the tank remains constant in all parts of this problem.

If the operation is started when the tank contains 10,000 lb of 20 mass per cent phosphoric acid solution, what is the concentration in the tank after 1 hr?

THE OVER-ALL ENERGY BALANCE

An over-all energy balance will now be obtained by the application of the principle of the conservation of energy to a control volume fixed in space, in much the same way as the principle of the conservation of mass was applied in the previous chapter. The first law of thermodynamics may be written as

$$\Delta E = Q - W \tag{4-1}$$

where

$$E = U + \frac{u^2}{2g_c} + \frac{gz}{g_c} \tag{4-2}$$

The terms on the right-hand side of this equation represent, respectively, the internal energy, the kinetic energy, and the potential energy of 1 lb of fluid. In Eq. (4-1) Q is the heat absorbed per pound of fluid, and W is the work of all kinds done per pound of fluid upon the surroundings. In computation, each term must, of course, be expressed in the same units—usually Btu/lb or (ft)(lb force)/lb. If it is, the mechanical equivalent of heat J need not appear in our equations. By considering the flow out of, the flow into, and the accumulation within the control volume, we write

$$\iint_A u\rho(\cos \alpha)E \, dA + \frac{d}{d\theta} \iiint_V E\rho \, d\check{V} = q - \dot{W} \tag{4-3}$$

where q and $\dot{W}$, as well as the two integrals, are expressed in energy per unit time. It is usual to divide the work $\dot{W}$ into two parts: the shaft work and the rest of the work, often called pV work. No other kinds of work (such as surface or electrical) are considered here, but they could be included. Accordingly, we have

$$\dot{W} = \dot{W}_s + \iint_A u\rho pV \cos \alpha \, dA \tag{4-4}$$

Fig. 4-1. Flow system.

where $\dot{W}_s$ is the shaft work. This work is purely mechanical and must be directly identifiable with a turning shaft or a moving piston rod. The integral in Eq. (4-4) is the net work done by the fluid as it flows into and out of the control volume. As one pound of fluid flows out at a point where the pressure is p, it displaces a volume V in the surroundings. Since the work is given by $\int_0^V p \, dV$, the work per pound of fluid is pV. The enthalpy is defined by the equation

$$H = U + pV \tag{4-5}$$

Therefore, the over-all energy balance is

$$\iint_A u\rho \cos \alpha \left(\frac{u^2}{2g_c} + \frac{gz}{g_c} + H\right) dA + \frac{d(\breve{E})}{d\theta} = q - \dot{W}_s \tag{4-6}$$

In this equation the volume integral has been replaced by its equivalent, the rate of change of the total energy in the control volume.

For the simple type of control surface defined in Fig. 4-1, Eq. (4-6) reduces to

$$\frac{w_2(u^3)_{\text{av},2}}{2g_c u_{b2}} + \frac{w_2 g(uz)_{\text{av},2}}{g_c u_{b2}} + \frac{w_2(uH)_{\text{av},2}}{u_{b2}} - \frac{w_1(u^3)_{\text{av},1}}{2g_c u_{b1}}$$

$$- \frac{w_1 g(uz)_{\text{av},1}}{g_c u_{b1}} - \frac{w_1(uH)_{\text{av},1}}{u_{b1}} + \frac{d(\breve{E})}{d\theta} = q - \dot{W}_s \tag{4-7}$$

The kinetic-energy terms are obtained as follows (ρ is taken as constant over the area of flow; $\cos \alpha = \pm 1.0$):

$$\frac{\rho}{2g_c} \iint_A u^3 \, dA = \frac{\rho}{2g_c} (u^3)_{\text{av}} A \tag{4-8}$$

where we define

$$(u^3)_{\text{av}} = \frac{1}{A} \iint_A u^3 \, dA \tag{4-9}$$

Since

$$w = u_b \rho A \qquad (4\text{-}10)$$

the final expression for the integral becomes

$$\frac{w(u^3)_{\text{av}}}{2g_c u_b}$$

In a similar fashion we define $(uz)_{\text{av}}$ and $(uH)_{\text{av}}$; the derivation of these expressions is left as an exercise for the reader.

It is usually necessary to solve Eq. (4-7) simultaneously with the over-all mass balance and the equation of state of the fluid. In the simplified case studied here, the over-all mass balance is given by Eq. (3-7).

Certain simplified forms of Eqs. (4-6) and (4-7) are so important that they will be given here. Let us write Eq. (4-7) as

$$\frac{1}{2g_c} \Delta \frac{w(u^3)_{\text{av}}}{u_b} + \frac{g}{g_c} \Delta \frac{w(uz)_{\text{av}}}{u_b} + \Delta \frac{w(uH)_{\text{av}}}{u_b} + \frac{d(\check{E})}{d\theta} = q - \dot{W}_s \qquad (4\text{-}11)$$

When input equals output, Δw equals zero; in this case $q = wQ$ and $\dot{W}_s = wW_s$. We obtain from Eq. (4-11), for $\Delta w = 0$,

$$\frac{1}{2g_c} \Delta \frac{(u^3)_{\text{av}}}{u_b} + \frac{g}{g_c} \Delta \frac{(uz)_{\text{av}}}{u_b} + \Delta \frac{(uH)_{\text{av}}}{u_b} + \frac{M}{w}\frac{dE}{d\theta} = Q - W_s \qquad (4\text{-}12)$$

If there is no accumulation of energy, $dE/d\theta$ is zero. If there are, in addition, negligible variations of velocity, height, and temperature over each of the two areas, there results the familiar general energy balance which appears in texts on thermodynamics:

$$\frac{\Delta u_b{}^2}{2g_c} + \frac{g}{g_c} \Delta z + \Delta H = Q - W_s \qquad (4\text{-}13)$$

It should be emphasized that Q or q represents all the heat transferred across the control surface, including that by conduction through the fluid. Problems involving reacting mixtures can be solved by Eq. (4-6), using for the value of H or U its thermochemical value; this procedure is illustrated in Example 4-4.

No attempt will be made here to present all the applications of the over-all energy balance, although a number of these applications are illustrated in the exercises and problems which follow. For instance, in a process involving a chemical reaction the ΔH term is usually so large that kinetic- and potential-energy terms are negligible. Conversely, in flow through a nozzle, the kinetic-energy term is important, and in the production of hydroelectric power, the potential-energy term is significant.

In most practical problems the variations in u or H across an inlet or outlet stream can be ignored. For example, the kinetic-energy term becomes important only at high velocities, but the velocity across a stream becomes more nearly uniform at higher Reynolds numbers. However, an awareness of the effect of these variations is important in applying the energy balance to each new situation; in certain cases there may be significant variations of temperature or velocity over a cross section. The best way to obtain an appreciation of these matters is to study the following examples and solve some numerical problems such as those given later in this chapter.

Example 4-1

In laminar flow the effects of the variations of velocity and temperature across a circular pipe may be significant. As an illustration, let us calculate the value of the kinetic-energy term of Eq. (4-12), $(u^3)_{av}/2g_c u_b$, in terms of u_b. For rodlike flow, the result is $u_b^2/2g_c$; for other velocity distributions, constants other than 2 appear in the denominator.

We substitute the equation for u as a function of r from Example 3-1 into Eq. (4-9) to obtain

$$(u^3)_{av} = \frac{u_{max}^3}{\pi r_i^2} \int_0^{2\pi} \int_0^{r_i} \left(1 - \frac{r^2}{r_i^2}\right)^3 r \, dr \, d\theta \tag{1}$$

This equation is similar to Eq. (2) of Example 3-1. Evaluation of the integral yields

$$(u^3)_{av} = \frac{(u_{max})^3}{4} \tag{2}$$

and so

$$\frac{(u^3)_{av}}{2g_c u_b} = \frac{(u_{max})^3}{8g_c u_b} \tag{3}$$

Since $u_b = u_{max}/2$, the final result is

$$\frac{(u^3)_{av}}{2g_c u_b} = \frac{u_b^2}{g_c} \tag{4}$$

As was remarked earlier, in laminar flow the kinetic-energy term is usually negligible. However, the analogous calculation of $(uH)_{av}/u_b$ gives a result which is frequently important, as in the case of heat transfer to a fluid in laminar flow. A computation of this sort is required in Prob. 4-7.

Example 4-2

A dilute solution at 70°F is added to a well-stirred tank at the rate of 180 lb/hr. A heating coil having an area of 10.0 sq ft is located in the tank and contains steam condensing at 300°F. The heated liquid leaves at 120 lb/hr and at the temperature of the solution in the tank, maintained uniform by effective agitation. There is 500 lb of solution at 100°F in the tank at the start of the operation. Calculate the outlet temperature after 1 hr.

The heat flux to the liquid is known empirically to be proportional to the temperature difference between the steam and the liquid in the tank. This observation is expressed mathematically by

$$\frac{q}{A} = U(t_s - t) \tag{1}$$

where U is the constant of proportionality, called the over-all heat-transfer coefficient. This quantity is, in general, a function of the properties of the two fluids involved, their flow patterns, and the shape and material of the coil. To simplify this problem, these factors are assumed to have a negligible effect, and U is taken as 70 Btu/(hr)(sq ft)(°F).

The over-all energy balance in the form of Eq. (4-11) is used for the solution. In most problems where there are large temperature changes combined with moderate velocities (i.e., less than 100 ft/sec), the potential- and kinetic-energy terms are negligible; such is the case in this problem. Since there are no turning shafts or moving piston rods, $\check{W}_s$ is zero also (work of stirring is negligible). Equation (4-11) then becomes

$$\Delta \frac{w(uH)_{\text{av}}}{u_b} + \frac{d\check{E}}{d\theta} = q \tag{2}$$

For the liquid considered here, essentially water, $H = C_p(t - t_o)$, where t_o is a constant reference temperature, and C_p is the specific heat of water. It will be assumed that the temperatures of the inlet and outlet streams given are the mixing-cup, or bulk, temperatures,[1] so that

$$\Delta \frac{w(uH)_{\text{av}}}{u_b} = w_2 H_2 - w_1 H_1 = C_p(w_2 t - w_1 t_1) - C_p t_o(w_2 - w_1) \tag{3}$$

In addition, we have the approximate relation

$$\check{E} = \check{U} = \check{H} = C_p M(t - t_o) \tag{4}$$

If Eqs. (1) to (4) are substituted into Eq. (2), there results

$$C_p w_2 t - C_p w_1 t_1 - C_p t_o(w_2 - w_1) + M C_p \frac{dt}{d\theta} + C_p(t - t_o)\frac{dM}{d\theta} = UA(t_s - t) \tag{5}$$

The over-all mass balance gives $dM/d\theta = 60$ and $M = 60\theta + 500$. t_o can be given any reasonable value; zero is the most convenient one to choose here. Making these substitutions in Eq. (5) and rearranging the results, one obtains

$$\frac{dt}{d\theta} + \frac{60C_p + w_2 C_p + UA}{C_p(60\theta + 500)} t = \frac{UAt_s + C_p w_1 t_1}{C_p(60\theta + 500)} \tag{6}$$

Upon inserting the numerical values $C_p = 1.0$, $w_2 = 120$, $U = 70$, $A = 10$, $w_1 = 180$, $t_s = 300$, and $t_1 = 70$, there results

$$\frac{dt}{d\theta} + \frac{880}{60\theta + 500} t = \frac{222,600}{60\theta + 500} \tag{7}$$

This is an ordinary, first-order, linear differential equation and is integrated to give

$$t = 253 + \frac{C}{(60\theta + 500)^{14.67}} \tag{8}$$

The constant of integration C is obtained from the requirement that $t = 100$ when $\theta = 0$, so the final equation is

$$t = 253 - \frac{6.07 \times 10^{41}}{(60\theta + 500)^{14.67}} \tag{9}$$

[1] The mixing-cup, or bulk, temperature, as the name implies, is the temperature a stream would have after passing through a device in which it was completely mixed. It can be defined mathematically as

$$t_b = \frac{1}{u_b A} \iint_A ut \, dA$$

For $\theta = 1$, t is 223°F; after a long period of operation, the temperature will reach a steady-state value of 253°F, if the tank does not overflow.

Example 4-3

The over-all energy balance in the form of Eq. (4-13) can be used to estimate the temperature drop of a gas flowing through an adiabatic throttling valve. The kinetic- and potential-energy terms are negligible; there is no heat transfer or shaft work, so

$$\Delta H = 0 \tag{1}$$

For an ideal gas, $\Delta H = C_p \, \Delta t$ and there is no temperature drop.

As an example using a real gas, let us consider steam entering the valve at 100 psia and 340°F and leaving at 52 psia. The enthalpy upstream[1] is $H_1 = 1194.3$ Btu/lb.

Since ΔH must be zero, the temperature downstream must be such that $H_2 = 1194.3$ at $p_2 = 52$; this temperature is 320°F.

Example 4-4

In part of a new process for making sulfuric acid, sulfur dioxide and oxygen enter the process at 1 atm and 50°C. The gases react completely in passing over a catalyst, and the sulfur trioxide produced is cooled to 50°C. Calculate the amount of heat removed in the process for every pound mole of SO_2 reacted.

The steady-state form of the energy balance is to be used; all terms are negligible except $\Delta \tilde{H}$ and $\tilde{Q}$, so that

$$\Delta \tilde{H} = \tilde{Q} \tag{1}$$

$\Delta \tilde{H}$ is found from the principles of thermochemistry:

$$\Delta \tilde{H} = \Delta \tilde{H}_{f,SO_3} - \Delta \tilde{H}_{f,SO_2}$$

where $\Delta \tilde{H}_f$ is the enthalpy of formation. From Perry, p. 243,

$$\begin{aligned} \Delta \tilde{H} &= -94.39 - (-70.94) \\ &= -23.45 \text{ kcal/g mole} \\ &= \tilde{Q} = -42{,}200 \text{ Btu/lb mole} \end{aligned}$$

The enthalpies of formation are given at 25°C, but the effect of a change to 50°C is small and will be neglected here. Thus approximately 42,000 Btu must be dissipated from the process for every pound mole of SO_2 reacted.

Examples 4-3 and 4-4 are essentially problems in thermodynamics. They are presented here to emphasize the fact that a great variety of problems can be viewed as applications of the over-all energy balance. The velocity-distribution and unsteady-state problems, Examples 4-1 and 4-2, require a more general form of the over-all energy balance than is usually encountered in beginning courses in physical chemistry or thermodynamics. We now turn to another example in order to introduce the important idea of the friction, or lost work, encountered in the flow of fluids.

[1] J. H. Keenan and F. G. Keyes, "Thermodynamic Properties of Steam," John Wiley & Sons, Inc., New York, 1936.

Example 4-5

Water is flowing through an insulated, horizontal pipe at steady state. Since $W_s = 0$, $Q = 0$, $\Delta u_b^2/2g_c = 0$, and $\Delta z g/g_c = 0$, ΔH must also be zero. For an incompressible liquid, since $\Delta U = C_v \Delta t \cong C_p \Delta t$,

$$\Delta H = C_p \Delta t + \frac{\Delta p}{\rho} \tag{1}$$

Thus

$$C_p \Delta t = \frac{-\Delta p}{\rho} \tag{2}$$

Experiment shows that there is a pressure drop through the pipe, and Eq. (2) shows that this effect will cause a rise in the temperature of the fluid. For instance, if $\Delta p = -5.0$ psi,

$$\Delta t = \frac{(5)(144)}{(62.4)(1)(778)} = 0.015°F$$

In the preceding example it has been shown that there can be a loss of pressure resulting in a decrease in the term $\Delta p/\rho$, with no corresponding gain in the other forms of mechanical energy, namely, $\Delta u^2/2g_c$, $\Delta z g/g_c$, and W_s. The gain in internal energy causes a scarcely perceptible temperature rise in the fluid; this mechanical energy is for all practical purposes "lost." The pressure loss is caused by frictional resistance to flow; the friction arises from the viscous nature of the fluid. In later chapters we shall see that this loss can be calculated from a knowledge of the properties of the viscous fluid, its velocity, and the geometry of the conduit. It is therefore convenient to write an energy balance in terms of this loss, variously referred to as the friction or the lost work. When this is done an equation is obtained involving only mechanical-energy terms; it is called the mechanical energy balance. The mechanical energy balance for a system in an unsteady state is complicated; only the case of steady-state flow will be considered here.

The lost work will be defined by reference to the batch work done by a pound of fluid as it passes from the inlet to the outlet.

$$W' = \int_{V_1}^{V_2} p \, dV - lw \tag{4-14}$$

This work can be visualized as that which would be done by a small piston and cylinder enclosing the pound of fluid as it flows; it differs from the work of Eq. (4-1), which includes the kinetic- and potential-energy effects.

The first law of thermodynamics may be written for this batch process

$$\Delta U = Q - W' \tag{4-15}$$

The Q here is that of Eq. (4-1). Equations (4-14) and (4-15) are combined to give

$$\Delta U = Q - \int_{V_1}^{V_2} p \, dV + lw \qquad (4\text{-}16)$$

The definition of enthalpy, Eq. (4-5), is written as

$$\Delta H = \Delta U + \Delta pV \qquad (4\text{-}17)$$

and ΔpV is replaced, using

$$\Delta pV = \int_{V_1}^{V_2} p \, dV + \int_{p_1}^{p_2} V \, dp \qquad (4\text{-}18)$$

Equations (4-16) to (4-18) are combined and solved for ΔH:

$$\Delta H = Q + \int_{p_1}^{p_2} V \, dp + lw \qquad (4\text{-}19)$$

If Eq. (4-19) is substituted for ΔH in Eq. (4-13), we obtain the mechanical energy balance, so called because it contains only mechanical-energy terms,

$$\frac{\Delta u_b{}^2}{2g_c} + \frac{g}{g_c} \Delta z + \int_{p_1}^{p_2} \frac{dp}{\rho} + lw + W_s = 0 \qquad (4\text{-}20)$$

The value of the integral depends on the path of the process and on the equation of state of the fluid. For an incompressible liquid the integral reduces to $\Delta p/\rho$. If, in addition, there is no shaft work or lost work (friction), Eq. (4-20) reduces to a form of Bernoulli's equation,

$$\frac{\Delta u_b{}^2}{2g_c} + \frac{g}{g_c} \Delta z + \frac{\Delta p}{\rho} = 0 \qquad (4\text{-}21)$$

Bernoulli's equation can also be obtained from a differential force balance, as will be shown in Chap. 12. Equation (4-20) is sometimes called the extended Bernoulli equation.

Equation (4-20) departs somewhat from our idea of an over-all balance, which we postulated as containing only terms which can be evaluated from a knowledge of the state of the inlet and outlet streams and the exchanges of heat and work with the surroundings. Nevertheless, Eq. (4-20) reduces in many cases to one which depends only on the end states; Eq. (4-21) is an example.

Since the integral in Eq. (4-20) can be expressed in terms of the inlet and outlet conditions for incompressible fluids, lw can be calculated in these cases from a knowledge of the externally measurable terms. However, the value of lw depends on the detailed nature of the flow, so that its independent calculation requires the use of a differential balance and the knowledge of the properties of the viscous fluid.

These latter methods for the calculation of lw from the differential momentum balance are used for flow through conduits, but not for flow through a pump or a turbine. For such machines it is convenient to divide the loss into lw_f, the loss in the conduit, and lw_t, the loss in the turbine.

$$lw = lw_f + lw_t \tag{4-22}$$

This equation applies to flow through a conduit including a turbine, for which, according to convention, $W_s > 0$. It is customary to take into account the loss in the turbine by defining an efficiency η_t by

$$\eta_t = \frac{W_s}{W_s + lw_t} \tag{4-23}$$

The shaft work W_s is the rate at which energy is transmitted by the turbine shaft. The sum $W_s + lw_t$ is the rate at which the fluid gives up its mechanical energy in the turbine.

If Eqs. (4-22) and (4-23) are incorporated into Eq. (4-20), there results

$$\frac{\Delta u_b^2}{2g_c} + \frac{g \, \Delta z}{g_c} + \int_{p_1}^{p_2} \frac{dp}{\rho} + lw_f + \frac{W_s}{\eta_t} = 0 \tag{4-24}$$

For a pump, we let

$$lw = lw_f + lw_p \tag{4-25}$$

Once again W_s is the rate at which energy is transmitted by the shaft. However, mechanical energy is absorbed by the fluid in the pump at the lower rate $W_s + lw_p$ because of the consumption of energy at the rate of lw_p to overcome friction. The terms W_s and lw_p will always have opposite signs when calculated for a pump. The efficiency for a pump is

$$\eta_p = \frac{W_s + lw_p}{W_s} \qquad W_s < 0 \tag{4-26}$$

so that

$$\frac{\Delta u_b^2}{2g_c} + \frac{g \, \Delta z}{g_c} + \int_{p_1}^{p_2} \frac{dp}{\rho} + lw_f + \eta_p W_s = 0 \tag{4-27}$$

The examples and problems which follow often involve the simultaneous use of the general energy balance and the mechanical energy balance. None of these illustrations will require the calculation of lw_f from a detailed analysis of the flow; such cases are reserved for Chaps. 7 and 15, when the mechanical energy balance will again be used in the analysis.

Example 4-6

Water is flowing from an elevated reservoir through a conduit to a turbine at a lower level and out of the turbine through a similar conduit. At a point in the conduit 300 ft above the turbine the pressure is 30 psia; at a point in the conduit 10 ft below the turbine the pressure is 18 psia. The water is flowing at 3600 tons/hr, and the output at the shaft of the turbine is 1000 hp. If the efficiency of the turbine is known to be 90 per cent, calculate the loss by friction in the conduit. If there were no heat transfer to the surroundings, how much would the water be heated in flowing through the conduit and turbine?

Let us start the solution of this problem by using Eq. (4-24). Since water can be treated as incompressible, the integral can be written as $\Delta p/\rho$; in addition, the inlet and outlet conduits are of the same diameter, so the kinetic-energy-difference term is negligible. (The latter statement does not invalidate the fact that the turbine itself operates on the principle of converting potential energy into kinetic energy.)

We write Eq. (4-24) as

$$\frac{g}{g_c}\Delta z + \frac{\Delta p}{\rho} + lw_f + \frac{\dot{W}_s}{w\eta_t} = 0 \tag{1}$$

and then

$$-310 + \frac{(-12)(144)}{62.4} + lw_f + \frac{(1000)(550)(3600)}{(3600)(2000)(0.90)} = 0$$

[550 (ft)(lb force)/sec = 1 hp].

Finally, we have

$$-310 - 27.7 + lw_f + 306 = 0$$
$$lw_f = 31.7 \text{ (ft)(lb force)/lb}$$

The temperature rise of the water can be calculated from the over-all energy balance,

$$\frac{g\,\Delta z}{g_c} + \Delta H = -W_s \tag{2}$$

from which

$$\Delta H = -275 + 310 = 35$$

$$C_p\,\Delta t + \frac{\Delta p}{\rho} = 35$$

$$C_p\,\Delta t + (-27.7) = 35$$

The temperature rise is, then,

$$\Delta t = \frac{35 + 27.7}{(1)(778)} = 0.0806°F$$

For steady flow the friction is, in general, given by

$$lw = \Delta U - Q + \int_{V_1}^{V_2} p\,dV \tag{3}$$

which reduces, for an incompressible fluid, to

$$lw = C_p\,\Delta t - Q \tag{4}$$

and for adiabatic flow of this fluid to

$$lw = C_p\,\Delta t$$
$$= 62.7 \text{ (ft)(lb force)/lb} \tag{5}$$

This represents the total loss of mechanical energy in the conduit and in the turbine.

Example 4-7

Helium, which behaves like an ideal gas for the conditions of this problem, flows steadily at low velocity into a converging-diverging nozzle (Fig. 4-2) at a pressure of 15 atm abs and a temperature of 200°F. At a point near the end of the diverging section of the nozzle, the pressure has fallen to 1 atm abs. Calculate the velocity and temperature at this point.

15 atm
200°F ———Helium———▸ 1 atm

Fig. 4-2.   Converging-diverging nozzle.
(Refer to Example 4-7.)

Variations of velocity and temperature across the diameter of the nozzle are small; there is no exchange of heat or shaft work with the surroundings, and the nozzle is horizontal.   The over-all energy balance then becomes

$$\frac{\Delta u_b^2}{2g_c} + \Delta H = 0 \tag{1}$$

For an ideal gas,

$$\Delta H = C_p \, \Delta t \tag{2}$$

so that once Δt is known, the velocity is readily calculated from these equations.

The process is isentropic (reversible), as thermodynamics would indicate for a frictionless, isolated process.   We can therefore calculate the downstream temperature by the formula

$$\frac{T_2}{T_1} = \left(\frac{p_1}{p_2}\right)^{(C_v - C_p)/C_p} \tag{3}$$

which is valid for the isentropic expansion of an ideal gas.

For helium, $\tilde{C}_p$ is 5 and $\tilde{C}_v$ is 3, so

$$T_2 = (660)(15)^{-\frac{2}{5}} = 223°\text{R}$$
$$= -237°\text{F}$$

From Eq. (2)

$$\Delta H = \frac{(5)}{4}(-237 - 200) = -546 \text{ Btu/lb}$$

so that

$$\frac{u_{b2}^2}{2g_c} = (546)(778)$$

and $u_{b2} = 5230$ ft/sec.

The velocity obtained is much greater than the velocity of sound, and such nozzles are used to propel rockets and jet aircraft.

PROBLEMS

4-1. A moving body possesses kinetic energy equal to the amount of work required to take it from zero velocity to velocity u.   By combining Newton's second law with the concept that work equals force times distance, show that this amount of work is $u^2/2g_c$ for a mass of 1 lb.

4-2. The potential-energy change in a flow process is written $g \, \Delta z/g_c$, which can be shown to be the amount of work required to raise a mass of one pound a distance Δz ft.

In most chemical-engineering problems the variation in g is correctly assumed to be negligible, so an approximate value of 32.2 ft/sec^2 is used which cancels numerically the proportionality constant g_c, having the value 32.2 (lb)(ft)/(lb force)(sec^2).

To emphasize the fact that g is not a constant and that the expression $g \, \Delta z / g_c$ does not represent the potential-energy change in all situations, derive an expression for the potential-energy change in raising an object of constant mass M a distance Δz above the earth's surface. The variation of g with the distance r from the center of the earth can be represented by the inverse-square law

$$g = 32.2 \left(\frac{r_o}{r}\right)^2$$

where r_o is the earth's radius (3960 miles). Find the numerical answer for the case of $\Delta z = 500$ miles and compare it with the answer obtained by taking g as a constant at 32.2 ft/sec^2.

4-3. In a chemical plant the water used in an absorption tower is pumped continuously from a pond through a well-insulated schedule-40, 3-in. pipe to a spray head at the top of the absorption tower. The temperature of the pond water is 60°F, and the vertical distance from the surface of the pond to the spray head is 100 ft. The rate of pumping is 200 gal/min, and the power input to the pump is 14.0 hp. The water may be assumed to have a flat velocity profile at the pipe discharge. Determine the temperature of the water as it enters the spray head, where the pressure is 3 psig.

4-4. Steam expands through an adiabatic converging nozzle. It enters the nozzle with a velocity of 20 ft/sec at a pressure of 400 psia and a temperature of 600°F. At the throat of the nozzle the steam pressure is 216 psia and the temperature is 460°F. Find the velocity of the steam in the throat of the nozzle. The velocity profile may be assumed to be flat at all points.

4-5. A gas enters a horizontal 3-in., schedule-40 pipe at a constant rate of 0.50 lb/sec. The gas is at a temperature of 70°F and a pressure of 1.15 atm. It has a molecular weight of 29. The pipe is wrapped with an 80-kw electric-heating coil which is covered with a thick layer of insulation.

At the point where the gas is discharged, the pressure is 1.05 atm. Find the temperature of the gas at this point. Assume that the gas behaves ideally and its heat capacity $C_p = 0.24$ Btu/(lb)(°F).

4-6. Water is to be drained from the bottom of an open cylindrical tank which has an ID of 10 ft. The initial depth of water in the tank is 4 ft. Estimate the time for all the water in the tank to drain through a 2-in. opening if the process is frictionless and the discharge pressure is 1 atm.

4-7. A viscous oil flows at a constant rate (**Re** $= 1000$) out of a tank through a smoothly rounded entrance and into a length of 2-in., schedule-40 steel pipe. At the pipe entrance the velocity is essentially uniform at 3.00 ft/sec across the pipe diameter, and the temperature is 200°F. At a point downstream in the pipe the temperature at the center line of the pipe is 120°F, and at the pipe wall, 80°F. Calculate the rate of heat flow to the surroundings from the fluid, Btu/hr, assuming a flat velocity profile and a temperature distribution across the pipe at the downstream point given by

$$t - t_s = (t_{\max} - t_s) \left[1 - \left(\frac{r}{r_i}\right)^2 \right]$$

Compare this result with that obtained using the same temperature profile and the isothermal laminar velocity distribution given in Example 3-1. The density of the oil is 54.0 lb/cu ft, and its specific heat is 0.45 Btu/(lb)(°F).

4-8. A cross-country pipeline transports oil at the rate of 5000 bbl/day. The pressure of the oil leaving pumping station A is 250 psig. The pressure at the inlet to the next station B is 115 psig. Station B is at an elevation 57 ft higher than station A. Find the lost work per pound of oil and the total theoretical power consumption (horsepower). Oil density, 48 lb/cu ft; 1 bbl = 42 gal.

4-9. (*a*) Write the over-all mass and energy balances for a process involving two separate entering streams and one leaving stream.

(*b*) Simplify these equations for the common case in which the variations of velocity and temperature across each stream are negligible.

(*c*) Finally, write the equations for steady state.

(*d*) Generalize the results of part (*a*) to apply to the case of m streams in and p streams out. Use summation symbols to make the equations as compact as possible.

4-10. Water is taken from the bottom of a large tank, where the pressure is 50 psig, and pumped to a nozzle discharging to the atmosphere 50 ft above the bottom of the tank. The flow rate is 100 lb/sec, and the nozzle velocity is 70 ft/sec. If the efficiency of the pump is 75 per cent and 10 hp is furnished to the pump shaft, calculate in (ft)(lb force)/lb (*a*) the friction in the pump; (*b*) the friction in the rest of the system.

4-11. Water flows from the bottom of a large tank where the pressure is 100 psig through a pipe to a turbine which produces 5.82 hp. The pipe leading from the turbine is 60 ft below the bottom of the tank. In this pipe the pressure is 50 psig, the velocity 70 ft/sec, and the flow rate 100 lb/sec. If the friction loss in the system, excluding the turbine, is 40 (ft)(lb force)/lb, find the efficiency of the turbine.

THE OVER-ALL MOMENTUM BALANCE

The over-all momentum balance is based on Newton's second law,

$$F_x = \frac{1}{g_c} \frac{d(Mu_x)}{d\theta} \tag{5-1}$$

This situation is inherently more complicated than those previously treated, because the force F_x and the momentum Mu_x are vectors. In order to describe force and momentum, their direction must be specified as well as their magnitude; for mass and energy, only the magnitude is required. In this treatment we shall consider only the x components of the vectors.

A control volume is defined just as was done in deriving the mass and energy balances. The force acting on the volume is given by the rate of change of the momentum of the fluid passing through the volume at any instant; this quantity is in turn made up of the flux of momentum summed over the entire control surface and the rate of change of the momentum within the volume (recall that the control surface is fixed in space).

$$\frac{1}{g_c} \iint_A u_x \rho u(\cos \alpha)\, dA + \frac{d}{d\theta} \iiint_{\check{V}} \frac{u_x \rho}{g_c}\, d\check{V} = F_x \tag{5-2}$$

The quantity $u_x \rho$ in this equation can be regarded as the concentration of x-directed momentum in (lb)(ft/sec)/cu ft, whereas $u(\cos \alpha)\, dA$ is the volumetric flow rate in cu ft/sec through dA. Thus $u_x \rho u(\cos \alpha)\, dA$ is the flow of x-directed momentum through dA.

The force F_x is composed of the sum of several forces. If there is an increase of pressure in the positive x direction, there is a resultant force F_{xp} directed in the negative x direction. If the control surfaces are within the fluid or at its boundary, there will be shearing stresses caused by viscosity; the resultant of these forces, also directed in the negative x direction, will be called the drag force F_{xd}.

Finally, the control volume may include solid objects such as pipe walls, and these objects may be acted on by forces arising outside the control volume. The resultant of these forces will be designated by R_x, taken positive in the positive x direction. For instance, if the control surface cuts through a cross section of a pipe in tension, R_x will have a certain, computable value.

Equation (5-2) is now rewritten in terms of these forces, and the volume integral is replaced by the derivative of the momentum of the mass within the control volume (written as P_x) with respect to time.

$$\iint_A \frac{u_x \rho}{g_c} u(\cos \alpha)\, dA + \frac{1}{g_c}\frac{dP_x}{d\theta} = R_x - F_{xp} - F_{xd} \tag{5-3}$$

If Eq. (5-3) is now applied to a section of conduit with its axis in the x direction as illustrated in Fig. 3-2, u and u_x become identical, ρA equals w/u_b, $\cos \alpha$ equals ± 1.0, and we have

$$\frac{1}{g_c}\Delta\left[\frac{w(u_x{}^2)_{\text{av}}}{u_b}\right] + \frac{1}{g_c}\frac{dP_x}{d\theta} = R_x - F_{xp} - F_{xd} \tag{5-4}$$

where

$$(u_x{}^2)_{\text{av}} = \frac{1}{A}\iint_A u_x{}^2\, dA \tag{5-5}$$

At steady state, Eq. (5-4) reduces to

$$\frac{w}{g_c}\Delta\frac{(u_x{}^2)_{\text{av}}}{u_b} = R_x - F_{xp} - F_{xd} \tag{5-6}$$

Equation (5-4) or (5-6) can be combined with the mass balance and the equation of state to find the relation between the forces caused by a flowing fluid and its velocity and properties.

If there is no variation in velocity across the areas A_1 and A_2, Eq. (5-4) becomes

$$\frac{1}{g_c}\Delta(wu_x) + \frac{1}{g_c}\frac{dP_x}{d\theta} = R_x - F_{xp} - F_{xd} \tag{5-7}$$

which applies whether the axis of the conduit is curved or not. If the conduit axis is curved, the analogous balance of y momentum must be solved in order to complete the analysis.

$$\frac{1}{g_c}\Delta(wu_y) + \frac{1}{g_c}\frac{dP_y}{d\theta} = R_y - F_{yp} - F_{yd} \tag{5-8}$$

A problem involving a curved conduit is illustrated in Example 5-3. Of course, in the most general case the z momentum must also be considered

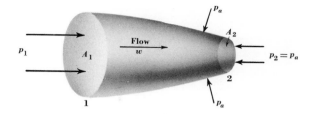

Fig. 5-1. Flow through converging nozzle.

simultaneously. If the conduits are not horizontal, suitable components of the force of gravity must be included on the right-hand side of the momentum equation.

In the analysis and design of rotating machinery such as turbines and rotary pumps, the momentum balance is conveniently written in terms of torque (moment) and angular momentum. We shall not consider this type of problem here; it is discussed in other texts, such as Hunsaker and Rightmire.[1] The study of the momentum balance will aid us in future work with the equations of motion and the boundary layer, as well as in the following examples and problems illustrating some immediate uses of the over-all momentum balance.

Example 5-1

Water is flowing at 150 gal/min through a horizontal converging nozzle (Fig. 5-1). The upstream ID is 3 in., and downstream ID is 1 in. Calculate the resultant force on the nozzle when it discharges to the atmosphere. Consider that the nozzle is attached at its upstream end and that frictional forces are negligible.

We must first compute the upstream pressure, or more specifically, Δp. This is accomplished by using Eq. (4-21), which neglects any friction in the flow.

$$\frac{\Delta u_b{}^2}{2g_c} + \frac{\Delta p}{\rho} = 0 \qquad (1)$$

The velocities have been assumed uniform across the nozzle cross sections. From the given flow rate,

$$w = \frac{(150)(8.33)}{60} = 20.85 \text{ lb/sec}$$

the velocities are calculated.

$$u_{b1} = \frac{w}{\rho A_1} = \frac{(20.85)(4)(144)}{(62.4)(3.14)(9)}$$

$$= 6.80 \text{ ft/sec}$$

$$u_{b2} = (6.80)(\tfrac{3}{1})^2 = 61.2 \text{ ft/sec}$$

[1] J. C. Hunsaker and B. G. Rightmire, "Engineering Applications of Fluid Mechanics," McGraw-Hill Book Company, Inc., New York, 1947.

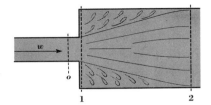

Fig. 5-2.   Expansion flow.

From Eq. (1),

$$\Delta p = -\left[\frac{(61.2)^2 - (6.80)^2}{(2)(32.2)}\right](62.4)$$

$$= -3580 \text{ lb force/sq ft} = -24.9 \text{ psi}$$

The momentum balance, Eq. (5-6), is used to obtain R_x:

$$\frac{w}{g_c}\Delta u_x + F_{xp} = R_x \tag{2}$$

The solution of this problem requires that the control volume include the nozzle walls, so that R_x enters into the force balance. At A_1 there is a force $p_1 A_1$ directed to the right in Fig. 5-1; at A_2, there is a force $A_2 p_a$ directed to the left. In addition, atmospheric pressure acting on the outside of the nozzle exerts a net force equivalent to $p_a(A_1 - A_2)$ directed to the left. Therefore the pressure force becomes

$$F_{xp} = A_2 p_a + p_a(A_1 - A_2) - p_1 A_1$$

$$= A_1(p_a - p_1)$$

We then substitute into Eq. (2):

$$\frac{(20.85)}{32.2}(61.2 - 6.80) + \frac{(3.14)(9)}{(4)}(-24.9) = R_x$$

$$35.2 - 175.8 = R_x = -140.6 \text{ lb force}$$

Because the resultant force R_x on the nozzle is negative, it is acting in the negative x direction, opposite to the direction of flow; the pipe wall is in tension since the nozzle is supported at its upstream end.

Example 5-2

When a fluid flows from a small pipe to one of larger diameter through a sudden expansion (Fig. 5-2), there is a mechanical energy loss caused by the resulting eddies. A gradual change in cross section, such as occurs in the nozzle of Example 5-1, is accompanied by very little lost work. Use the momentum balance to obtain an expression for lw for a sudden expansion for an incompressible fluid.

Let us consider the simple case for which the velocities in the two pipes do not vary across the diameter. Equation (5-6) becomes

$$\frac{w}{g_c}\Delta u_b = -F_{xp} \tag{1}$$

The control volume is chosen so as not to include the pipe wall, so R_x drops out. The boundaries of the control volume are planes 1 and 2. Flow through plane 1, however,

Fig. 5-3.   *Flow through a curved pipe.*

occurs only over the area A_o.   In addition, all the loss is assumed to be from eddies within the volume, making F_{xd} equal to zero.   Substituting $A_2(p_2 - p_1)$ for F_{xp} gives

$$\frac{w}{g_c} \Delta u_b = -A_2(p_2 - p_1) \tag{2}$$

It is assumed that p_1 and p_2 are uniform over the cross-sectional area; also, $p_o = p_1$.   Using the relations $w = u_{bo}\rho A_o$ and $u_{b2} = (A_o/A_2)u_{bo}$, this equation is changed to

$$\frac{u_{bo}^2}{g_c} \frac{A_o}{A_2}\left(1 - \frac{A_o}{A_2}\right) = \frac{\Delta p}{\rho} \tag{3}$$

The mechanical energy balance applied to the problem gives

$$\frac{u_{bo}^2}{2g_c}\left[1 - \left(\frac{A_o}{A_2}\right)^2\right] - lw = \frac{\Delta p}{\rho} \tag{4}$$

From the combination of these latter two equations we obtain the desired result:

$$lw = \frac{u_{bo}^2}{2g_c}\left(1 - \frac{A_o}{A_2}\right)^2 \tag{5}$$

In many situations the loss at the expansion is only a small part of the total loss and Eq. (5) is sufficiently accurate.   If the expansion loss is a large fraction of the total loss, a more precise expression is desirable and can be obtained by using the actual upstream velocity distribution in the analysis (Prob. 5-5).

Example 5-3

Water is flowing through a horizontal, right-angle bend of gradual curvature, illustrated in Fig. 5-3.   The velocity is 80 ft/sec, the pressure at the inlet is 20 psig, and the ID of the pipe is 2 in.   If friction can be neglected, calculate the magnitude and direction of the force required to hold the piece of pipe in equilibrium.   The control volume includes the pipe walls.

To work this problem, the momentum balance is solved first for the x direction and then for the y direction.   For the former,

$$\frac{w}{g_c}(u_{x2} - u_{x1}) = R_x - F_{xp} \tag{1}$$

The velocities are assumed constant across pipe cross sections.   Since there is no x component of velocity at point 2, $u_{x2} = 0$.   The x component of force caused by pressure arises from p_1 over the area A_1 and atmospheric pressure p_a over the rest of the pipe, except A_2.   The atmospheric pressure acts equally in all directions.   Thus the net value of F_{xp} is $-A_1(p_1 - p_a)$.

Fig. 5-4.   *Boundary layer on flat plate.*

$$R_x = -A_1(p_1 - p_a) - \frac{w}{g_c} u_{x1}$$

$$= \frac{\pi(4)}{4}(-20) - \frac{(80)(62.4)(\pi)(4)(80)}{(4)(144)(32.2)}$$

$$= -62.8 - 270 = -333 \text{ lb force} \tag{2}$$

By similar reasoning, we obtain

$$R_y = A_2(p_2 - p_a) + \frac{w}{g_c} u_{y2}$$

$$= 62.8 + 270 = 333 \text{ lb force} \tag{3}$$

The resultant force is directed as shown in Fig. 5-3, with $\beta = 45°$, and its magnitude is $333/\cos 45° = 471$ lb force.

PROBLEMS

5-1. Water is flowing through a horizontal diffuser consisting of a section of conduit for which the ID gradually increases from 2 to 4 in. The diffuser is constructed so that friction is negligible. Calculate the resultant force on the diffuser when the upstream pressure is 60 psig and the flow rate is 1000 gal/min.

5-2. Water flows through a horizontal 45° elbow of 2-in., schedule-40 steel pipe at 200 gal/min. If the upstream pressure is 50 psig and friction is neglected, calculate the resultant force on the elbow.

5-3. An incompressible fluid flows past one side of a flat plate of unit width. The flow far from the plate is everywhere uniform at u_o, and the plate is oriented parallel to the general flow. The viscous fluid flowing near the plate is slowed by the layers nearer the plate, and there is no slip at the plate surface. At the leading edge a boundary layer develops which becomes thicker with distance downstream. In fact, the boundary layer is defined as the zone in which the velocity changes from zero at the plate to the uniform stream velocity u_o some distance from the plate. At any distance downstream the thickness is δ, and the velocity parallel to the plate is approximated by

$$\frac{u_x}{u_o} = \frac{3}{2}\left(\frac{y}{\delta}\right) - \frac{1}{2}\left(\frac{y}{\delta}\right)^3 \qquad 0 \leq \frac{y}{\delta} < 1$$

$$\frac{u_x}{u_o} = 1.0 \qquad \frac{y}{\delta} \geq 1$$

Use the over-all momentum balance to find the drag force on one side of the plate as a function of u_o, ρ, and δ. There is no change in pressure. Choose the control surface so there is flow in and out only in the x direction; Fig. 5-4 illustrates this problem. A

Fig. 5-5. *Operation of an air ejector.*

streamline is a line (surface) across which no fluid flows; there is flow across the line $\delta(x)$ shown in the figure.

5-4. The ejector sketched in Fig. 5-5 is to be used to pump air to the atmosphere from a space at a pressure 2 in. of water less than atmospheric. The pipe is 3-in., schedule-40 steel pipe, and the cross-sectional area of the nozzle is small enough to neglect in comparison with the cross section of the 3-in. pipe. The injected air is pumped in at a pressure just sufficient to cause the air to leave the nozzle at 1100 ft/sec, about sonic velocity. The density of the air at all points changes very little and can be taken as constant at 0.075 lb/cu ft.

Find a relation between the flow rate of entrained air w_e and the flow rate of injected air w_i by writing the over-all momentum balance between 1 and 2 in Fig. 5-5. The two streams are well mixed at 2, and the velocity is constant across the pipe at 2 and just before 1. The drag force F_{xd} can be neglected. Calculate also the maximum flow rate of entrained air and the corresponding nozzle size.

5-5. An incompressible fluid flows from a small pipe, where it is in fully developed laminar flow, through a sudden expansion to a larger pipe, where the velocity is uniform. Derive an equation for lw, as was done in Example 5-2.

This problem[1] is sometimes considered with reference to the equation

$$\frac{\Delta u_b^2}{2g_c} + \frac{\Delta p}{\rho} + K_e \frac{u_{b1}^2}{2g_c} = 0 \tag{1}$$

Show that

$$K_e = 1 + \left(\frac{A_1}{A_2}\right)^2 - \frac{8}{3}\left(\frac{A_1}{A_2}\right) \tag{2}$$

This equation for K_e takes into account not only the lost-work term, but also the fact that $u_b^2/2g_c$ does not correctly represent the kinetic energy for laminar flow in the small pipe.

[1] W. M. Kays, *Trans. ASME*, **72:**1067 (1950). This article is concerned with the calculation of the pressure drop through a short heat exchanger, in which the expansion loss may be an appreciable fraction of the total loss.

FLOW MEASUREMENT
6

In the preceding chapters the three over-all balances have been developed, and they have enabled us to solve a number of problems. Before considering additional theory, the over-all balances will be applied in this chapter to the analysis of the common types of flowmeter. The over-all balances, together with some empirical observations, permit the practical solution of most flowmeter problems. Some important contributions to the understanding of flowmeter performance can also be obtained from the theory of flow of an ideal fluid, defined here as a fluid of zero viscosity.

Pitot Tube

Figure 6-1 shows the general appearance of a simple pitot tube. It consists of one tube with its opening normal to the direction of flow and a second tube in which the opening is parallel to the flow.

The velocity of flow is calculated from the difference between the pressure at the opening parallel to the flow, registering the static pressure, and the pressure in the impact tube, called the stagnation pressure. In Fig. 6-1 the difference between these two pressures is indicated by the difference in levels of the liquid in the manometer. Bernoulli's equation (4-21) can be written for the incompressible fluid at points 1 and 2. Since the velocity at 2 is zero,

$$\frac{u_1^2}{2g_c} = \frac{p_2 - p_1}{\rho} \tag{6-1}$$

The working equation for the pitot tube is usually written

$$u = C \sqrt{\frac{2g_c \, \Delta p}{\rho}} \tag{6-2}$$

The factor C is introduced to take into account deviations from Eq. (6-1); for most pitot tubes C is approximately unity, but for precise determina-

Fig. 6-1. *Schematic diagram of simple pitot*

tions of velocity the value should be determined by calibration of the instrument.

The value of Δp is related to the manometer reading by a simple hydrostatic analysis. This is approached most easily by applying Eq. (4-21) for the case of zero flow:

$$\Delta p = -\rho \, \Delta z \, \frac{g}{g_c} \tag{6-3}$$

Reference to Fig. (6-1) shows that

$$\Delta p = p_2 - p_1 = (p_2 - p_3) + (p_3 - p_4) \\ + (p_4 - p_5) + (p_5 - p_6) + (p_6 - p_1) \tag{6-4}$$

From Eq. (6-3) it is evident that two points at the same level joined by a continuous column of stagnant fluid are at the same pressure. Thus $p_4 - p_5$ is zero, and $p_2 - p_3$ equals $-(p_6 - p_1)$. The fluid between 6 and 1 is stagnant in the sense that there is no net flow in the vertical direction. These considerations reduce Eq. (6-4) to

$$\Delta p = (p_3 - p_4) + (p_5 - p_6) \tag{6-5}$$

By using Eq. (6-3) and the fact that $z_3 - z_4$ equals $-(z_5 - z_6)$, we obtain

$$\Delta p = \frac{g}{g_c} (\rho_m - \rho)(z_3 - z_4) \tag{6-6}$$

where ρ_m is the density of the manometer fluid. If $z_3 - z_4$ is called Δh, Eqs. (6-6) and (6-2) can be combined to give

$$u = C \sqrt{\frac{2g(\rho_m - \rho) \, \Delta h}{\rho}} \tag{6-7}$$

There are many possible manometer configurations (Perry, pp. 364–367), but they can all be analyzed by the procedure applied above.

In addition to the simple pitot tube which we have discussed, there exist many modifications. A compact design which makes use of concentric tubes is shown in Fig. 6-2. Static-pressure holes parallel to the flow are

Fig. 6-2.   Schematic diagram of compact pitot tube.

drilled in the outer tube.   This instrument can be mounted so that readings can be taken at various points across the pipe.

The pitot tube measures the point or local velocity; readings at successive points across a duct are used to obtain velocity profiles.   The bulk velocity is obtained from the profile in a conduit by the evaluation, numerical or graphical if necessary, of Eq. (3-5).

This treatment applies to incompressible fluids and approximately to gases at moderate velocities for which the pressure change is less than 15 per cent of the total pressure.

Venturi Meter

A venturi meter is shown in Fig. 6-3; the converging and diverging sections minimize losses by eddy formation.   Experimental measurements show that for $Re_1 > 10,000$ the friction loss from 1 to 3 is about 10 per cent of $(p_2 - p_1)/\rho$ when the tube is horizontal.   Referring to $(p_2 - p_1)/\rho$ as $\Delta p/\rho$, for incompressible fluids, we have

$$0.1 \frac{\Delta p}{\rho} + lw_{13} = 0 \tag{6-8}$$

Assuming the loss from 1 to 2 is roughly half lw_{13}, the mechanical energy balance for a horizontal tube from 1 to 2 is

$$\frac{\Delta p}{\rho} + \frac{\Delta u_b{}^2}{2g_c} - 0.05 \frac{\Delta p}{\rho} = 0 \tag{6-9}$$

Solution for u_{b2} gives

$$u_{b2} = 0.975 \sqrt{\frac{2g_c(-\Delta p)}{\rho(1 - \beta^4)}} \tag{6-10}$$

Fig. 6-3. *Venturi meter.* (Not to scale)

where β is the ratio of inside diameters D_2/D_1. The quantity $\sqrt{1/(1-\beta^4)}$ is called the velocity-of-approach factor; it is near unity for common values of β. For instance, for $\beta = 0.50$, $\sqrt{1/(1-\beta^4)} = 1.03$.

The coefficient 0.975 in Eq. (6-10) was obtained from the over-all loss to show the relation between these two quantities. For precision, the coefficient is obtained from a direct measurement of the flow rate w by independent means, such as weighing the amount of liquid collected in a given time. Equation (6-10) is then written

$$u_{b2} = C_v \sqrt{\frac{2g_c(-\Delta p)}{\rho(1-\beta^4)}} \tag{6-11}$$

For $\mathbf{Re}_1 > 10,000$, C_v is 0.98; for smaller Reynolds numbers the coefficient decreases rapidly, as shown in Perry, fig. 53, p. 407. This effect is partially caused by the nonuniform velocity distribution across the diameter in laminar flow. Some recent results for C_v are given by Jorissen.[1]

Orifice Meter

The orifice meter, illustrated in Fig. 6-4, operates on the same principle as the venturi meter but with some important differences. The orifice plate can easily be changed to accommodate widely different flow rates, whereas the throat diameter of a venturi is fixed, so that its range of flow rates is circumscribed by the practical limits of Δp. The orifice meter has a large permanent loss of pressure because of the presence of eddies on the downstream side of the plate; the shape of the venturi meter prevents the formation of these eddies and greatly reduces the permanent loss.

There are a number of customary positions for the pressure taps which lead to the manometer.

1. *Plate taps.* Radial holes are drilled in the orifice plate and emerge on opposite sides of the plate near the pipe wall.

2. *Corner taps.* Holes are drilled through the flange and emerge from the

[1] A. L. Jorissen, Discharge Coefficients of Herschel-type Venturi Tubes, *Trans. ASME*, **72**:1067 (1950), and **74**:905 (1952).

Fig. 6-4.   *Orifice meter.*

pipe wall in the corner adjacent to the orifice plate.   These holes are normal to the holes for plate taps.

3. *Flange taps.*   The centers of the holes are located 1 in. upstream and 1 in. downstream from the faces of the plate.

4. *Radius taps.*   One pressure tap is 1 pipe diameter upstream from the orifice plate, and the other tap is ½ pipe diameter downstream from the plate.

5. *Vena contracta taps.*   The upstream tap is usually 1 pipe diameter from the plate, and the downstream tap at the point of minimum pressure. This position is a function of the ratio of orifice and pipe diameters, as shown in Perry, fig. 51, p. 405.

6. *Pipe taps.*   The upstream tap is 2½ pipe diameters from the orifice plate, and the downstream tap 8 pipe diameters from the plate.   The downstream tap is at or beyond the point of maximum downstream pressure.

When using vena contracta taps, p_1 is measured far enough upstream to be in a region where the flow is little disturbed by the presence of the orifice; p_2 is measured at the vena contracta, which is the point of minimum static pressure and minimum cross section of the jet of fluid after it emerges from the orifice.   This jet enters the relatively stagnant fluid behind the orifice plate, and as the jet expands to fill the pipe downstream from the vena contracta, it entrains some of the surrounding fluid.   Most of the over-all loss in the orifice arises from this viscous interaction and accompanying eddy formation.

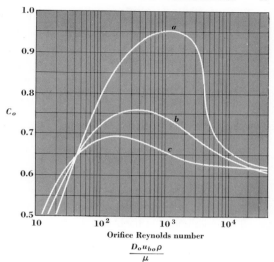

Fig. 6-5.   *Orifice coefficient in*
Eq. (6-15). (From John H. Perry
(ed.), "Chemical Engineers'
Handbook," 3d ed., fig. 50,
p. 405, McGraw-Hill Book
Company, Inc., New York, 1950.)
   a. $D_o/D_1 = 0.80$.
   b. $D_o/D_1 = 0.60$.
   c. $D_o/D_1 = 0.20$.

The flow up to the vena contracta is very similar to flow in a venturi. Thus Eq. (6-11) can be used to describe flow up to this point.   Equation (6-11) is rearranged into the form of the mechanical energy balance to yield

$$C_v{}^2 \frac{p_2 - p_1}{\rho} + \frac{u_{b2}{}^2 - u_{b1}{}^2}{2g_c} = 0 \tag{6-12}$$

The coefficient C_v, as we have seen, has a value of about 0.98 and can be related to the loss by

$$lw_{12} = (C_v{}^2 - 1) \frac{p_2 - p_1}{\rho} \tag{6-13}$$

Equation (6-12) contains the velocity term u_{b2}, but this is difficult to evaluate because the cross section of the jet at the vena contracta is not readily known.   Consequently, the downstream velocity is more conveniently taken as the velocity through the orifice itself.   To compensate for the error thus introduced, a discharge coefficient C_o is defined by

$$C_o{}^2 \frac{p_2 - p_1}{\rho} + \frac{u_{bo}{}^2 - u_{b1}{}^2}{2g_c} = 0 \tag{6-14}$$

If β is defined as D_o/D_1, Eq. (6-14) becomes

$$u_{bo} = C_o \sqrt{\frac{2g_c(p_1 - p_2)}{\rho(1 - \beta^4)}} \tag{6-15}$$

The discharge coefficient sometimes includes the velocity-of-approach factor.

The velocity distribution across the stream at the various points is not necessarily uniform, especially for laminar flow, so C_o also includes this effect.   Empirically determined values of C_o for sharp-edged orifices with corner taps are given in Fig. 6-5 as a function of β and the Reynolds number through the orifice.   The value of C_o is dependent on the location of the pressure taps.   Tabulations of C_o for flange taps, vena contracta taps, and pipe taps are available in "Fluid Meters: Their Theory and Application," part I.[1]

It is of interest to show that the discharge coefficient can be estimated from theory with some success.   Let us define a coefficient of contraction for the jet by

$$C_c = \frac{A_2}{A_o} \tag{6-16}$$

This coefficient is used to relate the velocities

$$u_{b2} = \frac{u_{bo}}{C_c} \tag{6-17}$$

and

$$u_{b1} = \beta^2 u_{bo} \tag{6-18}$$

These expressions are then substituted in Eq. (6-12) to give

$$\frac{p_2 - p_1}{\rho} = -\frac{1}{C_v{}^2} \left(\frac{1}{C_c{}^2} - \beta^4 \right) \frac{u_{bo}{}^2}{2g_c} \tag{6-19}$$

A similar equation is obtained by substituting for u_{b1} in Eq. (6-14) using Eq. (6-18).

$$\frac{p_2 - p_1}{\rho} = -\frac{1}{C_o{}^2} (1 - \beta^4) \frac{u_{bo}{}^2}{2g_c} \tag{6-20}$$

By equating the coefficients of $u_{bo}{}^2/2g_c$ in Eqs. (6-19) and (6-20) and rearranging, we obtain

$$C_o = C_v C_c \sqrt{\frac{1 - \beta^4}{1 - C_c{}^2\beta^4}} \tag{6-21}$$

The shape of the jet, i.e., the value of C_c, can be calculated from the theory of ideal fluids.   The results apply strictly only to a two-dimensional jet with a flat velocity profile flowing into a fluid of much lower density, but they give a good estimation of the value of C_c for a sharp-edged orifice. The values in Table 6-1 were obtained by von Mises[2] and are reproduced in standard texts on hydrodynamics.[3]   If the values of C_c from Table 6-1

[1] American Society of Mechanical Engineers, New York, 1937.

[2] R. von Mises, *Z. deut. Ing.*, **61**:447–451, 469–473, 493–497 (1917).

[3] H. Rouse and J. W. Howe, "Basic Mechanics of Fluids," p. 49, John Wiley & Sons, Inc., New York, 1953.

Table 6-1

β	0	0.1	0.2	0.3	0.4	0.5	0.6	0.7	0.8	0.9	1.00
C_c	0.611	0.612	0.616	0.622	0.631	0.644	0.662	0.683	0.722	0.781	1.000

are substituted into Eq. (6-21) for $C_v = 0.98$ together with various values of β, it is found that C_o departs very little from the empirical value of 0.61 given in Fig. 6-5 for $\mathbf{Re}_o > 50,000$. Equation (6-21) is not valid for lower $\mathbf{Re}$, for which C_o should include a correction for the upstream velocity distribution.

The use of an orifice meter is often limited by the magnitude of the permissible over-all pressure drop from 1 to 3. From the mechanical energy balance there results

$$\frac{p_3 - p_1}{\rho} + lw_{12} + lw_{23} = 0 \tag{6-22}$$

The value of lw_{12} is given by Eq. (6-13); lw_{23} is the expansion loss from 2 to 3 and can be calculated from Eq. (5) of Example 5-2.

$$lw_{23} = \left(1 - \frac{A_2}{A_1}\right)^2 \frac{u_{b2}{}^2}{2g_c} \tag{6-23}$$

Equation (6-16) and the definition of β are used to transform Eq. (6-23) to

$$lw_{23} = \frac{(1 - C_c\beta^2)^2}{C_c{}^2} \frac{u_{bo}{}^2}{2g_c} \tag{6-24}$$

Equations (6-13), (6-20), (6-22), and (6-24) are combined to give

$$\frac{p_3 - p_1}{\rho} = \left[\left(1 - \frac{1}{C_v{}^2}\right)\left(\frac{1}{C_c{}^2} - \beta^4\right) - \frac{(1 - C_c\beta^2)^2}{C_c{}^2}\right]\frac{u_{bo}{}^2}{2g_c} \tag{6-25}$$

Equation (6-25) is divided by Eq. (6-20) to give the result

$$1 - R = \frac{p_1 - p_3}{p_1 - p_2} = 1 - \frac{2C_c\beta^2C_v{}^2}{1 + C_c\beta^2} \tag{6-26}$$

The quantity R represents the fraction of the maximum pressure drop, that from 1 to 2, recovered downstream from the vena contracta; $1 - R$ is the fraction lost. Using $C_v = 0.98$ and values for C_c from Table 6-1, Eq. (6-26) yields Fig. 6-6.

The orifice discharge coefficient is significantly affected by flow disturbances which originate in valves, bends, and other fittings located upstream from the orifice. It is less affected by downstream disturbances. As a general rule, the meter should be placed 50 pipe diameters downstream and 10 pipe diameters upstream from any disturbances. It should be apparent that the necessary distances depend on the nature of the disturbance and

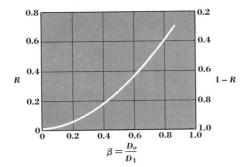

Fig. 6-6.   Over-all pressure change for orifice.

in many cases are much less than the general specifications given above. Perry (p. 407) tabulates recommended locations for many specific cases. The upstream distance can often be reduced by placing straightening vanes in the pipe, and recommendations for the use of these vanes are also given by Perry.

Our purpose in this discussion of orifice meters has been to show some applications of the over-all balances and to inquire briefly into the principles of flow through orifices. The extension of the formulas to compressible gases is discussed in Perry's Handbook, pp. 402 to 404. A much more detailed treatment of orifices is given by Stearns et al.[1] Not only are extensive tables of the discharge coefficient given, but much useful information is included about the location of the orifice with respect to upstream and downstream disturbances and about the details of orifice installation.

Rotameter

The rotameter is illustrated in Fig. 6-7. In the meters already studied, the area of the constriction remains constant and the pressure drop varies with flow rate; in the rotameter, the pressure drop remains nearly constant and the area of the constriction varies. The fluid flows vertically upward through the tapered rotameter tube, and the float comes to equilibrium at a point where the annular flow area is such that the velocity increase has produced the necessary pressure difference. A higher flow rate causes the float to rise to a point where the annular area is larger.

Equation (6-15) is adapted to the rotameter by defining a coefficient C_r by

$$u_{br} = C_r \sqrt{\frac{2g_c(p_1 - p_2)}{\rho}} \tag{6-27}$$

The factor $1/\sqrt{1 - \beta^4}$ is included in C_r; u_{br} is the velocity in the annular

[1] R. F. Stearns, R. R. Johnson, R. M. Jackson, and C. A. Larson, "Flow Measurement with Orifice Meters," D. Van Nostrand Company, Inc., Princeton, N.J., 1951.

Fluid out

Fluid in

Fig. 6-7.   *Operation of rotameter.*

constriction. The pressure difference, $p_1 - p_2$, is found by making a force balance on the stationary float. The downward force caused by gravity is balanced by the upward buoyant force plus the force exerted by the pressure difference across the float caused by the velocity increase in the annular constriction. Thus we write

$$\rho_f \check{V}_f \frac{g}{g_c} = \rho \check{V}_f \frac{g}{g_c} + A_f(p_1 - p_2) \tag{6-28}$$

and

$$p_1 - p_2 = \frac{\check{V}_f(\rho_f - \rho)g}{A_f g_c} \tag{6-29}$$

where $\check{V}_f$ = volume of float

     A_f = maximum cross-sectional area of float

The substitution of Eq. (6-29) into Eq. (6-27) gives

$$u_{br} = C_r \sqrt{\frac{2g\check{V}_f(\rho_f - \rho)}{A_f \rho}} \tag{6-30}$$

The coefficient of discharge C_r is given in Fig. 6-8 as a function of the Reynolds number in the annulus and the type of float. The Reynolds number is defined as

$$\mathsf{Re} = \frac{(D - D_f)u_{br}\rho}{\mu} \tag{6-31}$$

where D = diameter of tube at level of float

     D_f = maximum diameter of float

Above $\mathsf{Re} = 10,000$, C_r is constant for the floats shown in Fig. 6-8. Equation (6-30) then shows that u_{br} is constant when C_r is constant, for a given fluid and rotameter. The mass rate of flow or the upstream velocity is easily found from an over-all mass balance.

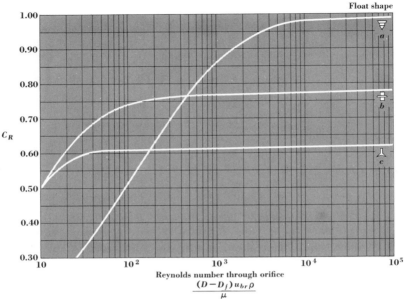

Fig. 6-8.   Rotameter discharge coefficients. (From G. G. Brown et al., "Unit Operations," fig. 145, p. 158, John Wiley & Sons, Inc., New York, 1950.)

$$w = u_{br}\rho A_r = u_{b1}\rho A_1 \tag{6-32}$$

Flow around float a shown in Fig. 6-8 resembles flow through a venturi in that the cross-sectional area for flow changes gradually. As a consequence, C_r approaches C_v at high Reynolds numbers. Flow around float c resembles flow through an orifice, with the result that C_r approaches C_o at high Re.

The annular area A_r is a function of the float position. Although the flow through a rotameter can be estimated from the geometry of the float and tube and the above equation, the manufacturer usually furnishes a reliable calibration. The above relations, particularly Eq. (6-30), permit the calibration for one fluid to be adapted for use with a different fluid.

Other Meters

An example of a nozzle is shown in Fig. 6-9. It has more over-all pressure loss than a venturi but less than an orifice; some models can be installed in a pipe in the same manner as an orifice plate.

There are many other types of meters besides the foregoing differential-pressure meters. They include weirs and notches for flow in open channels and various kinds of mechanical meters. The latter operate either on a

Fig. 6-9.   Flow nozzle.

positive-displacement principle, such as a wet test meter, or as a current meter, such as an anemometer.   There are many other more specialized types; for pictures and discussion of their operation, refer, for example, to Perry, pp. 410 to 412, and to Linford.[1]

Data on coefficients and operating and installation procedures are given in publications by the American Society of Mechanical Engineers[2] and the International Standards Association.[3]

PROBLEMS

6-1. A closed-U-tube manometer filled with mercury is attached to the underside of a line carrying water, as shown in Fig. 6-10.   At a point directly above the closed-U-tube-manometer tap, the upstream tap of an inverted U tube is located.   The inverted-U-tube manometer is filled with a liquid of specific gravity 0.5.   What are p_1 and p_2 in psia?

6-2. The following data were obtained in a pitot-tube traverse of a 3-in., schedule-40 steel pipe in which water at 58°F was flowing:

Distance from wall, in.	Manometer reading, in. carbon tetrachloride at 58°F
0.28	2.20
0.53	2.40
0.78	2.60
1.03	2.80
1.28	3.00
1.53	3.10
1.78	2.85
2.03	2.70
2.28	2.40
2.53	2.00
2.78	1.65

[1] A. Linford, "Flow Measurement and Meters," E. and F. N. Spoon Ltd., London, 1949.

[2] ASME Special Committee on Fluid Meters, "Fluid Meters," pts. 1 to 3, New York, 1931–1937.

[3] Rules for Measuring the Flow of Fluids by Means of Nozzles and Orifice Plates, Preliminary Recommendations, *ISA Bulls.* 9 and 12, December, 1935, and August, 1936.

Fig. 6-10. Orifice meter for Prob. 6-1.

At the same time that these measurements were being taken, a series of samples of the flow were taken by discharging the total stream into a weigh tank. The discharge rate was found to be 1400 lb of water in 194.4 sec. Find the pitot-tube coefficient.

6-3. Water at 60°F is flowing through a 3½-in., schedule-40 steel pipe. The corner taps of a 1-in. circular, square-edged orifice in the pipe are connected to a manometer containing methyl benzoate (specific gravity 1.10). The difference in fluid levels in the manometer is 5.2 in. Find the flow rate in the pipe.

6-4. During a laboratory experiment 4.5 cu ft of air at an upstream pressure of 749.5 mm Hg and a temperature of 84°F is passed through an orifice in 131 sec. The orifice diameter is 0.25 in. and is small compared with the pipe diameter. The pressure drop across the orifice is 5.6 in. of water. Calculate the orifice coefficient.

6-5. Water at 60°F is flowing through a 3-in., schedule-40 steel pipe at the rather low rate of 0.2 lb/sec. The liquid is metered by a sharp-edged orifice having a diameter of 2.28 in.

It is later found necessary to meter acetone at 40°F in the same system at the same rate of flow, 0.2 lb/sec. What will be the ratio of the pressure drop across the orifice using acetone to the pressure drop using water?

6-6. Air at 60°F is flowing through a 12-in.-diameter circular duct into a spray drier at the rate of 300 cu ft/min. The flow rate is to be measured using an orifice meter to which is attached a water manometer. Since the pressure in the air line is only 2 psig and the air must reach the drier at a pressure of at least 1.8 psig, it is essential that the permanent head loss due to the orifice not exceed 0.2 psi. Find the maximum manometer differential (in inches of water) which can be obtained under these conditions.

6-7. Water at 70°F is to be pumped through a length of 2-in., schedule-40 steel pipe, and its flow rate is to be measured by an orifice meter or a venturi meter. The water enters the pump at atmospheric pressure and leaves the meter at 70 psig at the same elevation as the pump entrance. At a flow rate of 100 gal/min the difference in mercury levels in the attached manometer is to be 10 in. How much will the daily cost of electrical energy to run the pump be reduced by using the venturi meter instead of the orifice meter? The motor-pump combination has an efficiency of 70 per cent. Electricity cost is 2 cents per kilowatthour.

6-8. A rotameter has the sight glass marked into 25 divisions. The float which is used is made of an unknown material, and its total volume is also unknown. Air at the rate of 3 cu ft/122 sec is allowed to flow through the meter. The following data were taken:

Temperature of air.................. 92°F
Static pressure..................... 2.05 in. water
Barometric pressure................ 29.49 in. Hg
Rotameter reading.................. 13.0
Weight of float in air.............. 4.62 g at 60°F
Weight of float in water........... 2.96 g at 60°F
Diameter of float.................. 0.50 in.
Diameter of tube at top............ 0.6482 in.
Diameter of tube at bottom......... 0.5128 in.

Calculate the rotameter coefficient.

CONCEPTS OF FLUID BEHAVIOR (I)

Viscosity of Newtonian Fluids

A fluid is distinguished from a solid in this discussion of viscosity by its behavior when subjected to an applied stress. Whereas an elastic solid deforms by an amount proportional to the applied stress, a fluid under similar circumstances continues to deform—i.e., flow—at a velocity which increases with increasing stress. These ideas are clarified by a quantitative definition of viscosity. In Fig. 7-1 a fluid in laminar motion is contained between two infinite parallel plates.

If the upper plate moves with a constant velocity relative to the lower one, a steady-state variation of velocity in the fluid between the plates is eventually achieved. For newtonian fluids, the shear stress τ (the applied force per unit area of plate needed to maintain the constant velocity) is proportional to Δu and inversely proportional to Δy.

$$\tau = \mu \frac{\Delta u}{\Delta y} \tag{7-1}$$

where μ is by definition the viscosity. Since μ as defined by Eq. (7-1) is really an average viscosity over the distance Δy and the curve of u versus y will not in general be a straight line, the relationship is made exact by letting Δy approach zero and using the definition of the derivative to obtain

$$\tau = \mu \frac{du}{dy} \tag{7-2}$$

The defining expression for μ is thus a differential equation, as are many other basic relations of physics.

The units for the viscosity given by Eq. (7-2) are (dynes)(sec)/sq cm or

Fig. 7-1.   Fluid shear between parallel plates.

(lb force)(sec)/sq ft.   The cgs unit, alternatively expressed as g/(cm)(sec), is called the poise, and the usual unit appearing in tables is the centipoise, equal to $\frac{1}{100}$ poise.   In the system of units commonly employed by engineers, viscosity is given in lb/(ft)(sec), and the defining equation is written

$$\tau = \frac{\mu}{g_c} \frac{du}{dy} \tag{7-3}$$

We shall follow this custom.   Centipoises are converted to lb/(ft)(sec) by multiplying by 6.72×10^{-4}, and to lb/(ft)(hr) by multiplying by 2.42.

If the viscosity of a fluid is divided by its density, a useful quantity, the kinematic viscosity, is obtained.   It is written as

$$\nu = \frac{\mu}{\rho} \tag{7-4}$$

where the cgs units are the stoke and the centistoke.   Of two fluids flowing in a given tube at a given velocity, the one having the lower kinematic viscosity will be the more susceptible to the development of turbulence. Deviations from straight-line flow are dampened by the viscous character of the fluid, and the inertia of a deviating element is proportional to its density.   Thus fluids with low viscosity and high density tend to support turbulence.   The Reynolds number expressed in terms of the kinematic viscosity becomes Du_b/ν.   It is therefore a measure of the ratio of the inertia effect to the viscous effect and of the likelihood of the development of turbulence.   It is interesting to note that at room temperature ν is 1.0 cs for water and 15.0 cs for air at atmospheric pressure.

The concept of a flux of mass, energy, or momentum has been used in Chaps. 3 to 5.   Let us now observe that Eq. (7-2) defines a flux of momentum. The shear stress τ can be written in the units (g)(cm/sec)/(sq cm)(sec), that is, momentum per unit area-second.   The argument can be put into more concrete terms by considering the interaction of two adjacent layers of a gas in which there is a velocity gradient $du/dy \neq 0$.   The random motions of the molecules in the faster-moving layer send some of them into the slower-moving layer, where they collide with the slower-moving molecules and tend to speed them up. In similar fashion the slower layer acts to retard the faster one. (Note that "slow" and "fast" refer to the velocities of the layers, not to the random molecular velocities which determine the temperature.) This exchange of molecules produces a transfer of momentum, and a certain force per unit area is required to overcome the drag between the layers and maintain the velocity gradient.

For a newtonian fluid the viscosity is a property of the fluid and thus a function of only the state (pressure, temperature, and composition) of the fluid, so that a plot of τ against du/dy gives a straight line of slope μ. If the flow in a channel as illustrated in Fig. 7-1 is laminar, so that all the layers of fluid slide over each other in the same direction, Eq. (7-3) can be integrated over a finite Δy, provided that τ is known as a function of y. In this way we shall obtain many useful results for problems with laminar flow.

In turbulent flow the velocity at any point is a function of time, and in terms of this instantaneous unsteady-state velocity, Eq. (7-3) still holds; after all, μ is a property of the fluid. In addition to the exchange of molecules between layers, macroscopic amounts of fluid are also exchanged, and momentum is transferred by this mixing process. For these reasons the ordinary viscosity is often called the molecular viscosity, whereas the viscosity which would be measured using Eq. (7-1) (u signifies now a time mean velocity) for turbulent flow in the channel of Fig. 7-1 is the sum of the molecular viscosity and a quantity called the eddy viscosity. The eddy viscosity attains values much larger than the molecular viscosity. It is not a property of the fluid, since it is a function of the extent of mixing (turbulence) in the fluid; it varies from point to point. Turbulent flow will be considered in detail in Chap. 13.

The student should know in general that the viscosity of a gas increases with increasing temperature; the viscosity of a liquid, which is much larger than that of the same substance in its vapor state at the same temperature, decreases with increasing temperature. The viscosity of an ideal gas is independent of pressure, but the viscosities of real gases and liquids usually increase with pressure.

Figure 7-2 gives the viscosities of a few substances and the effects of pressure and temperature. Some sources of detailed information on viscosities are Perry, "Chemical Engineers' Handbook"; Lange, "Handbook of Chemistry"; and Landolt-Börnstein, "Physikochemische Tabellen."

If no experimental viscosity data are available, there are several methods available by which this property can be estimated from the fundamental

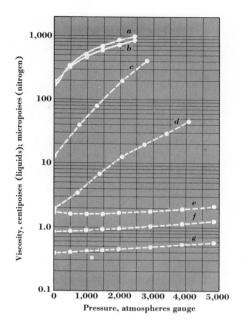

Fig. 7-2.   *Viscosities of 9,n-octyl heptadecane, water, and nitrogen.*

a.   Nitrogen, 25°C (4).
b.   Nitrogen, 75°C (4).
c.   n-Octyl heptadecane, 20°C (1).
d.   n-Octyl heptadecane, 99°C (1).
e.   Water, 0°C (2,3).
f.   Water, 20°C (2,3).
g.   Water, 75°C (2,3).

(1)   Pressure-Viscosity Report, ASME, New York, 1953.
(2)   P. W. Bridgman, "The Physics of High Pressure," G. Bell & Sons, Ltd., London, 1950.
(3)   J. H. Keenan and F. G. Keyes, "Thermodynamic Properties of Steam," John Wiley & Sons, Inc., New York, 1936.
(4)   F. Lazarre and B. Vodar, *Proc. Conf. Thermo. and Transport Properties of Fluids*, Inst. Mech. Engrs., London, 1958.

physical constants for a fluid.   Refer to Bird et al.[1] for an introduction to this subject.

Rheology of Nonnewtonian Fluids[2]

The science of the deformation and flow of materials is often called rheology; we now turn to another important branch of this subject, the behavior of nonnewtonian fluids.   For a newtonian fluid there is a linear relation between the shear stress τ and the velocity gradient du/dy.   (Many authors refer to the velocity gradient as the rate of shear.)   For nonnewtonian fluids, the relation is not linear; the character of the relation is used to classify the several types of nonnewtonian fluid.   The stress rates of shear curves for some of these types are shown in Fig. 7-3, a logarithmic plot of τ versus du/dy.

There is a large range of rate of shear over which the curves for many nonnewtonian fluids on Fig. 7-3 are essentially straight lines.   It is therefore convenient to write[3]

[1] R. B. Bird, W. E. Stewart, and E. N. Lightfoot, "Transport Phenomena," John Wiley & Sons, Inc., New York, 1960.
[2] A. B. Metzner, "Non-Newtonian Technology," *Advances in Chem. Eng.*, 1:77–153 (1956).
[3] This equation often is replaced in the literature by $du/dy = Kg_c\tau^n$.

Fig. 7-3.   *Shear behavior of fluids.*
a.   **Dilatant.**
b.   **Newtonian.**
c.   **Bingham-plastic.**
d.   **Pseudo plastic.**

$$\tau = \frac{K}{g_c}\left(\frac{du}{dy}\right)^n \tag{7-5}$$

This equation does not apply for precise work over a large range of du/dy; however, it is useful for many engineering applications. For newtonian fluids, which include all gases and most liquids of low molecular weight, n is unity and K is then the same as μ. The quantity n is often called the flow-behavior index, and K is the consistency index. We shall now discuss several types of nonnewtonian fluids.

Bingham-plastic Fluids.   These fluids require the application of a stress τ_p to cause any deformation. At stresses below τ_p they behave like solids, and at stresses above τ_p a plot of τ versus du/dy is linear, so that

$$\tau = \tau_p + \frac{\mu_p}{g_c}\frac{du}{dy} \qquad \tau \geqq \tau_p \tag{7-6}$$

where μ_p is a constant analogous to the viscosity of a newtonian fluid. This is the simplest kind of nonnewtonian behavior. It is exhibited by fluids such as drilling muds and suspensions of regular, granular solids which take on a rigid, three-dimensional structure when at rest.

Pseudoplastic Fluids.   Most nonnewtonian fluids fall into this group; they are typified by the curve in Fig. 7-3 having a slope between zero and unity. The slope often approaches unity at very high or very low values of the rate of shear; that is, the fluids become more newtonian.

If Eq. (7-5) is put in the form

$$\tau = \frac{K|du/dy|^{n-1}}{g_c}\frac{du}{dy} \tag{7-7}$$

the term $K|du/dy|^{n-1}$ is sometimes called the apparent viscosity. This quantity decreases with increasing shear rate for pseudoplastic fluids, for which n is less than 1.0. Solutions of polymers and other large elongated molecules behave in this way, as well as colloidal or ordinary suspensions of asymmetric particles. These molecules or particles are looked upon as entangled at low shear rates, but more nearly aligned with each other at higher rates, decreasing the apparent viscosity. At very low shear rates the effect of entanglement is less important, whereas at very high shear rates the particles are aligned so that the entanglement is small. This explains the shape of the curve for pseudoplastic fluids in Fig. 7-3; newtonian behavior (a slope of unity) is approached at very low and at very high shear rates.

Dilatant Fluids. The curve in Fig. 7-3 typifying dilatant fluids has a slope greater than unity; n is greater than 1.0. A dilatant fluid is often thought of as containing only enough liquid to fill the void between particles at rest or at very low shear rates; for these cases the fluid is almost newtonian. As the particles move over each other more rapidly, they need more room; the fluid as a whole dilates. Since there is no longer enough liquid to fill the larger void space, the apparent viscosity increases. This behavior is in accord with Eq. (7-7) for $n > 1.0$. Suspensions of starch, potassium silicate, and sand are examples of dilatant fluids.

Time-dependent Nonnewtonian Fluids. For these fluids, the shear stress is a function of time at constant shear rate. This type of behavior is complicated, and little progress has been made toward its analytical representation.

For a rheopectic fluid the shear stress increases with time at constant shear rate; for a thixotropic fluid it decreases with time. Many paints are thixotropic, a characteristic which aids their application with either a brush or a spray nozzle and retards their subsequent flow when applied to a vertical surface.

Most nonnewtonian fluids have apparent viscosities which are relatively high compared with the viscosity of water.

Laminar Flow in a Circular Tube

In Chap. 11 we shall derive the general partial differential equations which can be used to obtain velocity distributions for two- and three-dimensional flow systems; the viscous stress defined by Eq. (7-3) is an important part of the analysis. However, to show an immediate application of the definition of viscosity to a simple and important case, let us analyze the one-dimensional, steady, laminar flow of an incompressible fluid in a horizontal, circular tube of constant diameter in order to find the velocity distribution and pressure drop.

This problem will be solved by making a force balance on the cylindrical

Fig. 7-4.   *Forces acting on an element of fluid flowing in a circular tube.*

element of fluid shown in Fig. 7-4.   The analysis is an application of Eq. (5-6), which we write for this case as

$$\frac{w}{g_c} \Delta u_x = R_x - F_{xp} - F_{xd} \tag{7-8}$$

The momentum (velocity) difference is zero for an incompressible fluid, and there is no external force; the pressure force is $\pi r^2 \, \Delta p$, and the drag force is $\tau 2\pi r L$, so that Eq. (7-8) reduces to

$$\tau = \frac{-\Delta p}{2L} r \tag{7-9}$$

At the wall this equation becomes

$$\tau_s = \frac{-\Delta p D}{4L} \tag{7-10}$$

These two equations, unlike those to follow, apply to both laminar and turbulent flow, provided the time mean pressure and velocity are used for the latter.   The velocity distribution in laminar flow is found by substituting

$$\tau = \frac{\mu}{g_c}\left(-\frac{du}{dr}\right) \tag{7-11}$$

into Eq. (7-9).   This is Eq. (7-3) modified with a minus sign because du/dr is negative.   After rearrangement and the introduction of integral signs, the substitution gives

$$\frac{-\Delta p g_c}{2\mu L} \int_0^r r \, dr = -\int_{u_{\max}}^u du \tag{7-12}$$

The integrated result is

$$u = u_{\max} + \frac{\Delta p g_c}{4\mu L} r^2 \tag{7-13}$$

Since $u = 0$ at $r = r_i$ from the assumption of no slip at the wall, it follows that

$$u_{\max} = \frac{-\Delta p g_c r_i{}^2}{4\mu L} \tag{7-14}$$

and thus we obtain

$$u = u_{\max} \left[1 - \left(\frac{r}{r_i} \right)^2 \right] \tag{7-15}$$

Equation (7-15) is the parabolic velocity distribution which we used in Example 3-1 to show that $u_b = u_{\max}/2$ for laminar flow and in Example 4-1 to show that the kinetic-energy term in the over-all energy balance is $u_b{}^2/g_c$. Using the fact that $u_{\max} = 2u_b$, Eq. (7-14) can be written as

$$-\Delta p = \frac{8\mu L u_b}{g_c r_i{}^2} = \frac{32\mu L u_b}{g_c D^2} \tag{7-16}$$

This is the Hagen-Poiseuille equation for the pressure drop for steady-state, laminar flow in a horizontal, round pipe of constant cross section. From the mechanical energy balance, Eq. (4-27), it is seen that

$$lw_f = \frac{32\mu L u_b}{\rho g_c D^2} \tag{7-17}$$

for laminar flow (**Re** < 2100). Although the frictional loss in Eq. (7-17) was derived for a horizontal pipe, the analysis could have been made for a vertical pipe and would have given the same value for lw_f. If the velocity profile in the pipe is not changed by the orientation of the pipe, the expression for lw_f is not affected.

Example 7-1

Calculate the power required and the pressure which should be developed by a pump of 70 per cent efficiency in order to send 15 gal/min of 98 per cent sulfuric acid at 68°F from a tank at atmospheric pressure through 1000 ft of 2-in., schedule-40 steel pipe to a tank at 10 psig, where the level is 10 ft above that in the lower tank.

We calculate the bulk velocity and the Reynolds number in order to be sure that Eq. (7-17) is applicable.

$$u_b = \frac{15}{(60)(7.48)(0.0233)} = 1.431 \text{ ft/sec}$$

The cross-sectional area of the pipe, 0.0233 sq ft, is found in Perry, p. 415. The specific gravity of 98 per cent sulfuric acid is 1.836 (p. 185), and its viscosity is 26.0 cp (pp. 372–373). Thus

$$\textbf{Re} = \frac{(2.067/12)(1.431)(1.836)(62.4)}{(0.000672)(26.0)} = 1615$$

The flow is laminar, so Eq. (7-17) gives

$$lw_f = \frac{(32)(0.000672)(26.0)(1000)(1.431)}{(1.836)(62.4)(32.2)(2.067/12)^2} = 7.31 \text{ (ft)(lb force)/lb}$$

The work required is found from the mechanical energy balance, Eq. (4-27), which becomes

$$\frac{g}{g_c}\,\Delta z + \frac{\Delta p}{\rho} + lw_f + \eta_p W_s = 0$$

The kinetic-energy term and the expansion and contraction losses are negligible for this laminar-flow problem. Substitution of numerical values yields

$$10 + \frac{(10)(144)}{(62.4)(1.836)} + 7.31 + 0.70W_s = 0$$

and $W_s = -42.7$ (ft)(lb force)/lb.

The horsepower required is

$$\frac{(42.7)(3.83)}{550} = 0.298 \text{ hp}$$

for the flow rate of 3.83 lb/sec.

The pressure rise across the pump is given by

$$\frac{\Delta p}{\rho} + \eta_p W_s = 0$$

and

$$\Delta p = -\frac{(0.70)(-42.7)(62.4)(1.836)}{144}$$
$$= 23.8 \text{ psi}$$

Example 7-2

Find the relation between velocity and radial position for the laminar flow of a nonnewtonian fluid through a circular pipe at steady state. The stress rate of shear relation is given by

$$\tau = \frac{K}{g_c}\left(-\frac{du}{dr}\right)^n \tag{1}$$

This is Eq. (7-5), except for the minus sign, which is necessary in this case.

Equation (1) is substituted into Eq. (7-9) to yield

$$\frac{-\Delta p g_c}{2KL}\,r = \left(-\frac{du}{dr}\right)^n \tag{2}$$

Both sides of this equation are now raised to the $1/n$ power, and the equation is rearranged to give

$$\left(\frac{-\Delta p g_c}{2KL}\right)^{1/n}\int_0^r r^{1/n}\,dr = -\int_{u_{\max}}^u du \tag{3}$$

We find upon integration

$$u = \frac{n}{n+1}\left(\frac{-\Delta p g_c}{2KL}\right)^{1/n}(r_i)^{(n+1)/n}\left[1 - \left(\frac{r}{r_i}\right)^{(n+1)/n}\right] \tag{4}$$

and since $u = 0$ at $r = r_i$,

$$u = u_{\max}\left[1 - \left(\frac{r}{r_i}\right)^{(n+1)/n}\right] \tag{5}$$

This result, if compared with Eq. (7-15), shows that the velocity profile for the laminar flow of a nonnewtonian fluid can be greatly different from that of a newtonian fluid.

For pseudoplastic fluids, a relatively flat profile is obtained, and in the limit of an infinitely pseudoplastic fluid ($n = 0$) there is rodlike flow. For dilatant fluids, the profile is sharper, and for the limiting case of an infinitely dilatant fluid ($n = \infty$), the velocity is a linear function of the radius. The velocity profile is conical.

Further interesting cases of the laminar flow of both newtonian and nonnewtonian fluids will be found in the problems at the end of the chapter.

Fluxes of Momentum, Mass, and Energy

At the beginning of this chapter we showed that the shear stress τ can be regarded as a flux of momentum. For an incompressible fluid we can rewrite Eq. (7-3) as[1]

$$g_c \tau = -\nu \frac{d(u\rho)}{dy} \tag{7-18}$$

This equation is of the form: flux of momentum $[(\text{lb})(\text{ft/sec})/(\text{sq ft})(\text{sec})]$ equals a conductivity or diffusivity (sq ft/sec) times a gradient of momentum concentration $[(\text{lb})(\text{ft/sec})/(\text{cu ft})(\text{ft})]$. We insert the minus sign because the momentum is transferred toward the region of lower concentration of momentum (velocity). The kinematic viscosity is equivalent to a diffusivity of momentum. Equations in which flux equals diffusivity times concentration gradient are often called phenomenological equations; they represent an empirical method of correlating observed phenomena. Similar equations can be written for fluxes of mass, energy, electricity, and other entities.

The equation for the transfer of mass is written

$$J_A = -D_{AB} \frac{d\rho_A}{dy} \tag{7-19}$$

This relation applies to a binary mixture of A and B; J_A is the flux of A, D_{AB} is the diffusivity of A through the mixture of A and B, and ρ_A is the density (concentration) of A. The diffusivity, like the kinematic viscosity, has the units square feet per second. Component A flows from a region of high concentration of A to one of lower concentration. The flux is measured in lb $A/(\text{sec})(\text{sq ft})$ across an area perpendicular to the direction of the concentration gradient, expressed as (lb A/cu ft)/ ft.

The equation for the flux of energy is written

$$\frac{q}{A} = -k \frac{dt}{dy} \tag{7-20}$$

[1] The minus sign in this equation has been introduced to emphasize the analogy to heat and mass transfer. According to convention, the sign is positive, as in Eq. (7-3) and elsewhere in this book.

where k is the thermal conductivity. For a fluid of constant density and specific heat, this equation may be put into the form of Eqs. (7-18) and (7-19):

$$\frac{q}{A} = -\alpha \frac{d(C_p \rho t)}{dy} \tag{7-21}$$

where $\alpha = k/C_p \rho$. This coefficient is called the thermal diffusivity, and like ν and D_{AB}, its units are square feet per second. The energy flux is expressed as Btu/(sec)(sq ft), and the gradient of concentration of energy as (Btu/cu ft)/ ft. The energy flux is measured over an area perpendicular to the temperature gradient, and the energy flows from a region of high concentration of energy (temperature) to one of lower concentration.

In Chaps. 3 to 5 we saw many similarities among the over-all balances of mass, energy, and momentum. In the preceding paragraphs we have seen a rather striking similarity among the equations for the fluxes of these quantities. After a further general introduction to fluid behavior in Chap. 8, we shall study the differential balances of mass, energy, and momentum in Chaps. 9 to 11. In doing so we shall use the equations for the fluxes and the definitions of the various diffusivities, and we shall continue to find similarities among the three transport phenomena. In the present chapter we have discussed only viscosity and momentum transfer in detail. More extensive treatments of thermal conductivity and molecular diffusivity are deferred to the later parts of the book, which deal specifically with heat transfer and with mass transfer.

PROBLEMS

7-1. Derive the relations analogous to Eqs. (7-15) and (7-16) for the velocity distribution and for the pressure drop in laminar, newtonian flow through a slit of height y_o and infinite width.

7-2. Repeat Prob. 7-1 for a pseudoplastic fluid which follows the power law, Eq. (7-5), with $n = 0.5$.

7-3. Find the relation between u_{max} and u_b and also the expression for the pressure drop for a nonnewtonian fluid following Eq. (7-5) for laminar flow in a circular pipe.

7-4. Repeat Prob. 7-3 for a Bingham-plastic fluid.

7-5. Consider a newtonian fluid in laminar flow down a plane surface of infinite width. Find the velocity distribution within the liquid layer and the velocity at the free surface.

7-6. Oil is to be pumped at a rate of at least 1 gal/min through a horizontal line with an equivalent length of 1000 ft. The pump to be used has under these conditions a maximum discharge pressure of 14 psig. The line will discharge into a tank containing oil to a depth of 20 ft above the inlet. If the oil has a density of 50 lb/cu ft and a viscosity of 3 cp, what size schedule-40 pipe should be recommended for the line?

7-7. A pipeline 20 miles long delivers 5000 bbl/day of petroleum. The pressure drop over the line is 500 psi. Find the new capacity of the pipeline if a parallel, identical line is laid along the last 12 miles of the line. The pressure drop is to remain 500 psi, and the flow is laminar in all cases.

7-8. Glycerol is flowing at 140°F through a 100-ft length of vertical 1-inch, schedule-40 steel pipe. If the pressure at the lower end of the pipe is 20 psi greater than at the upper end, what is the mass rate of flow of glycerol? What is the direction of flow?

7-9. Find the expression for the velocity distribution and pressure drop for a fluid in laminar flow in the annular space between two horizontal, concentric pipes. In this derivation the momentum balance must be applied to a control volume of differential magnitude, namely, an annular shell of thickness dr. Show that this analysis results in the differential equation

$$\frac{d}{dr}\,(r\tau) = \frac{r\,\Delta p}{L}$$

from which the desired relations are obtained by the substitution of Newton's law [Eq. (7-3)] and two integrations.

CONCEPTS OF FLUID BEHAVIOR (II)

The chapters following this one lead to the derivation of the differential momentum balance. The momentum balances in the three directions are called the equations of motion, or the Navier-Stokes equations. These equations will be used to obtain the flow patterns and pressure drops for flow past objects and in conduits. Before setting out on this analytical approach, however, it is useful to learn about the results of experiments on flow for systems of simple geometry and the agreement between these and the results predicted by various theoretical arguments.

Streamlines and the Stream Function

In order to describe flow systems graphically it is common practice to use streamlines. We now consider their mathematical definition. To avoid unprofitable complications, only two-dimensional steady flow will be discussed, i.e., cases where there is no variation of velocity in the z direction taken perpendicular to the plane of the paper. A streamline is then defined as a line across which no fluid flows.

It is useful to define a quantity which is called the stream function ψ in such a way that streamlines represent lines of constant ψ. The velocity components u_x and u_y can be related to the orientation of the streamlines by the following analysis.

Consider two lines of constant ψ as shown by Fig. 8-1. The mass rate of flow through the space having a cross section defined by the two streamlines and a unit distance in the direction perpendicular to the paper is constant across any line, say C_1, joining the two streamlines and is given by

$$w = \int_{C_1} u\rho \cos \alpha \, ds \qquad (8\text{-}1)$$

where s = distance along line C_1 joining streamlines

α = angle between velocity vector and outward-directed normal to ds

The stream function is related to the mass rate of flow by

Fig. 8-1. *Sketch of streamlines.*

$$w = (\psi_2 - \psi_1)\rho_o \tag{8-2}$$

where ρ_o = a constant reference density

Equations (8-1) and (8-2) can also be written for a differential change in the stream function as

$$dw = \rho_o \, d\psi = u\rho \cos \alpha \, ds \tag{8-3}$$

The value of $\int \rho_o \, d\psi$ is the same for any path joining the streamlines. If the path C_2 is chosen, oriented in the y direction, then $ds = dy$ and $u \cos \alpha = u_x$, so that

$$\frac{\partial \psi}{\partial y} = u_x \frac{\rho}{\rho_o} \tag{8-4}$$

For path C_3, $ds = -dx$ and $u \cos \alpha = u_y$, giving

$$\frac{\partial \psi}{\partial x} = -u_y \frac{\rho}{\rho_o} \tag{8-5}$$

If ds is chosen so its normal coincides with the direction of flow, we obtain

$$\frac{d\psi}{ds} = u \frac{\rho}{\rho_o} \tag{8-6}$$

If ds coincides with the direction of flow, $\cos \alpha$ is zero and $d\psi/ds$ is zero; hence ψ is constant. Since a line of constant ψ is a streamline, it is evident that the velocity is directed along the streamlines. For an incompressible fluid, the velocity u is greatest where the streamlines on a particular graph are closest together. For a compressible fluid the flux $u\rho$ is greatest when the streamlines are closest together.

These ideas can be extended to three-dimensional flow by defining a stream surface in an analogous manner. For axially symmetric flow the two-dimensional representation is satisfactory, as illustrated in Fig. 8-2 for flow through a nozzle.

Ideal Fluids

An ideal fluid has a viscosity of zero, and the science dealing with such fluids is called theoretical hydrodynamics. During the latter half of the

Fig. 8-2.   Streamlines in a nozzle.

nineteenth century an elaborate mathematical theory of ideal fluids was developed, and the differential equations for flow of an ideal fluid were solved for many cases.   Since air and water have low viscosities, it was reasoned that they should behave like ideal fluids except at low Reynolds numbers.   Experiments showed that this was not true in many cases.   For example, practical problems, like the calculation of the pressure drop for water flowing through a conduit, could not be solved by using the equations of theoretical hydrodynamics.   Meanwhile, the empirical science of hydraulics, which bore very little resemblance to the theory of ideal fluids, had been developed by engineers to solve these problems.

It was not until the introduction of the idea of the boundary layer by Prandtl in 1904 that the two branches of fluid dynamics began to be reconciled.   The theory of ideal fluids is still regarded as satisfactory for the flow of fluids of low viscosity far from solid boundaries, but near the boundaries there is a thin layer where viscous friction is important.   In spite of its thinness, this layer profoundly affects the flow near an object and the drag exerted by the fluid on the object.

Let us look at a few results from the theory of ideal fluids for flow past a simple shape.   Figure 8-3 shows horizontal, two-dimensional flow past a cylinder of infinite length.   The fluid divides and flows around the cylinder with slip at the surface, since there can be no tangential or shear stresses in an ideal fluid.

The position of the streamlines can be obtained from calculations based on a type of ideal fluid flow called irrotational, or potential, flow.   Once this mathematical problem has been solved, Bernoulli's equation can be used to find the pressure distribution in the fluid.   This equation becomes, for horizontal flow along a streamline in an ideal incompressible fluid,

$$\frac{u^2 - u_o{}^2}{2g_c} + \frac{p - p_o}{\rho} = 0 \tag{8-7}$$

Because the velocity at A is zero, the pressure there is found to be

$$p = p_o + \frac{u_o{}^2 \rho}{2g_c} \tag{8-8}$$

Fig. 8-3.   Ideal flow around a cylinder.

This is the stagnation, or kinetic, pressure.   At points B and D the velocity is a maximum and the pressure falls to a minimum.   At point C the velocity is again zero.   Since the flow is symmetrical before and behind the cylinder, the force exerted by the pressure on the upstream half of the cylinder equals that on the downstream half.   As a result, there is no drag on the cylinder.   Near the curved surface of the cylinder, the inner layers of fluid travel faster than the outer layers, so that there is no net rotation of fluid; hence the term irrotational flow.   Furthermore, the fluid has zero viscosity, so that the sliding of these layers over each other is associated with no shearing stress.   These matters will be discussed mathematically in Chap. 12.

Figure 8-4 shows a comparison of the experimental pressure distribution around a cylinder with that predicted by ideal flow.   It can be seen that the theory gives results very different from the results of the experiments.

For flow past a flat plate the theory of ideal fluids gives zero drag force because there is slip at the surface.   Furthermore, there is no change in velocity or pressure in the fluid.   The drag actually observed for real fluids, therefore, is caused completely by viscous shear forces associated with the variation of velocity from zero at the surface of the plate to u_o in the undisturbed stream.   The drag on the plate can be calculated from theory by the integration of the differential momentum balance, as will be shown in Chap. 12, or it can be obtained from a knowledge of the velocity distribution near the plate and the use of the over-all momentum balance, as will be shown in Chap. 13.

The Boundary Layer

The boundary layer is the region near a solid where the fluid motion is affected by the solid boundary; just where the motion ceases to be affected

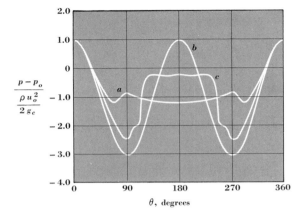

$$\frac{p - p_o}{\frac{\rho u_o^2}{2 g_c}}$$

θ, degrees

Fig. 8-4.   Pressure distribution in flow past a cylinder. (From Hermann Schlichting, "Boundary Layer Theory," 4th ed., fig. 1.9, p. 19, McGraw-Hill Book Company, Inc., New York, 1960.)
a.   *Measured, Re = 1.9 × 10⁵.*
b.   *Ideal-fluid theory.*
c.   *Measured, Re = 6.7 × 10⁵.*

is, of course, subject to an arbitrary definition.   Details of this matter will be considered in Chap. 12.   In the bulk of the fluid the flow is often assumed to be governed by the theory of ideal fluids.   By contrast, viscosity is important in the boundary layer, but the layer is relatively thin, so that the equations for flow in this region can be simplified and adequate solutions obtained for many cases.   This division of the problem of flow past an object into these two parts, as suggested by Prandtl, has proved to be of fundamental importance in fluid dynamics.

For flow past a flat plate the thickness of the boundary layer increases from zero at the leading edge, as shown in Fig. 8-5.   The Reynolds number for this case is defined as $xu_o\rho/\mu$, where x is the distance downstream measured from the leading edge.   Above a certain value of $\mathbf{Re}_x$, the flow becomes turbulent, although there remains a laminar sublayer, as shown in Fig. 8-5. The transition from laminar to turbulent flow on a smooth plate occurs in the range of Reynolds numbers 2×10^5 to 3×10^6.

If a fluid flowing with a uniform velocity u_o enters a conduit, a boundary layer builds up as shown in Fig. 8-6 and eventually fills the pipe.   Thus,

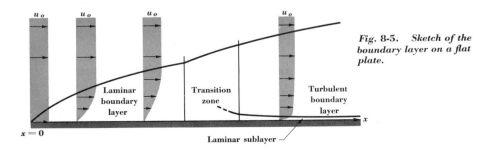

Fig. 8-5.   Sketch of the boundary layer on a flat plate.

Fig. 8-6.   Boundary layer near the entrance of a conduit.

in fully developed laminar or turbulent flow, the entire radius of the pipe is in the boundary layer. Downstream from the point where the boundary layer fills the pipe, the flow pattern is independent of x, so the Reynolds number based on the distance from the inlet has no further significance. Instead, the flow is characterized by the Reynolds number based on the pipe diameter, which we have used in all previous chapters. Therefore the quantity $Du_b\rho/\mu$ applies only to this fully developed flow region. If the boundary layer is turbulent and fills the pipe, as it usually does except very near the entrance to the pipe, a uniform laminar sublayer persists near the walls, just as with flow past a flat plate.

Boundary-layer Separation

In Chap. 12 a consideration of the order of magnitude of the various terms in the equations of motion when applied to a boundary layer will lead to the conclusion that there is negligible pressure variation in the direction normal to the surface. Consequently, the pressure within the boundary layer can be approximated by the pressure given by the ideal-flow pattern outside the boundary layer.

We defined the boundary layer with reference to a flat plate, but a boundary layer will also clearly exist on the surface of a cylinder, or on any other surface. In Fig. 8-7 the layers of fluid near the surface of the cylinder (of diameter D) are retarded by viscous friction, and after point B is passed, the fluid is also retarded by the unfavorable pressure gradient.

Fig. 8-7.   Separation in flow past a cylinder.

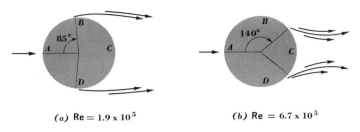

(a) Re = 1.9 x 10^5 (b) Re = 6.7 x 10^5

Fig. 8-8.   *Effect of turbulence on the point of separation.*

These two factors are enough at all but rather low Reynolds number $(Du_o\rho/\mu)$ to cause the fluid near the surface to come to rest and even to flow in the reverse direction, as shown in Fig. 8-7. The boundary layer then leaves the surface; this phenomenon is called separation.

If the flow rate past a cylinder is gradually increased above **Re** in the order of 1.0, separation starts at the rear stagnation point. This causes a change in the pressure and flow fields, and the separation point moves forward. The most forward position is at $\theta = 85°$, as shown in Fig. 8-8a. This occurs for a laminar boundary layer.

If the velocity past the cylinder is increased sufficiently to cause a transition to a turbulent boundary layer, the point of separation moves toward the rear of the cylinder, as shown in Fig. 8-8b. Because of the increased efficiency of momentum transfer in the turbulent flow, the velocity of the layers near the surface is increased. The higher kinetic energy of the fluid near the surface causes it to penetrate farther around the cylinder and establish a zone of higher pressure (Fig. 8-4), in accordance with the nearly ideal-flow behavior outside the boundary layer. Therefore the separation point moves to a new position past points B and D. For flow past a cylinder, most of the drag is caused by the difference in the pressure on the forward and the rear surfaces, so that the drag is actually decreased by the increase of velocity, which causes the change from a laminar to a turbulent boundary layer. Further increases in the Reynolds number, however, will cause an increase in the drag force.

The type of drag experienced by a bluff shape such as a cylinder, which is mostly caused by a pressure difference, is called form drag. The drag caused by viscous shear in the boundary layer is called skin friction; it is the only drag for flow past a flat plate. Form drag is predominant in flow past bluff, nonstreamlined objects at all except low Reynolds numbers and is often associated with the appearance of a wake. Skin friction is predominant in flow past streamlined bodies, for which the form drag is small.

Separation of the boundary layer is associated with other cases involving flow against a pressure gradient when the cross section available to flow increases. There is therefore separation at an orifice or other sudden expansion, as described in Chaps. 5 and 6. The boundary layer occupies the entire conduit upstream from the orifice, but it separates from the walls at the sudden expansion and forms a jet.

The Drag Coefficient

The drag force per unit area for two-dimensional flow past an infinitely long cylinder would be proportional to $\rho u_o{}^2$ by a momentum balance if it were assumed that the x momentum were reduced by the same proportion for all Reynolds numbers $Du_o\rho/\mu$. We could then write

$$F_d' \propto \frac{\rho u_o{}^2}{2g_c} \frac{A}{L} \tag{8-9}$$

where F_d' = drag force per unit length

$\dfrac{A}{L}$ = frontal area per unit length

The factor ½ is introduced by custom. Since A/L is proportional to the diameter of the cylinder, an equivalent expression is

$$F_d' \propto \frac{\rho u_o{}^2 D}{2g_c} \tag{8-10}$$

However, as the Reynolds number changes, the fractional decrease in x momentum *is* affected, so we write

$$F_d' = C_D \frac{\rho u_o{}^2 D}{2g_c} \tag{8-11}$$

or

$$C_D = \frac{2F_d' g_c}{\rho u_o{}^2 D} \tag{8-12}$$

where C_D is a function of the Reynolds number and is called the drag coefficient.

For flow past a sphere or other objects, C_D is defined slightly differently:

$$C_D = \frac{2F_d g_c}{\rho u_o^2 A} \tag{8-13}$$

F_d is the total drag on the object, and A is its frontal area.

The effects of variation of Reynolds number on the drag coefficient for flow past a cylinder are shown in Fig. 8-9. In Chap. 7 we found that the pressure drop (total drag) for laminar flow in a pipe was proportional to the bulk velocity u_b. This is approximately true for flow around a cylinder at low Reynolds numbers. Consequently, it can be seen from Eq. (8-12) that the drag coefficient C_D must be inversely proportional to u_o and the Reynolds number. The portion of the curve with a slope of approximately -1 indicates the range of Reynolds numbers for which the preceding approximation is valid. As the Reynolds number is increased, viscous effects become relatively less important. The sharp drop in C_D at approximately $\mathbf{Re} = 500{,}000$ corresponds to the transition from a laminar to a turbulent boundary layer. In general, the relation between C_D and Reynolds number must be found by experiment for flow past each specific shape.

THE DIFFERENTIAL MASS BALANCE

Single-component System

A mass balance will now be made over a differential element of volume in much the same way as it was made over a finite volume in Chap. 3.

Figure 9-1 shows the differential element of volume; we shall use as before the fact that output minus input plus accumulation must equal zero. In the x direction, output less input by mass flow is given by

$$[u_x\rho + d(u_x\rho)]\, dy\, dz - u_x\rho\, dy\, dz \tag{9-1}$$

The second term is the input in the x direction through the face of area $dy\, dz$ located at a distance x from the plane $x = 0$; the first term is the output through the parallel face located at $x + dx$. The expression (9-1) reduces to

$$d(u_x\rho)\, dy\, dz \tag{9-2}$$

It will be convenient to express the differential change in $u_x\rho$ over the distance dx by

$$d(u_x\rho) = \frac{\partial(u_x\rho)}{\partial x}\, dx \tag{9-3}$$

As a result the output minus input in the x direction is

$$\frac{\partial(u_x\rho)}{\partial x}\, dx\, dy\, dz \tag{9-4}$$

Similar expressions can be written for flow in the y and z directions. The rate of accumulation in the element is

$$\frac{\partial\rho}{\partial\theta}\, dx\, dy\, dz \tag{9-5}$$

so that the mass balance becomes

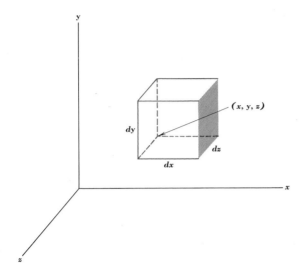

Fig. 9-1. *Differential element for mass balance.*

$$\frac{\partial(u_x\rho)}{\partial x}\,dx\,dy\,dz + \frac{\partial(u_y\rho)}{\partial y}\,dy\,dx\,dz + \frac{\partial(u_z\rho)}{\partial z}\,dz\,dx\,dy$$

$$+ \frac{\partial\rho}{\partial\theta}\,dx\,dy\,dz = 0 \qquad (9\text{-}6)$$

The similarity between this equation and Eqs. (3-4) and (3-7) should be noticed. The first three terms of Eq. (9-6) are equivalent to $\Delta(u\rho A)$, that is, Δw, and the fourth term to $dM/d\theta$.

From Eq. (9-6) we now write the equation of continuity[1] for a single-component, unsteady-state system.

$$\frac{\partial(u_x\rho)}{\partial x} + \frac{\partial(u_y\rho)}{\partial y} + \frac{\partial(u_z\rho)}{\partial z} + \frac{\partial\rho}{\partial\theta} = 0 \qquad (9\text{-}7)$$

This equation may be expanded to give

$$\rho\left(\frac{\partial u_x}{\partial x} + \frac{\partial u_y}{\partial y} + \frac{\partial u_z}{\partial z}\right) + u_x\frac{\partial\rho}{\partial x} + u_y\frac{\partial\rho}{\partial y} + u_z\frac{\partial\rho}{\partial z} + \frac{\partial\rho}{\partial\theta} = 0 \qquad (9\text{-}8)$$

Because the density of the fluid ρ is a function of x, y, z, and θ, one may write

$$d\rho = \frac{\partial\rho}{\partial x}\,dx + \frac{\partial\rho}{\partial y}\,dy + \frac{\partial\rho}{\partial z}\,dz + \frac{\partial\rho}{\partial\theta}\,d\theta \qquad (9\text{-}9)$$

The derivative with respect to time is

---

[1] Although Eq. (9-7) is referred to as the equation of continuity in fluid mechanics, some engineers also give this name to the steady-state form of Eq. (3-7), that is, $\Delta(u\rho A) = 0$.

$$\frac{d\rho}{d\theta} = \frac{\partial \rho}{\partial x}\frac{dx}{d\theta} + \frac{\partial \rho}{\partial y}\frac{dy}{d\theta} + \frac{\partial \rho}{\partial z}\frac{dz}{d\theta} + \frac{\partial \rho}{\partial \theta} \qquad (9\text{-}10)$$

The implications that follow from this equation can be understood if we postulate the existence of a movable instrument for measuring density at a point, just as a thermocouple could be thought to measure temperature at its tip. If the instrument is fixed in space, Eq. (9-10) is an expression of the rate of change of density at that point in space, but the equation becomes trivial:

$$\frac{dx}{d\theta} = \frac{dy}{d\theta} = \frac{dz}{d\theta} = 0 \qquad \text{so that} \qquad \frac{d\rho}{d\theta} = \frac{\partial \rho}{\partial \theta}$$

However, if the instrument tip moves at the same velocity as the adjacent fluid, then the components of the velocity of the instrument ($dx/d\theta$, $dy/d\theta$, and $dz/d\theta$) are identical with the velocity components of the fluid (u_x, u_y, and u_z). In the terminology of fluid dynamics, "the observer is moving with the fluid." The "observer" is, of course, the tip of the instrument. The rate of change of density to this moving observer is therefore

$$\frac{d\rho}{d\theta} = u_x \frac{\partial \rho}{\partial x} + u_y \frac{\partial \rho}{\partial y} + u_z \frac{\partial \rho}{\partial z} + \frac{\partial \rho}{\partial \theta} \qquad (9\text{-}11)$$

If the observer is moving, but not at the same velocity as the fluid, Eq. (9-10) holds; however, $dx/d\theta$ no longer equals u_x, nor does $dy/d\theta$ equal u_y, nor $dz/d\theta$ equal u_z.

The derivative defined by Eq. (9-11) is called the substantial, or material, derivative, and we shall write it as $D\rho/D\theta$ in order to distinguish it from the total derivative of the general case, Eq. (9-10). Using this new nomenclature, we write Eq. (9-8) as

$$\frac{\partial u_x}{\partial x} + \frac{\partial u_y}{\partial y} + \frac{\partial u_z}{\partial z} + \frac{1}{\rho}\frac{D\rho}{d\theta} = 0 \qquad (9\text{-}12)$$

Let us now use the idea of the substantial derivative to try to give a physical significance to the first three terms of Eq. (9-12). Consider a fluid element of unit mass moving with the fluid; the volume and density of the element change with time. By differentiating the relation $\rho V = 1$ with respect to time, we get

$$\rho \frac{DV}{D\theta} + V \frac{D\rho}{D\theta} = 0 \qquad (9\text{-}13)$$

or

$$\frac{1}{V}\frac{DV}{D\theta} + \frac{1}{\rho}\frac{D\rho}{D\theta} = 0 \qquad (9\text{-}14)$$

A comparison of Eqs. (9-14) and (9-12) shows that $\dfrac{1}{V}\dfrac{DV}{D\theta}$ is equal to the sum of $\partial u_x/\partial x$, $\partial u_y/\partial y$, and $\partial u_z/\partial z$. The physical interpretation for this relationship is that the first term in Eq. (9-14), which represents the rate of volumetric strain or expansion of the element, is really the same as the sum of the first three terms of Eq. (9-12), which represent the three linear rates of strain.

The analysis leading to Eq. (9-8), as well as that used in deriving the over-all balances of Chaps. 3 to 5, is based on the consideration of the flow in and out of an element of fixed size, fixed in space, and containing a variable mass. This is often called the point of view of Euler. On the other hand, the analysis which leads to Eq. (9-14) is based on a fixed mass of fluid as it moves in space; the volume of the element may vary. This point of view is referred to as that of Lagrange. The Lagrangian analysis is convenient and will be used in the next two chapters to derive the differential energy and momentum balances.

The main use of the equation of continuity will be to simplify the differential heat and momentum equations, with which it must hold simultaneously in flow problems.

At steady state, Eq. (9-8) is easily modified by setting $\partial \rho/\partial \theta$ equal to zero. For the common case of an incompressible fluid, at either steady or unsteady state, we have

$$\frac{\partial u_x}{\partial x} + \frac{\partial u_y}{\partial y} + \frac{\partial u_z}{\partial z} = 0 \qquad\qquad (9\text{-}15)$$

Two-component System

A differential mass balance can also be made for a component A in a binary mixture. In the over-all balance of Chap. 3 we did not include the effect of diffusion; this time let us include it in the differential balance, for the equation thus obtained will prove very useful in the later study of mass transfer by diffusion.

The entry of component A into the differential element through face $dy\,dz$ is by two mechanisms. One is the contribution resulting from the general movement of the fluid, this flux being $u_x\rho_A$ lb/(hr)(sq ft). The other is by molecular diffusion, which may be considered as a flux superimposed on the general movement of the fluid; this flux is written as J_{Ax} lb/(hr)(sq ft). The total flux is the sum of the individual fluxes, $u_x\rho_A + J_{Ax}$. It follows that the total flux out of the opposite face of the element is $(u_x\rho_A + J_{Ax}) + d(u_x\rho_A + J_{Ax})$. The difference, which is output minus input in the x direction, is

$$d(u_x\rho_A + J_{Ax})\, dy\, dz = \left[\frac{\partial(u_x\rho_A)}{\partial x} + \frac{\partial J_{Ax}}{\partial x}\right] dx\, dy\, dz \tag{9-16}$$

which is analogous to the expression (9-4).

It follows that the equation of continuity for component A in its three-dimensional form is then

$$\frac{\partial(u_x\rho_A)}{\partial x} + \frac{\partial(u_y\rho_A)}{\partial y} + \frac{\partial(u_z\rho_A)}{\partial z} + \frac{\partial\rho_A}{\partial\theta} + \frac{\partial J_{Ax}}{\partial x} + \frac{\partial J_{Ay}}{\partial y}$$

$$+ \frac{\partial J_{Az}}{\partial z} - r_A = 0 \tag{9-17}$$

or

$$\rho_A\left(\frac{\partial u_x}{\partial x} + \frac{\partial u_y}{\partial y} + \frac{\partial u_z}{\partial z}\right) + \frac{D\rho_A}{D\theta} + \frac{\partial J_{Ax}}{\partial x} + \frac{\partial J_{Ay}}{\partial y} + \frac{\partial J_{Az}}{\partial z}$$

$$- r_A = 0 \tag{9-18}$$

The term r_A in these equations has been added, as was R_i in Eq. (3-9); it is the rate of generation of component A in lb/(hr)(cu ft) within the element by chemical reaction. With the appropriate sign it may also represent the rate of consumption of component A. The term $\partial\rho_A/\partial\theta$ is the rate of accumulation of component A in lb/(hr)(cu ft).

The fluxes J_A can arise in many ways, such as thermal diffusion, pressure diffusion, ionic diffusion, or ordinary molecular diffusion. For a case involving only binary molecular diffusion we usually write

$$J_{Ax} = -D_{AB}\frac{\partial\rho_A}{\partial x} \tag{9-19}$$

Similar equations exist for the other two directions. If these equations are substituted into Eq. (9-17) and D_{AB} is constant, we obtain

$$\frac{\partial(u_x\rho_A)}{\partial x} + \frac{\partial(u_y\rho_A)}{\partial y} + \frac{\partial(u_z\rho_A)}{\partial z} + \frac{\partial\rho_A}{\partial\theta}$$

$$= D_{AB}\left(\frac{\partial^2\rho_A}{\partial x^2} + \frac{\partial^2\rho_A}{\partial y^2} + \frac{\partial^2\rho_A}{\partial z^2}\right) + r_A \tag{9-20}$$

The first three terms may be expanded to give

$$\rho_A\left(\frac{\partial u_x}{\partial x} + \frac{\partial u_y}{\partial y} + \frac{\partial u_z}{\partial z}\right) + u_x\frac{\partial\rho_A}{\partial x} + u_y\frac{\partial\rho_A}{\partial y} + u_z\frac{\partial\rho_A}{\partial z} + \frac{\partial\rho_A}{\partial\theta}$$

$$= D_{AB}\left(\frac{\partial^2\rho_A}{\partial x^2} + \frac{\partial^2\rho_A}{\partial y^2} + \frac{\partial^2\rho_A}{\partial z^2}\right) + r_A \tag{9-21}$$

If the density of the mixture is constant, $\partial u_x/\partial x + \partial u_y/\partial y + \partial u_z/\partial z$ equals zero, according to Eq. (9-15). Using the substantial derivative notation, Eq. (9-21) becomes

$$\frac{D\rho_A}{D\theta} = D_{AB} \left(\frac{\partial^2 \rho_A}{\partial x^2} + \frac{\partial^2 \rho_A}{\partial y^2} + \frac{\partial^2 \rho_A}{\partial z^2} \right) + r_A \tag{9-22}$$

If diffusion and chemical reaction are important, ρ may be changing with distance. This effect can be particularly significant in a gaseous system, so that Eq. (9-22) may be an oversimplification. This situation is somewhat complicated, and so we shall reserve a detailed discussion of this matter for the part of the book which deals specifically with mass transfer. The study of mixtures of more than two components is rather difficult and will not be included.

PROBLEMS

9-1. Use the definition of the stream function given in Chap. 8 and express the equation of continuity in terms of the stream function. What is shown by the result obtained? What remark can be made about the stream function for unsteady state?

9-2. Use a cylindrical shell of dimensions dz and dr to obtain the equation of continuity for flow in a circular pipe with axial symmetry. Assume ρ is constant. Could this equation be obtained from Eq. (9-8)?

9-3. Find the equation of continuity for component A in a binary mixture in a tubular reactor with axial symmetry. Use cylindrical coordinates. Assume ρ is constant.

9-4. Find the differential equation describing the concentration of component A (no reaction occurring) at any point in a spherical drop. The drop, which contains a binary mixture, is exposed to a medium of composition different from the drop, so that component A is diffusing at unsteady state from within the drop. Assume ρ is constant.

THE DIFFERENTIAL
ENERGY BALANCE

A differential energy balance could be written with reference to a constant-volume element fixed in space, as in the first part of Chap. 9. However, this time the point of view of Lagrange will be found simpler than that of Euler, so the element is chosen as a fixed mass moving with the fluid at the fluid velocity. The basis for any energy balance is the first law of thermodynamics, so we consider the internal-energy change of the element as it flows along and exchanges heat and work with the surrounding fluid. This is the same point of view as that used in the discussion leading to Eqs. (4-15) and (4-16). Equation (4-16), written as the rate of change of internal energy of one pound of moving fluid, is

$$\frac{DU}{D\theta} = \frac{DQ}{D\theta} - p\frac{DV}{D\theta} + \frac{D(lw)}{D\theta} \tag{10-1}$$

The term $DQ/D\theta$ is the rate of heat flow to the surface of the pound of fluid from the surrounding stream with which it is moving. In order to analyze this term it is convenient to apply Eq. (10-1) to a cubic differential element of mass $\rho\,dx\,dy\,dz$. We define a loss term Φ, which equals $\rho D(lw)/D\theta$ and has units of Btu/(hr)(cu ft). Hence we obtain the equation

$$\frac{DU}{D\theta}\rho\,dx\,dy\,dz = \rho\frac{DQ}{D\theta}dx\,dy\,dz - p\frac{DV}{D\theta}\rho\,dx\,dy\,dz + \Phi\,dx\,dy\,dz \tag{10-2}$$

It is now possible to relate $\rho(DQ/D\theta)\,dx\,dy\,dz$ to the heat fluxes across the faces of the cube. Since the heat term is positive for a net inflow, we write the inflow minus outflow as

$$\rho \frac{DQ}{D\theta} dx\, dy\, dz = \left(\frac{q}{A}\right)_x dy\, dz - \left[\left(\frac{q}{A}\right)_x + d\left(\frac{q}{A}\right)_x\right] dy\, dz + \left(\frac{q}{A}\right)_y dx\, dz$$

$$- \left[\left(\frac{q}{A}\right)_y + d\left(\frac{q}{A}\right)_y\right] dx\, dz + \left(\frac{q}{A}\right)_z dx\, dy$$

$$- \left[\left(\frac{q}{A}\right)_z + d\left(\frac{q}{A}\right)_z\right] dx\, dy \qquad (10\text{-}3)$$

or

$$\rho \frac{DQ}{D\theta} dx\, dy\, dz = -\left[\frac{\partial(q/A)_x}{\partial x} + \frac{\partial(q/A)_y}{\partial y} + \frac{\partial(q/A)_z}{\partial z}\right] dx\, dy\, dz \qquad (10\text{-}4)$$

By substituting Eq. (10-4) into Eq. (10-2) and rearranging, we obtain the differential energy balance in terms of the heat flux q/A.

$$\rho \frac{DU}{D\theta} + p\rho \frac{DV}{D\theta} = -\left[\frac{\partial(q/A)_x}{\partial x} + \frac{\partial(q/A)_y}{\partial y} + \frac{\partial(q/A)_z}{\partial z}\right] + \Phi \qquad (10\text{-}5)$$

It is often convenient to replace the internal energy by the enthalpy H, where

$$H = U + pV \qquad (10\text{-}6)$$

Taking the substantial derivative and multiplying by ρ, we get

$$\rho \frac{DH}{D\theta} = \rho \frac{DU}{D\theta} + p\rho \frac{DV}{D\theta} + \frac{Dp}{D\theta} \qquad (10\text{-}7)$$

so that the differential energy balance (10-5) written in terms of the enthalpy is

$$\rho \frac{DH}{D\theta} - \frac{Dp}{D\theta} = -\left[\frac{\partial(q/A)_x}{\partial x} + \frac{\partial(q/A)_y}{\partial y} + \frac{\partial(q/A)_z}{\partial z}\right] + \Phi \qquad (10\text{-}8)$$

The heat flux in laminar flow or for solids arises from heat flow by conduction, so that

$$\left(\frac{q}{A}\right)_x = -k \frac{\partial t}{\partial x} \qquad (10\text{-}9)$$

Similar equations exist for the other two directions. If these equations are substituted into Eq. (10-8), they give, for constant k,

$$\rho \frac{DH}{D\theta} - \frac{Dp}{D\theta} = k\left(\frac{\partial^2 t}{\partial x^2} + \frac{\partial^2 t}{\partial y^2} + \frac{\partial^2 t}{\partial z^2}\right) + \Phi \qquad (10\text{-}10)$$

For viscous fluids Φ is the rate at which work is done per unit volume to change the shape of the element. A detailed discussion of the relation of this work to the shearing stresses and in turn to the viscosity and the deformation is given in more specialized texts.[1] It is related to the lost work of Chap. 4 in that it is the rate of work lost per unit volume because of friction within the fluid. It is also referred to as the viscous-dissipation

---

[1] H. Lamb, "Hydrodynamics," 6th ed., p. 579, Dover Publications, New York, 1945.

term. Although lw is essential in the mechanical energy balance for the calculation of pressure drop, Φ usually has a negligible effect on the temperature of the fluid and may be omitted from the energy balance except when it is used for highly viscous fluids or velocities of the order of the sonic velocity.

Starting from thermodynamics, it can be shown that for an incompressible fluid the following equation holds:

$$\rho \frac{DH}{D\theta} = \rho C_p \frac{Dt}{D\theta} + \frac{Dp}{D\theta}$$

This can be substituted in Eq. (10-10) to give

$$\frac{Dt}{D\theta} = u_x \frac{\partial t}{\partial x} + u_y \frac{\partial t}{\partial y} + u_z \frac{\partial t}{\partial z} + \frac{\partial t}{\partial \theta} = \frac{k}{\rho C_p} \left(\frac{\partial^2 t}{\partial x^2} + \frac{\partial^2 t}{\partial y^2} + \frac{\partial^2 t}{\partial z^2} \right) \quad (10\text{-}11)$$

where Φ has been omitted. For a solid, the equation becomes

$$\frac{\partial t}{\partial \theta} = \frac{k}{\rho C_p} \left(\frac{\partial^2 t}{\partial x^2} + \frac{\partial^2 t}{\partial y^2} + \frac{\partial^2 t}{\partial z^2} \right) \quad (10\text{-}12)$$

and its ultimate simplification for a solid at steady state is

$$\frac{\partial^2 t}{\partial x^2} + \frac{\partial^2 t}{\partial y^2} + \frac{\partial^2 t}{\partial z^2} = 0 \quad (10\text{-}13)$$

This is Laplace's equation. The solution of the above equations for several important cases will be considered in detail in the section on heat transfer.

If heat is being generated within the element of fluid by a chemical reaction, a simple way of modifying Eq. (10-11) is to add a term involving q_r, the rate of heat generation in Btu/(hr)(cu ft).

$$\frac{Dt}{D\theta} = \frac{k}{\rho C_p} \left(\frac{\partial^2 t}{\partial x^2} + \frac{\partial^2 t}{\partial y^2} + \frac{\partial^2 t}{\partial z^2} \right) + \frac{q_r}{\rho C_p} \quad (10\text{-}14)$$

Equation (10-14), for an incompressible fluid, is very similar to Eq. (9-22), for mass transfer in a binary mixture.

$$\frac{D\rho_A}{D\theta} = D_{AB} \left(\frac{\partial^2 \rho_A}{\partial x^2} + \frac{\partial^2 \rho_A}{\partial y^2} + \frac{\partial^2 \rho_A}{\partial z^2} \right) + r_A \quad (9\text{-}22)$$

The analogy extends to $k/\rho C_p$, which has the same units as D_{AB}. Because of this similarity, $k/\rho C_p$ is often called the thermal diffusivity, as already mentioned at the end of Chap. 7. Having shown this analogy between mass and heat transfer, we shall proceed in the next chapter to develop similar equations for momentum transfer, for which similar analogies will become evident.

In presenting the basic differential equations for mass, heat, and momentum transfer in this portion of the book, we are leading up to the equations of motion of a fluid.   These equations will then be used to solve a number of isothermal-fluid-flow problems.   The equation of continuity for a single component must be simultaneously satisfied, as well as the equation of state of the fluid.   As presented here, the equations increase in complexity in going from mass to heat to momentum transfer.   Paradoxically, for fluid systems, the isothermal-momentum-transfer equation is the easiest to solve; for mass and heat transfer, the pertinent equations must in general be solved simultaneously with the momentum equation.   The detailed applications of Eq. (9-20) and Eq. (10-10) will be presented later, after those of the equations of motion.

PROBLEMS

10-1. Find the expression for the differential energy balance in cylindrical coordinates. Obtain first the equation analogous to Eq. (10-10) (k = const) and then its simplification for k, ρ, and C_p constant [analogous to Eq. (10-11)].

10-2. Find the equation analogous to Eq. (10-14) which would be convenient for a tubular reactor with axial symmetry.

10-3. It is desired to study the time required to cool the center of a hot ball bearing to a certain level.   Find the form of the energy balance which would be convenient for this unsteady-state heat-transfer problem.

THE DIFFERENTIAL
MOMENTUM BALANCE
11

EQUATIONS IN TERMS OF
THE SHEAR-STRESS COMPONENTS

We now proceed to the derivation of the equations of motion for a real fluid; these equations, which are based on Newton's second law, will permit the determination of the way the velocity varies with position. It will then be possible to find quantities such as the pressure drop in laminar flow. With certain modifications, the equations can also be used for turbulent flow, but this application will be discussed separately; in what follows the flow is considered laminar.

Newton's Second Law Applied to an Element of Fluid

The force-momentum balances apply in the three coordinate directions; the equation in the x direction is

$$F_x = \frac{M a_x}{g_c} \tag{11-1}$$

which can be written in terms of rate of change of momentum as

$$F_x = \frac{1}{g_c} \frac{d(M u_x)}{d\theta} \tag{11-2}$$

We apply this equation to a fluid element of constant mass moving with velocity of the fluid. This is the point of view of Lagrange, so for the same reasons given in Chap. 10, the derivative in Eq. (11-2) is written as a substantial derivative.

$$F_x = \frac{M}{g_c} \frac{Du_x}{D\theta} \qquad (11\text{-}3)$$

If the element of fluid is a differential mass $\rho \, dx \, dy \, dz$, Eq. (11-3) becomes

$$dF_x = \frac{1}{g_c} \rho \, dx \, dy \, dz \frac{Du_x}{D\theta} \qquad (11\text{-}4)$$

The Body Force

The force dF_x represents the resultant of all the forces acting in the x direction on the element. It is convenient to divide it into a body force X, expressed in lb force/lb, and the forces arising from the mechanical stresses on the surface of the element. A body force acts on the element as a whole; the force on a charged body in an electric field is an example. For the differential element, the body force in the x direction is

$$dF_{xB} = X\rho \, dx \, dy \, dz \qquad (11\text{-}5)$$

The only body force we consider is that caused by gravity. It can be written as

$$X = \frac{g}{g_c} \cos \beta \qquad (11\text{-}6)$$

in which β is the angle between the x direction and the direction in which gravity acts.

The Stresses on an Element of Fluid

Each of the six faces of the cube will be subjected to mechanical stresses arising from the adjacent fluid, and each of these stresses can in turn be resolved into three components, parallel to the three axes. Figure 11-1 shows the stress components acting in the x direction, and Fig. 11-2 illustrates the three stress components operating on a given face. These figures show the system used for the subscripts on τ. The first subscript indicates the face on which the stress is acting by giving the axis perpendicular to the face, and the second subscript gives the direction in which the stress acts. The stresses with the mixed subscripts, such as τ_{xy}, are shear stresses, tending to deform the element and change the angles between the faces. The convention for the positive direction of the shear stresses is illustrated in Fig. 11-3. The stresses with repeated subscripts, such as τ_{xx}, are normal stresses, which are closely related to the hydrostatic pressure. As is customary in mechanics, normal stresses are considered positive for tension. If the size of the elements illustrated by Figs. 11-1 and 11-3 approaches zero, the stresses on the opposite faces become identical in magnitude and

Fig. 11-1.   *Element of fluid showing stresses acting in the x direction.*

opposite in sign.   Consequently, the state of stress at a point can be completely described by the six components of shear stress and the three components of normal stress.

It can be shown that not all the shear-stress terms are independent by considering the possibility of rotation of the element.   For example, rotation about an axis parallel to the z axis may be caused by a torque produced by the stresses shown in Fig. 11-3.   From the principles of mechanics, the

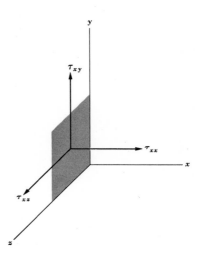

Fig. 11-2.   *Stresses on a single face of fluid element.*

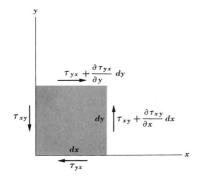

Fig. 11-3.   Shearing stresses causing moments about an axis parallel to the z axis.

torque equals the moment of inertia multiplied by the angular acceleration. This can be shown[1] to lead to the equation

$$\tau_{xy} - \tau_{yx} = \rho \text{ (radius of gyration)}^2 \text{ (angular acceleration)}$$

If the size of the fluid element approaches zero, the radius of gyration goes to zero, so that τ_{xy} must equal τ_{yx}. Similar procedures show that $\tau_{xz} = \tau_{zx}$ and $\tau_{yz} = \tau_{zy}$.

The normal stresses are related to the pressure by the following arbitrary definition:

$$- p = \tfrac{1}{3}(\tau_{xx} + \tau_{yy} + \tau_{zz}) \tag{11-7}$$

Since the normal stresses are positive for tension, and the pressure is positive for compression, the minus sign is necessary. If the velocity is not everywhere the same, the individual normal stresses will differ among themselves, and the absolute value of no one of them need equal the pressure.

The Equations of Motion in Terms of the Stresses

We refer again to Fig. 11-1 and write the net force in the x direction resulting from the variation of the appropriate stresses with position.

$$dF_{x,\text{ stresses}} = \left(\tau_{xx} + \frac{\partial \tau_{xx}}{\partial x}\, dx\right) dy\, dz + \left(\tau_{yx} + \frac{\partial \tau_{yx}}{\partial y}\, dy\right) dx\, dz$$
$$+ \left(\tau_{zx} + \frac{\partial \tau_{zx}}{\partial z}\, dz\right) dx\, dy - \tau_{xx}\, dy\ 'z - \tau_{yx}\, dx\, dz$$
$$- \tau_{zx}\, dx\, dy \tag{11-8}$$

This equation simplifies to

[1] J. G. Knudsen and D. L. Katz, "Fluid Dynamics and Heat Transfer," p. 31, McGraw-Hill Book Company, Inc., New York, 1958.

$$dF_{x,\,\text{stresses}} = \left(\frac{\partial \tau_{xx}}{\partial x} + \frac{\partial \tau_{yx}}{\partial y} + \frac{\partial \tau_{zx}}{\partial z} \right) dx\, dy\, dz \tag{11-9}$$

The force arising from the stresses, Eq. (11-9), and the body force, Eq. (11-5), are the only two forces acting in the x direction. The term dF_x in Eq. (11-4) is the sum of the above two forces, so the combination of Eqs. (11-4), (11-5), (11-6), and (11-9) gives

$$\frac{\rho}{g_c} \frac{Du_x}{D\theta} = \rho \frac{g}{g_c} \cos \beta + \frac{\partial \tau_{xx}}{\partial x} + \frac{\partial \tau_{yx}}{\partial y} + \frac{\partial \tau_{zx}}{\partial z} \tag{11-10}$$

Equation (11-10) is given in terms of the stresses; the reader will recall that these stresses may also be viewed as fluxes of x momentum. The term $(\partial \tau_{xx}/\partial x)(dx)(g_c)$ represents the net flux of x momentum out through the two planes of the cubical element perpendicular to the x axis; the term $(\partial \tau_{yx}/\partial y)(dy)(g_c)$ gives the net flux of x momentum out through the planes of the element perpendicular to the y axis; and $(\partial \tau_{zx}/\partial z)(dz)(g_c)$ has a similar meaning. The last three terms of Eq. (11-10) are comparable with three similar terms in Eq. (9-18) (fluxes of mass) and in Eq. (10-8) (fluxes of energy).

In addition to Eq. (11-10), there are similar equations for the y and z directions. Let us write all three equations for future reference.

$$\frac{\rho}{g_c} \frac{Du_x}{D\theta} = \rho X + \frac{\partial \tau_{xx}}{\partial x} + \frac{\partial \tau_{yx}}{\partial y} + \frac{\partial \tau_{zx}}{\partial z} \tag{11-11}$$

$$\frac{\rho}{g_c} \frac{Du_y}{D\theta} = \rho Y + \frac{\partial \tau_{xy}}{\partial x} + \frac{\partial \tau_{yy}}{\partial y} + \frac{\partial \tau_{zy}}{\partial z} \tag{11-12}$$

$$\frac{\rho}{g_c} \frac{Du_z}{D\theta} = \rho Z + \frac{\partial \tau_{xz}}{\partial x} + \frac{\partial \tau_{yz}}{\partial y} + \frac{\partial \tau_{zz}}{\partial z} \tag{11-13}$$

The next step is to obtain an equation which can be used to calculate a velocity distribution or a pressure drop. To do this we relate the stresses to the viscosity and the rate of deformation of the element. This deformation rate will be expressed in terms of the derivatives of the velocity components of the flowing fluid. If the fluid is nonnewtonian, Eq. (11-10) holds, but modification would need to be made in what follows in relating the stresses and strain rates through the ordinary viscosity.

THE STRESSES IN RELATION TO THE VISCOSITY[1]

Shear Stresses

Elastic solids deform according to Hooke's law, which states that stress is proportional to strain, i.e., to the amount of deformation, but for new-

---

[1] This treatment follows that of J. M. Kay, "An Introduction to Fluid Mechanics and Heat Transfer," appendix 4, Cambridge University Press, London, 1957.

Fig. 11-4. *Deformation caused by a shear in a one-dimensional flow.*

tonian fluids, the stress is proportional to the rate of deformation. The rate of deformation is sometimes called the rate of shear. The defining equation for viscosity in terms of rate of shear has been shown in Chap. 7 in a one-dimensional analysis to be

$$\tau = \frac{\mu}{g_c} \frac{du_x}{dy} \tag{11-14}$$

For more·complicated deformations it is convenient to define the rate of deformation as the rate of change of the angle ϕ, shown in Fig. 11-4. For the simple one-dimensional case, the change in the angle ϕ in time $d\theta$ can be expressed in radians, as the arc $(du_x/dy)\ dy\ d\theta$ divided by the radius dy:

$$d\phi = -\frac{(du_x/dy)\ dy\ d\theta}{dy} \tag{11-15}$$

The rate of deformation, therefore, is

$$\frac{d\phi}{d\theta} = -\frac{du_x}{dy} \tag{11-16}$$

which is substituted in Eq. (11-14) to give

$$\tau = -\frac{\mu}{g_c} \frac{d\phi}{d\theta} \tag{11-17}$$

Equation (11-17) is now used in the analysis of the deformation of the element $dx\ dy\ dz$. Figure 11-5 shows the shear-stress components which act on the faces perpendicular to the xy plane to produce the illustrated deformation. The change in the angle ϕ consists of two portions, as shown in Fig. 11-5b: one part is $(-\partial u_x/\partial y)\ d\theta$, as derived by reasoning similar to that leading to Eq. (11-5); the other part is $(-\partial u_y/\partial x)\ d\theta$. Therefore we obtain

(a) Before deformation   (b) After time $d\theta$

Fig. 11-5.   *Deformation caused by shear stresses.*

$$\frac{d\phi}{d\theta} = -\left(\frac{\partial u_x}{\partial y} + \frac{\partial u_y}{\partial x}\right) \tag{11-18}$$

Substitution of this into Eq. (11-17) gives

$$\tau_{xy} = \tau_{yx} = \frac{\mu}{g_c}\left(\frac{\partial u_x}{\partial y} + \frac{\partial u_y}{\partial x}\right) \tag{11-19}$$

In a similar way, the other shear stresses are found to be

$$\tau_{yz} = \tau_{zy} = \frac{\mu}{g_c}\left(\frac{\partial u_z}{\partial y} + \frac{\partial u_y}{\partial z}\right) \tag{11-20}$$

$$\tau_{zx} = \tau_{xz} = \frac{\mu}{g_c}\left(\frac{\partial u_x}{\partial z} + \frac{\partial u_z}{\partial x}\right) \tag{11-21}$$

Normal Stresses

The problem of the normal stresses is somewhat more involved.   First of all, by definition, we have

$$p = -\tfrac{1}{3}(\tau_{xx} + \tau_{yy} + \tau_{zz}) \tag{11-7}$$

For the specific case of a fluid at rest or in motion such that the velocity is everywhere the same, each normal stress is numerically equal to the pressure.   In general, the normal stress is visualized as made up of a contribution from the pressure and a contribution from the viscous stresses which are associated with the linear deformation of the element in the direction of the normal stress.   We state this idea mathematically for the x direction as

$$\tau_{xx} = -p + \sigma_x \tag{11-22}$$

We have already defined p in Eq. (11-7). This is combined with Eq. (11-22) as follows:

$$\sigma_x = \tau_{xx} + p \tag{11-23}$$

$$\sigma_x = \tau_{xx} - \tfrac{1}{3}(\tau_{xx} + \tau_{yy} + \tau_{zz}) \tag{11-24}$$

$$\sigma_x = \tfrac{2}{3}\tau_{xx} - \tfrac{1}{3}(\tau_{yy} + \tau_{zz}) \tag{11-25}$$

It will prove convenient to divide the normal viscous stress σ_x into two parts, so we arrange Eq. (11-25) into the form

$$\sigma_x = \tfrac{1}{3}(\tau_{xx} - \tau_{yy}) - \tfrac{1}{3}(\tau_{zz} - \tau_{xx}) \tag{11-26}$$

Similar equations can be derived for σ_y and σ_z. The quantity σ_x is substituted in Eq. (11-22) to give (11-27). Similar substitutions produce Eqs. (11-28) and (11-29). The designations (a) to (d) under the various groups in these three equations will be used as a convenient method of identification in subsequent discussions.

$$\tau_{xx} = \underset{(a)}{-p} + \underset{(b)}{\tfrac{1}{3}(\tau_{xx} - \tau_{yy})} - \underset{(c)}{\tfrac{1}{3}(\tau_{zz} - \tau_{xx})} \tag{11-27}$$

$$\tau_{yy} = \underset{(a)}{-p} - \underset{(b)}{\tfrac{1}{3}(\tau_{xx} - \tau_{yy})} + \underset{(d)}{\tfrac{1}{3}(\tau_{yy} - \tau_{zz})} \tag{11-28}$$

$$\tau_{zz} = \underset{(a)}{-p} + \underset{(c)}{\tfrac{1}{3}(\tau_{zz} - \tau_{xx})} - \underset{(d)}{\tfrac{1}{3}(\tau_{yy} - \tau_{zz})} \tag{11-29}$$

The effect of the normal stress τ_{xx} is to cause a deformation in the x direction. It will be assumed that the deformation rate in the x direction $\partial u_x/\partial x$ can be evaluated by adding the effects of the terms from the three equations for normal stress.

The contribution to $\partial u_x/\partial x$ by the pressure term is considered first; this is written as $(\partial u_x/\partial x)_a$. The variation of the pressure $Dp/D\theta$ causes a change in the density of the element; the rate of change is expressed by the equation of continuity:

$$-\frac{1}{\rho}\left(\frac{D\rho}{D\theta}\right) = \frac{\partial u_x}{\partial x} + \frac{\partial u_y}{\partial y} + \frac{\partial u_z}{\partial z} \tag{11-30}$$

The left-hand side of this equation is also equal to the rate of volumetric deformation (strain) $\dfrac{1}{V}\dfrac{DV}{D\theta}$, as was shown in Eq. (9-14). Since the pressure is equal in all directions, the contribution of pressure to the rate of deformation in the x direction is given by

$$\left(\frac{\partial u_x}{\partial x}\right)_a = \frac{1}{3}\frac{1}{V}\frac{DV}{D\theta} = \frac{1}{3}\left(\frac{\partial u_x}{\partial x} + \frac{\partial u_y}{\partial y} + \frac{\partial u_z}{\partial z}\right) \tag{11-31}$$

The other stress terms b, c, and d in Eqs. (11-27) to (11-29) will be examined in pairs chosen in such a way that the element can be considered

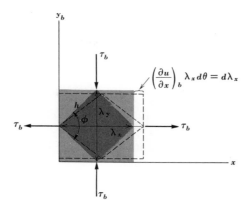

Fig. 11-6. *A contribution to the deformation caused by normal stresses (I).*

as subjected to pure shear, a case which is easy to analyze. In pure shear an element experiencing a compression in one direction equal in magnitude to a tension in the perpendicular direction behaves as though it were subjected to pure shear stresses on planes inclined at 45° to the axes. There are no normal stresses on these planes, and the shear stresses are equal in magnitude to the applied normal stresses on the outside of the element.[1]

We choose first the terms labeled (b) in Eqs. (11-27) and (11-28); these stresses act as shown in Fig. 11-6 with positive stresses in the x direction (tension) and negative stresses in the y direction (compression). The shear stress τ_b is also proportional to the rate of angular deformation.

$$\tau_b = -\frac{\mu}{g_c}\frac{d\phi}{d\theta} = \tfrac{1}{3}(\tau_{xx} - \tau_{yy}) \tag{11-32}$$

The quantity $d\phi/d\theta$ is to be found in terms of $(\partial u_x/\partial x)_b$, the contribution to $\partial u_x/\partial x$ of the stress term under study. Since there are no normal stresses acting on the element of side h of Fig. 11-6, the sides of this element will not change length with deformation. Figure 11-6 shows that the angle $\phi/2$ can be expressed by the relation

$$\tan\frac{\phi}{2} = \frac{\lambda_y}{\lambda_x} \tag{11-33}$$

The fact that the sides h are of constant length yields

$$\lambda_y{}^2 + \lambda_x{}^2 = \text{const} \tag{11-34}$$

and since λ_y approximately equals λ_x, it follows that

---

[1] These concepts are explained more fully in standard texts in mechanics. See, for example, S. Timoshenko, "Strength of Materials," 3d ed., chap. 2, D. Van Nostrand Company, Inc., Princeton, N.J., 1955.

$$d\lambda_y = -d\lambda_x \tag{11-35}$$

We next write Eq. (11-33) in differential form.

$$\tfrac{1}{2} \sec^2 \left(\frac{\phi}{2}\right) d\phi = \frac{\lambda_x \, d\lambda_y - \lambda_y \, d\lambda_x}{\lambda_x{}^2} \tag{11-36}$$

We substitute $-d\lambda_x$ for $d\lambda_y$ and use the fact that λ_x and λ_y differ only by a differential amount to obtain

$$\tfrac{1}{2} \sec^2 \left(\frac{\phi}{2}\right) d\phi = \frac{-2d\lambda_x}{\lambda_x} \tag{11-37}$$

We then divide Eq. (11-37) by $d\theta$ and set $\phi = 90°$ to get

$$\frac{d\phi}{d\theta} = \frac{-2}{\lambda_x} \frac{d\lambda_x}{d\theta} \tag{11-38}$$

From Fig. 11-6 we notice that $d\lambda_x$ equals $(\partial u_x/\partial x)_b \lambda_x \, d\theta$, and there results

$$\frac{d\phi}{d\theta} = -2 \left(\frac{\partial u_x}{\partial x}\right)_b \tag{11-39}$$

The desired stress is then found by combining Eqs. (11-32) and (11-39),

$$\tau_b = \frac{2\mu}{g_c} \left(\frac{\partial u_x}{\partial x}\right)_b \tag{11-40}$$

and we obtain finally

$$\left(\frac{\partial u_x}{\partial x}\right)_b = \frac{\tau_b g_c}{2\mu} \tag{11-41}$$

or

$$\left(\frac{\partial u_x}{\partial x}\right)_b = \frac{g_c}{2\mu} \frac{\tau_{xx} - \tau_{yy}}{3} \tag{11-42}$$

We have now considered two of the three stress components in Eqs. (11-27) to (11-29). In the third case we consider the element again in pure shear, as shown in Fig. 11-7. By reasoning similar to that leading to $(\partial u_x/\partial x)_b$ we find

$$\left(\frac{\partial u_x}{\partial x}\right)_c = \frac{g_c}{2\mu} \frac{\tau_{xx} - \tau_{zz}}{3} \tag{11-43}$$

The remaining two stresses in Eqs. (11-27) to (11-29), labeled (d), do not cause any distortion in the x direction; that is, $(\partial u_x/\partial x)_d = 0$.

The sum of the deformation rates considered above gives the rate of deformation in the x direction caused by the normal stresses.

$$\frac{\partial u_x}{\partial x} = \frac{1}{3} \left(\frac{\partial u_x}{\partial x} + \frac{\partial u_y}{\partial y} + \frac{\partial u_z}{\partial z}\right) + \frac{g_c}{2\mu} \frac{\tau_{xx} - \tau_{yy}}{3} + \frac{g_c}{2\mu} \frac{\tau_{xx} - \tau_{zz}}{3} \tag{11-44}$$

or

$$\frac{\partial u_x}{\partial x} = \frac{1}{3} \left(\frac{\partial u_x}{\partial x} + \frac{\partial u_y}{\partial y} + \frac{\partial u_z}{\partial z}\right) + \frac{\tau_{xx} g_c}{2\mu} - \frac{g_c}{2\mu} \frac{\tau_{xx} + \tau_{yy} + \tau_{zz}}{3} \tag{11-45}$$

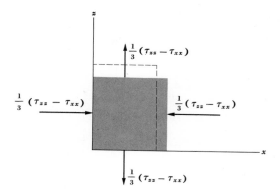

Fig. 11-7. *A contribution to the deformation caused by normal stresses (II).*

Using the definition of the pressure [Eq. (11-7)] and solving for τ_{xx}, we obtain

$$\tau_{xx} = -p + \frac{2\mu}{g_c}\frac{\partial u_x}{\partial x} - \frac{2}{3}\frac{\mu}{g_c}\left(\frac{\partial u_x}{\partial x} + \frac{\partial u_y}{\partial y} + \frac{\partial u_z}{\partial z}\right) \tag{11-46}$$

The equations for the stresses for the other two directions can be derived in a similar manner.

$$\tau_{yy} = -p + \frac{2\mu}{g_c}\frac{\partial u_y}{\partial y} - \frac{2}{3}\frac{\mu}{g_c}\left(\frac{\partial u_x}{\partial x} + \frac{\partial u_y}{\partial y} + \frac{\partial u_z}{\partial z}\right) \tag{11-47}$$

$$\tau_{zz} = -p + \frac{2\mu}{g_c}\frac{\partial u_z}{\partial z} - \frac{2}{3}\frac{\mu}{g_c}\left(\frac{\partial u_x}{\partial x} + \frac{\partial u_y}{\partial y} + \frac{\partial u_z}{\partial z}\right) \tag{11-48}$$

Navier-Stokes Equations

If Eqs. (11-19), (11-21), and (11-46) for the three stress components directed in the x direction are substituted into Eq. (11-11), we obtain the complete equation of motion for the x direction.

$$\frac{\rho}{g_c}\frac{Du_x}{D\theta} = \rho X - \frac{\partial p}{\partial x} + \frac{2\mu}{g_c}\frac{\partial^2 u_x}{\partial x^2} - \frac{2}{3}\frac{\mu}{g_c}\left(\frac{\partial^2 u_x}{\partial x^2} + \frac{\partial^2 u_y}{\partial x\,\partial y} + \frac{\partial^2 u_z}{\partial x\,\partial z}\right)$$
$$+ \frac{\mu}{g_c}\left(\frac{\partial^2 u_x}{\partial y^2} + \frac{\partial^2 u_y}{\partial y\,\partial x}\right) + \frac{\mu}{g_c}\left(\frac{\partial^2 u_x}{\partial z^2} + \frac{\partial^2 u_z}{\partial z\,\partial x}\right) \tag{11-49}$$

Rearranging, we have

$$\frac{\rho}{g_c}\frac{Du_x}{D\theta} = \rho X - \frac{\partial p}{\partial x} + \frac{\mu}{g_c}\left(\frac{\partial^2 u_x}{\partial x^2} + \frac{\partial^2 u_x}{\partial y^2} + \frac{\partial^2 u_x}{\partial z^2}\right)$$
$$+ \frac{1}{3}\frac{\mu}{g_c}\frac{\partial}{\partial x}\left(\frac{\partial u_x}{\partial x} + \frac{\partial u_y}{\partial y} + \frac{\partial u_z}{\partial z}\right) \tag{11-50}$$

Similar equations exist for the y and z directions. These three equations are called the Navier-Stokes equations, or the equations of motion; they are the basis of a large body of useful results obtained in fluid mechanics.

For incompressible flow, with which we shall deal for the most part, the equation of continuity gives

$$\frac{\partial u_x}{\partial x} + \frac{\partial u_y}{\partial y} + \frac{\partial u_z}{\partial z} = 0 \qquad (11\text{-}51)$$

and so the three Navier-Stokes equations for this case are

$$u_x \frac{\partial u_x}{\partial x} + u_y \frac{\partial u_x}{\partial y} + u_z \frac{\partial u_x}{\partial z} + \frac{\partial u_x}{\partial \theta}$$
$$= g_c X - \frac{g_c}{\rho} \frac{\partial p}{\partial x} + \nu \left(\frac{\partial^2 u_x}{\partial x^2} + \frac{\partial^2 u_x}{\partial y^2} + \frac{\partial^2 u_x}{\partial z^2} \right) \qquad (11\text{-}52)$$

$$u_x \frac{\partial u_y}{\partial x} + u_y \frac{\partial u_y}{\partial y} + u_z \frac{\partial u_y}{\partial z} + \frac{\partial u_y}{\partial \theta}$$
$$= g_c Y - \frac{g_c}{\rho} \frac{\partial p}{\partial y} + \nu \left(\frac{\partial^2 u_y}{\partial x^2} + \frac{\partial^2 u_y}{\partial y^2} + \frac{\partial^2 u_y}{\partial z^2} \right) \qquad (11\text{-}53)$$

$$u_x \frac{\partial u_z}{\partial x} + u_y \frac{\partial u_z}{\partial y} + u_z \frac{\partial u_z}{\partial z} + \frac{\partial u_z}{\partial \theta}$$
$$= g_c Z - \frac{g_c}{\rho} \frac{\partial p}{\partial z} + \nu \left(\frac{\partial^2 u_z}{\partial x^2} + \frac{\partial^2 u_z}{\partial y^2} + \frac{\partial^2 u_z}{\partial z^2} \right) \qquad (11\text{-}54)$$

These equations have a formidable appearance, which arises mostly from their being written in a general form applicable to a three-dimensional system lacking symmetry. Fortunately, many engineering problems can be solved by applying the equations in one- or two-dimensional form, as will be shown in the next chapters. As given above, Eqs. (11-52) to (11-54) are applicable to the laminar flow of a fluid of constant density and viscosity. The modifications required to adapt them for use with turbulent flow will be studied in Chap. 13.

PROBLEMS

12-1. For an ideal fluid, ν is zero, and Eqs. (11-52) to (11-54) become Euler's equations, a basic relation for this type of flow. If in addition the flow is irrotational, it can be shown that

$$\frac{\partial u_x}{\partial y} = \frac{\partial u_y}{\partial x} \qquad \frac{\partial u_x}{\partial z} = \frac{\partial u_z}{\partial x} \qquad \frac{\partial u_y}{\partial z} = \frac{\partial u_z}{\partial y}$$

Use these relations to show that Euler's equations become Bernoulli's equation for steady, irrotational, incompressible flow.

12-2. Write the Navier-Stokes equations for two-dimensional steady flow, and then write the equations in terms of the stream function ψ.

SOME SOLUTIONS OF THE
EQUATIONS OF MOTION
12

In the present chapter we shall study some applications of the differential momentum balance to isothermal flow; the results will complement the introductory discussion of laminar flow in a pipe in Chap. 7 and the qualitative discussion of flow past a flat plate in Chap. 8.

In Chap. 7 we wrote a force-momentum balance for a finite, cylindrical element of fluid in laminar flow in a cylindrical pipe. This analysis led to the Hagen-Poiseuille equation. In Chap. 11 we wrote a force balance for a differential element of fluid in a general situation; the shape of the conduit or immersed body was not specified. The result of this analysis was a set of nonlinear partial differential equations, the Navier-Stokes equations. Because of the mathematical complexity of these equations, exact solutions have been found for only relatively simple cases, for which many terms can be set equal to zero. Sometimes the whole problem is reduced to the solution of one equation rather than several equations simultaneously. This simplification can be made for laminar flow in a circular pipe; later in this chapter we shall use this procedure to obtain the equation for the parabolic velocity distribution from the Navier-Stokes equations.

After considering a few exact solutions of the Navier-Stokes equations, we shall study some approximations which simplify the differential equations and make it possible to solve them analytically. Terms will be left out which are not exactly zero, but which are small in comparison with the terms retained. The approximations we shall consider are called creeping flow, potential flow, and boundary-layer flow.

Laminar Parallel Flow between Flat Walls

One of the simplest types of fluid flow is the steady, laminar flow of an incompressible fluid between flat, parallel walls of infinite width, at a point far from the inlet or outlet of the channel. If the x axis is taken in the direction of flow, u_y and u_z are zero, and the equation of continuity gives

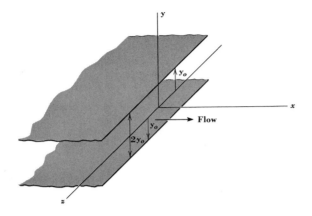

Fig. 12-1.   *Flow in a slit.*

$$\frac{\partial u_x}{\partial x} = 0 \tag{12-1}$$

Of the Navier-Stokes equations, we consider first (11-52); since $\partial u_x/\partial \theta = 0$, $u_y = 0$, $u_z = 0$, and $\partial u_x/\partial x = 0$, Eq. (11-52) reduces to

$$\frac{g_c}{\rho}\frac{\partial p}{\partial x} = g_c X + \nu \left(\frac{\partial^2 u_x}{\partial y^2} + \frac{\partial^2 u_x}{\partial z^2} \right) \tag{12-2}$$

or

$$\frac{\partial p}{\partial x} = \rho X + \frac{\mu}{g_c} \left(\frac{\partial^2 u_x}{\partial y^2} + \frac{\partial^2 u_x}{\partial z^2} \right) \tag{12-3}$$

If the channel is horizontal, the body force X is zero [Eq. (11-6)]. Figure 12-1 shows the orientation of the axes. The conduit extends indefinitely in the z direction, and its width is $2y_o$, as shown. There is therefore no change of u_x with z, and so $\partial^2 u_x/\partial z^2$ is zero, changing Eq. (12-3) to

$$\frac{\partial p}{\partial x} = \frac{\mu}{g_c}\frac{\partial^2 u_x}{\partial y^2} \tag{12-4}$$

We now consider briefly the remaining two Navier-Stokes equations. In Eq. (11-54), the body force Z is zero, as well as all the other terms involving u_z, so that $\partial p/\partial z$ is zero. If $2y_o$ is presumed to be small, Y can also be taken as negligible, and Eq. (11-53) reduces to $\partial p/\partial y = 0$. Thus p is independent of y and z, and $\partial p/\partial x$ can be written dp/dx. Since u_x, and thus $\partial^2 u_x/\partial y^2$, is not a function of x, we can say finally that dp/dx is a constant everywhere in the parts of the conduit subject to the condition of this problem. Thus the final differential equation to be solved is

$$\frac{d^2 u_x}{dy^2} = \frac{g_c}{\mu}\frac{dp}{dx} = \text{const} \tag{12-5}$$

The total pressure in the above equation for flow in a slit can be considered as the sum of the hydrostatic pressure (that pressure which would exist if there were no flow) and a quantity which is called the dynamic pressure. It is really the gradient of the dynamic pressure which causes flow; in a fluid at rest the total pressure gradient equals the hydrostatic pressure gradient, and the gradient of dynamic pressure is zero. If the above definition of the total pressure is inserted in the Navier-Stokes equations (11-52) to (11-54), it is found that the body-force terms disappear and that the total pressure is replaced by the dynamic pressure; the other terms in the equations are unaffected. Thus it is rigorously correct that $\partial p_d/\partial y$ and $\partial p_d/\partial z$ equal zero, even for a nonhorizontal conduit, and the equation

$$\frac{d^2 u_x}{dy^2} = \frac{g_c}{\mu} \frac{dp_d}{dx} = \text{const} \tag{12-6}$$

is true also for a nonhorizontal conduit. The original analysis for a horizontal conduit led to Eq. (12-5), which is not quite exact, since the total pressure at the bottom of the channel is slightly greater than at the top. However, there is no y gradient of dynamic pressure, and Eq. (12-6) is exact. In many texts on fluid dynamics the Navier-Stokes equations are written in terms of the dynamic pressure.

A first integration of Eq. (12-5) gives

$$\frac{du}{dy} = \frac{g_c}{\mu} \frac{dp}{dx} y \tag{12-7}$$

in which the constant of integration is zero because du/dy is zero at $y = 0$; the subscript on u has been dropped for convenience. A second integration yields

$$u = \frac{g_c}{2\mu} \frac{dp}{dx} (y^2 - y_o^2) \tag{12-8}$$

because u is zero at $y = y_o$. This equation is usually written as

$$u = -\frac{g_c}{2\mu} \frac{dp}{dx} (y_o^2 - y^2) \tag{12-9}$$

since we have $dp/dx < 0$ and $y^2 < y_o^2$. The maximum velocity u_{max} occurs at $y = 0$. Therefore Eq. (12-9) can be written alternatively as

$$u = u_{max} \left[1 - \left(\frac{y}{y_o} \right)^2 \right] \tag{12-10}$$

This equation can be used in conjunction with the over-all mass balance, as shown for several examples in Chap. 3, to give

$$\frac{dp}{dx} = -\frac{3\mu u_b}{g_c y_o^2} \tag{12-11}$$

The above relations could have been found by starting from a force balance on an element of fluid defined to take advantage of the symmetry of this

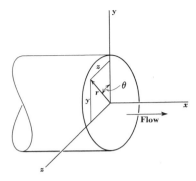

Fig. 12-2.   *Flow in a circular tube.*

system; this derivation was the subject of Prob. 7-1.   In the present discussion the equivalent result has been obtained from the Navier-Stokes equations, with attention to several theoretical details.

Laminar Flow in a Circular Pipe

This is another case of parallel flow, for which u_y, u_z, $\partial u_x/\partial x$, and $\partial u_x/\partial \theta$ are all zero for steady-state flow, far from the pipe inlet.   The axes are oriented as shown in Fig. 12-2.

The Navier-Stokes equations for an incompressible fluid reduce to

$$\frac{dp}{dx} = \frac{\mu}{g_c}\left(\frac{\partial^2 u}{\partial y^2} + \frac{\partial^2 u}{\partial z^2}\right) \tag{12-12}$$

In this equation, p may be interpreted as the dynamic pressure, particularly if the x axis is not horizontal, u replaces u_x, and dp/dx is a constant. These modifications follow from the same arguments used for the case of flow between flat walls.

In the present case u is a function of both y and z, so $\partial^2 u/\partial z^2$ cannot be set equal to zero.   The problem is made much easier to solve if cylindrical coordinates are used, for which

$$x = x \tag{12-13}$$
$$y = r \cos \theta \tag{12-14}$$
$$z = r \sin \theta \tag{12-15}$$

as shown in Fig. 12-2.   Conversely,

$$r = \sqrt{z^2 + y^2} \tag{12-16}$$

and

$$\theta = \tan^{-1}\frac{z}{y} \tag{12-17}$$

These relations may be used to transform Eq. (12-12) into its equivalent in cylindrical coordinates.

$$\frac{\partial^2 u}{\partial r^2} + \frac{1}{r}\frac{\partial u}{\partial r} + \frac{1}{r^2}\frac{\partial^2 u}{\partial \theta^2} = \frac{g_c}{\mu}\frac{dp}{dx} \tag{12-18}$$

The algebra involved in this transformation is quite tedious and is omitted here. Since the flow is symmetrical about the x axis, $\partial^2 u/\partial \theta^2$ is zero, and we obtain the following ordinary differential equation:

$$\frac{d^2 u}{dr^2} + \frac{1}{r}\frac{du}{dr} = \frac{g_c}{\mu}\frac{dp}{dx} = \text{const} \tag{12-19}$$

or

$$\frac{1}{r}\frac{d}{dr}\left(r\frac{du}{dr}\right) = \frac{g_c}{\mu}\frac{dp}{dx} = \text{const} \tag{12-20}$$

Equation (12-20) is integrated once, subject to the boundary condition that $du/dr = 0$ at $r = 0$. The result is then integrated again, subject to the condition that $u = 0$ at $r = r_i$, giving

$$u = -\frac{g_c}{4\mu}\frac{dp}{dx}(r_i^2 - r^2) \tag{12-21}$$

This result is analogous to Eq. (12-9) for flow through a slit and is easily converted to

$$u = u_{max}\left[1 - \left(\frac{r}{r_i}\right)^2\right] \tag{12-22}$$

which is the same as Eq. (7-15). An integration over the pipe cross section gives

$$\frac{dp}{dx} = -\frac{8\mu u_b}{g_c r_i^2} \tag{12-23}$$

Practical applications of (12-23), the Hagen-Poiseuille equation, have been given in Example 7-1 and Probs. 7-6 to 7-8.

Laminar Flow in an Annulus

Flow in the space between two concentric pipes is a common practical situation. For this case Eq. (12-20) still applies; an alternative derivation of this equation has been suggested in Prob. 7-9. The boundary condition for the first integration of Eq. (12-20) is $du/dr = 0$ at $r = r_{max}$, the radius at which the maximum velocity occurs. This gives

$$r\frac{du}{dr} = \frac{g_c}{2\mu}\frac{dp}{dx}(r^2 - r_{max}^2) \tag{12-24}$$

The second integration is subject to the condition that u is zero at the inner boundary r_1, giving

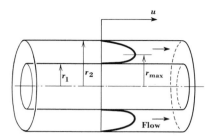

Fig. 12-3.   Velocity profiles for flow in an annulus.

$$u = \frac{g_c}{2\mu} \frac{dp}{dx} \left(\frac{r^2 - r_1{}^2}{2} - r_{max}^2 \ln \frac{r}{r_1} \right) \tag{12-25}$$

However, at $r = r_2$, u also is zero, so an alternative expression is

$$u = \frac{g_c}{2\mu} \frac{dp}{dx} \left(\frac{r^2 - r_2{}^2}{2} - r_{max}^2 \ln \frac{r}{r_2} \right) \tag{12-26}$$

These two equations permit r_{max} to be found in terms of r_1 and r_2:

$$r_{max} = \sqrt{\frac{r_2{}^2 - r_1{}^2}{2 \ln (r_2/r_1)}} \tag{12-27}$$

By an integration over the cross section of the annulus there results

$$\frac{dp}{dx} = - \frac{8\mu u_b}{g_c} \frac{1}{r_2{}^2 + r_1{}^2 - 2r_{max}^2} \tag{12-28}$$

The velocity profile predicted by Eq. (12-26) is shown in Fig. 12-3. For the limiting case of $r_1 = 0$, r_{max} becomes zero and Eqs. (12-26) and (12-28) reduce to the equivalent equations for the circular pipe, (12-21) and (12-23).

It must be remembered that these exact solutions of the equations of motion hold only for the isothermal, laminar, steady-state flow of an incompressible fluid far from the entrance of the channel. For a circular pipe **Re** must be less than 2100. The significance of Reynolds numbers for noncircular conduits will be discussed in Chap. 15.

No more exact solutions will be given here, but others are to be found in more specialized works.[1]

[1] J. G. Knudsen and D. L. Katz, "Fluid Dynamics and Heat Transfer," chap. 4, McGraw-Hill Book Company, Inc., New York, 1958; H. Schlichting, "Boundary Layer Theory," 4th ed., chap. 5, McGraw-Hill Book Company, Inc., New York, 1960; R. B. Bird, W. E. Stewart, and E. N. Lightfoot, "Transport Phenomena," chap. 2, John Wiley & Sons, Inc., New York, 1960.

Creeping Flow

The term creeping flow is used to describe flow at very low velocity, or to be more precise, at very low Reynolds numbers. The principal interest in this type of flow stems from the fact that it applies for the fall of small particles through a fluid; it is the basis of Stokes' law, which is useful in solving problems of settling and sedimentation. Creeping flow also occurs in certain problems in lubrication.

For Reynolds numbers less than unity, the viscous forces involved in flow outweigh the inertia forces. In flow around a sphere, for example, a fluid particle changes direction and velocity in a complex way, and if the inertia effects connected with these changes were important, it would be necessary to retain all the terms in all three Navier-Stokes equations. It will be recalled, however, that the substantial derivative in the statement of Newton's second law, (Eq. 11-4), is proportional to the force required to overcome the inertia of the fluid element. As a result, this term is omitted from the equations of motion representing creeping flow. Results based on this assumption have been found to agree with experiment at **Re** < 1. Thus the equations of motion for creeping flow of an incompressible fluid are

$$\frac{\partial p}{\partial x} = \frac{\mu}{g_c} \left(\frac{\partial^2 u_x}{\partial x^2} + \frac{\partial^2 u_x}{\partial y^2} + \frac{\partial^2 u_x}{\partial z^2} \right) \tag{12-29}$$

$$\frac{\partial p}{\partial y} = \frac{\mu}{g_c} \left(\frac{\partial^2 u_y}{\partial x^2} + \frac{\partial^2 u_y}{\partial y^2} + \frac{\partial^2 u_y}{\partial z^2} \right) \tag{12-30}$$

$$\frac{\partial p}{\partial z} = \frac{\mu}{g_c} \left(\frac{\partial^2 u_z}{\partial x^2} + \frac{\partial^2 u_z}{\partial y^2} + \frac{\partial^2 u_z}{\partial z^2} \right) \tag{12-31}$$

and the equation of continuity is

$$\frac{\partial u_x}{\partial x} + \frac{\partial u_y}{\partial y} + \frac{\partial u_z}{\partial z} = 0 \tag{12-32}$$

At the surface of the sphere, the tangential and normal velocities must be zero. The problem can be reduced to one of only two independent variables by the use of spherical coordinates. The mathematics required to achieve the equations describing the velocity distribution is long and complicated, so we merely state that the problem has been solved.[1] From the resulting pressure distribution over the sphere it can be shown by integration over the whole surface that the form drag caused by the pressure distribution is

---

[1] H. Lamb, "Hydrodynamics," 6th ed., pp. 597–598, Dover Publications, New York, 1945.

$$F_{d,\text{form}} = \frac{2\pi\mu r_o u_o}{g_c} \tag{12-33}$$

where r_o = radius of sphere

u_o = velocity of parallel flow far from sphere (or velocity of travel of sphere through a quiescent fluid)

From the velocity distribution and the basic relation between viscosity and shear stress at the surface, an integration over the whole surface of the sphere gives the total force arising from viscous drag—the skin friction.

$$F_{d,\text{skin}} = \frac{4\pi\mu r_o u_o}{g_c} \tag{12-34}$$

The total drag is then

$$F_d = \frac{6\pi\mu r_o u_o}{g_c} \tag{12-35}$$

which is the Stokes equation. The drag force is proportional to the velocity. The drag coefficient defined in Chap. 8 is found by combining Eqs. (12-35) and (8-13) to give

$$C_D = \frac{12\mu}{r_o u_o \rho} = \frac{24}{\mathsf{Re}} \tag{12-36}$$

Flow of an Ideal Fluid

Having just considered the case of flow at a very small Reynolds number, let us turn to the opposite extreme of flow at a very high Reynolds number, for which the inertia forces outweigh the viscous forces. We set the viscosity equal to zero in the Navier-Stokes equations and obtain the equations of motion for an ideal or inviscid fluid, called the Euler equations:

$$u_x \frac{\partial u_x}{\partial x} + u_y \frac{\partial u_x}{\partial y} + u_z \frac{\partial u_x}{\partial z} + \frac{\partial u_x}{\partial \theta} = g_c X - \frac{g_c}{\rho} \frac{\partial p}{\partial x} \tag{12-37}$$

$$u_x \frac{\partial u_y}{\partial x} + u_y \frac{\partial u_y}{\partial y} + u_z \frac{\partial u_y}{\partial z} + \frac{\partial u_y}{\partial \theta} = g_c Y - \frac{g_c}{\rho} \frac{\partial p}{\partial y} \tag{12-38}$$

$$u_x \frac{\partial u_z}{\partial x} + u_y \frac{\partial u_z}{\partial y} + u_z \frac{\partial u_z}{\partial z} + \frac{\partial u_z}{\partial \theta} = g_c Z - \frac{g_c}{\rho} \frac{\partial p}{\partial z} \tag{12-39}$$

The theory of ideal fluids is useful in aerodynamics, particularly in the calculation of the lift of airfoils. It is also useful in the general study of flow past immersed bodies, for it gives the pressure distribution at the outer edge of the boundary layer. Since the theory contains the postulate of zero viscosity, it implies slip at a solid surface. As previously discussed (Chap. 8), the effect of viscosity and shear must be considered in the boundary layer near a surface, for there actually is no slip at the surface. However, away from the surface, the assumption of an ideal fluid is often valid.

The aeronautical engineer finds the most opportunities to use the theory of ideal fluids, but it is important to all engineers in the general study of fluid dynamics. In this discussion, we shall restrict ourselves to the simple case of irrotational, or potential, flow. This name implies the absence of rotation, or vorticity, in the flow.

Potential Flow

The idea of an electric potential is familiar, and we also have dealt with the potential energy due to the field of gravity. For instance, for the z axis directed vertically upward, the body force Z is given by $- g/g_c$ in lb force/lb. Since the change in potential energy is equal to the work done in raising a mass of one pound in the z direction, we set

$$d\Omega = Z \, dz \tag{12-40}$$

where Ω is the potential energy, (ft)(lb force)/lb, and

$$Z = -\frac{g}{g_c} = \frac{d\Omega}{dz} \tag{12-41}$$

Here a force is expressed as a gradient of a potential. By analogy, we define a velocity potential $\phi(x,y)$ so that the velocity is equal to the gradient of a potential. Thus

$$u_x = \frac{\partial \phi}{\partial x} \tag{12-42}$$

and

$$u_y = \frac{\partial \phi}{\partial y} \tag{12-43}$$

It is convenient to restrict this discussion to two-dimensional flow. If these expressions for the velocities are substituted into the equation of continuity,

$$\frac{\partial u_x}{\partial x} + \frac{\partial u_y}{\partial y} = 0 \tag{12-44}$$

we get

$$\frac{\partial^2 \phi}{\partial x^2} + \frac{\partial^2 \phi}{\partial y^2} = 0 \tag{12-45}$$

This is Laplace's equation. If suitable boundary conditions are known, the equation can be solved to give $\phi(x,y)$, and the velocity at any point can then be obtained from Eqs. (12-42) and (12-43). This is simple enough, but we have merely assumed so far that the potential function

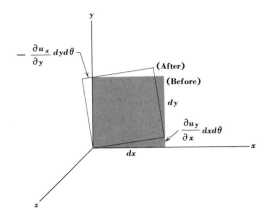

Fig. 12-4.   *Fluid element in rotational flow.*

exists.   Actually, it exists only if the flow fulfills certain requirements, which we shall now find.

Equations (12-42) and (12-43) can be differentiated to obtain

$$\frac{\partial u_x}{\partial y} = \frac{\partial^2 \phi}{\partial y\, \partial x} \tag{12-46}$$

and

$$\frac{\partial u_y}{\partial x} = \frac{\partial^2 \phi}{\partial x\, \partial y} \tag{12-47}$$

Since $\phi(x,y)$ is a single-valued function and all its second derivatives are assumed to exist, the right-hand sides of these two equations are identical, and we have

$$\frac{\partial u_y}{\partial x} - \frac{\partial u_x}{\partial y} = 0 \tag{12-48}$$

The quantity on the left-hand side of Eq. (12-48) is called the vorticity of the fluid; we shall see that it equals twice the angular velocity about an axis oriented in the z direction.

Consider the rotation of an element of fluid associated with the velocity gradients in Eq. (12-48).   These gradients may cause shear, or the sliding of one layer over the other; Fig. 12-4 illustrates a fluid element undergoing rotation.   The origin moves with the element, and the orientation of the element is shown before and after a time $d\theta$.   The average rotation of a differential element is one-half the sum of the rotation of the dx segment and the dy segment.   Since the angular velocity is equal to the rate of movement of the end of a radial arm divided by the radius, we have

$$\omega = \frac{1}{2}\left(\frac{\partial u_y}{\partial x} - \frac{\partial u_x}{\partial y}\right) \tag{12-49}$$

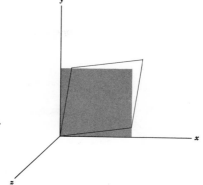

Fig. 12-5.   *Fluid element in irrotational flow.*

Thus the flow illustrated by Fig. 12-4 is rotational and does not meet the requirement of Eq. (12-48) for potential flow. On the other hand, the flow in Fig. 12-5 is irrotational; the element is deformed but suffers no net rotation. For this case, the requirement

$$\frac{\partial u_y}{\partial x} - \frac{\partial u_x}{\partial y} = 0 \qquad\qquad (12\text{-}48)$$

is met; the vorticity is zero. These definitions can be extended to three dimensions.

We have now shown that the velocity distribution for potential flow can be found from the solution of Laplace's equation (12-45) and that potential flow is irrotational because of the restriction imposed by Eq. (12-48). Euler's equations can now be used to find the pressure distribution. For steady-state, two-dimensional, irrotational, incompressible flow, the substitution of (12-48) and the x equivalent of (12-41) into Eq. (12-37) gives

$$u_x \frac{\partial u_x}{\partial x} + u_y \frac{\partial u_y}{\partial x} - g_c \frac{\partial \Omega}{\partial x} + \frac{g_c}{\rho} \frac{\partial p}{\partial x} = 0 \qquad\qquad (12\text{-}50)$$

This equation can be integrated to give

$$\tfrac{1}{2}(u_x{}^2 + u_y{}^2) - g_c\Omega + \frac{g_c p}{\rho} = f_1(y) \qquad\qquad (12\text{-}51)$$

Similarly, Eq. (12-38) gives

$$\tfrac{1}{2}(u_x{}^2 + u_y{}^2) - g_c\Omega + \frac{g_c p}{\rho} = f_2(x) \qquad\qquad (12\text{-}52)$$

Since the left-hand sides of these equations are identical, $f_1(y) = f_2(x) = $ const. Furthermore,

$$u_x{}^2 + u_y{}^2 = u^2 \qquad\qquad (12\text{-}53)$$

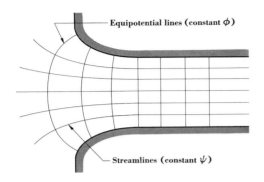

Equipotential lines (constant ϕ)

Streamlines (constant ψ)

Fig. 12-6.   Flow net for a rounded entry.

and so we have

$$\frac{u^2}{2g_c} - \Omega + \frac{p}{\rho} = \text{const} \qquad (12\text{-}54)$$

which is Bernoulli's equation.   It is alternatively expressed, for two points in the fluid, as

$$\frac{\Delta u^2}{2g_c} - \Delta\Omega + \frac{\Delta p}{\rho} = 0 \qquad (12\text{-}55)$$

Since

$$\Delta\Omega = -\frac{g}{g_c}\,\Delta z \qquad (12\text{-}56)$$

follows from Eq. (12-41), we obtain

$$\frac{\Delta u^2}{2g_c} + \frac{g}{g_c}\,\Delta z + \frac{\Delta p}{\rho} = 0 \qquad (12\text{-}57)$$

which is similar to Eq. (4-21).   The latter equation contains u_b rather than u, but the subscript is not really necessary, because the assumptions previously made imply that there can be no velocity variation over the planes at the inlet and outlet.   For irrotational, frictionless flow in this case, u and u_b are identical.

It will be recalled that Bernoulli's equation has been used in the analysis in Chap. 6 of the pitot tube and of the flow in an orifice up to the vena contracta.   For these flowmeters it is readily seen that the inertia terms do indeed outweigh the viscous terms.   The fluid is accelerated by changes in the flow cross section, and there is no extended rubbing against solid surfaces.   Since the flow in a jet emerging from an orifice is irrotational, the velocity across the jet is constant.   We mentioned in Chap. 6 that the coefficient of contraction for flow through an orifice has been calculated from ideal-fluid theory; this theory also applies for other cases involving relatively large inertia effects, such as flow over a weir, flow from large tanks into pipe entries, and flow through the rounded entry shown in Fig. 12-6.

The equipotential lines and streamlines in Fig. 12-6 (called the flow net) have been obtained from the solution of Laplace's equation (12-45), for boundary conditions corresponding to the shape given. The actual flow results have been found to agree well with the theoretical results shown. For potential flow, lines of constant ϕ and lines of constant ψ are everywhere perpendicular (orthogonal).

We know that Bernoulli's equation does not apply for ordinary, steady-state, parallel flow through a pipe of constant cross section. The term lw_f, which arises from the friction, or viscous shear, must be added [Eq. (4-27), for example, with W_s zero]. For this system, there is a velocity gradient across the pipe radius but no offsetting gradient in another direction; therefore, according to Eq. (12-48), the flow is rotational. We can, of course, draw streamlines for this rotational flow; the stream function ψ exists, since it is based only on the validity of the equation of continuity (Chap. 8). However, the potential function ϕ does not exist, for the flow is not irrotational. The rotation arising from shear, such as in laminar flow, is analogous to the rotation which can be given to a pencil held between the palms as one's hands are rubbed together. Similar remarks apply to boundary-layer flow.

We shall not give here the mathematical details of any solutions of Laplace's equation for ϕ. Many good discussions are available in books on fluid dynamics;[1] some knowledge of the theory of functions of a complex variable is necessary for anything more than an introduction to the subject.

Boundary-layer Flow

Certain terms in the Navier-Stokes equations are negligible when applied to laminar flow in a boundary layer; let us now investigate this case. These assumptions are valid only at high Reynolds numbers, for which the thickness of the boundary layer is small compared with distance from the leading edge. They are not valid at low Reynolds numbers, for which the region where viscosity is important extends relatively far from the wall, as, to mention an extreme case, in creeping flow. The theory of ideal fluids also holds at high Reynolds numbers, but since this theory requires slip of the fluid over a solid boundary, results obtained from it do not agree

[1] V. L. Streeter, "Fluid Dynamics," McGraw-Hill Book Company, Inc., New York, 1948 (an elementary text); Lamb, *op. cit.* (the classical treatise on hydrodynamics); L. M. Milne-Thomson, "Theoretical Hydrodynamics," 2d ed., The Macmillan Company, New York, 1950 (emphasis on vector notation).

Fig. 12-7.   Boundary-layer flow.

with physical reality for the layer of fluid near a boundary, where viscosity cannot be neglected and where the velocity is changing to its ultimate value of zero at the solid surface.   Recall from Chap. 8 that this physical unreality is particularly harmful in estimating the drag, for which ideal-fluid theory usually gives erroneous results.

We shall now see what simplifications can be made in applying the equations of motion to a two-dimensional, laminar, incompressible boundary layer at steady state.   We also neglect body forces (or use the dynamic pressure); the x and y equations are, then,

$$u_x \frac{\partial u_x}{\partial x} + u_y \frac{\partial u_x}{\partial y} = -\frac{g_c}{\rho} \frac{\partial p}{\partial x} + \frac{\mu}{\rho} \left(\frac{\partial^2 u_x}{\partial x^2} + \frac{\partial^2 u_x}{\partial y^2} \right)$$ (12-58)

and

$$u_x \frac{\partial u_y}{\partial x} + u_y \frac{\partial u_y}{\partial y} = -\frac{g_c}{\rho} \frac{\partial p}{\partial y} + \frac{\mu}{\rho} \left(\frac{\partial^2 u_y}{\partial x^2} + \frac{\partial^2 u_y}{\partial y^2} \right)$$ (12-59)

Figure 12-7 is a sketch of the boundary layer.   Its thickness is defined as the distance from the surface to the point where the velocity u_x has a value of $0.99u_o$; u_o is the velocity at the surface predicted by the theory of ideal fluids.

As first suggested by Prandtl,[1] since the boundary layer is presumed very thin and lies on a solid surface, u_y is very small compared with u_x, and $\partial u_x/\partial y$ is large compared with $\partial u_x/\partial x$.   This means that $u_x(\partial u_x/\partial x)$ and $u_y(\partial u_x/\partial y)$ are of about the same order of magnitude, and these in turn are comparable with $\frac{\mu}{\rho} \frac{\partial^2 u_x}{\partial y^2}$.   On the other hand, $\frac{\mu}{\rho} \frac{\partial^2 u_x}{\partial x^2}$ is negligible in comparison with the other terms in Eq. (12-58).

In Eq. (12-59), a similar analysis shows that all the terms containing u_y and its derivatives are small.   This leads to the conclusion that $\frac{g_c}{\rho} \frac{\partial p}{\partial y}$ is

[1] L. Prandtl, "Über Flüssigkeitsbewegung bei sehr kleiner Reibung," *Proc. III Intern. Math. Congr.*, Heidelberg, 1904. For a good nonmathematical discussion of fluid dynamics in general, see L. Prandtl, "The Essentials of Fluid Dynamics," Hafner Publishing Company, New York, 1949.

small; in other words, the pressure varies but little from the surface to the edge of the boundary layer. This result is important, for the variation of pressure with x can be found from potential flow, so that $\partial p/\partial x$ may be considered as given and as independent of y in the boundary layer.

The problem is now reduced to that of the simultaneous solution of the equation of motion for the x direction and the equation of continuity.

$$u_x \frac{\partial u_x}{\partial x} + u_y \frac{\partial u_x}{\partial y} = -\frac{g_c}{\rho}\frac{dp}{dx} + \frac{\mu}{\rho}\frac{\partial^2 u_x}{\partial y^2} \qquad (12\text{-}60)$$

$$\frac{\partial u_x}{\partial x} + \frac{\partial u_y}{\partial y} = 0 \qquad (12\text{-}44)$$

Since dp/dx is given by the potential, frictionless-flow solution, these two equations are sufficient to solve for the two unknowns u_x and u_y. In addition it is known that at $y = 0$, $u_x = u_y = 0$, and at $y = \delta$, $u_x = u_o$. For a curved boundary, x can be measured along the surface and y normal to the surface, if the radius of curvature is large compared with δ.

Flow Past a Flat Plate

For flow past a flat plate Eq. (12-60) is further simplified in that dp/dx is zero, since u_o is constant. The solution of this problem for laminar flow, giving u_x and u_y as a function of x and y, was first obtained by Blasius[1] and later elaborated upon by Howarth.[2] Equations (12-60) and (12-44), even though much simpler than the equations for the general case, still present considerable mathematical difficulty. The details of the solution will not be given in full, but the general procedure will be outlined.

Equations (12-60) and (12-44) can be reduced to a single partial differential equation by using the stream function, which we showed in Chap. 8 to be related to the velocities by the equations

$$u_x = \frac{\partial \psi}{\partial y} \qquad (12\text{-}61)$$

$$u_y = -\frac{\partial \psi}{\partial x} \qquad (12\text{-}62)$$

for an incompressible fluid. The stream function was defined so as to satisfy the equation of continuity. The substitution of Eqs. (12-61) and (12-62) into (12-44) will confirm this statement. If u_x and u_y in Eq. (12-60) are now replaced by using (12-61) and (12-62), there results

$$\frac{\partial \psi}{\partial y}\frac{\partial^2 \psi}{\partial x\, \partial y} - \frac{\partial \psi}{\partial x}\frac{\partial^2 \psi}{\partial y^2} = \nu \frac{\partial^3 \psi}{\partial y^3} \qquad (12\text{-}63)$$

[1] H. Blasius, *Z. Math. u. Phys.*, **56**:1 (1908); also *NACA Tech. Mem.* 1256.

[2] L. Howarth, *Proc. Roy. Soc. London*, **A164**:547 (1938).

This third-order, nonlinear partial differential equation must be solved for $\psi(x,y)$, subject to the boundary conditions already given.

The solution of a partial differential equation such as (12-63) cannot be obtained by any set mathematical technique, but usually depends on a trial-and-error procedure involving considerable mathematical and physical intuition. In the present case, the stratagem which leads to a solution arises from the fact that the velocity profiles at various points along the plate are similar—a conclusion which we may regard as based on physical intuition. Therefore the velocity at any point along the plate should be a unique function of y/δ. The boundary-layer thickness δ is a function of x, but it increases less rapidly than the first power of x. Since there is some evidence from other solutions (not given here) of the Navier-Stokes equations that δ is proportional to $\sqrt{x}$, let us say that u_x is a function of $y/\sqrt{x}$.

$$u_x = f_1 \left(\frac{y}{\sqrt{x}} \right) \tag{12-64}$$

Equation (12-63) is in terms of ψ, so we need a relation between ψ and u_x. We obtain this from Eq. (12-61). If we arbitrarily set $\psi = 0$ as the streamline at $y = 0$, $x = 0$, then we can write as an approximation, at a point x,

$$\psi = \frac{\partial \psi}{\partial y} \delta \tag{12-65}$$

The use of Eq. (12-61) and the fact that $\delta \propto \sqrt{x}$ permit us to write

$$\psi \propto u_x \sqrt{x} \tag{12-66}$$

and, using Eq. (12-64),

$$\psi \propto \sqrt{x} f_1 \left(\frac{y}{\sqrt{x}} \right)$$

$$\psi = (\text{const}) \sqrt{x} f_1 \left(\frac{y}{\sqrt{x}} \right) \tag{12-67}$$

Equations (12-64) and (12-67) form a basis for the simplification of Eq. (12-63). It is found that the substitution of Eqs. (12-64) and (12-67) into (12-63) changes the latter to an *ordinary* differential equation involving $f_1(y/\sqrt{x})$ and $y/\sqrt{x}$.

In place of the simple relations (12-64) and (12-67) given above, it is customary to define the quantities used to simplify Eq. (12-63) in terms of dimensionless variables, as follows:

$$\eta = y \sqrt{\frac{u_o}{\nu x}} \tag{12-68}$$

and

$$f(\eta) = \frac{\psi}{\sqrt{x\nu u_o}} \tag{12-69}$$

where η can be regarded as a dimensionless position variable and $f(\eta)$ as a dimensionless stream function. Equations (12-68) and (12-69) are called similarity transformations.

Using the rules of partial differentiation[1] and the above new quantities, Eq. (12-63) is transformed by a lengthy procedure into

$$f(\eta)\,\frac{d^2f(\eta)}{d\eta^2} + 2\,\frac{d^3f(\eta)}{d\eta^3} = 0 \tag{12-70}$$

or written more simply,

$$ff'' + 2f''' = 0 \tag{12-71}$$

Equations (12-68) and (12-69) have been contrived so that x, y, ψ, ν, and u_o are all eliminated in going from (12-63) to (12-71).

The boundary conditions on Eq. (12-71) are found from the definitions

$$u_x = \frac{\partial \psi}{\partial y} = u_o f' \tag{12-72}$$

and

$$u_y = -\frac{\partial \psi}{\partial x} = \frac{1}{2}\sqrt{\frac{\nu u_o}{x}}\,(\eta f' - f) \tag{12-73}$$

Thus, at $y = 0$, where $u_x = u_y = 0$, we have $\eta = 0$ and $f = f' = 0$, and at $y = \infty$, where $u_x = u_o$, $\eta = \infty$ and $f' = 1.0$.

Equation (12-71) has not been solved to give a closed form, but the following series solution has been obtained:

$$f = 0.664\eta^2 - 0.00705\eta^5 + 0.000153\eta^8 - 0.00000350\eta^{11} + \cdots \tag{12-74}$$

The derivation of this series and the determination of the constants from the boundary values are not given here.[2] Equation (12-74) can be used with Eqs. (12-72) and (12-73) to find the values of u_x and u_y, which are represented in Figs. 12-8 and 12-9. Figure 12-8 shows that the boundary-layer thickness is approximately

$$\delta = 5.0\sqrt{\frac{\nu x}{u_o}} \tag{12-75}$$

---

[1] A succinct summary of these rules is given by H. S. Mickley, T. K. Sherwood, and C. E. Reed, "Applied Mathematics in Chemical Engineering," 2d ed., pp. 209–213, McGraw-Hill Book Company, Inc., New York, 1957.

[2] See H. Schlichting, "Boundary Layer Theory," 4th ed., chap. 7, McGraw-Hill Book Company, Inc., New York, 1960. A table of $f(\eta)$ is given on p. 121.

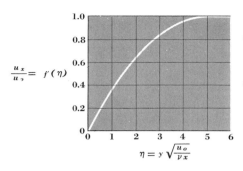

$$\frac{u_x}{u_o} = f'(\eta)$$

Fig. 12-8.   *Variation of u_x with position in the laminar boundary layer on a flat plate. (From Hermann Schlichting, "Boundary Layer Theory," 4th ed., fig. 7.8, p. 119, McGraw-Hill Book Company, Inc., New York, 1960.)*

Drag in Flow Past a Flat Plate

The drag on a flat plate is calculated from the shear stress at the surface. At any point on the surface a distance x from the leading edge,

$$\tau_s = \frac{\mu}{g_c}\left(\frac{\partial u_x}{\partial y}\right)_{y=0} \tag{12-76}$$

where τ_s is the shear stress at $y = 0$. Since we know u_x as a function of x and y from the solution for the laminar boundary layer, we obtain, from Eq. (12-76),

$$\tau_s = 0.332 \frac{\mu}{g_c} u_o \sqrt{\frac{u_o}{\nu x}} \tag{12-77}$$

where τ_s is a function of x. The total drag is given by

$$F_d = b \int_0^L \tau_s \, dx \tag{12-78}$$

for a plate of width b and length L. This drag is caused by skin friction;

Fig. 12-9.   *Variation of u_y with position in the laminar boundary layer on a flat plate. (From Hermann Schlichting, "Boundary Layer Theory," 4th ed., fig. 7.9, p. 120, McGraw-Hill Book Company, Inc., New York, 1960.)*

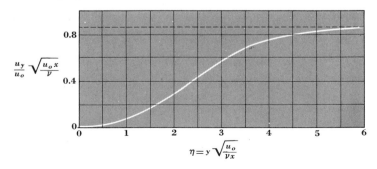

there is no form drag. The substitution of Eq. (12-77) into (12-78) yields

$$F_d = 0.332 \frac{\mu b u_o}{g_c} \sqrt{\frac{u_o}{\nu}} \int_0^L \frac{dx}{\sqrt{x}}$$

$$= \frac{0.664 b u_o}{g_c} \sqrt{\mu \rho L u_o} \tag{12-79}$$

and so

$$F_d = \frac{0.664 b}{g_c} \sqrt{\mu \rho L u_o{}^3} \tag{12-80}$$

The coefficient of drag related to the total drag on a plate of length L was defined in Chap. 8 and can be written for flow past one side of the plate as

$$C_D = \frac{F_d g_c}{\frac{1}{2} u_o{}^2 \rho A} \tag{12-81}$$

where A equals bL. Equations (12-80) and (12-81) may be combined to give

$$C_D = 1.328 \sqrt{\frac{\nu}{L u_o}} \tag{12-82}$$

Because the Reynolds number for this case is $L u_o / \nu$, the drag coefficient is given by

$$C_D = \frac{1.328}{\sqrt{\mathbf{Re}_L}} \tag{12-83}$$

This formula, as well as all the others derived above, applies only to the laminar boundary layer, for which $\mathbf{Re}_L$ is less than about 5×10^5. The results also are valid only for positions sufficiently far from the leading edge so that L (or x) is much greater than δ, as was assumed in simplifying the Navier-Stokes equation to obtain Eq. (12-60). The results obtained above for the velocity distribution and for the drag have been verified by many experiments.

The boundary-layer flow past many other shapes has been analyzed by the general method illustrated by the flow past a flat plate. The presence of the pressure-gradient term complicates the analysis in the general case, and the subject of separation and wakes is difficult to handle analytically. The chemical engineer is interested in flow past cylinders as on the shell side of a heat exchanger and past spheres or other particles in packed and fluidized beds. At present these problems are too complicated for an analytical approach, but future progress probably will come from using the principle of boundary-layer flow. Some progress has been made in relating the solution for flow past a single sphere to the flow through a bed of spheres.

The Blasius solution for the laminar boundary layer illustrates an im-

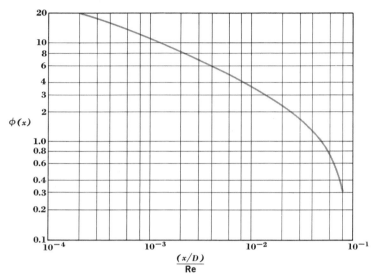

Fig. 12-10. Function for use with Eq. (12-85). [From H. L. Langhaar, Trans. ASME, 64 : A-55 (1942).]

portant point in the mathematical approach to engineering problems. The mathematician, armed with expert knowledge of analysis, is unable to solve the general Navier-Stokes equations as applied to most cases. Even the solution of the simple problem of flow past a flat plate required a knowledge of the physical situation and physical principles, plus some luck or intuition, to find out which terms could safely be dropped and what substitutions might be made to simplify the differential equation so as to arrive at its solution. This is one of the chief reasons why the engineer must acquire sufficient mathematical prowess to attack these analytical problems and not leave them solely to the mathematician.

Flow in the Entrance Section of a Conduit

The way in which the velocity profile develops has been illustrated in Fig. 8-6. For a rectangular duct of infinite width a boundary layer develops on both the top and bottom walls. This situation is similar to flow past a flat plate, and an estimate of the length of the entrance section (i.e., the length up to the point where $\delta = y_o$) might be made by using Eq. (12-75). However, this approximate procedure does not give a correct result, for the fluid in the central part of the duct does not continue to move at u_o but is accelerated in order to satisfy the equation of continuity. Similar remarks apply also to flow near the entrance to a circular tube.

Fig. 12-11. *Velocity profiles near a pipe entrance; laminar flow.*

Langhaar[1] has found an approximate solution of the equations of motion near the entrance to a circular pipe. The entrance length is given by

$$\frac{L_e}{D} = 0.0575 \; \text{Re} \tag{12-84}$$

He also finds for the velocity profile

$$\frac{u_x}{u_o} = \frac{I_o[\phi(x)] - I_o[(r/r_i)\phi(x)]}{I_2[\phi(x)]} \tag{12-85}$$

I_o and I_2 are modified Bessel functions of the first kind, and $\phi(x)$ is given in Fig. 12-10. Velocity distributions at several points near the entrance of a pipe are illustrated in Fig. 12-11.

Recapitulation

It is of interest to summarize the types of problems which can and cannot be solved by the application of the principles of fluid dynamics studied to this point.

1. The over-all balances permit us to calculate an input or an output of a process when a sufficient number of the other inputs and outputs are known. The over-all momentum balance, in particular, has given us a useful method for the analysis of flow through an orifice and other cases involving large inertia effects.

2. The differential momentum balance has enabled us to find solutions for the isothermal, laminar, steady-state flow of an incompressible fluid in a conduit far from its entrance. Similarly, a solution has been obtained for the laminar boundary layer on a flat plate.

3. On the other hand, we have not solved problems involving turbulent flow in a conduit or the turbulent boundary layer, or, for that matter, any boundary-layer flow past the point where separation occurs and a wake is formed. Some progress has been made in the analytical attack on these problems, but the main practical methods the engineer has for their solution depend on the idea of dimensional analysis and the use of considerable

[1] H. L. Langhaar, *Trans. ASME,* **A64:**55 (1942).

empiricism.   These methods are the subject of the next few chapters of this book.

PROBLEMS

12-1. Equation (12-5) can be applied to flow in a slit, one boundary of which moves with a constant velocity u_o.   Find the equation for the velocity as a function of y, u_o, and dp/dx, and sketch the profiles obtained when dp/dx is both positive and negative for u_o positive.

This type of flow is called Couette flow and is of importance in the hydrodynamic theory of lubrication.   If dp/dx is zero, it is called simple Couette flow; this case was used in connection with the first definition of viscosity, Fig. 7-1 and Eq. (7-3).

12-2. Find the equation for the velocity distribution within a film of liquid in laminar flow down a vertical, plane surface, neglecting the acceleration in the film.   In this case there is no pressure gradient in the direction of flow, but the body force (gravity) is important.   Find also the expression for the thickness of the film in terms of the bulk (average) velocity.

12-3. Use Eq. (12-35) to find the position of a small sphere of density ρ_o released from rest as a function of time.   The value of **Re** at the terminal (maximum) velocity is less than 1.0.   What is the expression for the terminal velocity?

12-4. The potential two-dimensional flow of a fluid from a large reservoir into a rectangular channel is described by the equations

$$x = \phi + e^\phi \cos \psi$$

$$y = \psi + e^\phi \sin \psi$$

Draw the streamlines and equipotential lines (i.e., the flow net) for this flow and identify the location of the channel walls.

12-5. For the two-dimensional, potential flow past an idealized pitot tube, the flow net is defined by

$$x = -\phi + \ln \sqrt{\phi^2 + \psi^2}$$

$$y = -\psi + \tan^{-1} \frac{\psi}{\phi}$$

Sketch the streamlines for this system.

12-6. The potential function for a certain flow is given by

$$\phi = xy$$

What might be the solid boundaries causing this flow?

12-7. The flow around a sphere of radius r_o is given in spherical coordinates by

$$\phi = \frac{u_o r_o^3}{2r^2} \cos \theta + u_o r \cos \theta$$

where θ is the angular-position variable.   Find the direction and magnitude of the velocity at $r = \frac{5}{4}r_o$ and $\theta = 30°$, if $\theta = 0$ corresponds to the forward stagnation point.

12-8. Air at 60°F and 1 atm is flowing past a flat plate at 30 ft/sec.   How thick is the boundary layer 1 ft from the leading edge?   Calculate also the drag on the first foot of a 1-ft-wide plate and the direction and magnitude of the velocity at $x = 1$ ft and $y = \delta/2$.

VELOCITY DISTRIBUTION AND DRAG WITH TURBULENT FLOW

13

SOME FUNDAMENTAL IDEAS ABOUT TURBULENCE

Most of the practical fluid-flow problems with which an engineer deals involve turbulent, rather than laminar, flow. There are a number of laminar-flow problems for which the equations of motion have been solved exactly, and many more for which the equations can be solved by certain approximations without greatly affecting the validity of the results. Several examples illustrating these assertions are to be found in the preceding chapter. However, for turbulent flow there exists not a single exact solution. The approximate equations describing turbulent flow depend on so many assumptions that it is difficult to tell whether agreement with experiment is the result of reasonable simplifications or of fortuitous cancellation of the errors arising from the assumptions. In spite of the difficulty of obtaining a complete, theoretical solution of the problem of turbulent flow, many very useful quantitative relations have been obtained by a combination of theoretical reasoning and empiricism, and we shall proceed to develop some of the more important ones, after first discussing the basic nature of turbulence.

The Origin of Turbulence

Turbulence usually appears in pipe flow for $\mathbf{Re} > 2100$ and for boundary-layer flow for $\mathbf{Re}_L > 5 \times 10^5$, but laminar flow has been obtained for considerably higher Reynolds numbers. The incipience of turbulence depends on the severity of disturbances in the flow, such as may occur at the pipe entrance; the more care taken to avoid disturbances, the higher is the Reynolds number at which laminar flow persists.

A theoretical analysis[1] has been developed for the calculation of the lowest possible Reynolds number for which turbulent flow may exist. The method consists in including in the analysis of laminar flow, using the equations of motion, a small sinusoidal fluctuation in the velocity; if the amplitude of the fluctuation increases with time, turbulence may develop; if the amplitude is damped, the Reynolds number is below that for which turbulence may exist.   The results of this theory agree with experiment, and they are of practical importance in aerodynamics.   For a streamlined body, such as an airfoil, the total drag can be appreciably reduced if laminar flow in the boundary layer can be caused to persist to a higher value of $\mathbf{Re}_L$ (i.e., farther from the leading edge).   The theory also accounts for the effect of various factors on the critical $\mathbf{Re}_L$.

Above the theoretical minimum Reynolds number there exists the possibility of two solutions for the equations of motion: a laminar solution and a turbulent one.   The persistence of laminar flow above the critical Reynolds number in the absence of any disturbance is an unstable case similar to the persistence of a pure vapor phase below the dew point or other phenomena of supersaturation.

Mean and Fluctuating Velocities

In this discussion of turbulent flow we shall consider only flow at steady state with respect to the mean flow; the meaning of this term will emerge from the following discussion.

In turbulent flow the velocity at a point varies chaotically with time in magnitude and direction, so that, strictly speaking, there is no such thing as steady state in turbulent flow.   However, we can define a mean velocity in the x direction by

$$\bar{u}_x = \frac{1}{\theta} \int_0^\theta u_x \, d\theta \tag{13-1}$$

where u_x is the instantaneous velocity, a function of time.   Since the frequency of the velocity fluctuation is large, θ need be only a few seconds. Similar definitions can be written for the other velocity components and for the pressure.   If all these mean quantities are constant over successive time intervals, the turbulent flow is said to be at steady state or, strictly speaking, at steady state with respect to the mean flow.

The instantaneous variables are conveniently expressed as the sum of a mean value and a fluctuating value, as follows:

[1] A summary of this subject is given by H. Schlichting, "Boundary Layer Theory," chaps. 16 and 17, McGraw-Hill Book Company, Inc., New York, 1960.

Fig. 13-1. *Velocity fluc-tuation in turbulent flow.*

$$u_x = \bar{u}_x + u_x' \qquad u_y = \bar{u}_y + u_y' \qquad u_z = \bar{u}_z + u_z' \qquad p = \bar{p} + p' \quad (13\text{-}2)$$

where u_x', u_y', u_z' = components of fluctuating velocity

$\qquad\qquad p'$ = fluctuating pressure

From these definitions, it is evident that

$$\bar{u}_x' = \frac{1}{\theta} \int_0^\theta u_x' \, d\theta = 0 \qquad\qquad\qquad\qquad (13\text{-}3)$$

Similarly, we find that $\bar{u}_y'$, $\bar{u}_z'$, and $\bar{p}'$ are zero. In addition, for parallel flow, we have

$$\bar{u}_y = 0 \qquad \bar{u}_z = 0 \qquad\qquad\qquad\qquad (13\text{-}4)$$

so that in this case

$$u_x = \bar{u}_x + u_x' \qquad u_y = u_y' \qquad u_z = u_z' \qquad\qquad (13\text{-}5)$$

A typical graph of u_x versus θ is shown in Fig. 13-1.

The Intensity of Turbulence

Turbulent flow is often described in terms of intensity, which is a meas-ure of the importance of the fluctuating velocity relative to the mean velocity. The quantity $\bar{u}_x'$ is zero because the time average of the positive values of u_x' equals the time average of the negative ones. However, the time average of the magnitude of the fluctuating-velocity component $\overline{|u'|}$ is not zero and gives a measure of the amplitude of the oscillations of the velocity. A more common way of expressing the average fluctuating veloc-ity is by using the quantity $\sqrt{\overline{u'^2}}$, called the root-mean-square fluctuating velocity. For parallel flow the intensity, or level of turbulence, is defined quantitatively by the expression

$$I = \frac{\sqrt{\frac{1}{3}(\overline{u_x'^2} + \overline{u_y'^2} + \overline{u_z'^2})}}{\bar{u}_x} \tag{13-6}$$

In the special case called isotropic turbulence, the three mean-square fluctuating velocities are equal, so that Eq. (13-6) is simplified to

$$I = \frac{\sqrt{\overline{u_x'^2}}}{\bar{u}_x} \tag{13-7}$$

The Scale of Turbulence

It has been found that the intensity alone does not completely characterize turbulent motion. Some method must also be available to specify the size of the eddies, usually referred to as the scale of turbulence. The velocity at one point in turbulent flow is often related to that at an adjacent point. Groups of fluid particles tend to move together and form eddies of sizes varying with the type of turbulence. Considering again the velocities at two separate points, if the second point is far enough from the first, there is no relation between the two velocities; the two points may be thought of as being in different eddies, or lumps of fluid.

Turbulence on a large scale in the atmosphere is familiar to us. Although two anemometers a mile apart in a flat region may indicate the same mean velocity, there is no correlation between the two instantaneous velocities; one varies in a random fashion with respect to the other. If the two instruments are brought closer together, a point is found where they start to indicate similar velocities at any instant, and the correlation between the two velocities increases as the distance between the points is reduced. Similar phenomena exist on a smaller scale in pipes or wind tunnels. A correlation coefficient is defined quantitatively by

$$R(y) = \frac{\overline{u_{x_1}' u_{x_2}'}}{\sqrt{\overline{u_{x_1}'^2}}\sqrt{\overline{u_{x_2}'^2}}} \tag{13-8}$$

for parallel flow in the x direction, where u_{x_1}' and u_{x_2}' are the fluctuating velocities read at the same instant at points 1 and 2, which are separated by a distance y. The correlation coefficient may vary with y, as shown in Fig. 13-2.

As one might suspect, there is no definite boundary between eddies; they merge gradually into each other. A scale of turbulence is often defined in relation to $R(y)$ by the equation

$$L = \int_0^\infty R(y)\, dy \tag{13-9}$$

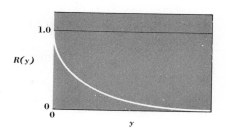

Fig. 13-2.   Variation of correlation coefficient with distance of separation.

An eddy in parallel flow might be considered to have a width of $2L$.

Many other correlation coefficients can be defined in terms of the various velocity components and their variation with the coordinate directions or with time.   The type of analysis introduced here is greatly extended in what is called the statistical theory of turbulence.

Turbulent Shear Stresses

Let us now investigate the application of the Navier-Stokes equations to the steady-state turbulent flow of an incompressible fluid.   The equation of continuity (11-51) is written

$$\frac{\partial u_x}{\partial x} + \frac{\partial u_y}{\partial y} + \frac{\partial u_z}{\partial z} = 0 \tag{13-10}$$

and then u_x is replaced by $\bar{u}_x + u'_x$, u_y by $\bar{u}_y + u'_y$, and u_z by $\bar{u}_z + u'_z$. The result is

$$\frac{\partial \bar{u}_x}{\partial x} + \frac{\partial \bar{u}_y}{\partial y} + \frac{\partial \bar{u}_z}{\partial z} + \frac{\partial u'_x}{\partial x} + \frac{\partial u'_y}{\partial y} + \frac{\partial u'_z}{\partial z} = 0 \tag{13-11}$$

Now we take the time average of Eq. (13-11) and use the following relations:

$$\overline{\frac{\partial u'_x}{\partial x}} = \frac{\partial \bar{u}'_x}{\partial x} \qquad \overline{\frac{\partial u'_y}{\partial y}} = \frac{\partial \bar{u}'_y}{\partial y} \qquad \overline{\frac{\partial u'_z}{\partial z}} = \frac{\partial \bar{u}'_z}{\partial z}$$

$$\overline{\frac{\partial \bar{u}_x}{\partial x}} = \frac{\partial \bar{u}_x}{\partial x} \qquad \overline{\frac{\partial \bar{u}_y}{\partial y}} = \frac{\partial \bar{u}_y}{\partial y} \qquad \overline{\frac{\partial \bar{u}_z}{\partial z}} = \frac{\partial \bar{u}_z}{\partial z}$$

and also

$$\bar{u}'_x = \bar{u}'_y = \bar{u}'_z = 0$$

The results are

$$\frac{\partial \bar{u}_x}{\partial x} + \frac{\partial \bar{u}_y}{\partial y} + \frac{\partial \bar{u}_z}{\partial z} = 0 \tag{13-12}$$

and

$$\frac{\partial u_x'}{\partial x} + \frac{\partial u_y'}{\partial y} + \frac{\partial u_z'}{\partial z} = 0 \tag{13-13}$$

The equation of continuity is satisfied for both the mean velocities and the fluctuating velocities.

We now turn our attention to the equation of motion for the x direction (11-52).

$$u_x \frac{\partial u_x}{\partial x} + u_y \frac{\partial u_x}{\partial y} + u_z \frac{\partial u_x}{\partial z} + \frac{\partial u_x}{\partial \theta} = -\frac{g_c}{\rho} \frac{\partial p}{\partial x} + \frac{\mu}{\rho} \left(\frac{\partial^2 u_x}{\partial x^2} + \frac{\partial^2 u_x}{\partial y^2} + \frac{\partial^2 u_x}{\partial z^2} \right) \tag{13-14}$$

The body force is omitted. It is convenient to change the left-hand side of Eq. (13-14) so that it becomes

$$\frac{\partial (u_x)^2}{\partial x} + \frac{\partial (u_x u_y)}{\partial y} + \frac{\partial (u_x u_z)}{\partial z} + \frac{\partial u_x}{\partial \theta} = \frac{-g_c}{\rho} \frac{\partial p}{\partial x} + \frac{\mu}{\rho} \left(\frac{\partial^2 u_x}{\partial x^2} + \frac{\partial^2 u_x}{\partial y^2} + \frac{\partial^2 u_x}{\partial z^2} \right) \tag{13-15}$$

It is easy to verify that the left-hand sides of these equations are identical, provided Eq. (13-10) holds. The next step in putting the equation of motion into a more instructive form is to substitute in Eq. (13-15) for the variables in terms of their mean and fluctuating values, and then to take the time average. We shall do this term by term. For the first term we have

$$\overline{\frac{\partial (u_x)^2}{\partial x}} = \overline{\frac{\partial (\bar{u}_x + u_x')^2}{\partial x}} = \overline{\frac{\partial}{\partial x} (\bar{u}_x^2 + 2\bar{u}_x u_x' + u_x'^2)} \tag{13-16}$$

Since $\bar{u}_x$ is constant with respect to time and $\overline{u_x'}$ is zero,

$$\overline{\frac{\partial (2\bar{u}_x u_x')}{\partial x}} = 0 \tag{13-17}$$

and for the first term in Eq. (13-15) we obtain

$$\overline{\frac{\partial u_x^2}{\partial x}} = \frac{\partial \bar{u}_x^2}{\partial x} + \frac{\partial \overline{u_x'^2}}{\partial x} \tag{13-18}$$

In these manipulations we have used the rule that $\overline{\partial u_x / \partial x} = \partial \bar{u}_x / \partial x$, etc. From the previous discussion of the intensity of turbulence it follows that $\overline{u_x'^2}$ is not zero, even though $\bar{u}_x'^2$ is.

For the second term we get

$$\overline{\frac{\partial (u_x u_y)}{\partial y}} = \overline{\frac{\partial}{\partial y} (\bar{u}_x \bar{u}_y + u_x' \bar{u}_y + \bar{u}_x u_y' + u_x' u_y')}$$

$$= \frac{\partial (\bar{u}_x \bar{u}_y)}{\partial y} + \frac{\partial (\overline{u_x' u_y'})}{\partial y} \tag{13-19}$$

Although $\bar{u}_x'$ and $\bar{u}_y'$ are both zero, the time-average product $\overline{u_x' u_y'}$ is not zero. Except for isotropic turbulence, there is a high degree of correlation between u'_x and u'_y at a point, as will be explained later. For the remaining terms we obtain, by similar analysis,

$$\frac{\overline{\partial(u_x u_z)}}{\partial z} = \frac{\partial(\bar{u}_x \bar{u}_z)}{\partial z} + \frac{\partial\overline{(u'_x u'_z)}}{\partial z} \tag{13-20}$$

$$\frac{\overline{\partial u_x}}{\partial \theta} = \frac{\partial \bar{u}_x}{\partial \theta} = 0 \tag{13-21}$$

$$\frac{\overline{\partial p}}{\partial x} = \frac{\partial \bar{p}}{\partial x} \tag{13-22}$$

and

$$\overline{\frac{\partial^2 u_x}{\partial x^2} + \frac{\partial^2 u_x}{\partial y^2} + \frac{\partial^2 u_x}{\partial z^2}} = \frac{\partial^2 \bar{u}_x}{\partial x^2} + \frac{\partial^2 \bar{u}_x}{\partial y^2} + \frac{\partial^2 \bar{u}_x}{\partial z^2} \tag{13-23}$$

Substituting Eqs. (13-18) to (13-23) into the time average of Eq. (13-15) gives

$$\frac{\partial \bar{u}_x^2}{\partial x} + \frac{\partial(\bar{u}_x \bar{u}_y)}{\partial y} + \frac{\partial(\bar{u}_x \bar{u}_z)}{\partial z} + \frac{\partial\overline{u'^2_x}}{\partial x} + \frac{\partial\overline{(u'_x u'_y)}}{\partial y} + \frac{\partial\overline{(u'_x u'_z)}}{\partial z}$$

$$= \frac{-g_c}{\rho}\frac{\partial \bar{p}}{\partial x} + \frac{\mu}{\rho}\left(\frac{\partial^2 \bar{u}_x}{\partial x^2} + \frac{\partial^2 \bar{u}_x}{\partial y^2} + \frac{\partial^2 \bar{u}_x}{\partial z^2}\right) \tag{13-24}$$

This equation has three additional terms which would not be obtained by merely replacing the variables in Eq. (13-15) by their mean values. Their meaning can be made clearer by writing the time mean of Eq. (11-11) with the body force $X = 0$ and $\partial \bar{u}_x/\partial \theta = 0$ as

$$\frac{D\bar{u}_x}{D\theta} = \frac{\partial \bar{u}_x^2}{\partial x} + \frac{\partial(\bar{u}_x \bar{u}_y)}{\partial y} + \frac{\partial(\bar{u}_x \bar{u}_z)}{\partial z} + \frac{\partial\overline{u'^2_x}}{\partial x} + \frac{\partial\overline{(u'_x u'_y)}}{\partial y} + \frac{\partial\overline{(u'_x u'_z)}}{\partial z}$$

$$= \frac{g_c}{\rho}\left(\frac{\partial \bar{\tau}_{xx}}{\partial x} + \frac{\partial \bar{\tau}_{yx}}{\partial y} + \frac{\partial \bar{\tau}_{zx}}{\partial z}\right) \tag{13-25}$$

The time-mean stresses are the result of the averaging of the stresses arising from the action of the ordinary viscosity. Let us define each of the total mean stresses by $\bar{\tau}_{xx}{}^t$, $\bar{\tau}_{yx}{}^t$, and $\bar{\tau}_{zx}{}^t$ as the sum of the corresponding viscous stresses and turbulent stresses.

$$\bar{\tau}_{xx}{}^t = \bar{\tau}_{xx} + \bar{\tau}_{xx}{}^r \tag{13-26}$$
$$\bar{\tau}_{yx}{}^t = \bar{\tau}_{yx} + \bar{\tau}_{yx}{}^r \tag{13-27}$$
$$\bar{\tau}_{zx}{}^t = \bar{\tau}_{zz} + \bar{\tau}_{zz}{}^r \tag{13-28}$$

The terms $\bar{\tau}_{xx}{}^r$, $\bar{\tau}_{yx}{}^r$, and $\bar{\tau}_{zz}{}^r$ are the turbulent-stress contributions.

We now arbitrarily write Eq. (11-11) for turbulent flow by replacing each velocity component by its time mean value and by replacing each stress component by the total mean stress.

$$\frac{\partial(\bar{u}_x{}^2)}{\partial x} + \frac{\partial(\bar{u}_x\bar{u}_y)}{\partial y} + \frac{\partial(\bar{u}_x\bar{u}_z)}{\partial z} = \frac{g_c}{\rho}\left(\frac{\partial\bar{\tau}_{xx}{}^t}{\partial x} + \frac{\partial\bar{\tau}_{yx}{}^t}{\partial y} + \frac{\partial\bar{\tau}_{zx}{}^t}{\partial z}\right) \tag{13-29}$$

For this equation to be correct, it must be consistent with Eqs. (13-25) to (13-28). This leads to the following definitions of the turbulent-stress contributions:

$$\bar{\tau}_{xx}{}^r = -\frac{\rho\overline{u_x'^2}}{g_c} \tag{13-30}$$

$$\bar{\tau}_{yx}{}^r = \frac{-\rho\overline{u_x'u_y'}}{g_c} \tag{13-31}$$

$$\bar{\tau}_{zx}{}^r = \frac{-\rho\overline{u_x'u_z'}}{g_c} \tag{13-32}$$

These stresses are also called the Reynolds stresses, or the apparent stresses. From Eqs. (11-46), (11-19), and (11-21), the total stresses for incompressible, steady, turbulent flow are

$$\bar{\tau}_{xx}{}^t = -\bar{p} + \frac{2\mu}{g_c}\frac{\partial\bar{u}_x}{\partial x} - \frac{\rho\overline{u_x'^2}}{g_c} \tag{13-33}$$

$$\bar{\tau}_{yx}{}^t = \frac{\mu}{g_c}\left(\frac{\partial\bar{u}_x}{\partial y} + \frac{\partial\bar{u}_y}{\partial x}\right) - \frac{\rho\overline{u_x'u_y'}}{g_c} \tag{13-34}$$

$$\bar{\tau}_{zx}{}^t = \frac{\mu}{g_c}\left(\frac{\partial\bar{u}_x}{\partial z} + \frac{\partial\bar{u}_z}{\partial x}\right) - \frac{\rho\overline{u_x'u_z'}}{g_c} \tag{13-35}$$

Not all the terms in Eqs. (13-33) to (13-35) appear in Eq. (13-24), because some are eliminated by the equation of continuity (13-12) for the incompressible fluid.

Interpretation of the Reynolds Stresses

The meaning of the Reynolds stresses can be made clearer by considering the case of parallel flow, for which $\bar{u}_z$ and $\bar{u}_y$ are zero.

Consider the flow between infinite parallel plates so that $\bar{u}_x$ is a function of y only. The quantity $\bar{\tau}_{yx}{}^t$ represents the total shearing stress in the x direction acting on a plane perpendicular to the y direction. The mean velocity may be distributed as shown in Fig. 13-3. At the center line $y = 0$, $\bar{u}_x = \bar{u}_{x,\max}$, and at the wall $y = y_o$, $\bar{u}_x = 0$. From Eq. (13-34) the contribution of the mean flow $\bar{\tau}_{yx}$ is $\dfrac{\mu}{g_c}\dfrac{d\bar{u}_x}{dy}$, just as in the case of laminar flow considered in Chap. 12. The Reynolds stress is $-(\rho/g_c)\overline{u_x'u_y'}$, and we should like to show that this term is different from zero and of the correct sign.

Fig. 13-3.   *Turbulent velocity distribution in a slit.*

Suppose a small packet of fluid having a mean velocity represented by A in Fig. 13-3 is transported, because of a positive u_y', to a region B, where $\bar{u}_x$ is smaller.   Since the packet will retain approximately its original velocity $\bar{u}_{xA}$, at B there is created a positive u_x', and $u_x'u_y'$ is positive.   On the other hand, if u_y' happens to be negative, the fluid is transported to a region C, where the mean velocity is greater than $\bar{u}_{xA}$; a negative u_x' is created, and $u_x'u_y'$ is again positive.   It is thus easy to see that $\overline{u_x'u_y'}$ will be a positive quantity, and so, from Eq. (13-31), the mean turbulent stress $\bar{\tau}_{yx}{}^r$ is negative.   This negative sign is to be expected, for $d\bar{u}_x/dy$ is negative, making the mean viscous stress $\dfrac{\mu}{g_c}\dfrac{d\bar{u}_x}{dy}$ also negative.

At the center of the conduit, where $d\bar{u}_x/dy$ is zero, a positive value of u_y' can no longer be associated with a positive value of u_x', so that $\overline{u_x'u_y'}$ is zero, as it must be, for there is no shear at the center line.

Because there is no velocity variation in the z direction, all the terms of Eq. (13-35) are zero.

Regarding Eq. (13-33), there is no possible turbulent flow for which $\overline{u_x'^2}$ is zero, so that the total normal stress must be different from the mean pressure.   If the intensity of turbulence decreases with x, the pressure will decrease with x less rapidly than would otherwise be the case.

Although the discussion of turbulence up to this point has given us some understanding of the behavior of turbulent flow, there is no way of calculating any fluctuating quantities and deducing a velocity distribution or a pressure drop from the equations of motion.   In order to make any progress in this direction, more simplifications must be made.

Eddy Viscosity and Mixing Length

By analogy with the molecular viscosity, an eddy kinematic viscosity can be defined for parallel flow by the equation

$$\bar{\tau}_{yx}{}^r = \frac{\rho \nu_e}{g_c} \frac{d\bar{u}_x}{dy} \tag{13-36}$$

so that

$$\bar{\tau}_{yx}{}^t = \frac{\rho}{g_c} (\nu + \nu_e) \frac{d\bar{u}_x}{dy} \tag{13-37}$$

This quantity ν_e, introduced by Boussinesq,[1] is also called the virtual, or apparent, viscosity. Unlike the ordinary viscosity, it is not a function of state and depends strongly on position. Unfortunately, we have no way of calculating ν_e, a priori, although it can be determined experimentally from a given distribution of $\bar{u}_x$ versus y.

We next define a quantity called the Prandtl mixing length, which will assist us in calculating the Reynolds stresses. Still considering flow between parallel walls and referring to Fig. 13-3, we define the mixing length in the following way. Consider again a small packet of fluid which is displaced from A to B in the y direction with a velocity u'_y. In reality, the lump of fluid will gradually lose its identity, but in the definition of the mixing length, it is assumed to retain its identity until it has traveled a distance ℓ defined as the Prandtl mixing length. For the small distance involved, we say

$$\frac{d\bar{u}_x}{dy} = \frac{\bar{u}_{x_B} - \bar{u}_{x_A}}{\ell} \tag{13-38}$$

As was mentioned in our previous discussion of Fig. 13-3, the packet of fluid can be assumed to retain its original velocity, so that $\bar{u}_{x_B} - \bar{u}_{x_A}$ is approximately $-u'_x$. Therefore we have

$$u'_x = -\ell \frac{d\bar{u}_x}{dy}$$

and, in general,

$$\overline{|u'_x|} = \ell \left| \frac{d\bar{u}_x}{dy} \right| \tag{13-39}$$

Prandtl also assumed that $\overline{|u'_y|}$ was of about the same absolute magnitude as $\overline{|u'_x|}$, so that

$$\overline{u'_x u'_y} = \ell^2 \left| \frac{d\bar{u}_x}{dy} \right|^2$$

Since the sign of $\overline{u'_x u'_y}$ depends on the sign of $d\bar{u}_x/dy$, we write this as

$$\overline{u'_x u'_y} = -\ell^2 \left| \frac{d\bar{u}_x}{dy} \right| \frac{d\bar{u}_x}{dy} \tag{13-40}$$

[1] T. V. Boussinesq, in Mémoires présentées par divers savants à l'Académie des Sciences de l'Institut de France, vol. 23, 1877.

Fig. 13-4. *Intensity of turbulence and velocity profile in a rectangular duct. (From Hermann Schlichting, "Boundary Layer Theory," 4th ed., fig. 18.3, p. 466, McGraw-Hill Book Company, Inc., New York, 1960.)*

$\bar{u}_{max}$ = 3.28 ft/sec

y = distance from center line

From Eqs. (13-31), (13-36), and (13-40), we get also

$$\bar{\tau}_{yx}{}^r = \frac{\rho \ell^2}{g_c} \left| \frac{d\bar{u}_x}{dy} \right| \frac{d\bar{u}_x}{dy}$$

and

$$\nu_e = \ell^2 \left| \frac{d\bar{u}_x}{dy} \right| \tag{13-41}$$

Although it may appear that the only result of this definition of ℓ has been to replace one empirical, noncomputable quantity with another, the mixing length is easier to estimate than ν_e. For instance, ℓ cannot be greater than the dimensions of the channel, and it should approach zero near the wall. As a matter of fact, in a later section it will be shown that some valuable results for the velocity distribution for turbulent flow in a pipe are obtained with the simple relation

$$\ell = Ky \tag{13-42}$$

where y in this equation is the distance from the wall, and K turns out to be a universal constant, 0.4.

Some Data on Turbulence

In order to illustrate the approximate magnitude of the quantities defined in the previous paragraphs, some experimental results are shown. Figure 13-4 gives the variation of the intensity of turbulence in a rectangular duct. Figure 13-5 shows the variation of the stress components for the same duct; a simple force balance such as that leading to Eq. (7-9) proves that $\bar{\tau}_{yx}{}^t$ must be a linear function of y.

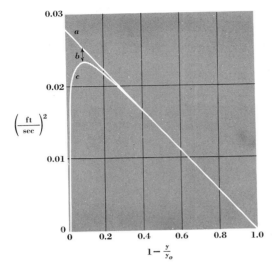

Fig. 13-5.   Shear stress in a rectangular duct.(From Hermann Schlichting,"Boundary Layer Theory," 4th ed., fig. 18.4, p. 466, McGraw-Hill Book Company, Inc., New York, 1960.)

$a.\ g_c\,\bar\tau^t_{yx}/\rho$

$b.\ g_c\,\bar\tau_{yx}/\rho = \nu\dfrac{d\bar u_x}{dy}$

$c.\ g_c\,\bar\tau^r_{yx}/\rho = -\,\overline{u'_x u_y'}$

y **is distance from center line**

The vertical axis is labeled $\left(\dfrac{\text{ft}}{\text{sec}}\right)^2$ with values 0, 0.01, 0.02, 0.03. The horizontal axis is labeled $1-\dfrac{y}{y_o}$ with values 0, 0.2, 0.4, 0.6, 0.8, 1.0.

TURBULENT FLOW INSIDE A SMOOTH, CIRCULAR PIPE

The Universal Velocity Distribution from the Prandtl Mixing Length

The Prandtl mixing length will now be used to derive an equation for the velocity distribution for fully developed turbulent flow inside a circular pipe.   We shall then show how this relation leads to a method of calculating the pressure drop in turbulent flow.

We start by dividing the fluid in the pipe into a central core, in which the shear stress approximately equals the Reynolds stress, and a thin, laminar sublayer near the wall, in which the influence of turbulence is negligible and the shear stress arises only from the molecular viscosity.   We shall see that a fuller analysis must include a buffer zone where both stresses are important.   The three zones are illustrated in Fig. 13-5.   For the present only the turbulent core and the laminar sublayer are considered.

In what follows, we drop the various subscripts and superscripts on the stresses and velocities.   The total stress τ is equal either to the Reynolds stress (for the core) or to the laminar stress (for the laminar sublayer); the velocity u is the time mean point velocity in the x direction.   The total stress varies from the wall to the center line according to Eq. (7-9), written here as

$$\tau = \tau_s \left(1 - \frac{y}{r_i} \right)$$

where τ_s = stress at wall

y = distance from wall

In the laminar sublayer, which is very thin, we neglect any variation in τ and write

$$g_c \tau_s = \mu \frac{du}{dy} = \text{const} \tag{13-43}$$

This equation is integrated to give

$$g_c \tau_s y = \mu u$$

or

$$u = \frac{g_c \tau_s}{\rho} \frac{y}{\nu} \tag{13-44}$$

The velocity in the laminar sublayer is proportional to the distance from the wall; this is in contrast with the parabolic velocity profile in the entire tube when there is laminar flow. We shall find it convenient to define what is called a friction velocity by the equation

$$u^* = \sqrt{\frac{g_c \tau_s}{\rho}} \tag{13-45}$$

In terms of this quantity, Eq. (13-44) can be written as

$$\frac{u}{u^*} = \frac{y u^*}{\nu} \tag{13-46}$$

In this equation the dimensionless velocity quotient on the left will be defined as u^+ and the dimensionless distance on the right as y^+. The latter quantity resembles a Reynolds number. It is then possible to write the velocity distribution in the laminar sublayer as

$$u^+ = y^+ \tag{13-47}$$

Let us now turn our attention to the turbulent core, in which we neglect any viscous stresses, and write

$$\tau = \frac{\rho \ell^2}{g_c} \left(\frac{du}{dy} \right)^2 \tag{13-48}$$

from Eqs. (13-36) and (13-41); du/dy is always positive, so the absolute-magnitude sign has been dropped.

In order to proceed, two assumptions are made, both of which are only rough approximations. Their only real justification is that they simplify the mathematics and that the final equations to which they lead agree well with experimental data. We assume that $\tau = \tau_s = \text{const}$ and that

$$\ell = Ky \tag{13-49}$$

where K is a constant.   The second assumption is reasonable, for we know that ℓ should decrease to zero at the wall, where the turbulence dies out. We then write Eq. (13-48) as

$$\frac{g_c \tau_s}{\rho} = K^2 y^2 \left(\frac{du}{dy}\right)^2 \tag{13-50}$$

and so

$$u^* = Ky \frac{du}{dy} \tag{13-51}$$

This equation is integrated to

$$u^* \ln y = Ku + c \tag{13-52}$$

and c is found from the condition that u must be zero at some small value of y, say y_o:

$$u^* \ln y_o = c \tag{13-53}$$

and

$$\frac{u}{u^*} = \frac{1}{K} \ln \frac{y}{y_o} \tag{13-54}$$

Since we are looking for a universal velocity profile, that is, one which will be of the form

$$u^+ = f(y^+) \tag{13-55}$$

for all flow rates, i.e., values of u^* or y_o, we must modify Eq. (13-54) to meet these conditions.   The variable y^+ is introduced by writing Eq. (13-54) as

$$u^+ = \frac{1}{K} \left(\ln \frac{yu^*}{\nu} - \ln \frac{y_o u^*}{\nu} \right) \tag{13-56}$$

or

$$u^+ = \frac{1}{K} \ln y^+ + c_1 \tag{13-57}$$

If Eq. (13-56) is to represent u^+ as a universal function of y^+, it is reasonable to suppose that $y_o u^*/\nu$, which might be written as $y_o{}^+$, is a universal constant representing the value of y^+ for a u^+ of zero.   The proof of the usefulness of these assumptions depends on whether Eq. (13-57), with K and c_1 taken as universal constants, fits the data on velocity distributions over a range of y and u^*, that is, **Re**.

Figure 13-6 shows a large amount of velocity-distribution data for a range of Reynolds numbers from about 4000 to 3.2×10^6.   It can be seen that Eq. (13-57) does fit the data well above $y^+ = 30$ and that the few data at low y^+ lie on the line $u^+ = y^+$ up to $y^+ = 5$.   Neither equation is satisfactory in the region $5 < y^+ < 30$, which we define as the buffer region

Fig. 13-6. *The universal velocity profile for flow in a smooth circular tube.*

and where we represent the velocity by an empirical equation of the form of (13-57). The universal velocity distribution is thus represented analytically by the equations

$$u^+ = y^+ \qquad\qquad 0 < y^+ < 5 \qquad\qquad (13\text{-}58)$$

$$u^+ = 5.0 \ln y^+ - 3.05 \qquad 5 < y^+ < 30 \qquad\qquad (13\text{-}59)$$

$$u^+ = 2.5 \ln y^+ + 5.5 \qquad 30 < y^+ \qquad\qquad (13\text{-}60)$$

The preceding analysis has been derived from the work of L. Prandtl and T. von Kármán. The experimental velocity distributions are largely the work of J. Nikuradse. For an account of the specific contributions of those responsible for this work, refer to books by Schlichting[1] and by Knudsen and Katz.[2] For some recent elaborations on the equations for the universal velocity distribution, refer to Deissler.[3]

The value of the mixing length can be calculated from velocity-distribution data by means of Eqs. (13-48) and (7-9); the results are shown in Fig. 13-7. Note that Eq. (13-60) gives K a value of 0.4 and that Fig. 13-7 verifies this value for the region near the wall but that Eq. (13-49) is not correct far from the wall. The data shown are for several Reynolds numbers and for both rough and smooth pipe; the mixing length is independent of both factors for sufficiently high **Re**.

[1] Schlichting, *op. cit.*, chaps. 18, 19, 20.

[2] J. G. Knudsen and D. L. Katz, "Fluid Dynamics and Heat Transfer," McGraw-Hill Book Company, Inc., New York, 1958.

[3] R. G. Deissler, Analysis of Turbulent Heat Transfer, Mass Transfer, and Friction in Smooth Tubes for High Prandtl and Schmidt Numbers, *NACA Rept.* 1210, 1955.

Fig. 13-7.   Mixing length as a function of radial position. (From Hermann Schlichting, "Boundary Layer Theory," 4th ed., fig. 20.5, p. 511, McGraw-Hill Book Company, Inc., New York, 1960.)

Equation (13-57) can be written for the velocity at the center of the pipe to give

$$u_{\max}^{+} = \frac{1}{K} \ln y_{\max}^{+} + c_1 \tag{13-61}$$

If Eq. (13-57) is subtracted from this, there results the so-called velocity-deficiency law,

$$u_{\max} - u = \frac{u^*}{K} \ln \frac{r_i}{y} \tag{13-62}$$

Since K is independent of the roughness of the pipe wall, Eq. (13-62) applies to both smooth and rough pipe. However, c_1 is a function of the roughness, as we shall see later.

The Flow Resistance from the Universal Velocity Distribution

We can easily find the bulk velocity in a pipe if we know how u varies with y.   Since u_b is $(1/A) \iint u \, dA$, we write, for a circular pipe, using Eq. (13-62),

$$u_{\max} - u_b = \frac{1}{\pi r_i{}^2} \int_0^{r_i} 2\pi(r_i - y) \frac{u^*}{K} \ln \frac{r_i}{y} \, dy \tag{13-63}$$

This equation is integrated to give

$$u_{\max} - u_b = \frac{3u^*}{2K} \tag{13-64}$$

The substitution of Eq. (13-61) for $u_{\max}$ yields

$$\frac{1}{K} \ln \frac{r_i u^*}{\nu} + c_1 - \frac{u_b}{u^*} = \frac{3}{2K} \tag{13-65}$$

Since $c_1 = 5.5$ and $K = 0.4$, this equation can be solved for a given u_b, r_i, and ν to give u^*. This term, the friction velocity, is related to τ_s by

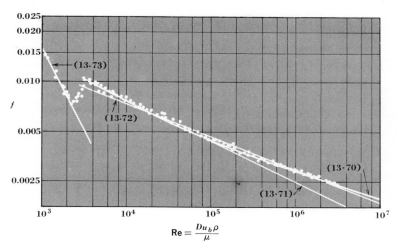

Fig. 13-8.   *Friction factors for pipe flow. (From Hermann Schlichting, "Boundary Layer Theory," 4th ed., fig. 20.1, p. 504, McGraw-Hill Book Company, Inc., New York, 1960.)*

Eq. (13-45).   The shear stress at the wall, τ_s, has been shown in Eq. (7-10) to be equal to $(-\Delta p)(r_i)/2L$, which gives the pressure drop per unit length of pipe.   However, let us put Eq. (13-65) into a more convenient form by defining a coefficient of resistance, as we did a drag coefficient in Eq. (8-13). For the present case we have

$$C_D = \frac{2F_d g_c}{\rho u_b{}^2 A} \tag{13-66}$$

in which A is the area of the inside wall of the pipe.

This equation is modified by using $F_d = \tau_s A$, and C_D is given the special symbol f for pipe flow:

$$f = \frac{2\tau_s g_c}{u_b{}^2 \rho} = \frac{2(u^*)^2}{u_b{}^2} \tag{13-67}$$

This coefficient is usually called the Fanning friction factor.   Equation (13-67) is also written as

$$u^* = u_b \sqrt{\frac{f}{2}} \tag{13-68}$$

The substitution of Eq. (13-68) into (13-65) results in

$$\frac{1}{K} \ln \frac{D u_b}{\nu} \sqrt{\frac{f}{8}} + c_1 - \frac{3}{2K} = \sqrt{\frac{2}{f}} \tag{13-69}$$

and the substitution of the numerical values of K and c_1, plus some rearrangement, gives the final equation[1]

[1] The symbol ln refers to a natural logarithm; log refers to a logarithm to the base 10.

$$\frac{1}{\sqrt{f}} = 4.06 \log (\mathbf{Re}\sqrt{f}) - 0.60 \tag{13-70}$$

This equation is compared with experimental data on smooth tubes in Fig. 13-8; also shown are the empirical equations of Blasius,

$$f = 0.079 \, \mathbf{Re}^{-\frac{1}{4}} \tag{13-71}$$

and a relation often used in the chemical-engineering literature,

$$f = 0.046 \, \mathbf{Re}^{-\frac{1}{5}} \tag{13-72}$$

Also shown is the relation for the laminar region,

$$f = \frac{16}{\mathbf{Re}} \tag{13-73}$$

which is obtained from the combination of Eqs. (7-10), (7-16), and (13-67).

TURBULENT FLOW INSIDE A ROUGH PIPE

In order to speak in a quantitative way about the effect of roughness on the velocity distribution or the pressure drop, we must first define a parameter which describes the roughness. We shall characterize a given roughness by the effective height of the protuberances, which we call e; the relative roughness is e/D. Although the quantity e is used to characterize a given roughness, a more exact procedure would require a description also of the spacing and orientation of the projections.

The relative roughness affects the flow in several ways. In laminar flow through commercial pipe, in which e/D is usually somewhat less than 0.01, the effect of wall roughness is negligible. The fluid fills the spaces between the protuberances, and the inner layers slide smoothly over a tube of effective diameter $D - 2e$. In turbulent flow the wall roughness also has no effect if it is smaller in height than the thickness of the laminar sublayer. In this case the pipe is said to be hydraulically smooth. However, if the irregularities enter into the main fluid stream, they increase the turbulence, change the velocity profile, and increase the flow resistance. Beyond a certain value of e, the effect of the roughness is so great that the inertia forces caused by the fluid flowing around the projections completely outweigh the viscous forces. In these circumstances the pipe is said to be completely rough. The thickness of the viscous sublayer is a function of the Reynolds number, so that the same pipe may be hydraulically smooth at one flow rate and completely rough at another.

Velocity Distribution in Rough Pipe

It has already been mentioned that Eq. (13-62) applies to both smooth and rough pipes. Since $u_{\max}$ may not be given, we shall find an equation of the form of (13-57) for rough pipe. This is done by simply assuming that y_o is proportional to e for completely rough pipe, giving

$$u^+ = \frac{1}{K} \ln \frac{y}{e} + c_2 \tag{13-74}$$

The coefficient K has its usual value of 0.4, and Nikuradse's experiments on pipes roughened by gluing carefully sized grains of sand to the walls show that Eq. (13-74) is valid for the completely rough region. For this case c_2 is 8.5; it applies at a roughness Reynolds number eu^*/ν above 70. The limit of the hydraulically smooth region is at eu^*/ν equal to 5; there is no simple equation to express the velocity distribution in the transition range between the hydraulically smooth and completely rough condition.

Flow Resistance in Rough Pipe

In the hydraulically smooth region the roughness has no effect on f, and in the completely rough region the variation of f can be found from Eqs. (13-74) and (13-64) with y equal to r_i, combined as follows:

$$\left(\frac{1}{K} \ln \frac{r_i}{e} + c_2 \right) - \frac{u_b}{u^*} = \frac{3}{2K} \tag{13-75}$$

By replacing u_b/u^* by $\sqrt{2/f}$ [Eq. (13-68)], there results

$$\sqrt{\frac{2}{f}} = \frac{1}{K} \ln \frac{r_i}{e} + c_2 - \frac{3}{2K} \tag{13-76}$$

Using $K = 0.4$ and $c_2 = 8.5$, Eq. (13-76) is transformed to

$$\frac{1}{\sqrt{f}} = 4.06 \log \frac{r_i}{e} + 3.36 \tag{13-77}$$

which is valid for completely rough pipe.

In laminar flow f is inversely proportional to the velocity, since the drag is proportional to the velocity. In hydraulically smooth turbulent flow the viscous effects (skin friction) are outweighed by the inertia (form-drag) effects: f is roughly proportional to $u_b^{-1/4}$, and the drag is proportional to $u_b^{7/4}$. We have now seen that in completely rough turbulent flow f is not a function of u_b, so that the drag is proportional to u_b^2—the importance of the viscous effects has shrunk to zero.

Nikuradse's data for artificially roughened pipes are shown in Fig. 13-9. The use of the methods of this chapter for flow in commercial pipe is discussed in Chap. 15.

Results for Flow Past a Flat Plate from a Momentum Balance

In Chap. 5 we obtained the drag by the use of the over-all, or integral, momentum balance; Prob. 5-3 provides an introduction to its use in

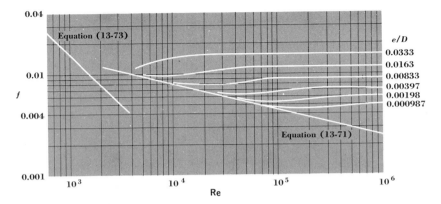

Fig. 13-9.   Friction factors for artificially roughened pipe. (From Hermann Schlichting, "Boundary Layer Theory," 4th ed., fig. 20.18, p. 521, McGraw-Hill Book Company, Inc., New York, 1960.)

boundary-layer flow. As with the over-all balances, it is necessary to know the velocity distribution. Since the Navier-Stokes equations cannot be solved for the velocity distribution in the turbulent boundary layer as they were for the laminar boundary layer in Chap. 12, we use the integral momentum balance with an empirical velocity distribution in order to get the drag in turbulent flow past a flat plate. This procedure is based on the work of von Kármán and also was used by Pohlhausen for boundary-layer flow with a pressure gradient.[1]

Application of the Over-all Momentum Balance to the Boundary Layer on a Flat Plate

The over-all momentum balance is to be applied to a control volume as shown in Fig. 13-10. There is flow only through the faces having areas designated by A_1, A_2, and A_3. The balance of x momentum is written from Eq. (5-3) as

$$\iint_A \frac{u_x \rho}{g_c} u \cos \alpha \, dA = -F_{xd} \tag{13-78}$$

for this steady-state flow with no pressure gradient. For A_1, $u \cos \alpha = -u_x$; for A_2, $u \cos \alpha = u_x$; and for A_3, $u_x = u_o$, the velocity outside the boundary layer. Equation (13-78) is then written

$$\iint_{A_2} u_x^2 \rho \, dA - \iint_{A_1} u_x^2 \rho \, dA + u_o \iint_{A_3} u \rho \cos \alpha \, dA = -g_c F_{xd} \tag{13-79}$$

[1] Schlichting, *op. cit.*, chaps. 21 and 22.

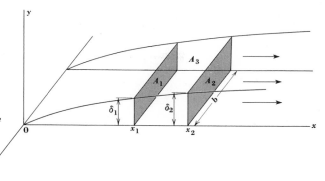

Fig. 13-10.   *Control volume for boundary-layer flow.*

The third integral can be replaced by using the over-all mass balance. For steady state, Eq. (3-3) becomes

$$\iint_A u\rho \cos \alpha \, dA = 0 \qquad (13\text{-}80)$$

and for the present case

$$\iint_{A_2} u_x\rho \, dA - \iint_{A_1} u_x\rho \, dA + \iint_{A_3} u\rho \cos \alpha \, dA = 0 \qquad (13\text{-}81)$$

The combination of Eqs. (13-81) and (13-79) yields

$$\iint_{A_2} u_x(u_o - u_x) \, dA - \iint_{A_1} u_x(u_o - u_x) \, dA = \frac{g_c F_{xd}}{\rho} \qquad (13\text{-}82)$$

for an incompressible fluid.

For the boundary layer on a plate of width b, $dA = b \, dy$, where y varies from zero to δ, and $F_{xd} = \tau_{s,\text{av}} b(x_2 - x_1)$.   Equation (13-82) is thus modified to

$$\int_0^{\delta_2} u_x(u_o - u_x) \, dy - \int_0^{\delta_1} u_x(u_o - u_x) \, dy = \frac{g_c \tau_{s,\text{av}}(x_2 - x_1)}{\rho} \qquad (13\text{-}83)$$

Given a velocity distribution, the integrals can be evaluated and the shear stress $\tau_{s,\text{av}}$ found.   However, this is the average stress over the length $x_2 - x_1$, and it is desirable to know τ_s at a point, so that it can be expressed in terms of the velocity gradient at a certain x.   The equation

$$g_c \tau_s = \mu \left(\frac{du}{dy}\right)_{y=0} \qquad (13\text{-}84)$$

gives τ_s at a certain x, where $(du/dy)_{y=0}$ has a certain value.   Therefore we arrange Eq. (13-83) to apply at a certain x by using the definition of a derivative (notice that each definite integral is a function of x only),

$$\lim_{(x_2 - x_1) \to 0} \frac{\int_0^{\delta_2} u_x(u_o - u_x)\, dy - \int_0^{\delta_1} u_x(u_o - u_x)\, dy}{x_2 - x_1} = \frac{g_c \tau_s}{\rho} \qquad (13\text{-}85)$$

so that

$$\frac{d}{dx} \int_0^{\delta} u_x(u_o - u_x)\, dy = \frac{g_c \tau_s}{\rho} \qquad (13\text{-}86)$$

Equation (13-86) applies at any point x along the plate; δ and τ_s are functions of x.

The Momentum Balance for the Laminar Boundary Layer

Before considering the turbulent boundary layer, it is of interest to apply Eq. (13-86) to the laminar boundary layer, because the results can be compared with the exact Blasius solution (Chap. 12). We shall find that an arbitrary velocity distribution gives results very close to the Blasius solution for the variation of δ and C_D with L.

The equation for u_x as a function of y is made on the similarity assumption that u_x/u_o is everywhere the same function of y/δ.

We know that $u_x = 0$ at $y = 0$, $u_x \cong u_o$ at $y = \delta$, and $du_x/dy \cong 0$ at $y = \delta$; it is easy to verify that the following simple equation fulfills these conditions.

$$\frac{u_x}{u_o} = \frac{3}{2}\left(\frac{y}{\delta}\right) - \frac{1}{2}\left(\frac{y}{\delta}\right)^3 \qquad (13\text{-}87)$$

This equation is substituted into Eq. (13-86) to give

$$\frac{d}{dx}\left(\delta \int_0^{1.0} \left\{ \left[\frac{3}{2}\left(\frac{y}{\delta}\right) - \frac{1}{2}\left(\frac{y}{\delta}\right)^3\right] - \left[\frac{3}{2}\left(\frac{y}{\delta}\right) - \frac{1}{2}\left(\frac{y}{\delta}\right)^3\right]^2 \right\} d\left(\frac{y}{\delta}\right) \right)$$

$$= \frac{g_c \tau_s}{\rho u_o^2} \qquad (13\text{-}88)$$

The evaluation of the integral transforms this equation to

$$\frac{d\delta}{dx} = \frac{280}{39} \frac{\tau_s g_c}{u_o^2 \rho} \qquad (13\text{-}89)$$

For the laminar boundary layer, Eq. (13-84) holds; we differentiate Eq. (13-87) to get

$$\left(\frac{du}{dy}\right)_{y=0} = \frac{3u_o}{2\delta} \qquad (13\text{-}90)$$

and by Eq. (13-84) we obtain

$$g_c \tau_s = \frac{3\mu u_o}{2\delta} \qquad (13\text{-}91)$$

Equations (13-91) and (13-89) give

$$\int_0^\delta \delta \, d\delta = \left(\frac{280}{39}\right)\left(\frac{3}{2}\right)\frac{\nu}{u_o{}^2}\int_0^L dx \tag{13-92}$$

and thus

$$\delta = 4.64 \sqrt{\frac{\nu L}{u_o}} \tag{13-93}$$

The equation

$$C_D = 1.29 \sqrt{\frac{\nu}{Lu_o}} = \frac{1.29}{\sqrt{\mathbf{Re}_L}} \tag{13-94}$$

can also be derived; the method is illustrated in Chap. 12. A comparison of Eq. (13-93) with (12-75) and of (13-94) with (12-82) shows the success of the momentum method; the equations are identical except for the numerical constants. Similar results can be obtained from other arbitrarily chosen velocity distributions. Such a case is the subject of Prob. 13-8.

The Momentum Balance for the Turbulent Boundary Layer

The above procedures will now be applied to the turbulent boundary layer on a flat plate. It would be desirable to adapt the logarithmic velocity distribution [Eqs. (13-58) to (13-60)] to boundary-layer flow. This can be done, but the derivation and resulting equations are long and complicated, so a simpler empirical velocity distribution will be used here.

In pipe flow the equation

$$\frac{u}{u_{\max}} = \left(\frac{y}{r_i}\right)^{\frac{1}{7}} \tag{13-95}$$

is valid up to $\mathbf{Re} = 10^5$; it is sometimes called the Blasius $\frac{1}{7}$-power law. We shall write this equation for the boundary layer on a plate as

$$\frac{u_x}{u_o} = \left(\frac{y}{\delta}\right)^{\frac{1}{7}} \tag{13-96}$$

The substitution of Eq. (13-96) into (13-86), with subsequent integration, yields

$$\frac{d\delta}{dx} = \frac{72}{7}\frac{\tau_s g_c}{\delta u_o{}^2} \tag{13-97}$$

Although Eq. (13-84) holds for the fluid adjacent to the wall even in the turbulent boundary layer, Eq. (13-96) does not hold as y goes to zero.

Therefore we use the Blasius resistance law for pipe flow, which is consistent with the $\frac{1}{7}$-power velocity distribution.

$$f = 0.079 \left(\frac{Du_b\rho}{\mu}\right)^{-\frac{1}{4}} \tag{13-71}$$

From Eq. (13-67) we have

$$\frac{g_c \tau_s}{\rho u_b{}^2} = \frac{f}{2} = \frac{0.079}{2}\left(\frac{D u_b}{\nu}\right)^{-\frac{1}{4}} \tag{13-98}$$

This equation, which applies for a pipe, is adapted for boundary-layer flow over a plate by the substitutions $D = 2\delta$ and $u_b = 0.817 u_{\max} = 0.817 u_o$, and the result is

$$\frac{g_c \tau_s}{\rho u_o{}^2} = 0.023\left(\frac{\delta u_o}{\nu}\right)^{-\frac{1}{4}} \tag{13-99}$$

for boundary-layer flow.

Equations (13-99) and (13-97) are combined and put into integral form to give

$$\int_0^\delta \delta^{\frac{1}{4}}\,d\delta = \frac{72}{7}(0.023)\left(\frac{u_o}{\nu}\right)^{-\frac{1}{4}}\int_0^L dx \tag{13-100}$$

and thus

$$\delta = 0.376\left(\frac{L u_o}{\nu}\right)^{-\frac{1}{5}} L \tag{13-101}$$

or

$$\delta = 0.376\,(\mathbf{Re}_L)^{-\frac{1}{5}}\,L \tag{13-102}$$

An integration of the drag force from $x = 0$ to $x = L$, as has been done in several previous cases [Eqs. (12-78) *et seq.*], gives

$$C_D = 0.072\,(\mathbf{Re}_L)^{-\frac{1}{5}} \tag{13-103}$$

In the above development the turbulent boundary layer has been assumed to extend to $x = 0$, whereas there really is a certain length on the forward part of the plate in which the boundary layer is laminar.

A comparison of the results for the laminar and for the turbulent boundary layers shows that δ increases as $L^{\frac{1}{2}}$ for laminar flow and as $L^{\frac{4}{5}}$ for turbulent flow. The drag in turbulent flow is greater than in laminar flow; F_d increases as $L^{\frac{1}{2}}$ in laminar flow and as $L^{\frac{4}{5}}$ in turbulent flow. These are quantitative arguments for attempting to maintain a laminar boundary layer on an airfoil, as discussed early in this chapter.

The Blasius formulas are not valid above $D u_b \rho / \mu = 10^5$ for pipe flow. Similarly, the use of Eqs. (13-102) and (13-103) is restricted to the range of $L u_o \rho / \mu$ of 5×10^5 to 10^7. Just as in the case of pipe flow, if the logarithmic velocity distribution is used in the derivations, a result is obtained which is valid to very high **Re**. For the flat plate the results of such an analysis can be represented by

$$C_D = \frac{0.455}{(\log \mathbf{Re}_L)^{2.58}} \tag{13-104}$$

Fig. 13-11.   *Drag coefficients for flow past a flat plate. (From Hermann Schlichting, "Boundary Layer Theory," 4th ed., fig. 21.2, p. 538, McGraw-Hill Book Company, Inc., New York, 1960.)*

In order to take into account the laminar boundary layer on the forward part of the plate, this equation is modified to give the Prandtl-Schlichting formula

$$C_D = \frac{0.455}{(\log \mathbf{Re}_L)^{2.58}} - \frac{A}{\mathbf{Re}_L} \tag{13-105}$$

where A is a function of the transition $\mathbf{Re}_L$, which is governed by the intensity of the turbulence of the external flow.   Values of A are given in Table 13-1.

Table 13-1

Transition $\mathbf{Re}_L$	A
3×10^5	1050
5×10^5	1700
1×10^6	3300
3×10^6	8700

Figure 13-11 shows some experimental data and the errors resulting from several of the preceding equations for C_D.

We shall not discuss quantitatively the flow along curved surfaces, for which there is a pressure gradient arising from the external potential flow, and the possibility of separation.   This situation is discussed in a qualitative way at the end of Chap. 8.

PROBLEMS

13-1. At successive equal time intervals of a few milliseconds, the following velocities were measured by means of hot-wire anemometers at two points 5 cm apart:

u_{x1}	77	78	75	75	70	73	78	83	81	77	72
u_{x2}	74	85	69	80	74	81	79	79	88	80	75

Calculate the mean velocity and the intensity of the turbulence (assume isotropic) at each point. What is the correlation coefficient for the velocities at the two points?

13-2. Find an expression for the eddy viscosity from the formula for the logarithmic velocity profile in the turbulent core and a knowledge of how τ varies with y. Sketch graphs of the eddy viscosity versus position in the pipe at constant **Re** and versus **Re** at a given position. Is the quantity ν_e/u^*r_i a function of **Re**? Of position?

13-3. Proceeding as in the previous problem, find a relation for the dimensionless Prandtl mixing length ℓ/r_i. Show how this quantity varies with position and **Re**.

13-4. Point out ways in which the velocity profile predicted by Eqs. (13-58) to (13-60) is inconsistent with the profile indicated by some simple physical principles. It will be helpful to consider the behavior of du/dy.

13-5. Water is flowing at 68°F through a smooth, horizontal tube of 2-in. ID. At a point ¾ in. from the wall, calculate the velocity, shear stress, eddy viscosity, and mixing length for a bulk velocity of (a) 50 ft/sec; (b) 5 ft/sec; (c) 0.05 ft/sec.

13-6. Water is flowing as in Prob. 13-5, but through a rough tube. Calculate the same four quantities at the same point for:

(a) $u_b = 50$ ft/sec, $e/r_i = 0.01$

(b) $u_b = 5$ ft/sec, $e/r_i = 0.03$

(c) $u_b = 5$ ft/sec, $e/r_i = 0.0005$

(d) $u_b = 0.05$ ft/sec, $e/r_i = 0.01$

13-7. Derive the Blasius resistance formula, Eq. (13-71), from the ⅐-power velocity distribution, Eq. (13-95), applied to flow in a pipe.

13-8. Use the over-all momentum balance to find the equations for δ and C_D analogous to Eqs. (13-93) and (13-94) for an assumed linear variation of the velocity in the laminar boundary layer on a smooth flat plate. For water at 68°F flowing by a plate at 2 ft/sec, find the thickness of the boundary layer 1 ft from the leading edge. What is the total drag up to this point in pounds force per foot of width?

13-9. Air at 68°F and 1 atm is flowing past a smooth, flat plate at 100 ft/sec. If the turbulence in the main stream is such that the transition from a laminar to a turbulent boundary layer occurs at an **Re**$_L$ of 5×10^5, how far from the leading edge is the point of transition? Calculate also the boundary-layer thickness 3 ft from the leading edge and the total drag per foot of width up to this point.

13-10. The boundary layer which forms at the entrance to a circular pipe may be considered to behave like the boundary layer on a flat plate. Estimate the length needed to reach fully developed flow (i.e., for the edge of the boundary layer to reach the center line) for water at 68°F entering a pipe of 2-in. ID at a uniform velocity of (a) 50 ft/sec; (b) 5 ft/sec; (c) 0.05 ft/sec.

Compare the results with the empirical rules given in Perry's Handbook. More exact treatments of this problem are to be found in texts on fluid dynamics.

DIMENSIONAL ANALYSIS WITH APPLICATIONS IN FLUID DYNAMICS

GENERAL REMARKS

In the preceding chapters we have treated a number of flow problems analytically by using the differential momentum balance. However, the flow problems in many engineering systems are so complicated that it is not possible to integrate the differential momentum balance. For instance, in flow past a cylinder, the curve of Fig. 8-9 for **Re** > 1.0 cannot be predicted theoretically, but must be obtained from experiment. Although the equations of motion have been solved for flow past a flat plate or in a circular pipe, they have not been solved for flow past a bank of tubes or through a bed of spheres, or for many other cases. When the analytical approach does not yield a solution, the technique of dimensional analysis often assists in the rational treatment of a problem. The advantages and limitations of the method will become apparent from the discussion and examples given later in this chapter.

Units and Dimensions

In most discussions of mechanics, it is customary to define the so-called fundamental units with reference to Newton's law,

$$F = Ma \qquad (14\text{-}1)$$

This procedure leads to the following relations:

Centimeter, gram, second (cgs) system:

$$1 \text{ dyne} = \frac{(1 \text{ g}) (1 \text{ cm})}{\text{sec}^2} \qquad (14\text{-}2)$$

Meter, kilogram, second (mks) system:

$$1 \text{ newton} = \frac{(1 \text{ kg}) (1 \text{ m})}{\sec^2} \qquad (14\text{-}3)$$

British mass system:

$$1 \text{ poundal} = \frac{(1 \text{ lb}) (1 \text{ ft})}{\sec^2} \qquad (14\text{-}4)$$

The kilogram and the meter are fixed by the mass and the length of carefully preserved standards kept by the International Bureau of Weights and Measures at Sèvres, France. The second is defined as 1/86,400 of a mean solar day; the mean is taken over a period of 12 months. The pound is defined as 0.4536 kg, and the foot as 0.3048 m. In the systems illustrated, the units of force are derived from the units of mass, length, and time, which are usually considered as fundamental in mechanics. In terms of dimensions,[1] we speak of an $[M]$, $[L]$, $[\theta]$ system, and force then has the dimensions of $[ML/\theta^2]$.

On the other hand, in the so-called American engineering system, the pound force is taken as a fundamental unit, so that we have

$$1 \text{ lb force} = \frac{(1 \text{ slug}) (1 \text{ ft})}{\sec^2} \qquad (14\text{-}5)$$

The pound force is defined as $(0.4536)(9.807)$, or 4.448 newtons, that is, 4.448 (kg)(m)/sec². In this $[F]$, $[L]$, $[\theta]$ system a slug is equal to one (lb force)(sec²)/ft, and mass has the dimensions of $[F\theta^2/L]$.

In this book we use four fundamental units and dimensions rather than three, namely, the second, foot, pound, and pound force. The pound force is defined as the force exerted on one pound (mass) which gives it an acceleration of 32.1740 ft/sec². This acceleration corresponds to the acceleration in the standard gravitational field. With this choice of units, it is necessary to use a dimensional constant in Newton's second law,

$$F = \frac{Ma}{g_c} \qquad (14\text{-}6)$$

so that

$$1 \text{ lb force} = \frac{(1 \text{ lb}) (32.17 \text{ ft})/\sec^2}{g_c} \qquad (14\text{-}7)$$

Therefore the constant g_c is

$$g_c = 32.17 \text{ (lb)(ft)/(lb force)(sec}^2) \qquad (14\text{-}8)$$

The pound force defined in this $[F]$, $[M]$, $[L]$, $[\theta]$ system has a definite

[1] The expression $\mu = [M/L\theta]$, for example, means that viscosity has the dimensions of $[M/L\theta]$.

fixed value and does not depend on the local value of g as do the pound weight or the kilogram weight. The value of g_c has, of course, been chosen so that one pound mass exerts a force of one pound force when exposed to the standard gravitational field of the earth.

The use of this system is in accord with most industrial measuring devices. It is rare indeed to find a set of "weights" in the United States calibrated in slugs or a pressure gauge in England which reads in poundals per square inch. As a matter of fact, even in countries in which the metric system is used, the unit of pressure, the bar (1 bar $= 10^6$ dynes/sq cm $=$ 0.9869 atm), is used less than the kg force/sq cm ($= 0.9628$ atm).

If the reader has the idea that a system of four fundamental dimensions is somehow less basic or more arbitrary than a system of three fundamental dimensions, we shall show presently that a system involving only two fundamental dimensions can also be devised. In other words, the number of fundamental dimensions can be chosen to suit the convenience of the analyst.

Dimensional Homogeneity

In order to be applicable with any consistent set of units, an equation must be dimensionally homogeneous; i.e., all the terms must have the same dimensions. In the $[F]$, $[M]$, $[L]$, $[\theta]$ system, the dimensional constant g_c is necessary in Newton's law to ensure dimensional homogeneity. Its numerical value depends on the system of units; for instance, it might equal 9.81 (kg)(m)/(kg force)(sec²). Any numbers which appear in dimensionally homogeneous algebraic equations are dimensionless. Equation (14-6) would no longer be dimensionally homogeneous if it were written as $32.2F = Ma$. This equation does not hold for any units other than those given in Eq. (14-8). On the other hand, in the $[M]$, $[L]$, $[\theta]$ system, Eq. (14-1) is dimensionally homogeneous. By defining one less fundamental dimension and letting F have the dimensions of Ma, g_c has a value of 1.0 with no dimensions.

A System of Two Fundamental Dimensions

As mentioned previously, a system consisting of only two fundamental dimensions in mechanics can be devised.[1] In considering the movements of stars and planets, Newton's formula for the gravitational attractive force between two masses M and M' is used.

[1] This treatment follows that of H. L. Langhaar, "Dimensional Analysis and Theory of Models," chap. 1, John Wiley & Sons, Inc., New York, 1951.

$$F = \frac{kMM'}{r^2} \tag{14-9}$$

where r = distance between centers of masses

k = a dimensional constant having a value in cgs system of 6.7×10^{-8} cu cm/(g)(sec^2)

It might be argued that calculations in astronomy could be simplified by giving k a value of unity, so let us define an astronomical unit of force by the equation

$$1 \text{ af} = \frac{(1 \text{ g})(1 \text{ g})}{1 \text{ sq cm}} \tag{14-10}$$

Thus, in this $[M]$, $[L]$ system, the dimensions of force are $[M^2/L^2]$ and the units of force are sq g/sq cm. One af is equivalent to 6.7×10^{-8} (g)(cm)/sec^2, that is, dynes.

The dimensions of time in this system can be found from Eq. (14-1) by setting

$$1 \text{ af} = 1 \text{ g} \frac{1 \text{ cm}}{(\text{at})^2} \tag{14-11}$$

in which time is measured in astronomical time units, at. Since force has the dimensions of $[M^2/L^2]$, time must have the dimensions of $[L^{3/2}/M^{1/2}]$, and its units are cm$^{3/2}$/g$^{1/2}$. One at is equivalent to $(6.7 \times 10^{-8})^{-1/2}$, or 3.86×10^3 sec.

Although it may seem strange to measure time in cm$^{3/2}$/g$^{1/2}$ rather than typical time units, it is really no more unusual than measuring force in (g)(cm)/sec^2 rather than typical force units. The choice of the fundamental dimensions is arbitrary, and we might even devise a system having the basic dimensions of density, viscosity, and surface tension; mass, length, and time would then all be derived quantities.

Dimensions Used in This Book

We have so far discussed only mechanical systems. If thermal effects are important, we use an energy dimension $[H]$ and a temperature dimension $[T]$. Thus the complete set of fundamental dimensions used in this book is $[F]$, $[M]$, $[L]$, $[\theta]$, $[H]$, $[T]$. Of course, this number could be reduced, not only with regard to the mechanical quantities, as already discussed, but also with regard to $[H]$, which has the dimensions $[FL]$.

The dimensions of the variables used can be inferred from the units given in the table of notation in Chap. 1. Obviously, another consistent system of units could replace the lb force, lb, ft, sec, Btu, °F system used.

APPLICATION IN FLUID DYNAMICS

Results from the Differential Momentum Balance

Even though it may not be possible to integrate the Navier-Stokes equations for a given problem, we can use them to find out how the variables must be grouped in an equation representing the solution of the problem. We begin by writing the x component of the Navier-Stokes equations for steady flow as

$$u_x \frac{\partial u_x}{\partial x} + u_y \frac{\partial u_x}{\partial y} + u_z \frac{\partial u_x}{\partial z} = g \cos \beta - \frac{g_c}{\rho} \frac{\partial p}{\partial x} + \nu \left(\frac{\partial^2 u_x}{\partial x^2} + \frac{\partial^2 u_x}{\partial y^2} + \frac{\partial^2 u_x}{\partial z^2} \right)$$

$$(14\text{-}12)$$

This equation is, of course, dimensionally homogeneous; each term has the dimensions $[L/\theta^2]$. Since we are interested mainly in the way in which the variables appear in an integrated form of Eq. (14-12), we write

$$\left[\frac{u^2}{L} \right] = \left[g - \frac{g_c p}{\rho L} + \frac{\nu u}{L^2} \right] \tag{14-13}$$

We have symbolized all the velocity components by a single characteristic velocity u and all the lengths by a characteristic length L. Equation (14-13) expresses a dimensional equality, but not a numerical equality. We now change the terms in Eq. (14-13) to a dimensionless form by dividing each term by u^2/L, obtaining

$$[1] = \left[\frac{gL}{u^2} - \frac{g_c p}{u^2 \rho} + \frac{\nu}{uL} \right] \tag{14-14}$$

Equation (14-14) is merely a functional relationship and can be written as

$$\frac{g_c p}{u^2 \rho} = f \left(\frac{u^2}{gL}, \frac{uL}{\nu} \right) \tag{14-15}$$

We recognize the dimensionless group uL/ν as the Reynolds number; u^2/gL is called the Froude number; and $g_c p/u^2 \rho$ is called the Euler number. Recalling that the left-hand side of (14-13) represents the effect of inertia and that the terms on the right-hand side represent, respectively, the gravity force, the pressure force, and the viscous force, it is clear that we can write

$$\mathbf{Eu} = \frac{g_c p}{u^2 \rho} \propto \frac{\text{pressure force}}{\text{inertia force}} \tag{14-16}$$

$$\mathbf{Fr} = \frac{u^2}{gL} \propto \frac{\text{inertia force}}{\text{gravity force}} \tag{14-17}$$

$$\mathbf{Re} = \frac{uL}{\nu} \propto \frac{\text{inertia force}}{\text{viscous force}} \tag{14-18}$$

Let us now see how Eq. (14-15) may be useful in the study of flow past an infinite cylinder. If we set p equal to the drag force per unit length divided by the diameter, we find

$$\mathbf{Eu} = \frac{g_c F_d'}{u^2 \rho D} = \frac{C_D}{2} \tag{14-19}$$

The second equality is a definition of the drag coefficient from Eq. (8-12). Since gravity effects are not important in a flow problem unless there is a free liquid surface involved, Eq. (14-15) becomes

$$C_D = f_1(\mathbf{Re}) \tag{14-20}$$

Once we have experimentally determined a curve of C_D versus $\mathbf{Re}$, say by measuring the drag force as a function of velocity for a given fluid and a given cylinder, this curve can be used to estimate the drag force for other cylinders and other fluids. Such a curve is given in Fig. 8-9. Although the use of dimensional analysis has not given an explicit relation among the variables, the form of the equation has been limited so that only a few experimental data are needed to permit a complete solution of the problem.

The drag coefficient is also a function of the Froude number when surface waves are formed, as in the testing of a ship model or sometimes in the agitation of the liquid in an open tank.

The method of dimensional analysis just illustrated, which starts from a differential equation, is discussed more extensively by Klinkenberg and Mooy[1] and in a different way by Schlichting.[2]

Buckingham's Pi Theorem

A dimensional analysis can also be made according to the method of Buckingham; for a rigorous mathematical derivation of the method, refer to Langhaar.[3] This method is applicable even when the pertinent differential equation is not known. We postulate that p is a function of all the variables and dimensional constants which we think may have some effect on flow:

$$p = f(L, u, \rho, \mu, g, C, \sigma, g_c) \tag{14-21}$$

To find the form of this function by pure empiricism would involve a large number of experiments. By dimensional analysis we are able to reduce the number of experiments needed for a solution of the problem.

[1] H. A. Klinkenberg and H. H. Mooy, Dimensionless Groups in Fluid Friction, Heat, and Material Transfer, *Chem. Eng. Progr.*, **44**:17 (1948).

[2] H. Schlichting, "Boundary Layer Theory," pp. 55–57, McGraw-Hill Book Company, Inc., New York, 1960.

[3] Langhaar, *op. cit.*, chaps. 3 and 4.

We have begun by assuming that the pressure (i.e., the pressure drop associated with flow) is influenced by the variables listed in Eq. (14-21). This assumption is based on some prior knowledge of the physical phenomena, but it is by no means always clear what variables should be included.[1]   The velocity of sound C and the surface tension σ have been included in order to make the problem a little more general than the one treated previously.

The method is based on the premise that any equation representing the behavior of the system must be dimensionally homogeneous, so that it would be possible to write it in the form of dimensionless groups by a procedure similar to that used to get Eq. (14-15).   Using π_i as a symbol for a dimensionless group, we then generalize this result and write

$$\pi_1 = f(\pi_2, \pi_3, \ldots, \pi_i) \tag{14-22}$$

Equation (14-21) must now be written in the form of Eq. (14-22), which involves only the dimensionless groups $\pi_1, \ldots, \pi_i$.

It is first necessary to know how many groups Eq. (14-21) will yield, i.e., the value i.   The value of i is given by

$$i = n - r \tag{14-23}$$

where n = number of variables

r = maximum number of these variables which will *not* form a dimensionless group

The quantity r is often equal to the number of fundamental dimensions. For the general fluid-flow problem we are considering, Eq. (14-21) shows that $n = 9$.   By trial and error we find that L, u, ρ, and g_c cannot be combined in any way so as to make a π.   This can be shown by writing

$$L^a u^b \rho^c g_c{}^d \tag{14-24}$$

and substituting for each variable its dimensions,

$$[L]^a \left[\frac{L}{\theta}\right]^b \left[\frac{M}{L^3}\right]^c \left[\frac{ML}{F\theta^2}\right]^d \tag{14-25}$$

Since $[F]$ occurs only in g_c, it is evident that there is no possibility of obtaining a dimensionless group by assigning proper values to a, b, c, and d. If any one of the other variables is added to the set in (14-25), it is possible to find values of the exponents which result in a dimensionless group, as will be shown presently.   Since r is 4, i must be 5; there are five possible independent dimensionless groups, $\pi_1, \ldots, \pi_5$.

There are a large number of possible sets of dimensionless groups, but from what we know about fluid dynamics, it appears desirable to have a

[1] An interesting discussion of this point, and dimensional analysis in general, is given by P. W. Bridgman, "Dimensional Analysis," chaps. 1–3, Yale University Press, New Haven, Conn., 1931.

group which depends on the presence of viscous effects (μ), one on gravity effects (g), one on high-velocity effects (C), one on surface-tension effects (σ), and one on pressure effects (p). We shall therefore choose our groups so that each of the variables μ, g, C, σ, and p appears in only one group. On the other hand, L, u, ρ, and g_c may have an effect in almost any group, so we make it possible for them to appear in any group. For π_1 we write

$$\pi_1 = L^a u^b \rho^c g_c^d p^e \tag{14-26}$$

In terms of the four fundamental dimensions,

$$[1] = \left[L^a \left(\frac{L}{\theta}\right)^b \left(\frac{M}{L^3}\right)^c \left(\frac{ML}{F\theta^2}\right)^d \left(\frac{F}{L^2}\right)^e \right] \tag{14-27}$$

The exponents on each variable must be such that the group is dimensionless, so this requires that the following equations be satisfied:

For $[M]$ $0 = c + d$ $\tag{14-28}$

For $[L]$ $0 = a + b - 3c + d - 2e$ $\tag{14-29}$

For $[\theta]$ $0 = -b - 2d$ $\tag{14-30}$

For $[F]$ $0 = -d + e$ $\tag{14-31}$

These four equations can be solved to give all the exponents in terms of one. We choose e and get $d = e$, $b = -2e$, $c = -e$, and $a = 0$. In addition, e can be arbitrarily set equal to unity, since all the π's are to appear in Eq. (14-22), which involves an unknown function of the π's. From these results we obtain

$$\pi_1 = \frac{g_c p}{u^2 \rho} = \mathbf{Eu} \quad \text{the Euler number} \tag{14-32}$$

For π_2 we set

$$\pi_2 = L^a u^b \rho^c g_c^d \mu^e \tag{14-33}$$

which gives ($e = -1$)

$$\pi_2 = \frac{Lu\rho}{\mu} = \mathbf{Re} \quad \text{the Reynolds number} \tag{14-34}$$

In a similar way the other π's are obtained by changing the fifth variable in Eqs. (14-26) and (14-33), successively, to g, C, and σ. The results are

$$\pi_3 = \frac{u^2}{Lg} = \mathbf{Fr} \quad \text{the Froude number} \tag{14-35}$$

$$\pi_4 = \frac{u}{C} = \mathbf{Ma} \quad \text{the Mach number} \tag{14-36}$$

$$\pi_5 = \frac{\rho u^2 L}{g_c \sigma} = \mathbf{We} \quad \text{the Weber number} \tag{14-37}$$

Equation (14-22) becomes, for this problem,

$$\textbf{Eu} = f(\textbf{Re},\textbf{Fr},\textbf{Ma},\textbf{We}) \tag{14-38}$$

This set of five π's is called a complete set; every π is independent of the others. Many other π's can of course be formed from those of the complete set; for instance,

$$\textbf{Re Fr} = \frac{u^3\rho}{\mu g} \tag{14-39}$$

This group might conceivably be useful in the analysis of a particular problem.

Fortunately, in many cases, the effects represented by many of the groups in Eq. (14-38) are negligible. The following cases, some of which have been treated analytically in previous chapters, may be mentioned:

1. *Flow of an ideal fluid.* This approximation can be applied to the calculation of the lift of an airfoil or the delivery of a fan, for which viscosity, gravity, surface-tension, and compressibility (Mach number) effects are negligible. Equation (14-38) becomes, for this case,

$$\textbf{Eu} = \frac{g_c p}{u^2\rho} = \text{const} \tag{14-40}$$

which can be recognized as a reduced form of Bernoulli's equation.

2. *Flow in conduits or past totally immersed objects,* for which only viscous friction is important.

$$\frac{g_c p}{u^2\rho} = \phi\left(\frac{Lu\rho}{\mu}\right) \tag{14-41}$$

Recall that $g_c p/u^2\rho$ is equivalent to C_D or f.

We have already noted that Eq. (14-15) becomes

$$C_D = f_1(\textbf{Re}) \tag{14-20}$$

when applied to flow past a cylinder. For flow in a smooth pipe, we have defined the friction factor f, so that

$$\frac{g_c F_d}{u^2\rho A} = \frac{g_c \tau_s}{u^2\rho} = \frac{f}{2} \tag{13-66}$$

Since we know

$$\tau_s = -\frac{\Delta p D}{4L} \tag{7-10}$$

the equation for f becomes

$$f = \frac{g_c(-\Delta p)D}{2\rho L u_b{}^2} = \phi(\textbf{Re}) \tag{14-42}$$

A plot of f versus **Re** has been given in Fig. 13-8.

3. *Flow past ship models.* Since surface waves are formed, the Froude number must be included.

$$\frac{g_c p}{u^2 \rho} = \frac{g_c F_d}{u^2 \rho A} = \phi \left(\frac{L u \rho}{\mu}, \frac{u^2}{Lg} \right) \tag{14-43}$$

4. *Flow at high velocity; ballistics.*

$$\frac{g_c F_d}{u^2 \rho A} = \phi \left(\frac{u}{C} \right) \tag{14-44}$$

This type of problem will be discussed further in Chap. 17.

5. *Flow of dispersions which are breaking up.*

$$\frac{g_c p}{u^2 \rho} = \phi \left(\frac{\rho u^2 L}{g_c \sigma} \right) \tag{14-45}$$

If two liquid phases are present, groups formed from the ratios of the properties of the two phases, such as ρ_1/ρ_2, ν_1/ν_2, etc., may also be important.

Models and Similitude

Models are useful in the design of ships and airplanes and in the scale-up of chemical process equipment. Since experiments with the full-scale object, called the prototype, would be difficult and expensive, it is customary to study the behavior of models. In the cases which we shall discuss, the model is geometrically similar to the prototype; the ratio of any two lengths in the model is the same as that of two corresponding lengths in the prototype. In other words, the model and the prototype have the same shape. The terms kinematic similarity and dynamic similarity are used to describe a point-to-point correspondence between the velocities and the forces, respectively, for flow past the model and the prototype. If there is complete similarity for flow past a model and its geometrically similar prototype, all the pertinent dimensionless groups will have the same values for the two flows. Equations (14-16) to (14-18) show that this means that the ratios of the pertinent forces are the same for the two flows. Flow in a given smooth circular pipe can be regarded as flow past a model. By the principle of similitude, we can then predict the effect of flow in pipes of other sizes, which can be regarded as prototypes. The shape of the pipe is fixed, so once a set of experiments has been made to determine a curve of **Eu** versus **Re**, no more experiments are necessary. Complete similarity exists at equal Reynolds numbers, for which the Euler numbers must also be equal.

The situation is different for flow past a model of a ship hull, which does not have a standard shape but is made geometrically similar to the proposed prototype. Therefore experiments with a model may be necessary every time a new shape of hull is proposed.

Let us consider the problem of estimating the drag on a 500-ft ship. Equation (14-43) can be written as

$$C_D = \phi(\mathbf{Re}, \mathbf{Fr}) \tag{14-46}$$

and the problem would be solved if **Re** and **Fr** could be varied independently so as to find the function ϕ. However, Eqs. (14-17) and (14-18) show that

$$\mathbf{Fr} = \frac{u\nu}{gL^2}\, \mathbf{Re}$$

As the velocity of a given model is varied, **Re** and **Fr** bear a fixed relation to each other if water is always the fluid, since ν/gL^2 is constant. Thus the general form of ϕ cannot be found with one model using only water as the fluid.

It can also be deduced that complete similarity between the model and the prototype cannot be achieved. For a prototype of $L = 500$ ft and a model of $L = 5$ ft, it would be necessary to use a velocity for the model one-tenth that for the prototype in order to maintain **Fr** constant. However, this variation results in a value of **Re** for the model only 0.001 times the **Re** of the prototype.

Naval architects resolve this problem by an approximation which involves changing Eq. (14-46) to

$$C_D = \phi_1(\mathbf{Re}) + \phi_2(\mathbf{Fr}) \tag{14-47}$$

$\phi_1(\mathbf{Re})$ is found from experiments on flow past completely immersed bodies, for which **Fr** has no effect. Experiments are also conducted on ship models to obtain data on C_D for flow in which surface waves are important. The function $\phi_2(\mathbf{Fr})$ is found from these data and from Eq. (14-47) by difference.

Application to Mixing

The behavior of a liquid being agitated by a propeller or turbine in a tank with a free liquid surface is very complicated and cannot be predicted by an analytical solution of the equations of motion. The technique of dimensional analysis is therefore useful, and we now apply it to the problem stated as follows:

$$P = f(D, \rho, \omega, g_c, \mu, g) \tag{14-48}$$

where P = power supplied to propeller

$\quad\ D$ = diameter of propeller

$\quad\ \omega$ = angular velocity of propeller

The other symbols have their usual meanings. For this case, $n = 7$,

Fig. 14-1.   Power number for an unbaffled mixer.
[From J. H. Rushton, E. W. Costich, and H. J.
Everett, Chem. Eng. Progr., 46:395–404
(1950).]

a.	**Fr** = 0.0863.
b.	**Fr** = 0.345.
c.	**Fr** = 0.777.
d.	**Fr** = 1.382.
e.	**Fr** = 2.160.

$r = 4$, and so $i = 3$.   Choosing D, ρ, ω, and g_c as possibly common to each dimensionless group, we obtain

$$\pi_1 = \frac{Pg_c}{\rho\omega^3 D^5} \qquad (14\text{-}49)$$

$$\pi_2 = \frac{D^2\omega\rho}{\mu} \qquad (14\text{-}50)$$

$$\pi_3 = \frac{D\omega^2}{g} \qquad (14\text{-}51)$$

The group π_1 is called the power number.   The linear speed u of the turbine blades, which may be chosen as characteristic, equals $\omega D/2$; substitution for ω in π_2 makes it evident that π_2 is the Reynolds number.   The group π_3 is the Froude number.

The power number is a function of both **Re** and **Fr** when there is a vortex at the liquid surface.   Just as for the ship model, it is not possible to achieve complete similarity between a small mixer and its prototype, or scaled-up version, using the same liquid.   However, in contrast to the case of the ship model, it is practical to conduct the experiments on the mixer model with a fluid of different ν.   By a suitable choice of liquid and temperature, it is then possible to achieve complete similarity between model and prototype.

By using different liquids, it is also possible to vary **Re** and **Fr** independently.   Using this method, Rushton, Costich, and Everett[1] have obtained

[1] J. H. Rushton, E. W. Costich, and H. J. Everett, Power Characteristics of Mixing Impellers, *Chem. Eng. Progr.*, **46**:395, 467 (1950).

Vortex formed without baffles   A properly baffled mixer

Fig. 14-2. Effect of baffles in mixers.

curves for a given mixer, which are shown in Fig. 14-1.[1] Such a curve can be used to predict the performance of only geometrically similar mixers. If the position of the impeller, depth of liquid, or ratio of impeller diameter to tank diameter is changed, the position of the curves in Fig. 14-1 may be changed.

In most industrial mixers for liquids, baffles are used to eliminate swirl, so that the Froude number is no longer important. The effect of the baffles is illustrated in Fig. 14-2. For a certain baffled mixer, the power number is a function of the Reynolds number only, as shown in Fig. 14-3. The shape of this curve resembles that for C_D as a function of **Re** for flow past a submerged object. At low Reynolds number, for which viscous effects are important, the slope of the curves in Fig. 14-1 or 14-3 approaches -1. At high Reynolds number C_D becomes constant as completely turbulent conditions are approached. A curve such as that shown in Fig. 14-3 applies only to geometrically similar mixers. As mentioned previously, if the position of the impeller, the depth of liquid, the ratio of impeller to tank diameter, or the relative size and position of the baffles is changed, a different curve may be obtained on a graph such as Fig. 14-3. Although

[1] In Figs. 14-1 and 14-2, N (revolutions/sec) replaces ω (radians/sec).

Fig. 14-3.   Power number for a baffled mixer. [From J. H. Rushton, E. W. Costich, and H. J. Everett, Chem. Eng. Progr., 46:467–476 (1950).]

the method discussed above permits the estimation of power consumption after scale-up, it says nothing about the effectiveness of mixing.

Rayleigh's Method

In this method Eq. (14-21) is arbitrarily written in the form

$$p = A L^a u^b \rho^c \mu^d g^e C^f \sigma^g g_c{}^h \qquad (14\text{-}52)$$

where A is a constant.

Since this equation must be dimensionally homogeneous in the dimensions $[F]$, $[M]$, $[L]$, and $[\theta]$, it is possible to write four simultaneous equations and solve for four of the exponents in terms of the other four and the arbitrary exponent of 1.0 on p. This procedure gives

$$\frac{g_c p}{u^2 \rho} = A \left(\frac{L u \rho}{\mu}\right)^{-d} \left(\frac{u^2}{L g}\right)^{-e} \left(\frac{u}{C}\right)^{-f} \left(\frac{\rho u^2 L}{g_c \sigma}\right)^{-g} \qquad (14\text{-}53)$$

where d, e, f, and g can have any values. There is no reason to suppose, in general, that $g_c p / u^2 \rho$ is the special function of other groups given by Eq. (14-53), although for many problems the function does have this form. In order to make the result more generally valid, Eq. (14-53) may be regarded as determining the form of one term in an infinite series, so we can write

$$\frac{g_c p}{u^2 \rho} = \phi \left(\frac{L u \rho}{\mu}, \frac{u^2}{L g}, \frac{u}{C}, \frac{\rho u^2 L}{g_c \sigma}\right) \qquad (14\text{-}54)$$

since many functions can be expanded in terms of an infinite series. Equation (14-54) is the same as the result obtained for this problem by the Buckingham method.

No new principles are involved in the application of dimensional analysis to problems in heat and mass transfer. Examples in these areas are reserved to the parts of the book dealing specifically with heat transfer and with mass transfer.

In order to show the complete process of obtaining a correlating equation from experimental data by the technique of dimensional analysis, the following example is given.

Example 14-1

In connection with fundamental studies on heat transfer to boiling liquids, measurements have been made on the rate of bubble formation and the size of bubbles formed by a gas issuing from a small orifice beneath the surface of the liquid. The method of dimensional analysis is to be used to correlate data on bubble size with the properties of the liquid.

We assume that the following equation represents the relation between bubble diameter D and the variables of the problem:

$$D = f(d, \rho, g_c, \sigma, \mu, g) \tag{1}$$

in which d is the diameter of the orifice. It is found by trial and error that no more than four of the seven variables can be found which do not make a dimensionless group; these variables are d, ρ, g_c, and g. These variables will be chosen as the ones which may appear in any of the three $(7 - 4 = 3)$ dimensionless groups. Any dimensional constant such as g_c should always be included among these variables. The other three have been chosen by elimination. We want D to appear in only one group, and we also want to represent the effect of viscosity and the effect of surface tension so that they each appear only in one group. The variables g, g_c, d, and ρ may appear in any group.

The expression for π_1 is

$$\pi_1 = d^a \rho^b g_c{}^c g^d D^e \tag{2}$$

By inspection, π_1 is D/d.

For π_2, we have

$$\pi_2 = d^a \rho^b g_c{}^c g^d \sigma^e \tag{3}$$

The dimensions are substituted to yield

$$[1] = [L]^a \left[\frac{M}{L^3}\right]^b \left[\frac{ML}{F\theta^2}\right]^c \left[\frac{L}{\theta^2}\right]^d \left[\frac{F}{L}\right]^e \tag{4}$$

from which result the four equations

For $[L]$	$0 = a - 3b + c + d - e$	(5)
For $[M]$	$0 = b + c$	(6)
For $[\theta]$	$0 = -2c - 2d$	(7)
For $[F]$	$0 = -c + e$	(8)

If e is set equal to 1.0, we find $c = 1$, $b = -1$, $d = -1$, and $a = -2$, so that we get

$$\pi_2 = \frac{g_c \sigma}{\rho g d^2} \tag{9}$$

From the equation

$$\pi_3 = d^a \rho^b g_c{}^c g^d \mu^e \tag{10}$$

we obtain

$$\pi_3 = \frac{\mu^2}{\rho^2 g d^3} \tag{11}$$

in which e has been set equal to 2 in order to avoid fractional exponents. The result of the dimensional analysis is then

$$\frac{D}{d} = f\left(\frac{g_c \sigma}{\rho g d^2}, \frac{\mu^2}{\rho^2 g d^3}\right) \tag{12}$$

Fig. 14-4. Correlation of data on bubble formation.

Let us now use Eq. (12) to correlate the data of Benzing,[1] part of which is reproduced in Table 14-1. Since these data are given in the cgs system, we get $g_c = 1.0$ in Eq. (12). We then plot in Fig. 14-4 log (D/d) versus log $(\sigma/\rho g d^2)$. Recall that a centipoise is 0.01 g/(cm)(sec) and that g is 981 cm/sec². From the straight line which can be drawn

Table 14-1

System	Liquid viscosity, cp	Liquid density, g/cu cm	Surface tension, dynes/cm	Bubble diameter, cm	
				Orifice diam., 0.293 cm	Orifice diam., 0.438 cm
Water–air	0.81	0.996	70.2	0.514	0.612
Water–H₂	0.81	0.996	70.2	0.516	0.630
7.5% ethanol sol'n–air	1.07	0.982	51.4	0.480	0.583
45% sugar sol'n–air	52.0	1.197	58.1	0.486	0.585
Wesson Oil–air	57.0	0.920	36.5	0.411	0.491

through the points on the graph, it is possible to derive the equation

$$\frac{D}{d} = 1.88 \left(\frac{\sigma}{\rho g d^2}\right)^{0.30} \tag{13}$$

If the variable $\mu^2/\rho^2 g d^3$ were important, it should be possible to draw lines through the points on Fig. 14-4 corresponding to successive values of this parameter. However, the points actually show no systematic variation with $\mu^2/\rho^2 g d^3$, so it can be concluded that D/d is independent of $\mu^2/\rho^2 g d^3$. This result is not surprising, for it is possible to show that the bubble size at a low rate of formation is governed only by a balance between the buoyant force and the force arising from surface tension.

If an equation of the form

$$\pi_1 = a\pi_2{}^b\pi_3{}^c \tag{14}$$

is assumed, the constants a, b, and c can be found by a technique known as the method of least squares. The exponent c is found to have a very small value (approximately

[1] R. J. Benzing, Low Frequency Bubble Formation at Horizontal Circular Orifices, *Ind. Eng. Chem.*, **47**:2087 (1955).

Fig. 14-5.   Performance of a centrifugal pump.

0.01), indicating that the group π_3 is of negligible importance in the equation.   The values found for a and b are 1.82 and 0.25, respectively.

PROBLEMS

14-1. Dimensional analysis is useful in the design of centrifugal pumps.   The pressure rise across a pump p (this term is proportional to the "head" developed by the pump) may be considered to be affected by the fluid density ρ, the angular velocity ω, the impeller diameter D, the volumetric rate of flow Q, and the fluid viscosity μ.   Find the pertinent dimensionless groups, choosing them so that p, Q, and μ each appear in one group only.   Find similar expressions replacing the pressure rise first by the power input to the pump, then by the efficiency of the pump.

14-2. Experiments show that the fluid viscosity actually has little effect on the performance of a centrifugal pump under usual conditions, so that one of the terms obtained in each part of Prob. 14-1 can be omitted.

Test data obtained on a centrifugal pump are shown in Fig. 14-5.   Estimate the ratios of size and speed of a geometrically similar pump to the size and speed of the pump for which the data are given if it is desired to operate the second pump at maximum efficiency, 1000 gal/min, and a pressure rise of 50 psi.

14-3. A rough method of scaling up liquid-mixing tanks and impellers is to keep the power input per unit volume constant.   If it is desired to increase the volume of a properly baffled liquid mixer by a ratio of 3, by what ratio must the tank diameter and impeller speed be changed?   The mixers are geometrically similar, and both operate in the completely turbulent region.

14-4. By the use of the Prandtl mixing length, we showed in Chap. 13 that the velocity distribution in turbulent flow inside a pipe can be given by Eq. (13-57), which may be written as

$$\frac{u}{u^*} = \phi\left(\frac{yu^*}{\nu}\right) \tag{A}$$

where $u^* = \sqrt{\tau_s g_c/\rho}$.   Obtain Eq. (A) by dimensional analysis.

SOME DESIGN EQUATIONS FOR THE
FLOW OF INCOMPRESSIBLE FLUIDS

15

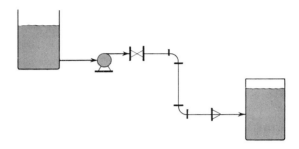

In the preceding chapters, an introduction to the principles of fluid dynamics has been given which should serve as a basis for the solution of many engineering problems. The over-all balances permit the solution of a variety of input-output problems. The equations of motion have been solved for some simple cases, and the technique of dimensional analysis plus experiment has been introduced for the treatment of more complicated situations. As mathematical and computational techniques improve, the number of situations which can be treated analytically will continually increase, so a thorough understanding of the principles underlying these techniques is essential to the engineer.

In discussing the theory we did not want to interrupt the continuity of the reasoning by dwelling on numerous practical examples; in this chapter we present the application of the principles of fluid dynamics to the flow of incompressible fluids in conduits, past immersed objects, and through packed beds.

The Mechanical Energy Balance

The solutions of many problems are based on the mechanical energy balance. This equation, written for the steady flow of an incompressible fluid, is

$$\frac{\Delta u_b{}^2}{2g_c} + \frac{g}{g_c}\Delta z + \frac{\Delta p}{\rho} + lw_f + \eta_p W_s = 0 \qquad (4\text{-}27)$$

for use with a pump, and is

$$\frac{\Delta u_b^2}{2g_c} + \frac{g}{g_c}\Delta z + \frac{\Delta p}{\rho} + lw_f + \frac{W_s}{\eta_t} = 0 \tag{4-24}$$

for use with a turbine. The use of these equations and their relation to the over-all energy balance have been discussed in Chap. 4. The main business of this chapter is to present concisely the methods of calculating lw_f for various practical flow situations.

In the discussions of pressure loss due to friction in Chaps. 13 and 14 the Fanning friction factor was defined as

$$f = \frac{g_c(-\Delta p)D}{2u_b^2 \rho L} \tag{14-42}$$

for the flow of an incompressible fluid in a horizontal pipe of uniform diameter with no pump. This means that Δu_b^2, Δz, and W_s are zero, so there results from Eqs. (4-27) and (14-42)

$$lw_f = \frac{2fLu_b^2}{g_c D} \tag{15-1}$$

This equation relates the loss to the pipe length and the Reynolds number. It is important to realize that Eq. (15-1) can also be used when the pipe is not horizontal and when there is a work term. This statement is illustrated in the equation

$$\frac{\Delta u_b^2}{2g_c} + \frac{g}{g_c}\Delta z + \frac{\Delta p}{\rho} + \eta_p W_s + \sum \frac{2fLu_b^2}{g_c D} + \sum lw_c + \sum lw_e = 0 \tag{15-2}$$

The summation sign is inserted before the term for the loss in straight pipe because this loss may result from flow in series through several sections of pipe of various lengths and diameters. The symbol $\sum lw_c$ stands for the sum of the contraction losses, and $\sum lw_e$ refers to the sum of the expansion losses. These effects have been discussed in Chaps. 5 and 6. It will be recalled that the loss in the pump is accounted for by the efficiency η_p.

Flow in Circular Pipes

The inner surfaces of commercial pipes are not necessarily hydraulically smooth, so the friction-factor chart in Fig. 15-1 contains curves for various degrees of relative roughness. Figure 15-1 is based on the data of many investigators as correlated by Moody.[1]

The curves for rough pipe have different shapes from those obtained by Nikuradse for pipes artificially roughened with sand (Fig. 13-9). The curves for commercial pipe become horizontal in the completely rough region, but they differ from those of Nikuradse in the transition region

---

[1] L. F. Moody, Friction Factors for Pipe Flow, *Trans. ASME*, **66**:671 (1944).

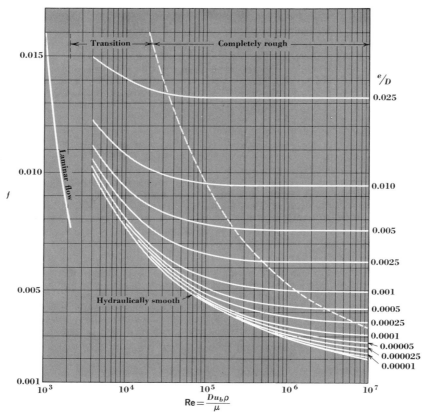

Fig. 15-1.   Friction factor vs. Reynolds number for commercial pipe. (From J. G. Knudsen and D. L. Katz, "Fluid Dynamics and Heat Transfer," fig. 7-21, p. 176, McGraw-Hill Book Company, Inc., New York, 1950.)

between rough and hydraulically smooth.   The relative-roughness parameters shown in Fig. 15-1 are the same as those for the lines in Fig. 13-9, which were defined to coincide with them in the completely rough zone. They were not found by actually measuring the heights of protuberances in commercial pipe.   Figure 15-2 enables one to find the relative roughness of various kinds of pipe.

The line in Fig. 15-1 for laminar flow is identical with Eq. (13-73); the line for turbulent flow for the hydraulically smooth regime is identical with Eq. (13-70); and the line for the completely rough regime is identical with Eq. (13-77).

If expansion and contraction losses make up a large fraction of the overall loss, as in a short heat exchanger, these losses should be calculated as

a.	Riveted steel	3.	Asphalted cast iron
b.	Concrete	4.	Commercial steel or wrought iron
1.	Cast iron	5.	Drawn tubing
2.	Galvanized iron		

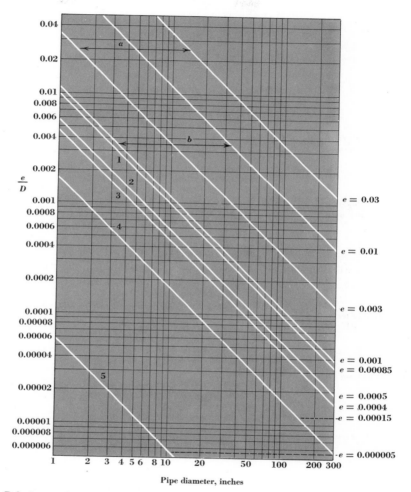

Fig. 15-2. *Relative roughness of commercial pipe. [From L. F. Moody, Trans. ASME, 66:671 (1944).]*

outlined in Chap. 5 and as given in detail by Kays.[1] In many cases, however, the losses at expansions, contractions, and fittings of various kinds are a small portion of the over-all loss, and Fig. 15-3 can be used. This nomograph gives the approximate equivalent length of straight pipe

[1] W. M. Kays, *Trans. ASME,* **72**:1067 (1950).

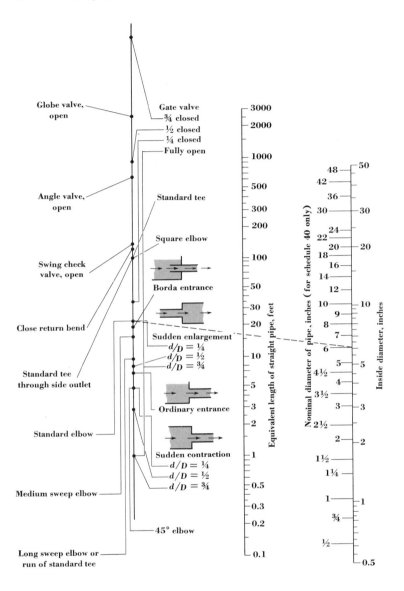

Fig. 15-3.   Equivalent lengths for friction losses. (Crane Co.)

which would have the same effect as a given fitting.   These lengths are added to the lengths of straight pipe between fittings, and the sums are used for the pertinent values of L in Eq. (15-2).   In this procedure the effects of $\Sigma \, lw_c$ and $\Sigma \, lw_e$ are included in the equivalent length, so these

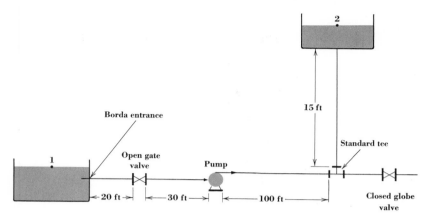

Fig. 15-4.   *Piping systems for Example 15-1. (Not to scale.)*

terms may be omitted.   The following example will explain more fully the use of these methods.

Example 15-1

Water at 60°F is pumped at 100 gal/min from a reservoir through a system of piping into an open tank, the level of which is maintained constant at 17 ft above the level of the reservoir.   Three-inch, schedule-40 steel pipe is used from the reservoir to the pump, and two-inch, schedule-40 pipe is used from the pump to the elevated tank.   The pipe lengths and fittings are shown in Fig. 15-4.   Calculate the power consumption of the pump if its efficiency is 70 per cent.

The solution of this problem is begun by writing the mechanical energy balance between the two planes at the liquid surfaces indicated by 1 and 2 in the figure.   Thus Δp is zero, Δu_b is zero, and Δz is 17 ft.   Equation (4-27) then yields

$$17 + lw_f + 0.70W_s = 0 \tag{1}$$

Once we have determined lw_f, this equation will permit the computation of W_s, and thus the power input.   The parts of this loss term are represented by the last three terms on the left side of Eq. (15-2).   Using Fig. 15-3, we find that for the 3-in. pipe, the equivalent length of the Borda entrance is 8 ft, and that of the open gate valve is 1.7 ft. The equivalent length of 3-in. pipe is, then, $8 + 20 + 1.7 + 30$, or 59.7 ft.   We also calculate the following quantities for the 3-in. pipe:[1]

$$w = \frac{(100)(62.6)}{(7.48)(60)} = 13.97 \text{ lb/sec}$$

$$u_b = \frac{13.97}{(7.393/144)(62.6)} = 4.35 \text{ ft/sec}$$

$$\mathbf{Re} = \frac{Du_b\rho}{\mu} = \frac{(3.068/12)(4.35)(62.6)}{(1.05)(6.72 \times 10^{-4})} = 9.87 \times 10^4$$

From Fig. 15-3, we find

[1] Pipe diameters and cross-sectional areas, viscosities, and densities are from Perry's Handbook.

$$\frac{e}{D} = 0.0006$$

From Fig. 15-1, the friction factor is

$$f = 0.0052$$

and so, for the 3-in. pipe, the loss is

$$lw_{f3} = \frac{2fLu_b{}^2}{g_cD} = \frac{(2)(0.0052)(59.7)(4.35)^2}{(32.2)(3.068/12)}$$

$$= 1.43 \text{ (ft)(lb force)/lb}$$

A similar calculation is made to find the loss in the 2-in. pipe. For the tee, $L = 12$ ft. There is no suitable point on Fig. 15-3 for the expansion loss into the upper tank, for which $d/D = 0$, but from Eq. (5) of Example 5-2, we find

$$lw_e = \frac{u_{b1}{}^2}{2g_c}\left(1 - \frac{A_1}{A_2}\right)^2$$

Since $A_1/A_2 = 0$, we have

$$lw_e = \frac{u_{b1}{}^2}{2g_c}$$

For the 2-in. pipe, we now calculate

$$u_b = 4.35 \ (3.068/2.067)^2 = 9.56 \text{ ft/sec}$$

$$\mathbf{Re} = \frac{(2.067/12)(9.56)(62.6)}{(1.05)(6.72 \times 10^{-4})} = 1.46 \times 10^5$$

Figure 15-2 yields

$$\frac{e}{D} = 0.0009$$

and so we have, from Fig. 15-1,

$$f = 0.0053$$

For the 2-in. pipe the loss is

$$lw_{f2} = \frac{(2)(0.0053)(100 + 12 + 15)(9.56)^2}{(32.2)(2.067/12)} + \frac{(9.56)^2}{2(32.2)}$$

$$= 22.4 + 1.43 = 23.8 \text{ (ft)(lb force)/lb}$$

The total loss term is then

$$lw_f = lw_{f3} + lw_{f2} = 1.4 + 23.8 = 25.2 \text{ (ft)(lb force)/lb}$$

This result is substituted into Eq. (1) to give

$$17 + 25.2 + 0.70W_s = 0$$

$$W_s = -60.3 \text{ (ft)(lb force)/lb}$$

The power requirement is then given by

$$\frac{(60.3)(13.97)}{550} = 1.53 \text{ hp}$$

In most problems the properties of the fluid are known; in the particular case just illustrated it was a straightforward procedure to calculate $\mathbf{Re}$ and

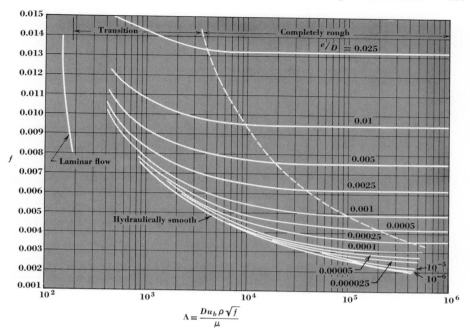

Fig. 15-5.   *Friction factor vs. Kármán number for commercial pipe.*

obtain f from Fig. 15-1 and then find lw_f from Eq. (15-1).   On the other hand, if the horsepower of the pump had been given instead of the flow rate, it would have been necessary to use a trial-and-error procedure to obtain the velocity (i.e., the flow rate) since u_b must be known to calculate both the friction factor and the Reynolds number.

In order to solve a problem in which the velocity is the unknown (that is, lw_f is given), the data of Fig. 15-1 are plotted so that the velocity need not be known to calculate the abscissa.   This is done by defining a variable Λ as follows:

$$\Lambda = \mathbf{Re}\sqrt{f} = \frac{D\rho}{\mu}\sqrt{\frac{lw_f g_c D}{2L}} \tag{15-3}$$

From the data in Fig. 15-1 it is easy to calculate values of Λ and find the corresponding values of f.   Figure 15-5 is a plot of f versus Λ; its use is illustrated in the following example.

Example 15-2

Hot water at 110°F flows from a constant-level tank through 2-in., schedule-40 steel pipe, from which it emerges 40 ft below the level in the tank.   The equivalent length of the piping system is 148 ft.   Calculate the rate of flow in gallons per minute.

If the input plane is at the level of the liquid in the tank and the output is at the end of the pipe, the mechanical energy balance reduces to

$$\Delta z \frac{g}{g_c} + \frac{\Delta u_b^2}{2g_c} + lw_f = 0 \tag{1}$$

or, since u_{b1} is zero and Δz is -40 ft,

$$-40 + \frac{u_b^2}{2g_c}\left(1 + \frac{4fL}{D}\right) = 0 \tag{2}$$

Equation (2) shows that the relative importance of the kinetic-energy term increases as L/D decreases.

In order to find f, and thus u_b, Fig. 15-5 is used. We calculate

$$\mathbf{Re}\,\sqrt{f} = \frac{D\rho}{\mu}\sqrt{\frac{lw_f g_c D}{2L}} \tag{3}$$

$$\mathbf{Re}\,\sqrt{f} = \frac{\left(\dfrac{2.067}{12}\right)(61.8)\sqrt{\dfrac{(40)(32.2)(2.067/12)}{(2)(148)}}}{(0.62)(6.72 \times 10^{-4})} \tag{4}$$

$$\mathbf{Re}\,\sqrt{f} = 2.21 \times 10^5$$

From Fig. 15-5, with $e/D = 0.0009$, $f = 0.0049$.

In the above calculation lw_f has been taken as 40, found from Eq. (1), neglecting the kinetic-energy term. If the latter is important, a correction can be made for it later. Equation (2) now becomes

$$-40 + \frac{u_b^2}{64.4}\left[1 + \frac{(4)(0.0049)(148)}{2.067/12}\right] = 0$$

and

$$-40 + \frac{u_b^2}{64.4}(1 + 16.82) = 0$$

and finally

$$u_b = \sqrt{\frac{(40)(64.4)}{17.82}} = 12.0 \text{ ft/sec}$$

From this value of u_b a new value of lw_f can be calculated from Eq. (1) and a new value of $\mathbf{Re}\,\sqrt{f}$ obtained. However, the latter is changed only by a few per cent, and the flow is still in the completely rough regime in Fig. 15-5, so f will not be changed from its old value. Therefore the correct answer is $u_b = 12.0$ ft/sec, and the flow rate is

$$(12.0)(0.0233)(60)(7.48) = 126 \text{ gal/min}$$

The group $\mathbf{Re}\sqrt{f}$ is sometimes called the Kármán number. If $1/\sqrt{f}$ is plotted versus $\log(\mathbf{Re}\sqrt{f})$, Eq. (13-70) shows that a straight line is obtained in the hydraulically smooth zone. Such a curve is given by Rouse,[1] for example.

It is left as an exercise for the reader to show that a plot of f versus $\mathbf{Re}\,f^{1/2}$

---

[1] H. Rouse and J. W. Howe, "Basic Mechanics of Fluids," p. 145, John Wiley & Sons, Inc., New York, 1953.

might be convenient for a case in which the total frictional loss and the volumetric flow rate are fixed but the pipe diameter is unknown.

Flow in Parallel Conduits

Flow in a network of pipe is often a complicated situation and may require the solution of many simultaneous, nonlinear equations. High-speed computing machines are useful in the calculation of the flows in the various parts of a large distribution system. The following simple example illustrates some of the principles involved.

Example 15-3

Water at 68°F flows from a constant-head tank through an equivalent length of 50 ft of 2-in., schedule-40 pipe to a point 15 ft below the liquid surface. At this point the line is divided; part of the water flows through an equivalent length of 30 ft of 1½-in. pipe to discharge at a point 30 ft below the level of the liquid in the tank, and the other part flows in parallel through an equivalent length of 40 ft of 1-in. pipe to discharge at a point 20 ft below the level in the tank. Find the bulk velocities in the three sections.

Referring to the 2-in. pipe as section 1, the 1½-in. pipe as section 2, and the 1-in. pipe as section 3, we write the mechanical energy balance for each section:

$$-15 + \frac{\Delta p_1}{\rho} + lw_{f1} = 0 \tag{1}$$

$$-15 + \frac{\Delta p_2}{\rho} + lw_{f2} = 0 \tag{2}$$

$$-5 + \frac{\Delta p_3}{\rho} + lw_{f3} = 0 \tag{3}$$

In order not to complicate the problem, kinetic-energy effects and losses at fittings, contractions, and expansions are omitted.

Since the over-all Δp from the surface of the liquid in the tank to the outlets of the two pipes is zero and Δp_2 must equal Δp_3, we have

$$\Delta p_1 = -\Delta p_2 = -\Delta p_3 \tag{4}$$

In addition, the over-all mass balance gives

$$w_1 = w_2 + w_3$$

and

$$u_{b1}D_1{}^2 = u_{b2}D_2{}^2 + u_{b3}D_3{}^2 \tag{5}$$

We must now proceed by trial and error. First Δp_1 is assumed, so that lw_{f1}, lw_{f2}, and lw_{f3} can be calculated from Eqs. (1) to (3). By the method illustrated in Example 15-2, u_{b1}, u_{b2}, and u_{b3} are then calculated.

If Eq. (5) is not satisfied using these values, a new Δp_1 is chosen until one is found for which Eq. (5) is satisfied.

Let us begin by choosing $\Delta p_1 = 0$, a reasonable choice which has the added virtue of simplifying the calculations. From Eqs. (1) to (3) we get $lw_{f1} = 15$, $lw_{f2} = 15$, and $lw_{f3} = 5$. We then find, for section 1,

$$\textbf{Re}\,\sqrt{f} = 1.46 \times 10^5 \qquad f = 0.0054$$
$$u_{b1} = 12.4 \text{ ft/sec}$$

For section 2,

$$\textbf{Re}\,\sqrt{f} = 1.29 \times 10^5 \qquad f = 0.0059$$
$$u_{b2} = 13.5 \text{ ft/sec}$$

For section 3,

$$\textbf{Re}\,\sqrt{f} = 3.41 \times 10^4 \qquad f = 0.0070$$
$$u_{b3} = 5.01 \text{ ft/sec}$$

Substituting the appropriate diameters, Eq. (5) becomes

$$u_{b1} = 0.607u_{b2} + 0.257u_{b3} \tag{6}$$

If the three velocities found above are substituted in Eq. (6), the right-hand side is 9.49 and the left-hand side is 12.4.

This result shows that the velocity in the 2-in. pipe is too large, so that Δp_1 should be chosen greater than zero. This change will *reduce* the friction loss in section 1. If $\Delta p_1/\rho$ is chosen as 3.5 (ft)(lb force)/lb, corresponding to $\Delta p_1 = +1.5$ psi, the resulting velocities will satisfy Eq. (6). The velocities are $u_{b1} = 10.8$ ft/sec, $u_{b2} = 9.12$ ft/sec, and $u_{b3} = 6.57$ ft/sec.

In obtaining this result, the trial-and-error process has been simplified by assuming that the f's remain constant as the u_b's are changed by the relatively small factors involved.

Flow in Conduits Other Than Circular

The following remarks apply only to turbulent flow; laminar flow for several cases has been discussed in Chap. 12.

Figures 15-1 and 15-5 can be used for turbulent flow in many noncircular conduits by replacing the diameter D by the equivalent diameter D_{eq} defined by the relation

$$D_{eq} = 4r_H \tag{15-4}$$

In this equation r_H is the hydraulic radius, in turn defined by the equation

$$r_H = \frac{A}{l_p} \tag{15-5}$$

where l_p = wetted perimeter of conduit
A = cross-sectional area of conduit

For a circular pipe it may be verified that this definition leads to the consistent result that $D = D_{eq}$.

As an example, for flow in an annulus, D_{eq} equals $D_2 - D_1$, and thus we obtain

$$lw_f = \frac{2fLu_b^2}{g_c(D_2 - D_1)} \tag{15-6}$$

and

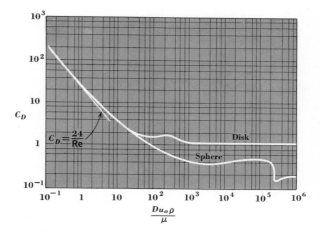

Fig. 15-6. Drag coefficients for spheres and disks. (From H. Rouse and J. W. Howe, "Basic Mechanics of Fluids," fig. 107, p. 181, John Wiley & Sons, Inc., New York, 1953.)

$$\mathbf{Re} = \frac{(D_2 - D_1)u_b\rho}{\mu} \tag{15-7}$$

The hydraulic radius can also be used with the friction-factor charts for flow in open channels or partially filled pipes.

Flow past Immersed Bodies

In Chap. 8 we discussed at some length flow past a cylinder; the results are expressed quantitatively in Fig. 8-9. In Chap. 14 we showed that the form of the coordinates of Fig. 8-9 could be obtained by dimensional analysis.

It is of interest also to know the drag in flow past spheres and disks; Fig. 15-6 presents the relation between C_D and $\mathbf{Re}$, where

$$C_D = \frac{2F_d g_c}{\rho u_o^2 A} \tag{8-13}$$

where $A = \pi D^2/4$, and where

$$\mathbf{Re} = \frac{Du_o\rho}{\mu}$$

In these equations, D is the diameter of the sphere or disk.

The curve for the sphere is similar to that for the cylinder; there is a sudden drop in C_D at $\mathbf{Re} \cong 3 \times 10^5$, where the point of separation moves downstream as the boundary layer becomes turbulent. The curve for the

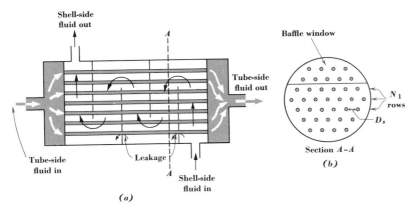

Fig. 15-7.   *Heat exchanger with baffles.*

disk does not have this sudden drop, for the point of separation can occur only at the sharp edge of the disk.

For **Re** < 1.0, Stokes' equation, discussed in Chap. 12, applies for both bodies.

Flow Normal to Banks of Tubes

Flow normal to a bank of tubes is encountered in air heaters and other heat exchangers. Figure 15-7a and b shows one way in which the fluid on the shell side of a heat exchanger may be caused to flow normal to the tubes by using baffles. There is flow across N_1 rows of tubes between baffles and flow parallel to the tubes in the baffle windows. There is also some leakage between the baffles and the tubes.

The Reynolds number and friction factor for flow past tube banks are defined in the literature in several ways. Some of the possible ways of defining the diameter in **Re** and f are as follows:

1. The flow is considered to be the sum of the effects obtained in flow past a single cylinder; the important dimension is thus the tube diameter.

2. The flow is considered to be the sum of the effects obtained in flow through rectangular orifices formed by the spaces between the tubes; the important dimension is thus the tube spacing D_s (Fig. 15-7b).

3. The situation is considered as flow through a noncircular conduit, and the hydraulic radius is defined as the free volume in the tube bank divided by the exposed surface area of the tubes. The important dimension is thus the equivalent diameter, $D_q = 4r_H$.

No attempt is made here to give a comprehensive survey of this problem, for which many correlations have been proposed. As an example, the following equation given by Donohue[1] is presented for turbulent flow across a bank of N_1 rows of staggered tubes:

$$f' = 0.99 \left(\frac{D u_{b,\max}\rho}{\mu}\right)^{-0.2} \tag{15-8}$$

for **Re** > 500. For this type of system laminar flow exists for **Re** < 100. The term $u_{b,\max}$ is the velocity based on the minimum cross-sectional area normal to the flow. The friction factor is defined by

$$f' = \frac{g_c(lw_f)}{2N_1 u_{b,\max}^2}\left(\frac{\mu}{\mu_s}\right)^{0.14} \tag{15-9}$$

where μ_s is the fluid viscosity at the average surface temperature of the tubes. The average bulk fluid temperature is used to find μ and ρ.

The factor $(\mu/\mu_s)^{0.14}$ can be used with turbulent flow in general to correct the friction factor for the effect of temperature variation in the fluid in the direction normal to the flow. For instance, for flow inside a heat-exchanger tube, the ordinate of Fig. 15-1 can be interpreted as

$$\frac{g_c lw_f D}{2u_b^2 L}\left(\frac{\mu}{\mu_s}\right)^{0.14}$$

This empirical method is based on the fact that the viscosity in the region of high shear near the wall has a large effect on f.

A survey of some of the numerous equations which have been proposed for flow across tube banks is given by Knudsen and Katz.[2]

Flow through Packed Beds

Flow of a fluid through a packed bed of granular particles occurs frequently in chemical processes. Some examples are flow through a fixed-bed catalytic reactor, flow through an adsorption or absorption column, and flow through a filter cake. An understanding of flow through packed beds is important in the study of fluidization and sedimentation. Two fluids may flow simultaneously, as in the absorption of a component in a gas by a liquid in a packed tower. In the present chapter, we treat only the flow of a single homogeneous fluid.

As for flow past tube banks, there exist many correlations for calculating the pressure drop in flow through a packed bed. This problem can be considered in the three ways mentioned in connection with flow past tube banks; we choose here a method based on the use of the hydraulic radius.

[1] D. A. Donohue, Heat Transfer and Pressure Drop in Heat Exchangers, *Ind. Eng. Chem.*, **41**:2499 (1949).

[2] J. G. Knudsen and D. L. Katz, "Fluid Dynamics and Heat Transfer," chap. 11, McGraw-Hill Book Company, Inc., New York, 1958.

This method is applicable to incompressible beds composed of nearly spherical particles; the bed porosities (fractional-void space) may range from about 0.3 to 0.6. More comprehensive discussions and reviews of the extensive literature are found in specialized treatises.[1] A successful method for the prediction of the behavior of flow through a bed from flow past a single sphere is given by Ranz.[2]

For a packed bed of N_p particles, the hydraulic radius is defined as

$$r_H = \frac{\text{void volume of bed}}{\text{surface area of packing}} \tag{15-10}$$

If the volume of a particle is v_p and the surface area of a particle is S_p, the specific surface of a particle is defined by

$$S_v = \frac{S_p}{v_p} \tag{15-11}$$

For a spherical particle

$$S_v = \frac{6}{D} \tag{15-12}$$

In considering packed beds of nonspherical particles, we shall use D as the effective particle diameter defined by the equation

$$D = \frac{6}{S_v} \tag{15-13}$$

We now substitute in Eq. (15-10) to find the hydraulic radius.

$$r_H = \frac{\epsilon v_p N_p/(1 - \epsilon)}{S_p N_p} = \frac{\epsilon}{1 - \epsilon} \frac{v_p}{S_p} \tag{15-14}$$

Here ϵ is the void fraction. This equation can be written as

$$r_H = \frac{\epsilon}{(1 - \epsilon)S_v} = \frac{1}{6} \frac{\epsilon}{1 - \epsilon} D \tag{15-15}$$

Since we know by definition that

$$\mathbf{Re} = \frac{4 r_H u_b \rho}{\mu}$$

we obtain

$$\mathbf{Re} = \frac{4\epsilon}{6(1 - \epsilon)} \frac{D u_b \rho}{\mu} \tag{15-16}$$

[1] M. Leva, M. Weintraub, M. Grummer, M. Pollchik, and H. H. Storch, Fluid Flow through Packed and Fluidized Systems, *U.S. Bur. Mines Bull.* 504, 1951; P. C. Carman, "Flow of Gases through Porous Media," Academic Press, Inc., New York, 1956; A. E. Scheidegger, "The Physics of Flow through Porous Media," The Macmillan Company, New York, 1957.

[2] W. E. Ranz, Friction and Transfer Coefficients for Single Particles and Packed Beds, *Chem. Eng. Progr.*, **48:**247 (1952).

In this equation, u_b is the average interstitial velocity at any cross section in the bed; it is more convenient to define a superficial velocity, u_{bs}, based on the cross section of the empty container,

$$u_{bs} = \epsilon u_b \tag{15-17}$$

and the Reynolds number is then

$$\mathbf{Re} = \frac{4}{6(1 - \epsilon)} \frac{D u_{bs} \rho}{\mu} \tag{15-18}$$

By a similar process, the equation for the friction factor becomes

$$f = \frac{4 g_c r_H (l w_f)}{2 L u_b{}^2} = \frac{g_c D (l w_f)}{3 L u_{bs}{}^2} \frac{\epsilon^3}{1 - \epsilon} \tag{15-19}$$

Ergun[1] has defined a Reynolds number and a friction factor similar to those given above but without the numerical constants.

$$\mathbf{Re}_p = \frac{D u_{bs} \rho}{\mu (1 - \epsilon)} \tag{15-20}$$

and

$$f_p = \frac{g_c D (l w_f) \epsilon^3}{L u_{bs}{}^2 (1 - \epsilon)} \tag{15-21}$$

For laminar flow $\mathbf{Re}_p < 1.0$; in this region, by analogy to flow in many other systems, we set f_p equal to a constant divided by $\mathbf{Re}_p$. An analysis of many experimental data indicates that the constant is 150, so for laminar flow we have

$$f_p = \frac{150}{\mathbf{Re}_p} \quad \text{or} \quad \frac{g_c D^2 \rho (l w_f) \epsilon^3}{\mu L u_{bs} (1 - \epsilon)^2} = 150 \tag{15-22}$$

This is referred to as the Kozeny-Carman equation. For a given bed and fluid, it predicts that the flow rate is proportional to the pressure drop, which is Darcy's law.

For completely turbulent flow, it is reasoned that f_p should approach a constant value and that all packed beds have the same relative roughness. The constant is found by experiment to be 1.75, so we have

$$f_p = 1.75 = \frac{g_c D (l w_f) \epsilon^3}{L u_{bs}{}^2 (1 - \epsilon)} \tag{15-23}$$

This is called the Burke-Plummer equation.

A consideration of flow at intermediate Reynolds numbers led Ergun to propose as a general equation

$$f_p = \frac{150}{\mathbf{Re}_p} + 1.75 \tag{15-24}$$

---

[1] S. Ergun, "Fluid Flow through Packed Columns," *Chem. Eng. Progr.*, **48:**89 (1952).

based on a relation suggested by Reynolds.[1]

There is no abrupt transition from laminar to turbulent flow in a packed bed. Equation (15-24) reduces to (15-23) for $\text{Re}_p > 10^4$ and to Eq. (15-22) for $\text{Re}_p < 1.0$.

If all the particles are not the same size, we define the mean specific surface as

$$S_{vm} = \Sigma \, x_i S_{vi} \tag{15-25}$$

in which x_i is the volume fraction. In terms of the mean effective diameter, we have

$$D_m = \frac{6}{S_{vm}} = \frac{6}{\Sigma \, x_i(6/D_i)} = \frac{1}{\Sigma \, (x_i/D_i)} \tag{15-26}$$

For example, the mean diameter for a mixture of 1- and 2-in. spheres containing equal volumes of each (i.e., equal masses, if all the spheres have same density) is 1.33 in., rather than 1.50 in. as given by a simple arithmetic average.

Example 15-4

Hydrocarbon vapors are cracked in a catalytic reactor which consists of a randomly packed bed of pellets shaped as cubes 0.20 in. long. The material of which the pellets are made has a density of 100 lb/cu ft, and the bulk density of the packed bed is 60 lb/cu ft. The container has a cross-sectional area of 1 sq ft, and the bed is 6 ft deep. Find the pressure drop through the bed if the superficial velocity is 3 ft/sec.

The density of the vapor is 0.040 lb/cu ft, and its viscosity is 0.015 cp.

We begin by calculating the void fraction.

$$\epsilon = \frac{\text{volume void}}{\text{volume bed}} = \frac{(\text{mass bed}/\rho_{\text{bed}}) - (\text{mass bed}/\rho_{\text{catalyst}})}{\text{mass bed}/\rho_{\text{bed}}}$$

$$= \frac{\rho_c - \rho_B}{\rho_c} = \frac{100 - 60}{100} = 0.40$$

Next we find the specific surface and thus D.

$$S_v = \frac{(6)(0.2)^2}{(0.2)^3} = \frac{6}{0.2} = 30 \text{ in.}^{-1}$$

$$D = \frac{6}{S_v} = 0.2 \text{ in.} = 0.0167 \text{ ft}$$

Now we calculate Re_p, f_p, and then $-\Delta p$.

$$\text{Re}_p = \frac{Du_{bs}\rho}{\mu(1 - \epsilon)} = \frac{(0.0167)(3)(0.040)}{(0.015)(6.72 \times 10^{-4})(0.60)} = 330$$

$$f_p = \frac{150}{\text{Re}_p} + 1.75 = 0.45 + 1.75 = 2.20$$

[1] O. Reynolds, "Papers on Mechanical and Physical Subjects," p. 83, Cambridge University Press, London, 1900.

$$-\Delta p = \frac{f_p L u_{bs}{}^2 (1 - \epsilon)\rho}{g_c D \epsilon^3} = \frac{(2.20)(6)(3)^2(0.60)(0.040)}{(32.2)(0.0167)(0.40)^3}$$

$$= 83.0 \text{ lb force/sq ft} = 0.577 \text{ psi}$$

Note on the Application of the Equations to Gases

Equation (14-42) can easily be adapted for use with the steady flow of a gas in a pipe of uniform cross section. As the pressure falls in the downstream direction, the density of the gas decreases and, according to the over-all mass balance, its velocity increases. It is therefore convenient to replace the velocity by the mass velocity, which is not affected by pressure or temperature. For a gas, we then write Eq. (14-42) for a differential length of uniform pipe as

$$-\rho \, dp = \frac{2 f G^2 \, dL}{g_c D}$$

The density is a function of the pressure and may be replaced in most circumstances by using the ideal-gas equation, so that we obtain

$$-\frac{M_m}{RT} \int_{p_1}^{p_2} p \, dp = \frac{2 f G^2}{g_c D} \int_0^L dL \tag{15-27}$$

for flow at constant temperature through a length of pipe, L.

Upon integration we obtain

$$-\frac{M_m}{2RT} (p_2{}^2 - p_1{}^2) = \frac{2 f L G^2}{g_c D} \tag{15-28}$$

and

$$-\frac{M_m}{2RT} (p_2 + p_1)(p_2 - p_1) = \frac{2 f L G^2}{g_c D}$$

and finally

$$-\Delta p = \frac{2 f L G^2}{g_c D \rho_{\mathrm{av}}} \tag{15-29}$$

where ρ_{av} is the density at the arithmetic mean pressure. If the temperature changes moderately, the arithmetic mean temperature can be used in figuring ρ_{av}.

In the above derivation, it has been assumed that the Reynolds number DG/μ does not change with pressure, and thus f remains constant. Recall that μ is not a function of pressure for an ideal gas.

It is extremely important to realize that Eq. (15-29) applies only to cases for which the relative pressure change $(-\Delta p)/p$ is small enough so that it does not cause a large change in velocity. If the downstream velocity becomes very large, the kinetic-energy term, which has been omitted in

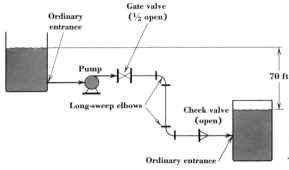

Fig. 15-8. *Sketch of piping system for Prob.* 15-1. *(Not to scale.)*

the above derivation, becomes important, and Eq. (15-29) no longer applies.   As the relative pressure drop rises above 20 or 30 per cent, so-called compressibility effects become important; for example, we shall find, in Chap. 17, that the velocity in adiabatic flow in a uniform pipe cannot exceed the velocity of sound.

In summary, it can be said that the equations in this book derived for the flow of incompressible fluids in a uniform conduit can be used for gases if $(-\Delta p)/p$ is not much more than 0.1 and if the density figured at the arithmetic average pressure is used.   It is convenient to replace u_b by G/ρ wherever possible.

PROBLEMS

15-1. A 35°API distillate is being transferred from a storage tank at 1 atm abs pressure to a pressure vessel at 50 psig by means of the piping arrangement shown in Fig. 15-8.

The liquid flows at the rate of 23,100 lb/hr through 3-in., schedule-40 steel pipe; the length of straight pipe is 450 ft.   Calculate the minimum horsepower input to a pump having an efficiency of 60 per cent.   The properties of the distillate at 80°F are viscosity, 3.4 cp; density, 52 lb/cu ft.

15-2. Water is to be withdrawn from a large main, in which the pressure is 35 psig, and carried through 175 ft of pipe to discharge to the atmosphere at a point 22 ft above the main.   What is the minimum diameter of pipe required to assure a flow of 275 gal/min?

15-3. Water is being heated from 80 to 150°F as it flows in the annulus of a horizontal-concentric-pipe heat exchanger.   The outer pipe is 2-in., schedule-40, and the inner pipe is 1-in., schedule-40, and the equivalent length of the exchanger is 200 ft.   What pressure drop is necessary to cause the water to flow at 45 gal/min?

15-4. Water is drawn from a reservoir and pumped an equivalent length of 2 miles through a horizontal, circular concrete duct of 10 in. ID ($e = 0.01$ ft).   At the end of this duct, the flow is divided into a 4- and a 3-in., schedule-40 steel pipe.

The 4-in. line has an equivalent length of 200 ft and rises to a point 50 ft above the surface of the water in the reservoir, where the flow discharges to the atmosphere. This flow must be maintained at a rate of 1000 gal/min.

The 3-in. line discharges to the atmosphere at a point 700 ft from the junction at the level of the surface of the water in the reservoir.

Calculate the horsepower input to the pump, which has an efficiency of 70 per cent.

15-5. A shell-and-tube heat exchanger is made from 70 tubes, each 14 ft long and made of 1-in., 16-gauge standard condenser tubing. These tubes are mounted inside a 16-in. (ID) shell, and fluid leaves and enters the header spaces at the ends of the exchangers by 3-in. pipes attached at the shell center line. If water flows through the tube side of the exchanger at a rate of 320 gal/min and an average temperature of 100°F, estimate the over-all pressure drop in pounds per square inch.

15-6. Air is heated from 80 to 120°F by blowing it over a bank of 40 rows of 1-in., 10-gauge condenser tubing. The tubes are 2 ft long and are placed vertically. There are 10 tubes per row set ½ in. apart; there is ½ in. between the outside tubes and the walls of the duct which contains the tube bank. The circulating fan supplies the air at a pressure of 1 in. of water. At what rate is heat being added to the air?

15-7. The tubes in the heater of Prob. 15-6 are heated by hot water which enters the tubes from the bottom. If the flow rate of the water is 475 gal/min and it enters at 200°F, estimate the pressure drop through the tubes.

15-8. Turpentine flows from a constant-head tank through 80 ft of 1½-in., schedule-40 steel pipe to a second constant-head tank, where the level is 50 ft below that in the first. There is an ordinary entrance at each tank, and there are two standard elbows and one open gate valve in the line.

(*a*) Find the flow rate in the line.

(*b*) Find the flow rate if a 0.40-in. orifice is inserted in a horizontal section of the pipe. If a mercury manometer is used with corner taps, what is the reading on this manometer?

15-9. A discussion of the economic pipe diameter is given in Perry's Handbook, pp. 384 to 385. Use the method outlined there and Eq. (13-72) for f and show the details of the derivation of a dimensionally homogeneous equation for the economic pipe diameter. Check your equation against the nomograph in Perry, p. 346.

15-10. The permeability K of a packed bed is defined for laminar flow by the equation

$$u_{bs} = K\frac{-\Delta p}{L\mu}$$

for horizontal flow. Make a suitable graph which shows the way in which the permeability varies with porosity for various particle diameters, assuming that the Kozeny-Carman equation is valid.

15-11. Calculate the pressure drop for air at 100°F and 1 atm flowing at 250 lb/hr through a bed of ½-in. spheres. The bed is 4 in. in diameter and 8 in. high and has a porosity of 0.38.

15-12. A gravity filter is made from a bed of granular particles. Fifty per cent by weight of the particles have a specific surface of 20 in.$^{-1}$, and the rest have a specific surface of 30 in.$^{-1}$ The bed porosity is 0.43. If the bed is 1 ft in diameter and 5 ft deep, at what rate (gallons per minute) will water at 75°F flow through the bed? There is a head of 10 in. of water above the bed.

FILTRATION AND FLUIDIZATION

16

In this chapter we turn to the study of two unit operations which illustrate important applications of the principles of fluid dynamics. These operations are characterized by the relative flow of a fluid and a single particle or bed of particles.

Filtration is one of a class of mechanical separations which involve the physical removal of a component as a separate phase, such as the separation of a solid from a liquid. Additional mechanical separations are centrifugation, sedimentation, screening, and flotation. The other category of separation depends on the tendency of a soluble component to concentrate in one phase or another. Examples of this class of unit operations are distillation, gas absorption, and liquid-liquid extraction.

Filtration on an industrial scale is similar to a simple laboratory filtration. A slurry is forced against a filter medium, which is a thin barrier or cloth made of natural, synthetic, or metallic fibers. The pores of the medium, or septum, are small enough to prevent the passage of some of the solid particles; others impinge on the fibers. Consequently, a cake builds up on the filter, and after the initial deposition, the cake itself serves as the barrier. The capacity of the device is governed by the rate of flow of the fluid filtrate through the ever-thickening bed formed by the solid particles.

Fluidization is another important unit operation and is used to achieve an intimate, uniform contact between a fluid and solid particles. As the velocity of a fluid passing up through a bed of particles is increased, a point is reached at which the upward force is sufficient to lift the particles and expand the bed. The individual particles are then no longer in continual contact, but are more or less free to move about through the bed. If the fluid velocity is increased further, the void fraction increases toward unity; the particles eventually are sufficiently separated so that they behave as single particles. If the upward force on a particle becomes significantly greater than its weight, it is swept completely out of the bed. Thus fluidization resembles flow through a packed bed at the minimum fluidizing velocity (a dense bed) and flow past a single particle at high velocity (an expanded bed).

Sedimentation, like filtration, is a means of separating a fluid from particles suspended in it. The suspension is placed in a tank, and the particles allowed to settle out; the fluid can then be removed from above the solid bed. It is interesting to notice that the sequence of events in a batch sedimentation is the reverse of that described above for fluidization. At first the particles in a suspension behave independently, but as they congregate in the bottom of the vessel, the effects of neighboring particles become important, as in fluidization. In sedimentation this situation is called hindered settling. The final state is that of a packed bed resembling a filter cake if the process is allowed to continue long enough.

In this chapter we shall analyze the operations of filtration and fluidization by combining the principles covered so far with some additional empirical information. Although typical equipment will be described, the reader is referred to Perry's Handbook for equipment details, as well as for discussions of the other unit operations involving mechanical separations.

FILTRATION

General Remarks

In this section we consider the filtration of a liquid containing an appreciable amount (say 1 per cent or more by volume) of suspended solid particles. This filtration is characterized by the formation of a cake of solid particles, which is removed from the apparatus intermittently or continuously. The other principal type of filtration is used to clarify or clean fluids containing relatively little solid, say up to 100 ppm by volume. In this operation, the particles are retained on or within the filter medium instead of by a cake of previously deposited solid. The filter can operate for relatively long periods before the pores become filled. Examples of this kind of filtration are air cleaners in a heating system and the filters used to remove dirt from a liquid ahead of a pump.

Three of the more important kinds of liquid-cake-filtration equipment are shown in Figs. 16-1 to 16-3. A plate-and-frame filter press is illustrated schematically in Fig. 16-1. The plates, frames, and filter cloths are pressed together as shown, and the entering slurry passes through lines leading to the frames. The cake is deposited against the filter cloths, which form the faces of the frames. The filtrate flows through the grooved channels on the faces of the plates and out through the openings at the

Fig. 16-1.   A plate-and-frame filter press. (T. Shriver and Co., Inc.)

tops of the plates.   When the frames have been filled with cake, washing can be done by introducing the washing liquid through washing plates.   It flows through the entire cake thickness.   The press is then opened, the solid removed, and another cycle of filtration started.   Pressure up to about 150 psi can be used with this type of filter.

A leaf-type filter is shown in Fig. 16-2.   The slurry, under pressure which can be considerably higher than 150 psi, is forced into the shell surrounding the filter leaves.   The filtrate is removed as shown from inside the leaves, and the cake forms on the outside.   In some models the leaves are rotated to agitate the slurry and to improve the uniformity of the cake. The wash liquid follows the same path as the filtrate.   When sufficient cake has been deposited, the shell is opened and the cake removed; sometimes air is blown into the leaves to aid in dislodging the cake.

The two filters already shown suffer from the disadvantages common to batch operations.   The advantages of continuous operation are achieved by the use of a rotary vacuum filter of the type shown in Fig. 16-3.   A vacuum is maintained on the interior of the rotating drum, which is covered on its curved surface by the filter medium.   The drum dips into a tank of slurry, and the filtrate passes through the medium and is removed through the axle of the filter.   The cake is continuously washed and removed as shown.   Offsetting the advantage of continuous operation is the fact that the filter illustrated has a maximum pressure differential of only 1 atm. It is not suitable for highly viscous filtrates or for liquids which cannot be

Fig. 16-2. *A leaf filter. (From W. L. Badger and J. T. Banchero, "Introduction to Chemical Engineering," p. 565, McGraw-Hill Book Company, Inc., New York, 1955.)*

exposed to the atmosphere. These disadvantages can be overcome by enclosing the filter in a shell which is maintained above atmospheric pressure.

Basic Equations

Figure 16-4 is a sketch of a section through a filter cake. In order to simplify the notation, the pressure on the downstream side of the medium is taken as zero; p_i is the pressure at the interface between the medium and the cake, and P is the upstream pressure.

We shall begin our analysis by considering a differential element of cake containing a mass of solid dM_c. This mass of solid is the solid carried by a volume of filtrate dV which has passed through the element of cake, plus the mass of solid carried by the liquid which adheres to the cake and remains in the element. This equality is written as

$$dM_c = \frac{\rho s}{1 - s} \, dV + \frac{(m - 1)s}{1 - s} \, dM_c \tag{16-1}$$

where ρ = density of filtrate

     s = mass fraction of solid in slurry

     m = mass ratio of cake when wet to cake when dry

Equation (16-1) can be rearranged to

$$dM_c = \frac{s\rho}{1 - ms} \, dV \tag{16-2}$$

We shall find it useful to express the mass of cake in terms of distance through the cake, x, by using the void fraction ϵ to obtain

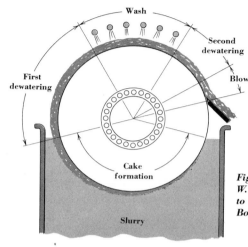

Fig. 16-3.   A continuous rotary filter. (From W. L. Badger and J. T. Banchero, "Introduction to Chemical Engineering," p. 569, McGraw-Hill Book Company, Inc., New York, 1955.)

$$dM_c = (1 - \epsilon)\rho_s A \ dx \qquad (16\text{-}3)$$

where ρ_s = density of dry solid
A = total area normal to flow

Since the particles making up a filter cake are relatively small, the flow is usually laminar and follows the Kozeny-Carman equation, written for a differential thickness as

$$\frac{d(lw_f)}{dx} = \frac{150\mu u_{bs}(1 - \epsilon)^2}{g_c D^2 \rho \epsilon^3} \qquad (15\text{-}22)$$

Using the mechanical energy balance for the usual case in which only pressure head is important and substituting $6/S_v$ for D, we get the following equation for the pressure drop over the cake:

$$-\frac{dp}{dx} = \frac{4.17 S_v{}^2 \mu u_{bs}(1 - \epsilon)^2}{g_c \epsilon^3} \qquad (16\text{-}4)$$

in which S_v is the specific surface defined in Chap. 15.

For many cakes the porosity and specific surface vary with position inside the cake. This effect is caused by the compressive pressure on the solid particles, which varies with position. This pressure, written as p_s, is the mechanical stress tending to compress the cake in the x direction, and it is defined by

$$p_s = P - p \qquad (16\text{-}5)$$

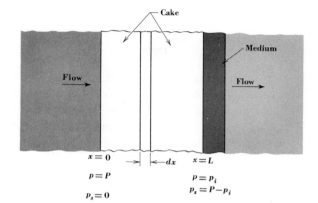

Fig. 16-4. Section through a filter cake.

$x = 0$ $\quad$ $\leftarrow dx$ $\quad$ $x = L$

$p = P$ $\qquad\qquad$ $p = p_i$

$p_s = 0$ $\qquad\qquad$ $p_s = P - p_i$

in which the upstream pressure P is constant. The "solid pressure" p_s increases from zero at $x = 0$ to a maximum value of $P - p_i$ at the medium. We write Eq. (16-4) in terms of p_s:

$$\frac{dp_s}{dx} = \frac{kS_v^2 \mu u_{bs}(1 - \epsilon)^2}{g_c \epsilon^3} \qquad (16\text{-}6)$$

in which the constant 4.17 has been replaced by k. In most discussions of filtration, k is given a value of 5.0, but this point has little importance, for studies have shown that k is by no means constant for all materials.[1]

It is conventional to characterize filter cakes by a term α, known as the specific cake resistance. To show the basis for the definition of this quantity, we express the distance x in Eq. (16-6) in terms of the mass of dry cake M_c, which is contained between $x = 0$ and $x = x$. Equation (16-3) is combined with Eq. (16-6) to obtain

$$\frac{dp_s}{dM_c} = \frac{kS_v^2 \mu u_{bs}(1 - \epsilon)}{g_c A \rho_s \epsilon^3} \qquad (16\text{-}7)$$

The specific cake resistance, which has units of feet per pound, is defined by

$$\alpha = \frac{kS_v^2(1 - \epsilon)}{\rho_s \epsilon^3} \qquad (16\text{-}8)$$

Equation (16-7) can then be written as

$$\frac{dp_s}{dM_c} = \frac{\alpha \mu u_{bs}}{g_c A} \qquad (16\text{-}9)$$

and α is seen to include all properties dependent on the cake. It is also a function of p_s for certain substances.

[1] H. P. Grace, *Chem. Eng. Progr.*, **49**:303 (1953).

Filter performance is usually specified in terms of filtrate volume, which is related to the mass of the cake by Eq. (16-2); Eq. (16-9) becomes

$$\frac{dp_s}{dV} = \frac{\alpha\mu qs\rho}{g_c A^2(1 - ms)} \tag{16-10}$$

in which u_{bs} has been replaced by q/A, q being the volumetric rate of flow. To apply this equation to a cake of finite thickness we integrate Eq. (16-10) between 0 and V, where V is the volume of filtrate equivalent to a cake of thickness L. It should be emphasized that this integration is performed across the cake at any instant for which P and q are given. We obtain from Eq. (16-10)

$$\int_0^{P-p_i} \frac{dp_s}{\alpha} = \frac{\mu qs\rho}{A^2 g_c(1 - ms)} \int_0^V dV \tag{16-11}$$

Thus we have

$$P - p_i = \frac{\alpha_{av}\mu qs\rho V}{A^2 g_c(1 - ms)} \tag{16-12}$$

where

$$\alpha_{av} = \frac{P - p_i}{\int_0^{P-p_i} (dp_s/\alpha)} \tag{16-13}$$

The quantity p_i is related to the pressure drop over the filter medium. For a given value of q, it is the upstream pressure at the start of filtration. However, since q may vary during the course of a filtration, p_i may not be a constant; it is desirable to relate this quantity to q and to the properties of the medium. It is customary to write the following equation, for which the fluid pressure on the downstream side of the medium is zero as usual:

$$p_i = \frac{\mu R_m q}{g_c A} \tag{16-14}$$

The quantity R_m defined by this equation is called the resistance of the medium and is a constant for a given medium and slurry. A comparison between Eqs. (16-14) and (16-12) shows that the resistance of the medium is

$$R_m = \frac{\alpha_{av}s\rho V_m}{(1 - ms)A} \tag{16-15}$$

This equation shows that the resistance of the medium may be expressed in terms of the resistance of a hypothetical layer of cake, which corresponds to the collection of a hypothetical volume of filtrate V_m. The resistance of a typical filter medium is equivalent to a few tenths of an inch of cake.

We use the definition of R_m to replace p_i in Eq. (16-12) and obtain

$$P = \left[\frac{s\rho V\alpha_{av}}{(1 - ms)A} + R_m\right]\frac{\mu q}{g_c A} \tag{16-16}$$

If α is constant throughout the cake (in other words, α is independent of the mechanical compressive stress p_s) and equal to α_{av}, the cake is said to be *incompressible*. Such cakes are formed from slurries of regularly shaped, crystalline particles. Unfortunately, most slurries form *compressible* filter cakes, for which α is a function of p_s, and α_{av} must be evaluated for the conditions of interest by the use of Eq. (16-13). This procedure requires a knowledge of α as a function of p_s and will be discussed later in this chapter.

In interpreting the results of filtration experiments on an incompressible slurry with a given filtering apparatus, it is simpler to write Eq. (16-16) as

$$P = (K_1 V + K_2)q \tag{16-17}$$

where

$$K_1 = \frac{s\rho\mu\alpha_{av}}{(1 - ms)A^2 g_c} \tag{16-18}$$

and

$$K_2 = \frac{R_m \mu}{A g_c} \tag{16-19}$$

For a given incompressible slurry K_1 and K_2 are constant. Computations using Eq. (16-17) can be relatively simple, for K_1 and K_2 can be expressed using arbitrary units such as pounds per square inch and gallons. However, if it is desired to use Eqs. (16-18) and (16-19) to calculate, for example, α_{av} and R_m from experimental values of K_1 and K_2, consistent units must be used. These equations show the effect of the several variables on K_1 and K_2; for instance, if the temperature is changed so that the viscosity doubles, K_1 and K_2 will double.

The result of the analysis thus far is an expression [Eq. (16-16) or (16-17)] giving the instantaneous pressure drop P across the filter as a function of the rate of flow q and the cake thickness corresponding to the filtrate volume V. During an actual filtration cycle the cake thickness increases from 0 to L_f, corresponding to an increase in filtrate collected from 0 to V_f. The pressure and flow rate may change during the deposition of the cake. The time θ_f required for the deposition of the cake and the collection of a volume V_f is obtained by writing the rate as

$$q = \frac{dV}{d\theta} \tag{16-20}$$

and integrating this equation to give

$$\int_0^{\theta_f} d\theta = \int_0^{V_f} \frac{dV}{q} \tag{16-21}$$

The flow rate q may be replaced using Eq. (16-17).

$$\theta_f = \int_0^{V_f} \frac{(K_1 V + K_2)\, dV}{P} \tag{16-22}$$

We now have the general equations needed to analyze most filtration problems. We consider next their application to the various types of filter operation.

Incompressible Filter Cakes

Constant-pressure Operation. If slurry is fed to a filter from a constant-head tank, the pressure at the upstream face of the cake is constant. Since the pressure at the downstream face of the medium is usually 1 atm, the quantity P in the equations given in the preceding section is known and constant. The effect of the pressure drops in the channels leading to and from the filter cake should also be considered, but it is usually sufficiently accurate to include these effects in R_m (or K_2).

In most industrial filtrations the pressure is furnished by a centrifugal pump rather than a constant-head tank. However, constant-pressure filtration is used in much laboratory and research work and, of necessity, with continuous rotary filters.

For an incompressible cake Eq. (16-22) can be integrated analytically, since P, K_1, and K_2 are constant. The result is

$$\theta_f = \frac{K_1}{2P} V_f{}^2 + \frac{K_2}{P} V_f \tag{16-23}$$

The values of K_1 and K_2 for a given slurry can be found from data on V_f versus θ_f collected from experiments at constant pressure with a laboratory filtration apparatus. To calculate K_1 and K_2, Eq. (16-23) is written as

$$\frac{\theta_f}{V_f} = \frac{K_1}{2P} V_f + \frac{K_2}{P} \tag{16-24}$$

and the experimental data are used to make a graph of θ_f/V_f versus V_f. The slope and intercept of the best straight line through the points can be used to calculate K_1 and K_2.

The values of K_1 and K_2 obtained apply only to the slurry and filter used. If only the size of the filter, that is, A, is changed, it is simple to calculate new values of K_1 and K_2 based on Eqs. (16-18) and (16-19). For instance, if the filter area is increased by a factor of 10, K_1 is reduced by a factor of 100 and K_2 by a factor of 10. Changes in μ, s, and m can be similarly accounted for. For an incompressible cake α_{av} is a constant for a given suspended solid, and R_m is constant for a given medium. If a reliable value of α_{av} is known from other experiments, it can be used in Eq. (16-18) to calculate K_1 directly.

Fig. 16-5. *Performance curve for a centrifu-gal pump.*

    a. **Filtration pressure.**
    b. **Pressure at medium.**

Constant-rate Operation. If slurry is fed to a filter by means of a positive displacement pump, the rate, which we shall call q_o, is approximately constant. The integration of Eq. (16-21) for this type of operation gives

$$V_f = q_o \theta_f \tag{16-25}$$

or at any moment during the filtration,

$$V = q_o \theta \tag{16-26}$$

Equation (16-17) shows that the filtration pressure P increases from p_i linearly with volume of filtrate collected at a constant rate, $q = q_o$. The pressure may be related to time by combining Eqs. (16-26) and (16-17) to give

$$P = K_1 q_o^2 \theta + K_2 q_o \tag{16-27}$$

A plot of P versus θ for a known q_o obtained from data on a constant-rate filtration permits the calculation of K_1 and K_2. These constants can also be calculated from values of α_{av} and R_m, if they are available. Note that p_i is constant and equal to $K_2 q_o$; it does not decrease with time as in constant-pressure filtration.

Variable-rate–Variable-pressure Operation. If slurry is fed by a centrifugal pump, the pressure and rate are related by a curve such as that shown in Fig. 16-5.

Values of K_1 and K_2 can be found from a filtration experiment measuring P at various values of V. The curve of P as a function of q is determined by the characteristics of the pump used. Equation (16-17) shows that values of P/q can be plotted against V, permitting the computation of K_1 and K_2 from the slope and intercept of the best straight line through the points.

The time θ_f required to collect a volume of filtrate V_f is given by the graphical or numerical integration of Eq. (16-21). The variation of q with V is given by the simultaneous solution of Eq. (16-17) and the relation given by the line representing filtration pressure as a function of flow rate in Fig. 16-5.

The Filtration Cycle. After the desired quantity of cake has been collected, the mother liquor is usually removed by washing with a suitable solvent. Washing occurs at constant rate and pressure, and Eq. (16-17) is easily adapted to give the relation between the wash rate q_w and the pressure P_w:

$$P_w = (K_1 V_f + K_2) q_w \qquad (16\text{-}28)$$

Recall that V_f is a constant, representing the total filtrate collected during the deposition of the cake. The time of washing is given by

$$\theta_w = \frac{V_w}{q_w} \qquad (16\text{-}29)$$

After washing has been completed, additional time is needed for draining and dumping the cake and cleaning and refilling the filter. If the sum of these times is θ_d, the total cycle time θ_c is given by

$$\theta_c = \theta_f + \theta_w + \theta_d \qquad (16\text{-}30)$$

The capacity C of the filter is defined in terms of filtrate volume as

$$C = \frac{V_f}{\theta_c} \qquad (16\text{-}31)$$

We shall consider in Example 16-3 the problem of finding the value of V_f which gives the maximum capacity C.

The same parts of the filtration cycle also occur with a continuous rotary filter. In this apparatus the times θ_f, θ_w, and θ_d are determined by the arrangement of the various compartments in the rotating drum, by the radius of the drum, and by its speed of rotation.

Example 16-1

A small leaf filter is used to find the filtering characteristics of a slurry which forms an incompressible cake. A test made on a suspension was run at a constant rate of 0.3 gal of filtrate per minute and gave the following results:

Time, min......................	1	2	3	5	10	20
Pressure drop across filter, psi...............	7.0	11.1	15.0	23.2	43.0	81.7

Using the same suspension and filter, the filtration cycle will be run in the following way. The filtrate is forced through at a constant rate of 0.5 gal/min until the pressure differential reaches 50 psi. The filtration is then continued at constant pressure (50 psi) until the total filtrate collected is 15 gal. The cake is then washed with 3.0 gal of water; 10 min is needed to dump and clean the filter. Find the capacity of this filtration cycle in gallons per hour.

Since the cake is incompressible, K_1 and K_2 in Eq. (16-27) are constant, and a graph of the test data given yields a straight line when P is plotted versus θ. The intercept is at $P = 2.92$ psi, so that we have

$$K_2 q_o = 2.92$$
$$K_2 = 2.92/0.3 = 9.73$$

The slope is 4.01, giving

$$K_1 q_o{}^2 = 4.01$$
$$K_1 = 4.01/0.09 = 44.6$$

For the constant-rate portion of the proposed filtration cycle, with $q_o = 0.5$ gal/min, Eq. (16-27) becomes

$$P = (44.6)(0.5)^2 \theta + 9.73(0.5)$$
$$= 11.15\theta + 4.86$$

For $P = 50$ psi, this equation gives $\theta = 4.04$ min, and so $V_{f_1} = 2.02$ gal. We next consider the constant-pressure part of the filtration. Since Eq. (16-23) is based on constant-pressure filtration right from the start, it does not apply; we must use Eq. (16-22), written as

$$\theta_f - \theta_{f_1} = \int_{V_{f_1}}^{V_f} \frac{(K_1 V + K_2)\, dV}{P}$$

In θ_{f_1} min (4.04) we have collected V_{f_1} gal (2.02) of filtrate. The above equation permits us to find the total time of filtration θ_f needed to obtain V_f gal (15.0) of filtrate.

$$\theta_f = \frac{K_1}{2P}(V_f{}^2 - V_{f_1}{}^2) + \frac{K_2}{P}(V_f - V_{f_1}) + \theta_{f_1}$$

$$= \frac{(44.6)}{2(50)}(225 - 4.07) + \frac{9.73}{50}(15 - 2.02) + 4.04$$

$$= 98.7 + 2.53 + 4.04 = 105.3 \text{ min}$$

The reader should be sure he understands why it would have been wrong to use Eq. (16-23) with $V_f = 12.98$ gal.

The time θ_f in Eq. (16-30) has been calculated; since θ_d is given as 10 min, it remains to calculate θ_w. Equations (16-28) and (16-29) are combined to give

$$\theta_w = \frac{V_w(K_1 V_f + K_2)}{P}$$

and so we have

$$\theta_w = \frac{(3.0)[(44.6)(15) + 9.73]}{50}$$

$$= 40.7 \text{ min}$$

The total cycle time is

$$\theta_c = 105.3 + 40.7 + 10$$
$$= 156.0 \text{ min}$$

and the capacity is

$$C = 15/156 = 0.0962 \text{ gal/min, or } 5.77 \text{ gal/hr}$$

Example 16-2

A suspension containing 225 g of carbonyl iron powder, Grade E, per liter of a solution of 0.01 N NaOH is to be filtered, using a leaf filter. Estimate the size (area) of the filter needed to obtain 100 lb of dry cake in 1 hr of filtration at a constant pressure drop of 20 psi.

Grace[1] has obtained experimental data for this slurry and found that the cake is incompressible, that α_{av} is 10^{11} ft/lb, and that the void fraction ϵ is 0.40. The resistance of the medium is taken as that offered by 0.10 in. of cake.

Since the cake is incompressible, Eq. (16-23) will apply, and Eqs. (16-18) and (16-19) can be used to find K_1 and K_2. We first calculate K_1 by

$$K_1 = \frac{s\rho\mu\alpha_{av}}{(1 - ms)A^2 g_c}$$

Assuming the filtrate to have the properties of pure water, we find

$\rho = 62.4$ lb/cu ft
$\mu = (1)(2.42) = 2.42$ lb/(ft)(hr)
$s = 225/1225 = 0.184$

The following formula for m is easily worked out:

$$m = \frac{(1 - \epsilon)\rho_s + \epsilon\rho}{(1 - \epsilon)\rho_s} = \frac{(0.6)(7) + (0.4)(1)}{(0.6)(7)}$$

$$= 1.093$$

(The specific gravity of the powder has been taken as 7.)

$$g_c = 4.16 \times 10^8 \text{ (lb)(ft)/(lb force)(hr}^2)$$

The value for K_1 is then

$$K_1 = \frac{(62.4)(0.184)(2.42)(10^{11})}{[1 - (1.093)(0.184)](4.16)(10^8)A^2}$$

$$= \frac{8460}{A^2}$$

The value of K_2 is found from

$$K_2 = \frac{R_m\mu}{A g_c}$$

and

$$R_m = \frac{\alpha_{av}s\rho V_m}{(1 - ms)A}$$

In the latter equation, we must find V_m. A material balance gives, as in Eqs. (16-2) and (16-3),

$$\frac{V_m}{A} = \frac{(1 - \epsilon)\rho_s L_m(1 - ms)}{s\rho}$$

$$= \frac{(0.60)(7)(0.1/12)(0.789)}{(1)(0.184)} = 0.1503$$

Thus

[1] *Ibid.*

$$R_m = \frac{(10^{11})(62.4)(0.184)(0.1503)}{(0.789)} = 2.18 \times 10^{11}$$

We get, finally,

$$K_2 = \frac{(2.18 \times 10^{11})(2.42)}{4.16 \times 10^8 A} = \frac{1270}{A}$$

In order to use Eq. (16-23),

$$\theta_f = \frac{K_1}{2P} V_f{}^2 + \frac{K_2}{P} V_f$$

we must calculate the value of V_f corresponding to $M_{cf} = 100$ lb.

$$V_f = \frac{1 - ms}{s\rho} M_{cf}$$

$$= \frac{(0.789)}{(62.4)(0.184)} (100) = 6.86 \text{ cu ft}$$

Equation (16-23) can finally be used:

$$1 = \frac{8460}{A^2(2)(2880)} (6.86)^2 + \frac{1270}{A(2880)} (6.86)$$

and this becomes

$$A^2 - 3.03A - 69.0 = 0$$
$$A = 9.96 \text{ sq ft}$$

A leaf filter having about this surface might consist of 10 leaves, each roughly 10 in. in diameter.

Example 16-3

The filter described in the preceding example is to be operated at maximum capacity. Fifteen minutes is needed for dumping and cleaning, and the volume of wash water used in any one cycle is one-tenth the volume of filtrate collected. All other conditions are as given in Example 16-2. From the value of the area $A = 9.96$ sq ft, we find

$$K_1 = 8460/99.2 = 85.4$$
$$K_2 = 1270/9.96 = 127.3$$

Equation (16-23), with $P = 2880$, gives

$$\theta_f = 0.01482 V_f{}^2 + 0.0442 V_f$$

From Eqs. (16-28) and (16-29) we obtain

$$\theta_w = \frac{0.1 V_f(K_1 V_f + K_2)}{P} = 0.00297 V_f{}^2 + 0.00442 V_f$$

Using $\theta_d = 0.25$, the time for a cycle is

$$\theta_c = 0.01779 V_f{}^2 + 0.0486 V_f + 0.25$$

and the capacity is

$$C = \frac{V_f}{\theta_c} = \frac{V_f}{0.01779 V_f{}^2 + 0.0486 V_f + 0.25}$$

Liquid entrance

Movable piston

Stainless steel porous plates

Cake of test material

Fig. 16-6.   Compression-permeability apparatus.

This equation shows that the capacity is zero for $V_f = 0$, rises to a maximum value, and approaches zero as V_f becomes very large.   For small values of V_f, an excessive portion of the time is spent in cleaning and dumping, and for large values of V_f, the cake is thick and q becomes very small.   The maximum capacity is found by the condition $dC/dV_f = 0$; the differentiation of the equation for C and the substitution of $dC/dV_f = 0$ gives $V_f = 3.76$ cu ft, corresponding to 0.251 in. of cake.   The maximum capacity is 5.52 cu ft/hr; each cycle lasts 0.682 hr.

Compressible Filter Cakes

If α is not constant but is a function of p_s, the filter cake is said to be compressible.   With incompressible cake it is possible to perform small-scale filtration experiments to find values of K_1 and K_2, and then use these values in the design of another filter operating with a changed A, P, or q. With a compressible cake the results of such an experiment can be extrapolated only to a different value of A (i.e., filter size).   The relation between P and q must be the same in the two filters.   This is so because α_{av}, and thus K_1 and K_2, are functions of both P and q.   In order to define the behavior of a filter for a given compressible substance, many filtration experiments must be made.   Therefore it is better to use the more basic equations (16-13) and (16-16) and find the relation between α and p_s by means of the experimental procedure discussed below.

The relation between α and p_s can be found using the apparatus sketched in Fig. 16-6; this procedure is called the compression-permeability technique and was applied to the study of filter cakes by Ruth.[1]   A cake of the material to be studied is contained in a cylinder and held between a fixed porous stainless-steel plate and a movable one.   The latter is attached to

[1] B. F. Ruth, *Ind. Eng. Chem.*, **38**:564 (1946).

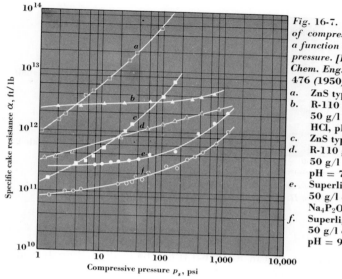

Fig. 16-7.   *Specific resistance of compressible filter cakes as a function of solid compressive pressure.* [*From H. P. Grace, Chem. Eng. Progr.,* 46:467–476 (1950).]

a.   ZnS type B, pH = 9.07.
b.   R-110 grade TiO_2, 50 g/l of 0.01 N HCl, pH $\doteq$ 3.45.
c.   ZnS type A, pH = 9.10.
d.   R-110 grade TiO_2 (flocculated), 50 g/l of distilled water, pH = 7.8.
e.   Superlight $CaCO_3$, 50 g/l of 0.01 M $Na_4P_2O_7$, pH = 10.3.
f.   Superlight $CaCO_3$ (flocculated), 50 g/l of distilled water, pH = 9.8.

a piston, and the solid pressure p_s can be varied by applying a known force to the piston by means of a hydraulic press. For a given value of p_s the specific cake resistance is determined by measuring the pressure drop experienced by a liquid flowing across the cake at a known rate. The cake porosity ϵ is also measured. The pressure drop across the cake is kept low compared with p_s by using a thin cake and a low rate of flow.

Compression-permeability measurements have been made by Grace[1] for a number of substances. Figures 16-7 and 16-8 show some of his results.

Let us now consider how the data of these figures can be used to calculate the time θ_f required to obtain a quantity of filtrate V_f. The method of feeding to the proposed filter will determine the relation between P and q. Some experiments must be run with the filter medium to find the value of R_m; the pressure p_i can then be calculated from Eq. (16-14) for a given q. With the relations between p_i and q, and α and p_s, known, Eq. (16-13) is next used to calculate α_{av} for the series of P's and q's which are to be used during the cycle. Equation (16-16) is then used to find the V's which correspond to the various values of q. Finally, the filtration time θ_f is found from Eq. (16-21) and the relation between q and V. This procedure is illustrated in Example 16-4. If the curve for α versus p_s happens to be a straight line

[1] *Loc. cit.*

a. ZnS type B, pH = 9.07.
b. R-110 grade TiO₂,
    50 g/l of 0.01 N
    HCl, pH = 3.45.
c. ZnS type A, pH = 9.10.
d. R-110 grade TiO₂ (flocculated),
    50 g/l of distilled water,
    pH = 7.8.
e. Superlight CaCO₃,
    50 g/l of 0.01 M
    Na₄P₂O₇, pH = 10.3.
f. Superlight CaCO₃ (flocculated),
    50 g/l of distilled water,
    pH = 9.8.

Fig. 16-8. *Void fraction of compressible filter cakes as a function of solid compressive pressure. [From H. P. Grace, Chem. Eng. Progr., 49:303 (1953).]*

on a log-log plot, the integral in Eq. (16-13) can be evaluated analytically by substituting for α an expression of the form

$$\alpha = \beta p_s{}^{\gamma} \tag{16-32}$$

in which β and γ are empirical constants obtained from the best-fitting straight line.

The data obtained from filtration experiments do not have a high degree of reproducibility. For instance, the state of agglomeration of the particles in the suspension is difficult to control, and it apparently has an important effect on the porosity and specific resistance of the cake formed. It is therefore advisable to use a liberal safety factor in the design of filtration equipment.

A more complete exposition of recent developments in filtration is given in a series of articles by Tiller.[1]

Example 16-4

A battery of leaf filters having a total area of 2500 sq ft is to be used to filter a suspension of 50 g of R-110 grade TiO₂ (flocculated) per liter of water. The properties of this suspension are given in Figs. 16-7 and 16-8. The filter will be fed by a pump having the characteristic curve shown in Fig. 16-5. Find the time required to obtain 20,000 lb of dry cake. For R_m a value of 2×10^{11} ft⁻¹ may be used; m is 1.64.

During the course of the filtration the pressure and rate will follow the curve given in Fig. 16-5. Values of α_{av} as a function of P must be calculated from Eq. (16-13),

[1] F. M. Tiller, *Chem. Eng. Progr.*, **49**:467 (1953), and **51**:282 (1955); *AIChE J.*, **2**:170 (1958).

and so p_i must be known for every P and its corresponding q. Equation (16-14) is used to calculate p_i.

$$p_i = \frac{\mu R_m q}{g_c A}$$

$$= \frac{(1)(2.42)(2 \times 10^{11})q}{(4.16 \times 10^8)(2500)} = 0.466q$$

It will be convenient to use in the calculations the pressure in pounds per square inch and the rate in gallons per minute, defined as p_i' and q' (the primes on any pressure symbol will indicate pounds per square inch).

$$p_i' = \frac{(0.466)(60)q'}{(144)(7.48)} = 0.0260q'$$

This equation is plotted as a straight line in Fig. 16-5, and it is thus possible to obtain $P' - p_i'$ as a function of q'. Filtrate (water) will flow through the empty filter at 400 gal/min with a pressure drop of 10.4 psi.

Since the curve of α versus p_s in Fig. 16-7 is a straight line, Eq. (16-32) can be used to represent the variation of α, giving

$$\alpha = 3.52 \times 10^{11}(p_s')^{0.266}$$

The substitution of this expression into Eq. (16-13) gives

$$\alpha_{av} = \frac{3.52 \times 10^{11}(P' - p_i')}{\int_0^{P'-p_i'} \frac{dp_s'}{(p_s')^{0.266}}}$$

The value of α_{av} is not affected by the units used for the pressures. Integration gives

$$\alpha_{av} = 2.58 \times 10^{11}(P' - p_i')^{0.266}$$

and the following table can be constructed:

q'	P'	$P' - p_i'$	$\alpha_{av} \times 10^{-11}$
400	10.4	0	
300	20.0	12.4	5.04
200	27.6	22.6	5.92
100	33.0	30.5	6.40
50	34.5	33.0	6.54

It is now possible to relate the filtrate volume collected to the rate of flow by Eq. (16-16).

$$P = \left[\frac{s\rho V \alpha_{av}}{(1 - ms)A} + R_m \right] \frac{\mu q}{g_c A}$$

For this problem, $s = 0.0476$ and $1 - ms = 0.922$. Substituting the appropriate values and rearranging, we obtain

$$V = \frac{0.598 \times 10^{16}}{\alpha_{av}} \left(\frac{P'}{q'} - 0.0260 \right)$$

Fig. 16-9.   *Graphical integration for Example* 16-4.

We now have sufficient information to find V as a function of q'.

q'	V
400	0
300	482
200	1132
100	2850
50	6070

The time required is found from

$$\theta_f = \frac{7.48}{60} \int_0^{V_f} \frac{dV}{q'}$$

by a graphical integration.   The volume of filtrate is given by

$$V_f = \frac{(1 - ms)M_{cf}}{s\rho}$$

$$= \frac{(0.922)(20,000)}{(62.4)(0.0476)} = 6220 \text{ cu ft}$$

The integration, which is illustrated by Fig. 16-9, yields $\theta_f = 8.53$ hr.   This corresponds to about $1\frac{1}{2}$ in. of cake.   A cycle for maximum capacity would require a much shorter filtration time.

FLUIDIZATION

Minimum Fluidization Velocity

As the flow rate upward through a packed bed is increased, a point is reached at which the frictional drag is enough to overcome the net down-

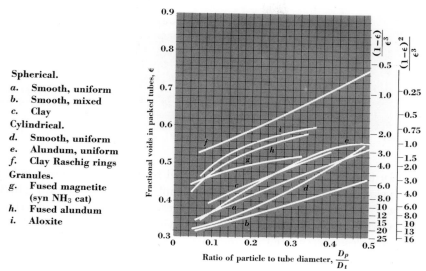

Fig. 16-10. *Void fraction of beds of typical solid particles. (From Max Leva,* "*Fluidization," fig. 3-7, p. 54, McGraw-Hill Book Company, Inc., New York, 1959.)*

ward force exerted on the bed by gravity. The bed is supported at the bottom by a screen, but is free to expand upward, as it will if the velocity is increased above the minimum fluidization velocity. In order to find this velocity, we write the net downward force as

$$F_g = (\rho_s - \rho)AL(1 - \epsilon)\frac{g}{g_c} \tag{16-33}$$

The upward force on the bed F_d is obtained starting from Eq. (15-21) for flow through a packed bed. The following equation defines the friction factor f_p:

$$f_p = \frac{g_c D(lw_f)\epsilon^3}{Lu_{bs}^2(1 - \epsilon)} \tag{15-21}$$

and f_p is evaluated by

$$f_p = \frac{150}{\mathbf{Re}_p} + 1.75 \tag{15-24}$$

Since the upward drag force is the same as $A\,\Delta p$, or $lw_f\rho A$, we obtain

$$F_d = \frac{(150/\mathbf{Re}_p + 1.75)\rho Lu_{bs}^2(1 - \epsilon)A}{Dg_c\epsilon^3} \tag{16-34}$$

At incipient fluidization, $F_d = F_g$. Equating (16-34) and (16-33) and replacing $\mathbf{Re}_p$ by $Du_{bs}\rho/\mu(1 - \epsilon)$, there results

$$(\rho_s - \rho)g = \frac{150(1 - \epsilon)\mu u_{mf}}{D^2\epsilon^3} + \frac{1.75\rho u_{mf}^2}{D\epsilon^3} \tag{16-35}$$

Fig. 16-11.   Void fraction in expanded fluidized beds.

In this equation, u_{bs} has been replaced by u_{mf}, the minimum fluidization velocity.   Once ϵ is known, it is a simple matter to solve Eq. (16-35) for u_{mf} using the quadratic formula.   Although it is best to determine the void fraction experimentally for a given particle and vessel, Fig. 16-10 provides an estimate for a few common materials.[1]

Terminal Velocity

At the onset of fluidization, the void fraction in the bed is near its minimum, which is about 0.35 to 0.50 for spherical particles.   Let us now consider the other extreme, for which only one particle is suspended in the "bed" and the void fraction is approximately 1.0.   The velocity past the particle is the same as the maximum velocity at which the object would fall through a large body of the still fluid.   At this terminal velocity the upward drag force is given by Eq. (8-13), written as

$$F_d = \frac{C_D \pi \rho u_o^2 D^2}{8 g_c} \tag{16-36}$$

for a sphere.   The value of C_D is found from the Reynolds number and Fig. 15-6.   The downward force is

$$F_g = (\rho_s - \rho)\frac{\pi D^3}{6}\frac{g}{g_c} \tag{16-37}$$

Equations (16-36) and (16-37) combine to give

$$\rho_s - \rho = \frac{3 C_D \rho u_t^2}{4 D g} \tag{16-38}$$

in which the terminal velocity u_t has replaced u_o.

There is no convenient analytical expression for C_D which holds for all Reynolds numbers.   For **Re** < 1.0, Stokes' law, Eq. (12-36), holds, and so the terminal velocity is

$$u_t = \frac{(\rho_s - \rho)g D^2}{18 \mu} \qquad \textbf{Re} < 1.0 \tag{16-39}$$

[1] M. Leva, M. Weintraub, M. Grummer, M. Pollchik, and H. H. Storch, Fluid Flow through Packed and Fluidized Systems, *U.S. Bur. Mines Bull.* 504, 1951.

*Fig. 16-12.   Pressure drop in
fixed and fluidized beds.*

For **Re** between about 500 and 200,000, C_D is almost constant at 0.44.
This substitution gives an equation often referred to as Newton's law:

$$u_t = \left[\frac{3D(\rho_s - \rho)g}{\rho} \right]^{\frac{1}{2}} \qquad 500 < \textbf{Re} < 200{,}000 \qquad (16\text{-}40)$$

If the Reynolds number does not fall within these two ranges, a trial-and-
error solution can be reached using Fig. 15-6.

The Expanded Bed

At velocities intermediate between the minimum fluidizing velocity and
the terminal velocity, the bed is expanded above the volume it would
occupy at u_{mf}.   A satisfactory empirical procedure for estimating the void
fraction, i.e., the bed expansion, as a function of u_{bs} is to plot a straight
line on a graph of log ϵ versus log u_{bs} (or log G) as shown in Fig. 16-11.
Once u_{mf} and u_t are known, such a graph shows how the bed behaves at
intermediate velocities.

The pressure drop varies as a function of velocity, as shown in Fig. 16-12.
Above the minimum fluidizing velocity the pressure drop stays almost
constant.   The void fraction can be calculated from Eq. (16-35) by replac-
ing u_{mf} by the actual u_{bs}, but only to about $\epsilon = 0.80$.   Below u_{mf}, Δp is
calculated with the aid of Eq. (15-21).

The type of fluidization which has been discussed so far is known as
batch, or dense-phase, fluidization ($u_{mf} < u_{bs} < u_t$).   If the velocity exceeds u_t, the particles are carried along with the fluid out of the limited
space so far considered.   This condition is called continuous, or dilute-
phase, fluidization.   If air is the fluid, it is identical with the process of
pneumatic transport.

If the motion of the particles in a dense-phase fluidized bed is quite
random, so that every particle seems to travel independently of the others,

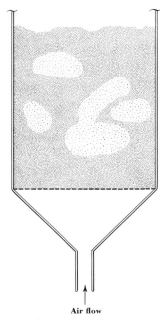

Air flow

Fig. 16-13.   Aggregative fluidization.

the process is known as particulate fluidization. The bed "boils" uniformly, although there is generally circulation of the particles up and down in the bed. Particulate fluidization occurs almost exclusively with liquids. It is also called homogeneous fluidization; the Froude number u_{mf}^2/gD is usually less than 1.

Although a bed fluidized by a liquid will follow a line such as that in Fig. 16-11 almost up to $\epsilon = 1.0$, a bed fluidized by a gas becomes unstable and nonhomogeneous far below $\epsilon = 1.0$. The particles are grouped together in aggregates, and bubbles of gas travel up between the denser parts of the bed, as illustrated in Fig. 16-13. This condition is characteristic of a bed in a state of aggregative, or heterogeneous, fluidization. The Froude number is usually greater than 1. The bed expands more than it would if it were homogeneous, because of the presence of the gas bubbles. The upper level of the bed is not constant, but fluctuates with the passing of the bubbles and aggregates. For large particles and high ratios of bed height to bed diameter, slugging occurs, which is an extremely unstable type of aggregative fluidization.

Heat and Mass Transfer

The use of a fluidized bed is advantageous in processes for which it is essential that the temperature and concentration be as uniform as possible.

In the catalytic cracking of gas oil to make gasoline and light hydrocarbons, heat can be supplied to the reaction without excessive temperature gradients in the bed.   In addition, the spent catalyst is conveniently removed, regenerated, and returned by fluidized transport.   Fluid beds are used for other heterogeneous catalytic reactions, for reactions between a solid and a fluid, and for the drying of solid particles.

The processes mentioned above benefit from the fact that heat and mass are transferred from one point to another within a fluid bed much more effectively than in a fixed bed.   On the other hand, transfer rates between the individual particles and the fluid may be lower than in a fixed bed, and transfer from a surface within the bed (the wall of the container or heating coils) is not always drastically improved over that in a fixed bed.

The reader interested in more details and design equations on fluidization is referred to books by Leva[1] and by Zenz and Othmer.[2]   Some of the principles of fluidization are illustrated in the following example.

Example 16-5

Thirty pounds of solid spherical particles is to be contacted in a batch fluidized bed with water flowing at a rate of 2000 lb/hr.   Estimate the diameter and height of the bed if it is expanded to 1.3 times the volume formed by a fixed bed.   The particles are 0.10 in. in diameter and have a specific gravity of 1.10.   The temperature is 68°F.

This problem may be solved by constructing a graph like Fig. 16-11 from a calculation of the minimum fluidizing velocity and the terminal velocity.   We use Eq. (16-35),

$$(\rho_s - \rho)g = \frac{150(1 - \epsilon)\mu u_{mf}}{D^2\epsilon^3} + \frac{1.75\rho u_{mf}^2}{D\epsilon^3}$$

where $\epsilon = 0.36$ is found from Fig. 16-10, assuming the bed diameter is much larger than the particle diameter.   Numerical values are used to yield

$$(62.4)(1.10 - 1.0)(4.16 \times 10^8) = \frac{150(1 - 0.36)(2.42)}{(0.1/12)^2(0.36)^3} u_{mf} + \frac{1.75(62.4)u_{mf}^2}{(0.1/12)(0.36)^3}$$

and

$$u_{mf}^2 + 256u_{mf} - 9260 = 0$$

Thus u_{mf} is found to be 32.0 ft/hr.

A first attempt is made to find the terminal velocity by Eq. (16-40), since the large diameter of the particles will result in a large **Re**.

$$u_t = \left[\frac{3D(\rho_s - \rho)g}{\rho}\right]^{1/2}$$

$$= \left[\frac{3(0.1/12)(1.10 - 1.00)(4.16 \times 10^8)}{1.00}\right]^{1/2}$$

$$= 1020 \text{ ft/hr}$$

$$\textbf{Re} = \frac{Du_t\rho}{\mu} = \frac{(0.1/12)(1020)(62.4)}{2.42} = 219$$

[1] M. Leva, "Fluidization," McGraw-Hill Book Company, Inc., New York, 1959.
[2] F. A. Zenz and D. F. Othmer, "Fluidization and Fluid-particle Systems," Reinhold Publishing Corporation, New York, 1960.

Fig. 16-14.   *Bed expansion in Example 16-5.*

This Reynolds number means that Eq. (16-40) cannot be used; Fig. 15-6 must be used. If C_D is estimated as 0.80, Eq. (16-38) becomes

$$u_t = \left[\frac{4(0.1/12)(1.10 - 1.0)(32.2)}{3(0.8)(1.0)} \right]^{1/2} = 760 \text{ ft/hr}$$

and **Re** = 1.64, at which C_D is about 0.8. Using the values found for u_{mf} and u_t, Fig. 16-14 is constructed.

For a 30 per cent bed expansion, $1 - \epsilon$ must be $0.64/1.3 = 0.492$, so that $\epsilon = 0.508$. At this void fraction Fig. 16-14 shows that the velocity must be 94 ft/hr. We then calculate

$$G = u_{bs}\rho = (94)(62.4) = 5870 \text{ lb/(hr)(sq ft)}$$

$$A = \frac{2000}{G} = \frac{2000}{5870} = 0.341 \text{ sq ft}$$

The corresponding diameter is 0.659 ft (7.90 in.).
The bed volume is

$$V = \frac{30}{(1.1)(62.4)(0.492)} = 0.889 \text{ cu ft}$$

The bed height is then

$$L = 0.889/0.341 = 2.61 \text{ ft}$$

PROBLEMS

16-1. A test of a certain leaf filter shows that if the pressure is maintained constant at 50 psig, the initial rate of collection is 10 gal/min, and 1 hr is needed to collect 100 gal of filtrate. What is the maximum hourly capacity of this filter if 15 gal of wash water is used and the time for dumping and cleaning is 20 min?

16-2. A small leaf filter is run at constant rate. It is found that the initial pressure is 5 psig and the pressure after 20 min of operation, during which 30 gal of filtrate is collected, is 50 psig. If this filter is used with the same slurry in a constant-pressure filtration at 50 psig, how much filtrate is collected in 20 min?

16-3. Find the quantity of cake which can be obtained in 1 hr of operation of a leaf filter with an area of 1000 sq ft working at 150 psig on a slurry of 100 g/l of ZnS, type B. Use the data in Figs. 16-7 and 16-8. The resistance of the medium is equivalent to 0.05 in. of cake.

16-4. (*a*) A homogeneous sludge, 15 per cent solid by weight, forming a uniform incompressible cake, is filtered through a batch leaf filter at a constant difference in pressure of 60 psi. One inch of cake is deposited in one hour with a filtrate volume of 1800 gal. Three minutes is required to drain the liquor from the filter. Two minutes is required to fill the filter with water. Washing proceeds exactly as filtration, using 400 gal. Opening, dumping, and closing take 6 min. Assume the filtrate to have the same properties as the wash water, and neglect the resistances of the filter cloth and flow line. Determine the maximum daily capacity of this filter operating on this slurry. Assume the ratio of wash water to filtrate is constant at a value of 400/1800.

(*b*) The sludge feed of part (*a*) is available in unlimited quantities. It is a waste stream from a plant and is ordinarily discarded. A neighboring plant is willing to buy the solid at $4.65 per 1000 lb and will buy whatever quantity is available. A laborer, who is paid $2 per hour, must be on hand for all parts of the cycle except during filtering and washing, when his time will be charged to other parts of the plant. Calculate the optimum batch size, the daily production of solid, and the daily profit. The filter of part (*a*) will be used. Take into account only the income from the sale and the cost of the laborer's time.

16-5. A continuous rotary filter is being used with a slurry which forms an incompressible cake. The resistance of the medium is negligible. What is the effect on the capacity of the filter of doubling the speed of rotation?

HIGH-SPEED FLOW
17

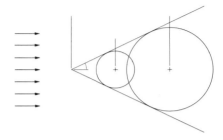

Compressible Fluids

The mass, energy, and momentum equations derived in previous chapters are applicable in their general form to compressible fluids, but we have considered in detail so far only their application to incompressible fluids. However, it has been pointed out that the equations which apply to incompressible fluids may often be used for compressible fluids if the fractional change in pressure is not large. Compressibility effects are unimportant in a change from 30 to 29 psia, but very important in a change from 2 to 1 psia.

Change in pressure is often associated with the passage of a gas through a turbine or a compressor. Considerable attention is usually given to this type of compressible flow in books on thermodynamics; operations of this type are analyzed by means of the mechanical energy balance, Eq. (4-20), and the general energy balance, Eq. (4-13).

Compressions and expansions through compressors or turbines are often analyzed assuming adiabatic and reversible (isentropic) operation. Another operation involving compressible fluids is the Joule-Thomson expansion, which is adiabatic and irreversible. It may occur in a valve or orifice, or in a long section of insulated pipe.

An additional situation in which compressibility plays an important part occurs in the study of tall columns of fluid in which gravity causes a variation of pressure and density with height. This effect is important in meteorology and in the production of natural gas from deep wells.

In none of the examples just mentioned is there necessarily any connection between compressibility and a high velocity of the gas (above 100 ft/sec, say). The former examples will not be considered further, whereas high-speed flow is the subject of this chapter. This flow is often associated with the passage of a gas through a nozzle or a length of pipe at high pressure differential. As will become apparent in the ensuing discussion, these situations are characterized by the fact that the kinetic energy of the compressible fluid becomes appreciable in comparison with the thermal energy. The kinetic energy assumes this importance as the velocity approaches that of sound in the gas. In addition to the well-publicized applications of the principles of the flow of compressible fluids to high-speed flight and missiles, these principles have important applications in the design of chemical processing equipment like ejectors and blowdown pipes.

The Differential Balances for One-dimensional Compressible Flow

In this study of compressible flow we shall assume that the flow is one-dimensional. This assumption is true in a pipe of constant cross section far downstream from the entrance, but it is an approximation for flow through a nozzle, in which the cross section is variable. For flow in a nozzle, therefore, it is not correct to let $\partial(u_y\rho)/\partial y$ and $\partial(u_z\rho)/\partial z$ equal zero in the equation of continuity (9-7). Rather than try to adapt this differential balance to the approximation of one-dimensional flow in a nozzle, we turn to the over-all mass balance. Equation (3-4) holds if the surfaces A_1 and A_2 are oriented normal to the flow. The approximations introduced in this chapter consist essentially in neglecting the curvature of the control surfaces and in assuming that $u = u_b = u_x$ at any point on any plane perpendicular to the axis of the conduit. For steady flow, if the distance between the surfaces 1 and 2 approaches żero, Eq. (3-4) becomes

$$d(u\rho A) = 0 \tag{17-1}$$

The differential mass balance will be used in this form in this chapter.

In obtaining the form of the differential energy balance which is convenient for one-dimensional compressible flow, we start from Eq. (4-13) rather than Eq. (10-10). For steady adiabatic flow with no shaft work, Eq. (4-13) can be written

$$\frac{u\,du}{g_c} + \frac{g}{g_c}\,dz + dH = 0 \tag{17-2}$$

Since Eqs. (17-1) and (17-2) contain only perfect differentials, they can be integrated to give the corresponding over-all balances whether the flow is reversible (frictionless) or not.

For pipe flow, we shall find the differential form of Eq. (4-20) to be useful.

$$\frac{u\,du}{g_c} + \frac{g}{g_c}\,dz + \frac{dp}{\rho} + d(lw_f) = 0 \tag{17-3}$$

Stationary wave front

Fig. 17-1.   *Sketch for the derivation of the sonic velocity.*

The presence of the friction term in this equation is not consistent with the assumption of a uniform velocity distribution, but the error introduced is small.   Unlike Eqs. (17-1) and (17-2), the path must be known in order to integrate the term dp/ρ in Eq. (17-3).   For some irreversible flows this path is not defined.   For reversible (frictionless) flow, Eq. (17-3) becomes the differential form of Bernoulli's equation.

$$\frac{u\,du}{g_c} + \frac{g}{g_c}\,dz + \frac{dp}{\rho} = 0 \tag{17-4}$$

For adiabatic, reversible flow dH equals dp/ρ, so Eqs. (17-4) and (17-2) become identical.

Velocity of Sound

In order to be able to discuss the important role of the sonic velocity in high-speed flow, we now derive the equation for the speed of sound in a fluid in terms of the properties of the fluid.   It will be recalled from elementary physics that sound waves are pressure waves caused by the mechanical vibration of the source of the sound.   In ordinary sound these pressure variations follow each other in rapid succession; the velocity of sound is the same as that at which any individual pulse travels.

If a diaphragm or piston is located at the right end of a cylinder filled with gas, a sudden small movement of the surface to the left will increase the pressure in the gas adjacent to the surface.   This region of higher pressure then travels to the left at the sonic velocity.   Ahead of the wave front the velocity of the undisturbed fluid is zero, and behind it there is a small velocity to the left du, caused by the increase in pressure dp and the accompanying increase in density $d\rho$ as the wave front passes.   If the piston comes to rest after its initial movement, the pressure some distance behind the wave front almost returns to its original value.   In the production of ordinary sound waves the piston, or diaphragm, vibrates about a constant mean position, and alternate bands of pressure and rarefaction travel down the tube.

An expression for the velocity of sound can be obtained from an analysis of conditions ahead of and behind the wave front. The analysis is made easier by choosing a situation in which the wave front is stationary; this is the case if the wave travels into a region where the gas velocity to the right is equal to the sonic velocity C, as illustrated in Fig. 17-1. The velocity to the right of the wave front is $C + du$, in which du is negative. The cross-sectional area of the stream tube is the same on both sides of the front.

The analysis of the flow in Fig. 17-1 begins with the use of Eq. (17-1). The increase in pressure across the wave front is differentially small for this steady, one-dimensional flow. Since dA is zero, we have

$$u \, d\rho + \rho \, du = 0 \qquad (17\text{-}5)$$

The small compression across the wave front occurs so quickly that it is adiabatic, and it is also assumed to be reversible. Therefore Bernoulli's equation (17-4) can be used in differential form ($dz = 0$):

$$\frac{u \, du}{g_c} + \frac{dp}{\rho} = 0 \qquad (17\text{-}6)$$

Equations (17-5) and (17-6) are combined to eliminate du and written as

$$u^2 = g_c \frac{dp}{d\rho} \qquad (17\text{-}7)$$

However, u is actually the sonic velocity C. In rewriting Eq. (17-7) we make the derivative more explicit by showing that the change in pressure with density occurs along an adiabatic, reversible path; i.e., the entropy S is constant.

$$C^2 = g_c \left(\frac{\partial p}{\partial \rho} \right)_S \qquad (17\text{-}8)$$

Equation (17-8) holds for a real fluid. In terms of the specific volume ($V = 1/\rho$), it becomes

$$C^2 = -g_c V^2 \left(\frac{\partial p}{\partial V} \right)_S \qquad (17\text{-}9)$$

In the present treatment, we concern ourselves principally with ideal gases, for which

$$\left(\frac{\partial p}{\partial \rho} \right)_S = \frac{kp}{\rho} \qquad (17\text{-}10)$$

This equation is derived from the relation for the adiabatic, reversible expansion of an ideal gas.

$$pV^k = p\rho^{-k} = \text{const} \qquad (17\text{-}11)$$

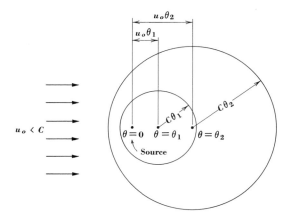

Fig.17-2.*Flow past a point source of sound at subsonic velocity.*

The velocity of sound for an ideal gas is thus

$$C = \sqrt{\frac{g_c k p}{\rho}} \qquad (17\text{-}12)$$

or

$$C = \sqrt{\frac{g_c k R T}{M_m}} \qquad (17\text{-}13)$$

Equation (17-13) shows that the square of the velocity of sound is proportional to the absolute temperature of the ideal gas, that is to say, to the internal energy of the gas. (C_p and C_v are assumed constant.) Since the kinetic energy of a flowing gas is proportional to u^2, the ratio u^2/C^2 is the ratio of the kinetic energy to the internal energy. It has already been mentioned in Chap. 14 that u/C is called the Mach number. The velocity of sound in air at room temperature is roughly 1100 ft/sec, so that at 110 ft/sec, $\mathbf{Ma}^2$ is only 0.01; kinetic-energy effects do not become important until somewhat higher Mach numbers are reached.

High-speed Motion of an Immersed Body

Another way in which the velocity of sound is related to high-speed flow is brought out by a study of the movement of a point source of sound in a fluid. At rest, successive wave fronts leave the source at the same speed in all directions and form concentric circles (two-dimensional flow) about the point. If the body moves to the left (or the fluid to the right) at a subsonic velocity, the pressure fronts travel with respect to the moving source, as shown in Fig. 17-2. At speeds of the source to the left above the

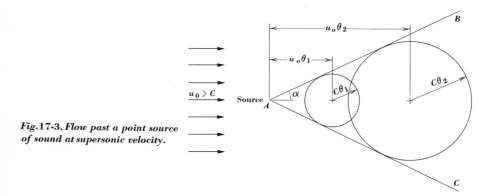

Fig. 17-3. Flow past a point source of sound at supersonic velocity.

velocity of sound, the centers of the circles are swept downstream so fast that there is a region relative to the source into which the pressure disturbance does not penetrate, as shown in Fig. 17-3. The progress of the wave front at times θ_1, θ_2, etc., is shown in the two figures. The lines AB and AC in Fig. 17-3 are called Mach lines, and the angle α is called the Mach angle. This angle is given by

$$\alpha = \sin^{-1}\frac{C}{u_o} = \sin^{-1}\frac{1}{\mathsf{Ma}} \qquad (17\text{-}14)$$

In the motion of a real body through a fluid at supersonic velocity, shock waves are generated at the front and rear of the body, even if it is not a point source of sound. Sudden pressure changes occur at the shock lines. Figure 17-4 represents a Schlieren[1] photograph of flow past a tapered body at above sonic velocity.

FLOW IN AN ISENTROPIC NOZZLE

Basic Relations

In a nozzle the cross section of flow, density, pressure, and velocity change smoothly but rapidly with distance along a streamline. A venturi is a form of nozzle.[2] Because of the rapidity of the changes of pressure

---

[1] A Schlieren photograph is obtained by using a method of illumination which causes regions of differing density to become visible on film. This method is described in L. Prandtl, "Essentials of Fluid Mechanics," p. 275, Hafner Publishing Company, New York, 1952.

[2] The word nozzle is used here in a general sense; in Chap. 6 we distinguished between a venturi and a nozzle used as flowmeters.

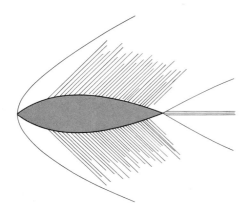

Fig. 17-4.   Sketch of a Schlieren photograph of supersonic flow past a tapered body.

and temperature in a nozzle, the wall surface is insufficient to transfer any appreciable amount of heat to the fluid.   The flow is therefore considered adiabatic.   Because of the smooth variation of the dimensions and the short length of the nozzle, the effect of eddies and skin friction is negligible. The flow is thus considered as reversible; since it is also adiabatic, it is isentropic.

Bernoulli's equation can be applied to flow in an isentropic nozzle, for which $lw_f = 0$.   These conditions are identical with those leading to Eq. (17-6), which is now written as

$$\int_{u_o}^{u} u \, du = -g_c \int_{p_o}^{p} \frac{dp}{\rho} \tag{17-15}$$

in which u_o and p_o are the conditions at the entrance to the nozzle, and u and p are at any point downstream in the nozzle.   The flow is assumed one-dimensional, and the velocity and other variables are constant over any given cross section.   For an ideal gas Eq. (17-11) holds, and we write it as

$$\rho = \rho_o \left(\frac{p}{p_o} \right)^{1/k} \tag{17-16}$$

This equation relates the density at any point to the pressure at that point and the conditions at the nozzle entrance.   At the nozzle entrance we also let u_o be zero, for u_o^2 is usually much less than u^2.

The substitution of Eq. (17-16) in Eq. (17-15), followed by integration, gives

$$u^2 = \frac{2kg_c p_o}{(k-1)\rho_o} \left[1 - \left(\frac{p}{p_o} \right)^{(k-1)/k} \right] \tag{17-17}$$

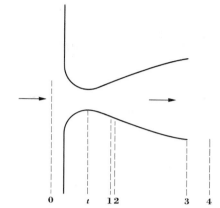

Fig. 17-5.   *A converging-diverging nozzle.*

0   t 1 2   3   4

This equation relates the velocity at any point in the nozzle to the pressure at that point and the inlet conditions.

The general energy balance can also be written for flow in the nozzle. In differential form, for adiabatic, horizontal flow, Eq. (17-2) becomes

$$\frac{u\,du}{g_c} = -dH \tag{17-18}$$

Integration yields ($u_o = 0$)

$$u^2 = 2g_c(H_o - H) \tag{17-19}$$

For an ideal gas, with C_p constant, Eq. (17-19) becomes

$$u^2 = 2g_c C_p(T_o - T) \tag{17-20}$$

The mass balance does not reduce to Eq. (17-5), since dA is in general not zero. The mass balance is conveniently written as

$$u\rho A = w = \text{const} \tag{17-21}$$

Let us now apply the basic relations we have derived to flow in a converging-diverging nozzle.

Converging-Diverging Nozzle

A typical converging-diverging nozzle is shown in Fig. 17-5. The behavior of the flow in the nozzle depends on whether the sonic velocity is reached or not.

Subsonic Flow. If p_3 equals p_o (refer to Fig. 17-5 for the meaning of the subscripts), there is no flow. If p_3 is slightly below p_o, the nozzle behaves qualitatively like the venturi already studied in Chap. 6. The pressure decreases and the velocity increases according to Eq. (17-17) until the throat t is reached; thereafter the pressure begins to increase and the velocity decreases until the nozzle outlet 3 is reached; p_3 and p_4 are equal. At the throat the extreme values of all the variables are reached. At this point du, $d\rho$, dp, and dA are all zero, so Eq. (17-1) is satisfied at the throat, as in the rest of the nozzle.

Supersonic Flow. As the pressure p_3 is reduced, the maximum velocity, which occurs at the throat of the nozzle, is increased. We shall next show that the highest value u_t can attain is the velocity of sound at the temperature of the gas (ideal) at the throat. In order for a change in p_3 to have an effect on conditions upstream, the change in pressure must be transmitted upstream. This pressure wave travels to the left (Fig. 17-5) at the sonic velocity, so if the velocity of gas flow to the right at any point reaches the sonic velocity, the advance of the pressure wave is brought to a halt. Since the velocity at the throat of the nozzle is higher than anywhere else in the nozzle for subsonic flow, the sonic velocity is the maximum attainable at the throat. The effect of any further reduction in pressure downstream below that required to produce the velocity of sound in the throat cannot be transmitted through the throat. Thus the conditions between 0 and t are unchanged for all values of $p_3 \leqq p_{3c}$, where p_{3c} represents the pressure at outlet 3 required to give the sonic velocity at the throat. The pressure at the throat is readily calculated by substituting for u in Eq. (17-17) the value u_t, which equals C_t, or $\sqrt{g_ckRT/M_m}$. This procedure yields

$$p_{tc} = p_o \left(\frac{2}{k+1} \right)^{k/(k-1)} \tag{17-22}$$

For the common gases p_{tc}/p_o is a little more than 0.5.

It is worth noting that the maximum velocity at the throat ($u_t = C_t$) is less than the velocity of sound at the entrance conditions (C_o). Equations (17-11), (17-12), and (17-22) can be combined to give

$$C_t = C_o \sqrt{\frac{2}{k+1}} \tag{17-23}$$

If the pressure p_3 is lowered below the value which gives the sonic velocity in the throat, a shock (i.e., a sudden change in pressure) is set up somewhere downstream from the throat of the nozzle. Shock in a nozzle will be discussed in more detail in a later section. However, there is one value of p_3/p_o for which no shock occurs in a properly designed nozzle with sonic velocity at the throat. The flow is then isentropic from 0 to 3, and the velocity downstream from t is above sonic velocity in the nozzle. Equations (17-17), (17-19), (17-20), and (17-21) apply all through the

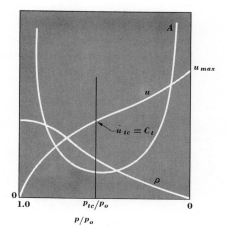

Fig. 17-6. *Velocity, density, and area as a function of pressure in a converging-diverging nozzle.*

nozzle. Unlike flow for which $p_t/p_o > p_{tc}/p_o$, the velocity, density, and pressure do not reach extreme values at the throat of the nozzle. Figure 17-6 shows how these quantities vary. As the cross-sectional area decreases in the converging part of the nozzle, the velocity increases and becomes sonic at the throat. In the diverging part of the nozzle the velocity continues to increase and the pressure to fall. Figure 17-6 shows that there is only one value of A_3 (i.e., only one nozzle) for a particular p_3, which lies between p_{tc} and 0. There is a finite limit to the velocity attainable, no matter how large A becomes; this velocity can be found from Eq. (17-17) by setting $p = 0$.

The way in which the pressure varies with distance through the nozzle is shown in Fig. 17-7. If p_3 is high enough so that the sonic velocity is nowhere reached, the curve leading to p_{3a} is obtained. At p_{3c} the sonic velocity is reached in the throat, and if p_3 is anywhere below p_{3c} except at p_{3b}, a shock will form downstream from the nozzle throat. With p_{3b}, the flow is supersonic everywhere in the diverging section.

If the nozzle is shortened, so that A_3 is smaller, p_{3b} becomes larger, as shown in Figs. 17-6 and 17-7. If the nozzle is shortened sufficiently to become simply a converging nozzle, $p_{3b} = p_{3c} = p_{tc}$; the sonic velocity cannot be exceeded unless there is a diverging section.

Let us now show in another way that the sonic velocity must exist at the throat whenever $p_3 < p_{3c}$. Equation (17-6) must always hold in the absence of shock; it leads to Eq. (17-17). For $p_3 > p_{3c}$ the sonic velocity is not reached, and we have seen that the mass balance in the form

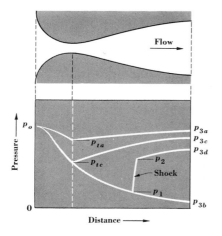

Fig. 17-7. *Pressure distribution in flow through a converging-diverging nozzle.*

$$u\rho \, dA + uA \, d\rho + \rho A \, du = 0 \qquad (17\text{-}24)$$

is satisfied at the throat, where $dA = 0$, since $d\rho$ and du are also zero. However, for $p_3 < p_{3c}$, $d\rho$ and du are not zero, so at the throat Eq. (17-24) becomes Eq. (17-5). Since the simultaneous solution of Eqs. (17-5) and (17-6) has already been shown to yield the formula for the sonic velocity, we have an alternative proof that this velocity must exist in the throat for $p_3 \leqq p_{3c}$.

Shock in a Nozzle

Referring once again to Figs. 17-5 and 17-7, let us consider what happens if p_4 is below p_{3c} but not equal to p_{3b}. If p_4 is less than p_{3b}, the pressure in the nozzle follows the path leading to p_{3b} and then the flow suddenly expands just outside the nozzle exit, forming the pattern of oblique shock waves shown in Fig. 17-8a. If p_4 is slightly greater than p_{3b}, there is a pattern of shock waves formed just outside the nozzle in which the flow is compressed from p_{3b} to p_4. A further increase in p_4 causes the shock pattern to move into the nozzle. The flow in the three cases mentioned so far is too complicated to be treated by an elementary analysis. However, if p_4 is raised so that it is not very much below p_{3c}, as shown at p_{3d}, the shock occurs quite far up into the nozzle, and it is concentrated into a single transverse shock. These four situations are illustrated in Fig. 17-8; the last one mentioned is next further analyzed.

The pressure at the upstream side of the shock shown in Fig. 17-8d is

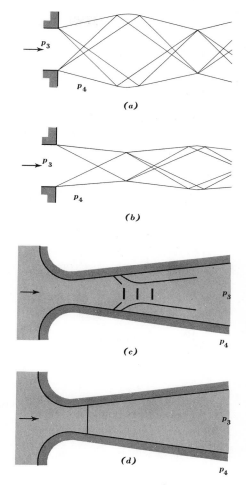

Fig. 17-8.   *Shock patterns accompanying supersonic flow in a nozzle. (a) p_4 slightly less than p_{3b}. (b) p_4 slightly greater than p_{3b}. (c) p_4 somewhat higher than in (b) above. (d) p_4 just below p_{3c} (transverse shock).*

p_1 in Figs. 17-5 and 17-7; the pressure on the downstream side is p_2. The thickness of the shock wave in air is in the order of 10^{-4} in. Because of the thinness of the shock, we can set A_2 equal to A_1, and the over-all mass balance becomes

$$u_1\rho_1 = u_2\rho_2 = G_1 \tag{17-25}$$

This equation should not be written in differential form; there is a finite jump in u, ρ, and p.

The energy balance must likewise be written in its over-all (integral) form,

$$\frac{u_2{}^2 - u_1{}^2}{2g_c} = H_1 - H_2 \tag{17-26}$$

or, for an ideal gas,

$$\frac{u_2{}^2 - u_1{}^2}{2g_c} = C_p(T_1 - T_2) \tag{17-27}$$

The flow within the shock is not reversible, as it is in the rest of the nozzle. Therefore the mechanical energy balance [Eq. (4-20) or (17-3)] is not useful; we can evaluate neither lw_f nor $\int dp/\rho$ for the unknown, irreversible path. However, the over-all momentum balance, Eq. (5-6), is helpful. For one-dimensional flow, applied to the gas within the shock, the equation becomes

$$\frac{w}{g_c}(u_2 - u_1) = R_x - F_{xp} - F_{xd} \tag{17-28}$$

R_x is zero since the nozzle wall is not within the control volume; F_{xd} is zero since the drag force on the wall is negligible for the short length involved. The pressure force is given by $A_1(p_2 - p_1)$, and w is $u_1\rho_1 A_1$. We have thus

$$\frac{u_1\rho_1}{g_c}(u_2 - u_1) = p_1 - p_2 \tag{17-29}$$

By using appropriate thermodynamic formulas for an ideal gas with Eqs. (17-25), (17-27), and (17-29), the following simple relation is obtained relating the velocities on either side of the shock wave:

$$u_1 u_2 = C_t{}^2 \tag{17-30}$$

The algebra involved in the derivation of Eq. (17-30) is long and complicated. The velocity u_1 is supersonic, and it can be shown that u_2 is subsonic; this fact has already been used in drawing the pressure profile in Fig. 17-7 which ends at p_{3d}. With supersonic flow the pressure decreases in the diverging section; with subsonic flow it increases.

Rather than go through the algebra leading to Eq. (17-30) we give a graphical illustration of the simultaneous solution of Eqs. (17-26) and (17-29). By using Eq. (17-25) it is possible to eliminate the velocities from these equations and obtain, from Eq. (17-26),

$$\frac{G^2}{2g_c}\left(\frac{1}{\rho^2} - \frac{1}{\rho_1{}^2}\right) = H_1 - H \tag{17-31}$$

and from Eq. (17-29),

$$\frac{G^2}{g_c}\left(\frac{1}{\rho} - \frac{1}{\rho_1}\right) = p_1 - p \tag{17-32}$$

(The subscript 2s have been removed in these equations.)

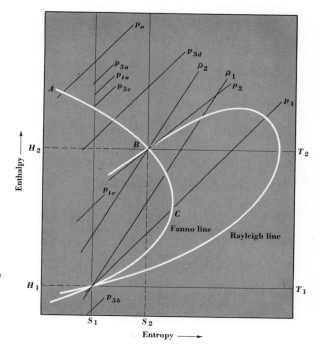

Fig. 17-9. *Graph of Rayleigh and Fanno lines.*

In order to use these equations we must know at what upstream pressure or velocity the shock occurs. If p_1 is known, u_1, ρ_1, and thus G can be calculated by the relations already considered for isentropic flow from 0 to 1. We now use an H-S diagram (Mollier diagram) to continue the solution. The quantities p_1 and ρ_1 define a point on the chart shown in Fig. 17-9, so that H_1, S_1, and T_1 are also known.

Successive values of ρ can now be chosen, and the corresponding values of H calculated by Eq. (17-31); these points define a curve called a Fanno line shown in Fig. 17-9.   In a similar way Eq. (17-32) can be used to calculate successive values of p from values of ρ, defining a curve called a Rayleigh line.   These two equations must hold simultaneously across the shock wave, so the values of p_2, ρ_2, and the other pertinent variables are found from the second intersection of the lines shown in Fig. 17-9.   The positions of the curves are, of course, changed as G, ρ_1, or p_1 is changed.

Also shown in Fig. 17-9 are lines representing the state of the gas in other parts of the nozzle.   From the entrance pressure p_o the path is downward along a vertical line through p_{tc} to p_1; at the shock the pressure jumps to p_2, and from p_2 to p_3 the path is upward along a vertical line of constant entropy.   Note that the entropy increases from 1 to 2.   A rarefaction shock from 2 to 1 is impossible, for the entropy cannot decrease for the adiabatic process.   There is always the possibility that a disturbance in the flow may cause a shock and a jump from supersonic to subsonic flow; the reverse cannot occur.

The other cases in Fig. 17-7 can also be followed on Fig. 17-9.   For subsonic flow the path descends along a vertical line to p_{ta} and then ascends the same line to p_{3a}.   If p_3 is lowered to p_{3c}, the path is similar, but the lowest pressure is now p_{tc}.   If p_3 equals p_{3b}, the entire flow is isentropic and follows the vertical path from p_o to p_{tc} to p_{3b}.

Stagnation Temperature and Pressure

In the study of high-speed flow it is important to realize that a stationary probe may not indicate the same temperature and pressure as would be registered by a probe moving with the fluid.   The temperature which would be attained by the fluid if its velocity were brought to zero adiabatically is called the stagnation temperature.   An ordinary thermocouple, say in the form of a cylinder, will measure a temperature somewhere between the stagnation temperature and the true temperature.   The fluid reaches the stagnation temperature only at the forward stagnation point of the cylinder.

The stagnation temperature for subsonic flow of an ideal gas is identified with T_o in Eq. (17-20).   This equation applies between the point 0, at which the velocity is zero, and a point in an adiabatic (not necessarily isentropic) flow at which the velocity and temperature are u and T.   The temperatures T_o and T differ appreciably only if kinetic-energy effects are important.   This point may be brought out by expressing the stagnation temperature in terms of the Mach number.   Let us divide the left-hand side of Eq. (17-20) by C^2 and the right-hand side by the equivalent quantity from Eq. (17-13), kg_cRT/M_m.   There results

$$\frac{u^2}{C^2} = \frac{2C_pM_m}{kRT}\,(T_o - T) \tag{17-33}$$

For an ideal gas we have, from thermodynamics,

$$\frac{C_pM_m}{R} = \frac{k}{k-1} \tag{17-34}$$

Equations (17-33) and (17-34) are easily combined and rearranged to give

$$\frac{T_o}{T} = 1 + \left(\frac{k-1}{2}\right) \mathsf{Ma}^2 \tag{17-35}$$

The stagnation and the true temperature differ appreciably only at velocities in the order of hundreds of feet per second.

In computing the stagnation pressure, it is assumed that the operation of slowing the fluid to zero velocity is performed reversibly as well as adiabatically (i.e., isentropically). Equation (17-11) then holds, and it can be combined with the ideal-gas law, $p/\rho = RT/M_m$, to give

$$\frac{T_o}{T} = \left(\frac{p_o}{p}\right)^{(k-1)/k} \tag{17-36}$$

By combining Eq. (17-36) with (17-35) it is found that the stagnation pressure is given by

$$\frac{p_o}{p} = \left[1 + \left(\frac{k-1}{2}\right)\mathbf{Ma}^2\right]^{k/(k-1)} \tag{17-37}$$

The form of Eq. (17-37) is rather unwieldy; it is convenient to expand the right-hand side by the binomial theorem, obtaining

$$\frac{p_o - p}{p} = \frac{k}{2}\mathbf{Ma}^2 + \frac{k}{8}\mathbf{Ma}^4 + \frac{k(2-k)}{48}\mathbf{Ma}^6 + \cdots \tag{17-38}$$

It will be recalled, however, that even with incompressible fluids an instrument like a pitot tube registers a pressure higher than the true, or static, pressure. Thus Eq. (17-38) contains both the effect of compressibility and the effect ordinarily observed at low velocities. The effect of compressibility can be separated out of Eq. (17-38) by the following procedure. We write, for incompressible flow,

$$\frac{p_o' - p}{p} = \frac{1}{p}\frac{\rho u^2}{2g_c} = \frac{k}{2}\mathbf{Ma}^2 \tag{17-39}$$

This equation is obtained from the integration of Eq. (17-4) ($dz = 0$) with ρ constant and from Eq. (17-12). The quantity $p_o' - p$ has been referred to in Chap. 12 as the dynamic pressure; p_o' is the stagnation pressure for incompressible flow. The effect of compressibility is now found by dividing Eq. (17-38) by Eq. (17-39), giving

$$\frac{p_o - p}{p_o' - p} = 1 + \tfrac{1}{4}\mathbf{Ma}^2 + \frac{2-k}{24}\mathbf{Ma}^4 + \cdots \tag{17-40}$$

The effect of compressibility is not appreciable below a Mach number of 0.2 or so.

In isentropic flow, such as in a nozzle, both the stagnation temperature and pressure remain constant as the actual temperature and pressure vary. In adiabatic flow with friction, the stagnation temperature is constant, but the stagnation pressure decreases with distance downstream.

The equations given for the stagnation pressure apply only to subsonic flow. If a probe is inserted into a supersonic stream a shock forms at or upstream from the probe and the flow is no longer isentropic; Eqs. (17-37) and (17-38) give a stagnation pressure which is too low.

We illustrate the use of the principles of operation of an isentropic nozzle by the following example.

Example 17-1

Several nozzles will be considered, all having upstream conditions given by $p_o = 10$ atm, $T_o = 3000°R$, and as usual, $u_o = 0$. The fluid is air. The large reservoir at these conditions is connected by a nozzle to a second large space maintained at p_4. We consider the following possibilities.

(a) Converging nozzle, $p_4 = 1$ atm. Since p_4 is obviously below about $\frac{1}{2}p_o$, the sonic velocity is achieved at the throat, where the pressure is

$$p_{tc} = p_o \left(\frac{2}{k+1}\right)^{k/(k-1)} \tag{17-22}$$

or

$$p_{tc} = 10 \left(\frac{2}{1.4+1}\right)^{1.4/(1.4-1)}$$

$$= 5.27 \text{ atm}$$

The temperature at the throat is found from Eq. (17-36), written as

$$T_{tc} = T_o \left(\frac{p_{tc}}{p_o}\right)^{(k-1)/k}$$

$$= 3000(0.527)^{0.286} = 3000(0.833)$$

$$= 2500°R$$

The velocity at the throat is

$$u_t = C_t = \sqrt{\frac{kg_cRT}{M_m}} \tag{17-13}$$

$$C_t = \sqrt{\frac{(1.4)(32.2)(1544)(2500)}{29}} = 2450 \text{ ft/sec}$$

The mass flow is governed by the throat diameter, which we choose as 2 in., so that $A_t = 0.0218$ sq ft. From the ideal-gas law, $\rho_t = 0.0838$ lb/cu ft. We have then

$$G_t = u_t \rho_t = (2450)(0.0838) = 205 \text{ lb/(sec)(sq ft)}$$

and

$$w = G_t A_t = (205)(0.0218) = 4.47 \text{ lb/sec}$$

Just outside the nozzle there will be shock waves across which the pressure falls from 5.27 to 1 atm.

(b) Consider now a converging-diverging nozzle with no shock inside the nozzle; p_4 still equals 1 atm. What are the conditions at the nozzle outlet, and what is the diameter the outlet must have?

We let $p_3 = 1$ atm and use Eq. (17-17) written as

$$u_3^2 = \frac{2kg_cRT_o}{(k-1)M_m}\left[1 - \left(\frac{p_3}{p_o}\right)^{(k-1)/k}\right]$$

$$= \frac{(2)(1.4)(32.2)(1544)(3000)}{(0.4)(29)}\left[1 - (\frac{1}{10})^{0.286}\right]$$

$$u_3 = 4170 \text{ ft/sec}$$

By using Eq. (17-36) as in part (a), we find

$$T_3 = 3000(\tfrac{1}{10})^{0.286} = 1550°R$$

Equation (17-13) gives $C_3 = 1932$ ft/sec, so that $\mathbf{Ma_3} = 2.16$. The density at 3 is 0.0257 lb/cu ft, so the nozzle area at the outlet is

$$\frac{A_3}{A_t} = \frac{u_t \rho_t}{u_3 \rho_3}$$

$$= \frac{(2450)(0.0838)}{(4170)(0.0257)} = 1.92$$

$$A_3 = 0.0418 \text{ sq ft}$$

$$D_3 = 2.77 \text{ in.}$$

Although a high velocity is reached at the outlet of this nozzle, the mass-flow rate has not been increased over that in part (a).

(c) Find the nozzle outlet area for $p_4 = 8$ atm which will cause a transverse shock to occur at $p_1 = 4.0$ atm.

We first find the conditions just ahead of the shock, starting by using Eq. (17-17).

$$u_1^2 = \frac{2(1.4)(32.2)(1544)(3000)}{(0.4)(29)} [1 - (\tfrac{4}{10})^{0.286}]$$

$$u_1 = 2880 \text{ ft/sec}$$

Proceeding as in part (b), we find also $T_1 = 2310°R$, $\rho_1 = 0.0689$ lb/cu ft, and $A_1 = 1.035 A_t$ or $D_1 = 2.04$ in. The shock occurs very close to the throat.

From Eq. (17-30) we calculate u_2.

$$u_2 = \frac{C_t^2}{u_1} = \frac{(2450)^2}{2880} = 2090 \text{ ft/sec}$$

From the mass balance we have

$$\rho_2 = \frac{u_1 \rho_1}{u_2} = \frac{2880(0.0689)}{2090} = 0.0950 \text{ lb/cu ft}$$

Equation (17-24) can now be used to find p_2.

$$\frac{u_1 \rho_1}{g_c}(u_2 - u_1) = p_1 - p_2$$

$$\frac{(2880)(0.0689)(2090 - 2880)}{32.2} = p_1 - p_2$$

$$p_2 - p_1 = 4870 \text{ lb force/sq ft}$$

and p_2 is 6.31 atm. From the ideal-gas law, T_2 is 2630°F. Equation (17-15) now applies once more between the downstream side of the shock 2 and the nozzle outlet 3. It is integrated to give

$$u_3^2 = \frac{2 k g_c p_2}{(k-1)\rho_2}\left[1 - \left(\frac{p_3}{p_2}\right)^{(k-1)/k}\right] + u_2^2$$

$$= \frac{(2)(1.4)(32.2)(13{,}330)}{(0.4)(0.0950)} [1 + (8/6.31)^{0.286}] + 4.37 \times 10^6$$

$$u_3 = 1470 \text{ ft/sec}$$

We can also find $T_3 = 2820°R$, $\rho_3 = 0.1130$ lb/cu ft, and $A_3/A_t = 1.24$ or $D_3 = 2.22$ in. As a check on the calculations, u_3 can be calculated from Eq. (17-20).

$$u_3{}^2 = \frac{2g_cC_p}{M_m}\,(T_o - T_3)$$

$$= \frac{2(32.2)(7)(778)}{(29)}\,(3000 - 2820)$$

$$u_3 = 1470 \text{ ft/sec}$$

FLOW IN A PIPE OF UNIFORM DIAMETER

Adiabatic Flow

A fluid flowing adiabatically through a pipe of constant cross section passes through a series of states given by Eq. (17-31), the Fanno equation. The mass velocity G is constant, and ρ_1 and H_1 are known initial values; Eq. (17-31) gives values of ρ and H downstream from point 1. For a single-phase fluid, these two properties fix all other properties such as the temperature, pressure, and entropy.

The states of the fluid are graphically represented by a Fanno line, such as the one shown in Fig. 17-9. The point A can be chosen to represent the initial condition; as the pressure falls downstream from A, the states pass through B to C. At point C the maximum entropy is reached, and it is not possible to proceed any farther along the Fanno line in an adiabatic process. The velocity at the end of the pipe (represented by point C) is the maximum that can be attained. For a differential change at C, dS is zero, and so the flow is both adiabatic and reversible (isentropic). Therefore the maximum velocity at C is the sonic velocity.

Point C can occur only at the end of a pipe, but the state of the gas at the end of the pipe can be anywhere on the line ABC, depending on the length of the pipe and the pressure drop. A new value of G defines a new Fanno line; such a line is a line of constant G.

We have so far discussed the properties of a fluid in adiabatic flow in a pipe without relating them to the length of pipe. This relation can be obtained by using Eq. (17-3). Substituting for the last term on the left-hand side of this equation by the use of Eq. (15-1), we obtain

$$\frac{u\,du}{g_c} + V\,dp + \frac{2fu^2\,dL}{g_cD} = 0 \tag{17-41}$$

In Eq. (17-41) ρ has been replaced by $1/V$. Since the mass velocity G is u/V, Eq. (17-41) can be divided by V^2 to give

$$\frac{G^2}{g_c}\frac{dV}{V} + \frac{dp}{V} + \frac{2fG^2\,dL}{g_cD} = 0 \tag{17-42}$$

The first term of Eq. (17-42) can be integrated directly since G^2/g_c is constant. In the third term $2G^2/g_cD$ is constant, and f varies only if the viscosity varies. The Reynolds number is DG/μ; the value of μ may vary in adiabatic flow, but the effect on f can usually be neglected. Equation (17-42) is then integrated between V_1 and V_2, p_1 and p_2, and 0 and L to give

$$\frac{G^2}{g_c} \ln \frac{V_2}{V_1} + \int_{p_1}^{p_2} \frac{dp}{V} + \frac{2fG^2L}{g_cD} = 0 \tag{17-43}$$

In dealing with adiabatic, reversible flow through a nozzle (G varies with L), we set the third term of Eq. (17-41) equal to zero and integrated the second term by the substitution given by Eq. (17-16). This equation was valid along a path of constant entropy, and the result was expressed as Eq. (17-17).

In dealing with adiabatic, irreversible flow through a pipe of constant cross section (G constant), we must retain the third term of Eq. (17-41). We integrate the second term by a relation which gives a relation between V and p along a path of constant G (S increases). Such a relation is given by Eq. (17-26), (17-27), (17-31), or (17-32). Let us choose Eq. (17-27) and replace u by GV and T by pVM_m/R. The result is

$$\frac{G^2}{2g_c} (V^2 - V_1{}^2) = \frac{C_pM_m}{R} (p_1V_1 - pV) \tag{17-44}$$

which is a form of the Fanno equation. Equation (17-44) is now solved for p, and $k/(k-1)$ is substituted for C_pM_m/R [Eq. (17-34)].

$$p = \left(\frac{G^2V_1{}^2}{2g_c} - \frac{G^2V^2}{2g_c} + \frac{kp_1V_1}{k-1}\right)\frac{k-1}{kV} \tag{17-45}$$

From this equation dp is found and substituted in the integral of dp/V. This integral is then evaluated between V_1 and V_2, and the resulting equation, after some rearrangement, is

$$\frac{(k+1)G^2}{2kg_c} \ln\left(\frac{V_2}{V_1}\right) + \frac{1}{2}\left[\frac{(k-1)G^2V_1{}^2}{2kg_c} + p_1V_1\right]\left(\frac{1}{V_2{}^2} - \frac{1}{V_1{}^2}\right)$$

$$+ \frac{2fG^2L}{g_cD} = 0 \tag{17-46}$$

In Eq. (17-46) one can, of course, replace the V's by $(1/\rho)$'s if so desired. The equation is rigorously correct for the adiabatic, irreversible, one-dimensional flow of an ideal gas of constant k through a pipe of constant diameter, if it can be assumed that f is constant.

In most practical situations, it is found that the temperature does not fall appreciably from points 1 to 2. In this case, the second term of Eq. (17-43) is very simply integrated by the substitution of RT/M_mp for V, giving

$$\frac{G^2}{g_c} \ln\left(\frac{V_2}{V_1}\right) + \frac{M_m}{2RT_{av}} (p_2{}^2 - p_1{}^2) + \frac{2fG^2L}{g_cD} = 0 \tag{17-47}$$

This equation is Eq. (15-28) plus the kinetic-energy term. It can be solved for the downstream conditions or for G by assuming T_{av} equals T_1. These results then permit the calculation of T_2 by Eq. (17-27), and the use of Eq. (17-47), this time with $T_{av} = (T_1 + T_2)/2$, can be repeated. The final result of this procedure is approximate to the extent that the correct T_{av} is not really equal to the arithmetic average of T_1 and T_2. The correct value of T_{av} could of course be obtained from the substitution of the results, using Eq. (17-46), into Eq. (17-47). As with all similar averaging procedures, the less difference there is between the quantities being averaged, the less difference there is between the correct average and any arbitrarily chosen average.

Let us consider the problem of finding G in a pipe of known length and diameter for which the inlet conditions (at 1) are given. The pipe discharges into a space where the pressure is p_4. Unless the sonic velocity is reached at the end of the pipe, p_4 equals p_2. When the calculations have been completed, using Eq. (17-46) or (17-47) with p_2 equal to p_4, it is necessary to check the velocity at 2 to make sure that the sonic velocity C_2 is not exceeded, i.e., that we have not followed the Fanno line ABC in Fig. 17-9 beyond the point C. If the velocity at 2 is subsonic, the problem is solved. If it is supersonic, the conditions used at 2 are not possible; the value of p_2 must be chosen somewhat higher than p_4. Values of p_2 are tried with Eq. (17-46) or (17-47) until the correct one is found, for which $u_2 = C_2$.

When there is sonic velocity at 2, p_4 can have any value equal to or less than p_2, and the flow in the pipe is not affected. A pressure wave cannot be transmitted into the end of the pipe against the sonic velocity. If the pipe is lengthened ($p_4 < p_2$), p_2 and T_2 are reduced, so that C_2 (that is, u_2) is reduced. Since V_2 is increased, from Eq. (17-1) the mass velocity G is reduced in the longer pipe, even though p_2/p_1 is decreased. This pressure ratio is not limited to about $\frac{1}{2}$, as in a converging nozzle [Eq. (17-22)], but can fall to an arbitrarily low value in a long pipe.

Isothermal Flow

For a sufficiently long pipe, heat can be transferred to the fluid fast enough so that the flow is essentially isothermal. Equation (17-47) then holds, and T_{av} is simply T_1. The maximum velocity attainable at 2 is given by the speed of transmission of a pressure difference isothermally rather than adiabatically. This velocity, which we shall call C_i, is not the sonic velocity. It can be found, however, by the same reasoning as that leading to Eqs. (17-12) and (17-13). Equation (17-7) applies just as for adiabatic flow, but $dp/d\rho$ is now evaluated along a path of constant temperature rather than constant entropy. Thus Eq. (17-8) is replaced by

$$C_i^2 = g_c \left(\frac{\partial p}{\partial \rho}\right)_T \tag{17-48}$$

For an ideal gas, we have

$$\left(\frac{\partial p}{\partial \rho}\right)_T = \frac{RT}{M_m} \tag{17-49}$$

so that the velocity of propagation of a pressure disturbance under isothermal conditions is given by

$$C_i = \sqrt{\frac{g_c p}{\rho}} \tag{17-50}$$

or

$$C_i = \sqrt{\frac{g_c RT}{M_m}} \tag{17-51}$$

These equations are analogous to Eqs. (17-12) and (17-13).

Since differences between adiabatic and isothermal flow are accentuated by increasing values of u_2, the greatest difference between these flows is at the maximum values of u_2. These maxima are represented, for instance, by Eqs. (17-13) and (17-51). For this extreme case the velocity for adiabatic flow is $\sqrt{k}$ (about 1.2 for air) times the velocity for isothermal flow.

Practical calculations for the flow of compressible fluids through pipe are facilitated by procedures and charts given by Lapple[1] and reproduced by Brown et al.[2] Further details on compressible flow can be obtained from books such as those by Hunsaker and Rightmire[3] or Liepmann and Puckett.[4]

Example 17-2

We shall study the flow out of the same reservoir considered in Example 17-1, but the diverging section of the nozzle will be replaced by 8.93 ft of straight pipe of 2-in. ID. At the reservoir, $p_o = 10$ atm and $T_o = 3000°R$. The beginning of the pipe is point 1, and the end of the pipe is point 2. The pipe discharges into a large space at p_4. Let us consider the values of p_4 required to cause a few different flows through the pipe and find the value of p_4 below which p_4 has no further effect on the flow.

We shall assume that the pipe is sufficiently rough and the Reynolds number suf-

[1] C. E. Lapple, *Trans. AIChE*, **39**:385 (1943).

[2] G. G. Brown et al., "Unit Operations," chap. 15, John Wiley & Sons, Inc., New York, 1950.

[3] J. C. Hunsaker and B. G. Rightmire, "Engineering Applications of Fluid Mechanics," McGraw-Hill Book Company, Inc., New York, 1947.

[4] H. W. Liepmann and A. E. Puckett, "Introduction to the Aerodynamics of Compressible Fluids," John Wiley & Sons, Inc., New York, 1947.

ficiently high so that f is constant at 0.010 for the flows chosen. We study, first, isothermal flow, followed by adiabatic flow.

1. *Isothermal flow in the pipe*

(a) $p_1 = 9.5$ atm. This pressure results in a relatively low pressure drop and flow rate from the reservoir to the beginning of the pipe so that the sonic velocity will probably not be reached at the end of the pipe. The flow is isentropic from 0 to 1 so we calculate, as follows, from Eq. (17-36):

$$T_1 = 3000(9.5/10)^{0.286} = 2950°\text{R}$$

From Eq. (17-17):

$$u_1{}^2 = \frac{(2)(1.4)(32.2)(1544)(3000)}{(0.4)(29)}\left[1 - \left(\frac{9.5}{10}\right)^{0.286}\right]$$

$$u_1 = 723 \text{ ft/sec}$$

We find also $\rho_1 = 0.1282$ lb/cu ft, and so

$$G = u_1\rho_1 = 723(0.1282) = 92.7 \text{ lb/(sec)(sq ft)}$$

In order to find the pressure at 2, we use Eq. (17-47), written in the form

$$\frac{G^2}{g_c}\ln\left(\frac{p_1}{p_2}\right) + \frac{M_m}{2RT_1}(p_2{}^2 - p_1{}^2) + \frac{2fG^2L}{g_cD} = 0$$

The first term in this equation is small compared with the others except at the highest velocities. Thus a first estimate of p_2 can be obtained by the omission of the first term; the result is $p_2 = 8.38$ atm. The final value of p_2 is found by trial; for $p_2 = 8.20$ atm we have

$$\frac{(92.7)^2}{32.2}\ln\left(\frac{9.50}{8.20}\right) + \frac{29}{(2)(1544)(2950)}\left[(17{,}380)^2 - (20{,}150)^2\right]$$

$$+ \frac{2(0.01)(92.7)^2(8.93)}{(32.2)(\frac{6}{12})} \overset{?}{=} 0$$

(The pressures must be expressed in pounds force per square foot.)
    After the evaluation of each term we have

$$39.0 - 331 + 285 = -7$$

The correct value of p_2 is somewhat less, say 8.15 atm. The kinetic-energy term is small but not negligible for this flow. At this pressure ρ_2 is 0.1098 lb/cu ft, so that

$$u_2 = \frac{G}{\rho_2} = \frac{92.7}{0.1098} = 845 \text{ ft/sec}$$

In order to have the flow described above, p_4 must be held at 8.15 atm. If it is increased, G is lowered; if it is decreased, G is raised.
    (b) Let us find the value of p_2 which gives the maximum flow rate. The maximum velocity u_2 is given by Eq. (17-51).

$$u_2 = C_i = \sqrt{\frac{g_cRT}{M_m}}$$

$$C_i = \sqrt{\frac{(32.2)(1544)(T_1)}{29}}$$

We must proceed by trial. A value of p_1 is chosen, so that G and T_1 are determined. Then p_2 and u_2 are found, following the procedure of part (a), until a value of p_1 is found such that $u_2 = C_i$ at T_1. Only the last (successful) trial is given here.

For $p_1 = 9.0$ atm, we have $T_1 = 2910°R$, $\rho_1 = 0.1230$ lb/cu ft, and $u_1 = 1034$ ft/sec, so that $G = 127$ lb/(sec)(sq ft). For this value of T_1, C_i is 2230 ft/sec. As in part (a), p_2 must be found by trial. For $p_2 = 4.16$ atm, Eq. (17-47) becomes

$$\frac{(127)^2}{32.2}\ln\left(\frac{9.0}{4.16}\right) + \frac{(29)[(8800)^2 - (19{,}100)^2]}{(2)(1544)(2910)} + \frac{2(0.01)(127)^2(8.93)}{32.2(\frac{2}{12})} \overset{?}{=} 0$$

Evaluation of the terms gives

$$389 - 925 + 536 = 0$$

and $\rho_2 = 0.0569$ lb/cu ft, $u_2 = 2230$ ft/sec.

To achieve the above flow, p_4 can be 4.16 atm; if p_4 is increased, G is decreased; but if p_4 is decreased, G is not changed from 127 and p_2 remains at 4.16 atm.

2. Adiabatic flow in the pipe

(a) $p_1 = 9.5$ atm. An approximate value of the temperature change in the pipe for adiabatic flow can be found from the use of the results of part 1a with Eq. (17-20).

$$u_2{}^2 - u_1{}^2 = 2g_cC_p(T_1 - T_2)$$

$$T_1 - T_2 = \frac{(845)^2 - (723)^2}{(2)(32.2)(\frac{7}{29})(778)} = 15.9°R$$

This relatively small temperature change shows that the results for isothermal flow apply to a good de ree of approximation to the adiabatic flow.

(b) $p_1 = 9.0$ atm. A calculation based on the results of part 1b gives $T_1 - T_2 = 323°R$. This temperature change is too large to neglect, and it will have a definite effect on the flow conditions. To illustrate this effect, we shall calculate the values of p_2, T_2, and u_2, which are obtained for $p_1 = 9.0$ atm; that is, $G = 127$ lb/(sec)(sq ft).

The problem is solved by using Eq. (17-46), which we write in terms of densities as

$$\frac{(k+1)G^2}{2kg_c}\ln\left(\frac{\rho_1}{\rho_2}\right) + \frac{1}{2}\left[\frac{G^2(k-1)}{2g_ck\rho_1{}^2} + \frac{p_1}{\rho_1}\right](\rho_2{}^2 - \rho_1{}^2) + \frac{2fG^2L}{g_cD} = 0$$

The only unknown in this equation is ρ_2; it is found by trial. The last (correct) value of $\rho_2 = 0.066$ lb/cu ft gives

$$\frac{(2.4)(127)^2}{(2.8)(32.2)}\ln\left(\frac{0.1230}{0.066}\right)$$

$$+ \frac{1}{2}\left[\frac{(127)^2(0.4)}{(2)(32.2)(1.4)(0.1230)^2} + \frac{19{,}080}{0.1230}\right][(0.066)^2 - (0.123)^2]$$

$$+ \frac{2(0.01)(127)^2(8.93)}{32.2(\frac{2}{12})} \overset{?}{=} 0$$

and

$$268 - 807 + 536 = -3$$

This check is close enough. We also find $u_2 = 127/0.066 = 1925$ ft/sec, and from Eq. (17-20), $T_2 = 2910 - 217 = 2693°R$. From the ideal-gas law, $p_2 = 4.46$ atm. The speed of sound at 2 is given by Eq. (17-13) as 2540 ft/sec. For adiabatic flow, G can be made greater than 127 lb/(sec)(sq ft).

HIGH-SPEED BOUNDARY-LAYER FLOW

Before leaving the subject of high-speed flow, we shall make a few qualitative observations about high-speed flow in the boundary layer along a flat plate.   In an isentropic nozzle the temperature falls as the gas expands; there is no friction.   In a pipe of constant cross section the tendency for the temperature to fall as an ideal gas expands is offset, except at high velocities, by the heat generated by friction (Joule-Thomson expansion). In the boundary layer on a flat plate the pressure does not fall, so there is no tendency for the gas to cool.   The temperature is thus increased by the heat generated by friction in the boundary layer.   This frictional heat increases with increasing velocity.   Since Mach numbers far above unity can be attained in this type of flow, very high temperatures may be reached in the boundary layer.   These last remarks apply to incompressible as well as compressible fluids.

Without giving the proof here, it can be shown[1] that the temperature at the surface of the flat insulated plate is given approximately by the stagnation temperature,

$$T_o = T_\infty \left(1 + \frac{k - 1}{2} \mathsf{Ma}^2 \right) \tag{17-52}$$

for air and similar gases.   For a temperature in the air far from the plate (T_∞) of 400°R, for $k = 1.4$, and for a Mach number of 10, the temperature at the plate surface is about 8400°R.   Since there are no known materials which will remain solid at such temperatures, the surfaces of a rocket may be coated with a poorly conducting material which is consumed during flight.   This vaporization of the solid because of frictional heating in the boundary layer is called ablation.

PROBLEMS

17-1. Complete the solution of Prob. 5-4 by calculating the pressure and temperature in the nozzle when the flow rate of entrained air is a maximum.   The air should leave the nozzle at 1150 ft/sec and at the same pressure and density as the entrained air.

17-2. Air is flowing from a reservoir through a converging nozzle to the surroundings at 1 atm.   If the diameter at the throat of the nozzle is 1½ in., calculate the mass-flow rates for reservoir pressures of 2, 3, and 5 atm.   The stagnation temperature is 200°F.

17-3. Air leaves a reservoir where it is at $p_o = 10$ atm and $t_o = 300$°F and flows through a converging-diverging nozzle.

(a) If the area at the nozzle outlet is twice the area at the throat, find the highest outlet pressure which causes the sonic velocity at the throat.   Calculate also the outlet velocity.

(b) For an outlet pressure 15 per cent below that found in part (a), find the location of the transverse shock and the velocities on either side of it.   Find also the velocity at the nozzle outlet.   What are the stagnation pressure and temperature at the outlet?

17-4. Steam from a large reservoir at 100 psia and 500°F flows reversibly through a converging-diverging nozzle at 1 lb/sec.   Calculate the pressure and area at the throat and the velocity and area at the nozzle exit if it is designed to discharge to the atmosphere

---

[1] H. Schlichting, "Boundary Layer Theory," 4th ed., chap. 15, McGraw-Hill Book Company, Inc., New York, 1960.

with no pressure shock.   Consider steam as a real gas and use a Mollier diagram to obtain its properties.

17-5. Find approximately the highest velocity which can be obtained with a converging-diverging nozzle with the reaction between oxygen and ethyl alcohol occurring in the upstream reservoir.

17-6. Suggest at least two possible methods for obtaining, on a laboratory scale, a flow having a Mach number of 10.

17-7. Plot on an *H-S* diagram the Fanno and Rayleigh lines of interest in the study of a transverse shock with steam; the upstream conditions are $u_1 = 2500$ ft/sec, $t_1 = 220°F$, $p_1 = 10$ psia.

17-8. Natural gas, which may be assumed to be pure methane, is to be pumped through a 100-mile section of 40-in.-ID pipeline at the rate of 150 million cu ft/24 hr (measured at 50°F and atmospheric pressure).   To what pressure must the gas be compressed in order to get a pressure of 10 psig at the discharge end of the line?   Assume isothermal flow at 60°F and no change in elevation.   Methane may be considered an ideal gas to simplify the problem.

17-9. Air is flowing adiabatically in a straight pipe of 1½ in. ID.   At a point 10 ft from the discharge point the pressure is 100 psig and the temperature is 200°F.   The discharge is to the atmosphere.   Find the mass-flow rate.   Also find the mass-flow rate if the given pressure and temperature exist (*a*) 20 ft and (*b*) 150 ft from the exit.

17-10. Steam is contained in a large tank at 800°F and 500 psia.   How fast will it flow out through a 10-ft length of 2-in.-ID pipe having a rounded entrance?   The flow is adiabatic.

HEAT TRANSFER

INTRODUCTION TO HEAT TRANSFER

Scientists and philosophers have speculated on the nature of heat for many centuries. Galileo is said to have constructed one of the first thermometers, a device in which the expansion of air was used as a measure of temperature. Numerous other temperature-measuring instruments were proposed and used before Fahrenheit described the first mercury thermometer in 1724.

Among the early investigators was Franklin, who in 1757 reported a series of observations on the thermal conductivity of metallic, ceramic, and wooden materials, with particular reference to teapot handles. Newton proposed in 1701 that the rate of cooling of a body was proportional to the temperature difference between the body and its surroundings, a relation which was true within the limits of experimental accuracy attainable in the eighteenth century. Scheele (1724–1786) observed that heat from a stove could move through air without warming it but could be absorbed by glass. He proposed that heat transferred in this fashion be called radiant heat.

The examples given above are typical of the numerous studies of heat transfer which were begun as a result of observations of a nonindustrial world. Although engineers are primarily concerned with applying the principles of heat transfer to industrial problems, they should not overlook the fact that the natural world furnishes many examples of heat-transfer phenomena which can increase their understanding of principles that apply elsewhere.

Mechanisms

Heat transfer is the transfer of energy occurring as a result of a driving force which we call temperature difference. There are three mechanisms by which heat transfer can occur:

Conduction. Heat can be conducted through solids, liquids, and gases. Most illustrations of heat conduction are chosen with an opaque solid as the conducting substance, because in such materials conduction is the only method by which heat can be transferred. Heat is conducted by the transfer of energy of motion between adjacent molecules. The kinds of motion depend on the molecular state of the system and range from the vibration of atoms in a crystal lattice to the random motion of molecules in a gas. It is known that there are supplementary mechanisms in certain cases, as, for example, the transfer of energy by free electrons in metallic solids.

Convection. This term implies transfer of heat due to bulk transport and mixing of macroscopic elements of liquid or gas. Because motion of a fluid is involved, heat transfer by convection is partially governed by the laws of fluid mechanics. If convection is induced by density differences resulting from temperature differences within the fluid, it is said to be natural convection. However, if the motion of the fluid is the result of an outside force, as might be exerted by a pump impeller, then it is called forced convection.

Radiation. The transfer of heat by radiation is energy transfer by electromagnetic radiation, or photons, having a certain range of wavelengths. It follows that the same laws that govern the special range of radiation which we call visible light also govern the radiation of the energy we call heat. Although energy can be transferred by radiation through gases, liquids, and solids, these media absorb some or all of the energy, so that energy is radiated most efficiently through empty space.

Illustrations

Both our natural and man-made surroundings contain numerous illustrations of the separate and combined mechanisms of heat transfer. For example, the temperature in the earth's crust has been observed experimentally to increase with depth at a rate which is usually between 0.01 and 0.02°F/ft. This indicates that heat is being conducted continuously to the earth's surface from its interior. This heat transfer has little effect on surface conditions because the conduction rate [roughly 0.01 Btu/(hr)(sq ft)] is far less than the rate at which heat is transferred to and from the surface by other mechanisms.[1] Examples of industrial heat-transfer processes in which conduction is the predominant mechanism are thermal curing of rubber, heat-treatment of steel forgings, and heat flow through the walls of heat exchangers.

[1] B. Gutenberg (ed.), "Internal Constitution of the Earth," Dover Publications, New York, 1951.

An example illustrating a process which is primarily convective is the operation of the steam "radiator." In this apparatus condensing steam in the radiator gives up heat which, after flowing through the radiator wall by conduction, is discharged into the atmosphere. Some heat is lost from the surface by radiation, but contrary to the name of the device, this amount is small compared with the total amount of heat given up. In fact, the common practice of painting radiators with aluminum or other light-colored paint does much to lessen radiation, as we shall see later. Heat is transferred by conduction into the air surrounding the radiator, and this step is followed by natural convection caused by the resulting density differences. If the air were moved by the action of a fan, the transfer would be achieved by combined forced and natural convection.

The most obvious example of the radiation mechanism is the transport of heat to the earth from the sun. The difficulty of transporting heat a distance of 93 million miles through a near vacuum rules out serious thought of contributions by conduction and convection. It is of interest to note that measurements of solar radiation striking the earth, which vary with time and location, indicate a heat-transfer rate normal to the sun's rays of approximately 440 Btu/(hr)(sq ft).

An industrial example of a heat-transfer process in which radiation is predominant is the operation of a furnace for heating petroleum. The tube still, as it is called, is essentially a room constructed of fire-resistant materials into which a combustible mixture of gases is injected and burned. Petroleum flows through a network of tubes suspended near the walls and ceiling. The combustion gases, which may have a temperature as high as 2000°F, transfer heat to the outer tube surfaces primarily by the mechanism of radiation and to a lesser extent by conduction and convection.

Heat is seldom transferred by a single mechanism, but usually by a combination of mechanisms operating in series or in parallel, as in the examples just discussed. The analysis of many heat-transfer problems, however, does not require that all parts be solved with equal care. With experience, the engineer will usually be able to recognize the predominant mechanisms and can base his calculations on these while neglecting many minor effects.

CONDUCTION AND
THERMAL CONDUCTIVITY

The Fourier Equation for Heat Conduction

The basic equation for steady-state heat conduction is known as Fourier's equation.[1] Written for conduction in one direction, it is

$$q = -kA \frac{dt}{dx} \tag{19-1}$$

where q = heat-conduction rate in x direction
  A = cross-sectional area normal to heat flow
dt/dx = temperature gradient in x direction
  k = a proportionality constant known as thermal conductivity of conducting medium

Steady-state conduction means that the heat-transfer rate q through a given cross section in the system does not vary with time.[2] The thermal conductivity k is a function of the molecular state of the medium; for a single-phase system it is usually considered to be dependent on temperature and pressure. If the temperature varies greatly across the system, this may cause a significant variation of k with position. The cross-sectional area normal to heat flow may also be dependent on position. The minus sign in the equation is present because it is usually convenient to make q positive in the positive x direction.

Thermal Conductivity

In this chapter we shall look only briefly at the subject of thermal conductivity. For the purpose of this book it is enough that a student have

[1] J. B. J. Fourier, "Théorie analytique de la chaleur," Gauthier-Villars, Paris, 1822.
[2] Electrical engineers and physicists use the term steady state to designate, in addition, systems in which there is a steady periodic variation.

some knowledge of the conduction mechanisms and the magnitudes of the thermal conductivity in various systems. For information beyond this, the student is referred to textbooks on modern physics and physical chemistry in which detailed discussions of the properties of matter rightly belong.

Solids.   The thermal conductivity of homogeneous solids varies widely, as may be seen in the few examples shown in Table 19-1. It is typical

Table 19-1.   *Thermal Conductivities of Solids*†
[k, Btu/(hr)(ft)(°F)]

Material	t, °F	k	t, °F	k
Metals:				
Aluminum.........................	32	117	212	119
Copper............................	32	224	212	218
Iron (pure).......................	64	39.0	212	36.6
Steel (1% C)......................	64	26.2	212	25.9
Silver............................	32	242	212	238
Nonmetals:				
Asbestos (density 36.0 lb/cu ft)........	32	0.087	212	0.111
Brick (fused alumina)................	800	1.8		
Corkboard (density 10 lb/cu ft)........	86	0.025		

† From J. H. Perry, "Chemical Engineers' Handbook," 3d ed., McGraw-Hill Book Company, Inc., New York, 1950.

that metallic solids have higher thermal conductivities than nonmetallic solids.

Among the metallic solids, inspection of thermal-conductivity data reveals that the solids with high thermal conductivities are also the ones which are known to have high electrical conductivities. This was first reported by Wiedemann and Franz in 1853 when they noted that the ratios of thermal conductivity to electrical conductivity for metals at a specified temperature were approximately the same. The fact that this relation does not apply to nonmetallic solids has led to the supposition that heat is conducted through solids by a dual mechanism. One mechanism, which applies only to electrical conductors, assumes that heat, like electricity, is conducted by free electrons which move through the lattice of a metal in a manner analogous to molecules moving in a gas. This theory, which is the basis of the Wiedemann-Franz relation, is supported by the fact that carefully grown crystals of very pure metallic elements often have very high thermal conductivities. For example, values for the thermal conductivity of copper at very low temperatures have been measured in the range of 5000 to 7000 Btu/(hr)(ft)(°F). It is assumed that the lattice dislocations more prevalent in commercially prepared copper cause the decrease from these values to the commonly used figure of 220 Btu/(hr)(ft)(°F).

The second mechanism by which heat is conducted in solids is the transmission of energy of vibration between adjacent atoms or molecules in the direction of decreasing temperature. This accounts for the fact that the Wiedemann-Franz equation does not apply to materials regarded as nonconductors of electricity. The oscillation-transfer mechanism is present, but not usually significant, when heat is being conducted through metallic solids. However, it is the controlling mechanism for nonmetallic substances. Although heat-transfer rates for these substances are small compared with the rates obtained through metals, the thermal conductivities of nonmetallic substances are not insignificant, as are the electrical conductivities.

Liquids. In the measurement of the thermal conductivity of a liquid it is essential that all heat transfer by natural convection be eliminated. As might be supposed, this is done by using very thin liquid layers with small temperature differences and by arranging the apparatus so that heat flows in a downward direction.

The thermal conductivities of most liquids are rather small, the exceptions being liquids regarded as metallic. A few values for common substances are given in Table 19-2.

Table 19-2. *Thermal Conductivities of Liquids*†
[k, Btu/(hr)(ft)(°F)]

Material	t, °F	k	t, °F	k
Benzene.............	86	0.092	140	0.087
n-Hexane.............	86	0.080	140	0.078
Mercury.............	82	4.8	140	5.6
n-Nonane.............	86	0.084	140	0.082
Sodium.............	212	49	410	46
Water...............	32	0.343	200	0.393

† From J. H. Perry, "Chemical Engineers' Handbook," 3d ed., McGraw-Hill Book Company, Inc., New York, 1950.

Several theories have been proposed for predicting the thermal conductivity of liquids. One of the earliest theories was that of Bridgman,[1] who proposed a mechanism whereby energy is handed down rows of molecules with the velocity of sound. The over-all energy-transfer rate is considered to be the rate of transfer per row multiplied by the number of rows per unit of cross-sectional area. This product divided by dt/dx provides an

[1] P. W. Bridgman, *Proc. Natl. Acad. Sci. U.S.*, **9**:341 (1923).

expression for the thermal conductivity k of the liquid.   Although the model proposed is simple, the equation can be used to predict the thermal conductivities for many liquids, such as water and acetone, within 10 per cent of the measured values.

Gases.   The conduction of heat in a gas is basically the mechanism of a random walk (diffusion and collision).   The molecules of high-temperature gas diffuse among the molecules of low-temperature gas, collide with them, and give up kinetic energy.   In a system behaving according to the simple kinetic theory of gases, the number of molecules per unit of volume is directly proportional to the pressure on the system.   As the mean free path of a molecule during a walk in such a system is inversely proportional to the pressure, it follows that the thermal conductivity should be independent of pressure.   This has been found to be approximately true of most gases near atmospheric pressure.   It is not true, however, at very low pressures where the thermal conductivity of a gas obviously must approach zero, nor is it true at even moderately low pressures when the dimensions of the container are less than the mean free path of the gas molecules (a so-called Knudsen gas).   At high pressures, where the simple kinetic theory of gases does not apply, it is to be expected that there would be a dependence upon pressure.

It is worth noting that there is a relationship between the viscosity and thermal conductivity of a gas.   Gas viscosity is a measure of the drag exerted by diffusion of gas molecules from a zone moving at one mean velocity into gas molecules in a zone moving at a different mean velocity. This is similar to heat conduction, except that in the case of conduction, the quantity being transported is kinetic energy associated with random motion of the molecules rather than directed momentum.

Table 19-3 gives the thermal conductivities of some common gases.

Table 19-3.   Thermal Conductivities of Gases†
[k, Btu/(hr)(ft)(°F), at approximately atmospheric pressure]

Material	t, °F	k	t, °F	k
Hydrogen............	32	0.100	212	0.129
Methane............	32	0.0175	122	0.0215
n-Butane............	32	0.0078	212	0.0135
n-Hexane............	32	0.0072	68	0.0080
Air................	32	0.0140	212	0.0183

† From J. H. Perry, "Chemical Engineers' Handbook," 3d ed., McGraw-Hill Book Company, Inc., New York, 1950.

Since the mechanism of heat conduction in a gas is a function of its tendency to diffuse, it is to be expected that light gases such as hydrogen would have relatively high thermal conductivities.   This is what actually happens. The data given in Table 19-3 for the paraffin hydrocarbons show a typical decrease of thermal conductivity with increase of molecular weight in a homologous series.

General Remarks on Thermal Conductivity

As was mentioned earlier, thermal conductivity is, in general, a function of temperature and pressure.   The effect of pressure on the conductivities of solids and liquids has received very little attention from engineers, probably because of their primary concern with applications at atmospheric pressure and also partly because of the masking effects of other variables such as the presence of impurities.   As mentioned earlier, the thermal conductivity of an ideal gas is independent of pressure.   The effects of high pressure on the thermal conductivities of gases have been the subject of recent investigations; in general, conductivities have been found to increase with pressure.

Thermal conductivities of gases, liquids, and solids are moderately dependent on temperature, as can be seen by inspection of Tables 19-1 to 19-3. In general, an increase in temperature causes the conductivity of a gas to increase and the conductivity of a solid or liquid to decrease.   However, there are many exceptions to these generalizations; in fact, there are some substances for which conductivities pass through maxima or minima with change in temperature.

In considering thermal conductivities it is apparent that the magnitudes of the values decrease markedly as we consider them in the order of decreasing density.   Most of the common substances encountered in engineering work have conductivities to be found in the following ranges:

	k, $Btu/(hr)(ft)(°F)$
Gases	0.001–0.1
Liquids	0.01–1.0
Solids	1.0–100

One result of this difference in magnitude is that within a given two-phase material the effective thermal conductivity may be quite difficult to predict.   A conductivity computed simply on the basis of weight or volume fraction may not be even close to the correct value.   Rather elaborate geometrical models have been postulated and analyzed mathematically to determine effective thermal conductivity, but even these have not proved very successful.   The principal reason for this, aside from oversimplification of the model, lies in the fact that in a two-phase system, such as porous insulation, some heat is transferred by convection and radiation as well as by conduction. A good discussion of this subject is given by Jakob.[1]

An interesting example of conduction in a two-phase system is found in studies of conduction through fine powders. At sufficiently high pressures the mean free path of the gas molecules is much smaller than the dimensions of the cavities in the powder and the conductivity of the system lies between the values for the solid and the gas. Below a certain pressure, which is a function of the pore size, the gas in the pores behaves as a Knudsen gas, with the result that its thermal conductivity is lower than the conductivity of the gas at the same pressure in a large free volume. As a result, the conductivity of the porous system may be lower than either the conductivity of the solid or the gas as measured under ordinary conditions.

The conductivities of homogeneous mixtures of solids, liquids, or gases are often as hard to predict as the conductivities of two-phase systems. Some experimental measurements have been made employing mixtures, but in general, few experimental data or theoretical methods are available for liquids and solids. Theoretical methods for mixtures of gases are somewhat more reliable.

[1] M. Jakob, "Heat Transfer," vol. I, chap. 6, John Wiley & Sons, Inc., New York, 1949.

STEADY-STATE HEAT CONDUCTION

In this chapter the Fourier conduction equation will be used in the analysis of one-dimensional, steady-state heat flow in solid systems that are geometrically simple. The flat wall and the hollow cylinder, in addition to being simple, are the commonest shapes with which engineers must deal.

Flat Wall

In the application of the Fourier conduction equation,

$$q = -kA \frac{dt}{dx} \tag{20-1}$$

to a flat wall, it is apparent that if heat is flowing normal to the principal surfaces, the area term A is constant. Furthermore, if the conductivity is assumed to be constant, then q at any cross section is proportional to the temperature gradient dt/dx. If energy is neither generated nor accumulated in the wall, q is identical at all cross sections and so is dt/dx. A sketch of the system and a graphical representation of its temperature profile are given in Fig. 20-1.

If the thermal conductivity varies with temperature, dt/dx is not constant. If heat flow and area remain constant at all cross sections and k increases with decreasing temperature, the temperature gradient must diminish in the direction of decreasing temperature. Thus the curve representing temperature in steady-state flow for this system is concave upward.

The integration of Eq. (20-1) is readily performed when q, k, and A are constant, and this gives

$$q = \frac{kA(t_1 - t_2)}{\Delta x} \tag{20-2}$$

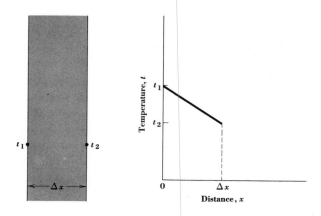

Fig. 20-1. Heat conduction in a flat wall.

The equation can also be integrated and solved for the temperature at a point x.

$$t = -\frac{q}{kA}\, x + t_1 \tag{20-3}$$

This equation indicates the linearity of temperature with distance when the conditions are as stated.

Multilayer Flat Wall

When heat is conducted through a flat wall consisting of layers of different substances, a situation is produced comparable with an electrical system in which a number of resistances are connected in series. The thermal system is shown in Fig. 20-2.

The Fourier equation can be written for each of these layers, and for steady state the heat flow q is the same for all three walls. By analogy with Eq. (20-2) we can write

$$q = k_a A\, \frac{t_1 - t_2}{\Delta x_a} = k_b A\, \frac{t_2 - t_3}{\Delta x_b} = k_c A\, \frac{t_3 - t_4}{\Delta x_c} \tag{20-4}$$

The over-all temperature difference is usually specified in engineering systems, so an equation for heat flow as a function of $t_1 - t_4$ will be derived. Rewriting the equalities given in (20-4) we get

$$t_1 - t_2 = q\, \frac{\Delta x_a}{k_a A}$$

$$t_2 - t_3 = q\, \frac{\Delta x_b}{k_b A}$$

$$t_3 - t_4 = q\, \frac{\Delta x_c}{k_c A}$$

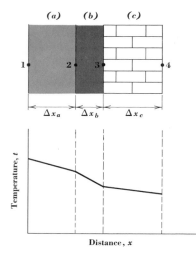

Fig. 20-2.   *Conduction in a multilayer flat wall.*

Adding these equations gives

$$t_1 - t_4 = q \left(\frac{\Delta x_a}{k_a A} + \frac{\Delta x_b}{k_b A} + \frac{\Delta x_c}{k_c A} \right)$$

or

$$q = \frac{t_1 - t_4}{\Delta x_a/k_a A + \Delta x_b/k_b A + \Delta x_c/k_c A} \tag{20-5}$$

If the integrated form of the Fourier equation (20-2) is considered analogous to Ohm's law for electric conduction, then the quantity $\Delta x/kA$ is a measure of the resistance to heat flow. The denominator of Eq. (20-5) is the over-all resistance, which is the sum of the individual resistances.

Figure 20-2 shows temperature gradients for the different layers of solid. Because q/A is the same for all layers, it follows that $k(\Delta t/\Delta x)$ is the same for all layers; thus $\Delta t/\Delta x$ is inversely proportional to the thermal conductivity.

One of the assumptions implicit in the usual analysis of heat flow through multilayer walls is that there is negligible resistance to the flow of heat at each interface. This may not always be true. Surface roughness such as scale can prevent a close junction of the two solids, and the intervening space, if filled with air, will offer a resistance which may be important in comparison with the solid-layer resistances. Although the air gap may be narrow, the low thermal conductivity of air (less than 1 per cent of the thermal conductivity of most solids) can make this thermal resistance $\Delta x/kA$ significant. Investigations have shown that the interfacial resist-

Fig. 20-3.   *Heat conduction in a hollow cylinder.*

ance is diminished by forcing the surfaces together under large pressures, as might be expected.

An important application of heat conduction through multilayer walls occurs in the use of fins which are attached by crimping, soldering, or welding to the outer surface of a tube to increase the heat-transfer rate. Vibration or exposure to cycles of increasing and decreasing temperature (thermal cycles) can cause these fins to become loosened from the tube surface, with a serious decrease in the heat-transfer rate.

Example 20-1

A cold-storage room has walls constructed of a 4-in. layer of corkboard contained between double wooden walls, each ½ in. thick. Find the rate of heat loss in Btu/(hr)(sq ft) if the wall surface temperature is 10°F inside the room and 70°F outside the room. In addition, find the temperature at the interface between the outer wall and the corkboard.

Although thermal conductivity is a function of temperature, it is often assumed to be constant at the arithmetic average temperature of the layer involved. The conductivities of many materials have not been measured over a temperature range; in addition, other factors such as the density (in the case of corkboard) and the presence of impurities (e.g., moisture) can have an effect on the conductivity. Data limitations such as these often have a direct effect on the accuracy of the solution and guide the engineer in determining the degree of simplification he can use in his calculations.

In this problem the thermal conductivity of corkboard is given "at approximately room temperature" in Perry (p. 458) as 0.0225 and 0.025 Btu/(hr)(ft)(°F), corresponding to densities of 7.0 and 10.6 lb/cu ft. A value of 0.024 will be chosen for the solution. The thermal conductivity of several varieties of wood is given in Perry, p. 457. Fir is one of the cheaper woods and is commonly used in wall construction; its thermal conductivity of 0.062 Btu/(hr)(ft)(°F) (given only at 60°C) will be used here.

$$\text{Thermal resistance of each wood layer} = \frac{\Delta x}{kA} = \frac{(\frac{1}{2})(\frac{1}{12})}{(0.062)(1)}$$

$$= 0.67 \text{ (hr)(°F)/Btu}$$

$$\text{Thermal resistance of corkboard} = \frac{\frac{4}{12}}{(0.024)(1)}$$

$$= 13.9 \text{ (hr)(°F)/Btu}$$

The heat loss, using Eq. (20-5), is

$$q = \frac{70 - 10}{0.67 + 13.9 + 0.67} = 3.9 \text{ Btu/hr}$$

The temperature at the interface between the outer wooden wall and the corkboard can be determined by rearranging the equations for the individual temperature drops which led to Eq. (20-5). This gives the temperature drop over the outer layer of wood,

$$t_1 - t_2 = \frac{(\Delta x / kA)_{\text{wood}}(t_1 - t_4)}{\sum \Delta x / kA}$$

$$= (0.67/15.3)(60)$$

$$= 2.6°F$$

Therefore the interface temperature t_2 is 67.4°F.

Hollow Cylinder

The conduction of heat in the walls of a hollow cylinder can be described mathematically by the Fourier equation written in rectangular coordinates [Eq. (20-1)], but the equation is usually written in cylindrical coordinates for convenience. For the example shown in Fig. 20-3, the equation is

$$q = -kA \frac{dt}{dr} \tag{20-6}$$

The area normal to heat flow is

$$A = 2\pi r L$$

The equation can be integrated and solved for the heat-transfer rate q in terms of the boundary conditions:

$$q \int_{r_1}^{r_2} \frac{dr}{r} = -2\pi L k \int_{t_1}^{t_2} dt \tag{20-7}$$

$$q = \frac{2\pi L k(t_1 - t_2)}{\ln (r_2/r_1)} \tag{20-8}$$

This equation can be multiplied by $r_2 - r_1$ in both numerator and denominator to produce

$$q = \frac{2\pi L k(r_2 - r_1)}{\ln (r_2/r_1)} \frac{t_1 - t_2}{r_2 - r_1}$$

$$= k \frac{A_2 - A_1}{\ln (A_2/A_1)} \frac{t_1 - t_2}{r_2 - r_1} \tag{20-9}$$

$$q = kA_{lm} \frac{\Delta t}{\Delta r} \tag{20-10}$$

The area term in Eq. (20-10), A_{lm}, is the log mean area $(A_2 - A_1)/[\ln (A_2/A_1)]$. The temperature difference Δt is $t_1 - t_2$ instead of $t_2 - t_1$. This usage is contrary to mathematical practice but is conventional in writing integrated heat-transfer equations for which the direction of heat flow is usually clearly understood.

Equation (20-10) is similar in form to Eq. (20-2) for conduction in a flat wall, the principal difference being in the area terms. In most engineering applications (e.g., pipes), $r_2/r_1 \ll 2$. In these circumstances the arithmetic mean area may be used in Eq. (20-10), with a consequent error in q less than 4 per cent.

Integration of Eq. (20-6) to give a relation for the temperature t at any radial position r shows that t is a linear function of $\ln r$, rather than of r as in the case of a flat wall.

Multilayer Cylinder

The analysis of multilayer cylinders is done by combining the modes of analysis for multilayer flat walls and single hollow cylinders.

Consider the case of three concentric hollow cylinders, e.g., a pipe with two layers of insulation around it. The thicknesses of the three layers will be designated Δr_a, Δr_b, and Δr_c, and the temperature drops over the individual layers Δt_a, Δt_b, and Δt_c. The total heat-transfer rate, which will be the same for all the cylinders, can be written by analogy with Eq. (20-10).

$$q = \left(kA_{lm}\frac{\Delta t}{\Delta r}\right)_a = \left(kA_{lm}\frac{\Delta t}{\Delta r}\right)_b = \left(kA_{lm}\frac{\Delta t}{\Delta r}\right)_c \tag{20-11}$$

The individual temperature drops may be found by rearranging (20-11).

$$\Delta t_a = q\left(\frac{\Delta r}{kA_{lm}}\right)_a$$

$$\Delta t_b = q\left(\frac{\Delta r}{kA_{lm}}\right)_b$$

$$\Delta t_c = q\left(\frac{\Delta r}{kA_{lm}}\right)_c$$

Adding and rearranging these three equations gives

$$q = \frac{\Delta t_{\text{over-all}}}{(\Delta r/kA_{lm})_a + (\Delta r/kA_{lm})_b + (\Delta r/kA_{lm})_c} \tag{20-12}$$

If the resistance concept is applied to this problem, the individual resistances are the terms written as $\Delta r/kA_{lm}$, and as in the case of the multilayer flat wall, the over-all resistance is simply the sum of the individual resistances in series.

Example 20-2

A 6-in., schedule-80 steel pipe is covered with a 4-in. layer of 85 per cent magnesia insulation. The temperature of the inner surface of the pipe is 475°F, and the temperature of the outer surface of the insulation is 100°F.   Calculate the rate of heat loss per foot of pipe and the temperature at the interface between the pipe and the insulation.

The thermal conductivity of the steel pipe can be taken as 25.9 Btu/(hr)(ft)(°F) (Perry, p. 456), and that of the 85 per cent magnesia as 0.038 (Perry, p. 458).   The OD of the pipe is 6.625 in., and the ID is 5.761 in.

For the pipe $A_{lm} = \dfrac{\pi}{12} \dfrac{6.625 - 5.761}{\ln (6.625/5.761)}$

$= 1.61$ sq ft

For the insulation $A_{lm} = \dfrac{\pi}{12} \dfrac{14.625 - 6.625}{\ln (14.625/6.625)}$

$= 2.65$ sq ft

Resistance of pipe $= \dfrac{\Delta r}{kA_{lm}} = \dfrac{0.432/12}{(25.9)(1.61)}$

$= 0.00086$ (hr)(°F)/Btu

Resistance of insulation $= \dfrac{4/12}{(0.038)(2.65)}$

$= 3.30$ (hr)(°F)/Btu

Rate of heat loss calculated from Eq. (20-12) $= q = \dfrac{375}{0.00086 + 3.30}$

$= 113$ Btu/hr

The thermal resistance of the insulation is so large compared with the resistance of the steel that it is of little importance in the problem to evaluate accurately such terms as the log mean area of the steel.   Although the arithmetic mean area would suffice for calculation of the steel resistance, the use of the arithmetic mean area for the insulation would have introduced an error of 10 per cent.

It is apparent that the temperature drop over the steel is very small.   Therefore the temperature at the steel-insulation interface is nearly the same as the temperature on the inside surface of the steel.

Interface temperature $= 475 - \left(\dfrac{0.00086}{3.30 + 0.00086} \right) (375)$

$= 474.9$°F

Example 20-3

A heating element is constructed from carbon in the shape of a bar 3 in. wide, ½ in. thick, and 3 ft long.   When a potential of 12 volts is applied to the ends of the bar, its surface reaches a uniform temperature of 1400°F, as indicated by an optical pyrometer. What is the temperature at the center of the bar?   The electrical resistivity of the bar is 1.30×10^{-4} (ohm)(ft), and its thermal conductivity is 2.9 Btu/(hr)(ft)(°F).

Only heat conduction normal to the largest faces of the bar will be considered, since heat leaves the bar principally through these faces.   A differential equation is obtained by writing an energy balance on a differential segment dx of the bar, as shown in Fig. 20-4.

Heat flow into element $= -kA \dfrac{dt}{dx}$ Btu/hr   (1)

where $A = (\tfrac{3}{12})(3) = 0.75$ sq ft.

Fig. 20-4. Heat conduction in a bar with generation (Example 20-3).

$$\text{Heat flow out of element} = -kA \left(\frac{dt}{dx} + d\,\frac{dt}{dx} \right)$$

$$= -kA \left(\frac{dt}{dx} + \frac{d^2t}{dx^2}\,dx \right) \qquad \text{Btu/hr} \qquad (2)$$

To obtain the rate of heat generation in the element:

$$\text{Electrical resistance of bar} = \frac{(1.30 \times 10^{-4})(3)}{(\tfrac{1}{24})(\tfrac{3}{12})}$$

$$= 0.0375 \text{ ohm}$$

$$\text{Rate of heat generation in entire bar} = \frac{(12)^2}{0.0375}$$

$$= 3830 \text{ watts [or 419,000 Btu/(hr)(cu ft)]}$$

$$\text{Rate of heat generation in element} = 419,000A\,dx \qquad \text{Btu/hr} \qquad (3)$$

A heat balance on the element gives the following equation:

Heat flow in + rate of heat generation = heat flow out

The terms in this expression are given as Eqs. (1), (2), and (3). These are combined to give

$$-kA\,\frac{dt}{dx} + 419,000A\,dx = -kA \left(\frac{dt}{dx} + \frac{d^2t}{dx^2}\,dx \right)$$

which reduces to

$$\frac{d^2t}{dx^2} = -\frac{419,000}{k} \qquad (4)$$

This equation could have been obtained by simplifying the general form of the differential energy balance (10-14).

Equation (4) becomes

$$\frac{d^2t}{dx^2} = -\frac{419,000}{2.9}$$

$$= -145,000°F/sq \ ft$$

This is integrated to give

$$\frac{dt}{dx} = -145,000x + C_1$$

If the bar is symmetrical, $dt/dx = 0$ at $x = 0$, so $C_1 = 0$. A second integration is performed to get the temperature

$$t = \frac{-145,000x^2}{2} + C_2$$

As a second boundary condition we use $x = \frac{1}{24}$ ft, $t = 1400°F$, and obtain

$$C_2 = 1400 + (145,000/2)(\tfrac{1}{24})^2$$

$$= 1526$$

The equation for the temperature distribution in the bar is

$$t = -72,500x^2 + 1526$$

At the center of the bar the temperature is 1526°F.

PROBLEMS

20-1. The outer wall of the cold-storage room described in Example 20-1 is exposed to air which is at a temperature of 70°F and has a dew point of 60°F. If the air is permitted to diffuse freely through the walls of the wood and cork, it will start to condense at the point where the wall temperature is 60°F and it will freeze at 32°F. Find the zones of moisture and frost in the wall.

20-2. To prevent free diffusion of air and moisture within cold-storage insulation, its surfaces are usually sealed with some material which is impervious to diffusion. Assuming that the corkboard of Example 20-1 and Prob. 20-1 is treated in this way, though the wood is still pervious, find the minimum thickness of cork which will prevent condensation of moisture at the outer cork-wood interface. All the other conditions of Example 20-1 and Prob. 20-1 apply.

20-3. A furnace is to be built with a layer of firebrick $[k = 0.85 \ \text{Btu}/(\text{hr})(\text{ft})(°F)]$ on the inside. This is covered with an 8.5-in. layer of insulating brick $[k = 0.09 \ \text{Btu}/(\text{hr})(\text{ft})(°F)]$ and then by 6 in. of building brick $[k = 0.50 \ \text{Btu}/(\text{hr})(\text{ft})(°F)]$ on the exterior. The interior of the furnace is at 2100°F, and the exterior is at 150°F. Determine the thickness of firebrick necessary to keep the temperature of the insulating brick below 1700°F. Calculate the inside temperature of the building brick.

20-4. The term "thermopane" is given to a window which in a certain case consists of two layers of glass, each ¼ in. thick, separated by a layer of dry, stagnant air, also ¼ in. thick. If the temperature drop over the composite system is 30°F, find the heat loss through such a window, 10 ft long and 4 ft wide. If the window replaces a single glass pane, ⅜ in. thick, at a difference in cost of $120, find the number of days of operation under the specified temperature conditions to pay for the window. Coal with a heating value of 13,200 Btu/lb costs $20 per ton. The furnace efficiency can be assumed to be 50 per cent. The thermal conductivity of the window glass is 0.5 Btu/(hr)(ft)(°F).

20-5. A brewery fermentation tank 37 ft in diameter is situated in a room which has a temperature of 60°F. The tank is constructed of ⅜-in. welded steel plate with a ½-in. glass lining. The temperature at the interface between the glass and the contents of the tank is known to be 120°F. Assuming that the resistance offered by the air film on the outside of the tank equals the combined resistances of the glass and steel, calculate the temperature at the glass-steel interface and the temperature at the steel-air interface. The thermal conductivity of the glass is 0.45 Btu/(hr)(ft)(°F).

20-6. A cylindrical exhaust duct has a constant inside temperature of 600°F. It is insulated on the exterior with a 4-in. layer of rock wool which has an outer surface temperature of 100°F. The duct has an ID of 3.5 in. and ¼-in.-thick walls of a ceramic material with a thermal conductivity of 0.88 Btu/(hr)(ft)(°F). Find the rate of heat loss from the duct per lineal foot. The thermal conductivity of rock wool is represented by the equation $k = 0.025 + 0.00005t$, where t is in °F and k is in Btu/(hr)(ft)(°F).

20-7. A hollow sphere contains a source which emits heat at a constant rate. Find the heat flow in terms of the temperature difference across the wall of the sphere, the thermal conductivity, and the inner and outer radii of the sphere.

20-8. A 60-ft length of Nichrome IV ribbon, 0.051 in. thick and 0.50 in. wide, is used as a heating element. The surface temperature of the ribbon is 1400°F when the voltage drop is 110 volts. Find the maximum temperature in the ribbon under these conditions. The product of electrical resistivity and thermal conductivity of Nichrome IV is 25.7×10^{-6} (Btu)(ohm)/(hr)(°F).

UNSTEADY-STATE HEAT CONDUCTION
21

Unsteady-state heat conduction is of importance to engineers in many circumstances. It may control the rate at which process equipment is brought to stable operating conditions, and it is also important in determining the processing time of many solid articles. For example, the curing time of objects made of molded plastic or rubber is often dependent on the time required to bring the center to some specified temperature without causing thermal damage to the material at the surface. There are also many applications of unsteady-state-conduction theory in the heat-treating and casting of metals.

A slightly different class of problems is characterized by a periodic variation of temperature. Internal-combustion engines, compressors, and automatic-firing weapons generate heat periodically; the dissipation of this heat causes regular periodic temperature fluctuations in the surroundings. Another example is the effect of diurnal, atmospheric-temperature variations on large structures such as bridges and on small structures such as growing plants.

Fundamental Equations

The basic differential equation for unsteady-state conduction in a solid is a special case of the differential energy balance which was derived in Chap. 10. The same equation applies to a stagnant, incompressible fluid. For constant thermal conductivity and no heat generation the differential energy balance was written

$$\frac{\partial t}{\partial \theta} = \frac{k}{\rho C_p}\left(\frac{\partial^2 t}{\partial x^2} + \frac{\partial^2 t}{\partial y^2} + \frac{\partial^2 t}{\partial z^2}\right) \qquad (10\text{-}12)$$

258

Special cases which are of interest include the problem of unsteady-state conduction in only one direction, for which Eq. (10-12) reduces to

$$\frac{\partial t}{\partial \theta} = \frac{k}{\rho C_p} \frac{\partial^2 t}{\partial x^2} \tag{21-1}$$

and the case of steady-state conduction in three directions, where $\partial t/\partial \theta = 0$, and Eq. (10-12) becomes

$$\frac{\partial^2 t}{\partial x^2} + \frac{\partial^2 t}{\partial y^2} + \frac{\partial^2 t}{\partial z^2} = 0 \tag{21-2}$$

When Eq. (10-12) is written for steady-state conduction in only one direction, we obtain

$$\frac{d^2 t}{dx^2} = 0$$

which is readily integrated to give a linear relation between temperature and distance. This was shown earlier in Eq. (20-3), obtained by integrating the Fourier conduction equation.

The differential energy balance can also be obtained in cylindrical coordinates by writing an energy balance on a control volume which has the shape of a hollow cylinder. The equation obtained for no flow and no heat generation is

$$\frac{\partial t}{\partial \theta} = \frac{k}{\rho C_p} \left(\frac{\partial^2 t}{dr^2} + \frac{1}{r} \frac{\partial t}{\partial r} + \frac{1}{r^2} \frac{\partial^2 t}{\partial \phi^2} + \frac{\partial^2 t}{\partial z^2} \right) \tag{21-3}$$

If there is negligible axial conduction, $\partial^2 t/\partial z^2 = 0$, and if there is no variation of temperature with angular position, $\partial^2 t/\partial \phi^2 = 0$. The derivation of Eq. (21-3) is left as an exercise for the reader. Many engineering systems involve cylindrical shapes, and Eq. (21-3) and its simplifications are more useful in describing these systems than Eq. (10-12), which is expressed in rectangular coordinates.

Example 21-1

Problems of heating or cooling spheres are best solved using the differential energy balance written in spherical coordinates. Derive this equation for the case where there is no variation of temperature with angular position.

The center of the sphere is chosen as the origin of the coordinate system. At a radial distance r from the center, we have a spherical surface at a uniform temperature t. At distance $r + dr$ is another surface at temperature $t + dt$. These two surfaces can be considered as the boundaries of the control volume.

$$\text{Rate of heat flow into control volume} = -k(4\pi r^2) \frac{\partial t}{\partial r} \tag{1}$$

Rate of heat flow out of control volume

$$= -k[4\pi(r + dr)^2]\left[\frac{\partial t}{\partial r} + d\left(\frac{\partial t}{\partial r}\right)\right]$$

$$= -4\pi k(r^2 + 2r\ dr + \overline{dr^2})\left(\frac{\partial t}{\partial r} + \frac{\partial^2 t}{\partial r^2}\ dr\right) \qquad (2)$$

The net heat flow in can be found by subtracting (2) from (1). After this is done, all second- and third-order differentials can be dropped (because they are negligible), giving

$$\text{Net heat flow} = 4\pi k\left(r^2\frac{\partial^2 t}{\partial r^2}\ dr + 2r\frac{\partial t}{\partial r}\ dr\right) \qquad (3)$$

The rate of accumulation of energy in the control volume is

$$(4\pi r^2\ dr)\rho C_p\frac{\partial t}{\partial \theta} \qquad (4)$$

which is equal to the net heat flow in.

Therefore we have

$$4\pi k\left(r^2\frac{\partial^2 t}{\partial r^2}\ dr + 2r\frac{\partial t}{\partial r}\ dr\right) = (4\pi r^2\ dr)\rho C_p\frac{\partial t}{\partial \theta} \qquad (5)$$

from which we obtain the equation for unsteady conduction,

$$\frac{\partial t}{\partial \theta} = \frac{k}{\rho C_p}\left(\frac{\partial^2 t}{\partial r^2} + \frac{2}{r}\frac{\partial t}{\partial r}\right) \qquad (6)$$

Solutions of the Fundamental Equations[1]

The equations for unsteady conduction which have been presented are all partial differential equations. There are two common methods of solving these equations: the "separation of variables" method and the method which uses integral transforms (usually Laplace transforms).

Both methods can be used to obtain solutions of the more common equations. However, the method of Laplace transforms is better suited to some of the more difficult problems.

The method of separation of variables is illustrated in Example 21-2. It can be followed by students who have a modest knowledge of differential equations. The method of Laplace transforms is more difficult and will not be illustrated.

Example 21-2

A rubber sheet ½ in. thick is to be cured at 292°F for 50 min. If the sheet is initially at 70°F and heat is applied from both surfaces, find the time required for the temperature

---

[1] Methods of solving the heat-conduction equations are presented in most textbooks on applications of mathematics in engineering. Three books that might be recommended are H. S. Mickley, T. K. Sherwood, and C. E. Reed, "Applied Mathematics in Chemical Engineering," 2d ed., McGraw-Hill Book Company, Inc., New York, 1957; C. R. Wylie, "Advanced Engineering Mathematics," 2d ed., McGraw-Hill Book Company, Inc., New York, 1960; and H. S. Carslaw and J. C. Jaeger, "Operational Methods in Applied Mathematics," 2d ed., Oxford University Press, London, 1947.

292°F   ₵   292°F

x

¼ in

$x = 0$ $x = x_o$

Fig. 21-1.   *Unsteady-state heat conduction in a rubber sheet (Example 21-2).*

at the center of the sheet to reach 290°F. It can be assumed that the surfaces are brought to 292°F as soon as curing is begun and held at that temperature throughout the process. The thermal diffusivity $k/\rho C_p$ of rubber can be taken as 0.0028 sq ft/hr.

The differential equation for unsteady heat conduction in one direction is

$$\frac{\partial t}{\partial \theta} = \frac{k}{C_p \rho} \frac{\partial^2 t}{\partial x^2} \tag{21-1}$$

The origin is chosen at the center of the sheet, so that x is the distance from the center, as shown in Fig. 21-1, and x_0 is the half thickness.

In solving partial differential equations it is usually convenient to define the variables so that they range between zero and 1 or between zero and infinity and are dimensionless. Therefore Eq. (21-2) will be expressed in terms of the following redefined variables:

$$Y = \frac{292 - t}{292 - 70} \qquad n = \frac{x}{x_o} \qquad \tau = \frac{k\theta}{C_p \rho x_o{}^2} \tag{1}$$

Equation (21-2) becomes

$$\frac{\partial Y}{\partial \tau} = \frac{\partial^2 Y}{\partial n^2} \tag{2}$$

as can be proved by substituting the new variables (1) in Eq. (2) and performing the indicated partial differentiations.

A solution to Eq. (2) is obtained by postulating that such a solution can be written as the product of two terms,

$$Y = \tau N \tag{3}$$

where τ is a function of only the quantity τ, in which time is the variable, and N is a function of only n, in which distance is the variable. If $Y = \tau N$ is a solution, it can be differentiated as stated in (2) and yields

$$N \frac{\partial \tau}{\partial \tau} = \tau \frac{\partial^2 N}{\partial n^2} \tag{4}$$

This equation can be rearranged to give only terms which depend on τ on the left side of the equation and only terms which are a function of n on the right side.

$$\frac{1}{\tau}\frac{\partial \tau}{\partial \tau} = \frac{1}{N}\frac{\partial^2 N}{\partial n^2} \tag{5}$$

Since time and distance are independent of each other in this problem, the left side of this equation is independent of distance and the right side is independent of time. Hence each side must be constant. This constant we shall call, for convenience, $-a^2$. Thus we can write two ordinary differential equations,

$$\frac{d\tau}{d\tau} + a^2\tau = 0 \tag{6}$$

and

$$\frac{d^2N}{dn^2} + a^2N = 0 \tag{7}$$

The solution of Eq. (6) is simply

$$\tau = C_1 e^{-a^2\tau} \tag{8}$$

The student of differential equations will recognize Eq. (7) as a second-order, ordinary differential equation with constant coefficients. The solution is written as

$$N = C_2 \sin an + C_3 \cos an \tag{9}$$

Having obtained expressions for τ and N, we can now write the solution for the partial differential equation (2), which we originally postulated as Eq. (3).

$$\begin{aligned} Y &= \tau N \\ &= C_1 e^{-a^2\tau}(C_2 \sin an + C_3 \cos an) \end{aligned} \tag{10}$$

This equation contains four constants, C_1, C_2, C_3, and a; however, C_1 can be combined with C_2 and C_3, so that only three boundary conditions are needed to complete the solution. These are:

1. The system is symmetrical, so no heat is conducted across the center line ($x = 0$). Therefore, at $n = 0$, $\partial Y/\partial n = 0$.
2. At the surface ($x = x_o = \frac{1}{48}$), the temperature is constant at 292°F at all times. Thus, when $n = 1$, $Y = 0$.
3. Initially ($\theta = 0$), the entire sheet is at 70°F. Therefore, when $\tau = 0$, $Y = 1$.
Boundary condition 1 is used first.

$$\frac{\partial Y}{\partial n} = C_1 e^{-a^2\tau}(C_2 a \cos an - C_3 a \sin an)$$

When $n = 0$, $\sin an = 0$; however, $\cos an = 1$. Therefore

$$\frac{\partial Y}{\partial n} = aC_1C_2 e^{-a^2\tau}$$

For this to be equal to zero and still preserve a general solution, the term C_2 must equal zero. After this simplification the general solution can be written

$$Y = Ae^{-a^2\tau} \cos an \tag{11}$$

where A includes both C_1 and C_3.
Boundary condition 2 is next employed.

$$0 = Ae^{-a^2\tau} \cos a$$

This condition is realized for many values of a such as $\pi/2$, $3\pi/2$, $5\pi/2$, etc.

The substitution of one of these values for a in Eq. (11) would meet the requirement of the second boundary condition, but it is not possible to represent an arbitrary temperature distribution in the slab by a cosine curve. However, it is possible to represent an arbitrary function by an infinite series of cosine terms, provided each term is multiplied by a suitable coefficient. Therefore we can write the general solution as

$$Y = A_1 e^{-(\pi/2)^2 \tau} \cos\left(\frac{\pi}{2}\right) n + A_2 e^{-(3\pi/2)^2 \tau} \cos\left(\frac{3\pi}{2}\right) n$$

$$+ A_3 e^{-(5\pi/2)^2 \tau} \cos\left(\frac{5\pi}{2}\right) n + \cdots$$

$$+ A_i e^{-[(2i-1)\pi/2]^2 \tau} \cos\left[\frac{(2i-1)\pi}{2}\right] n + \cdots \quad (12)$$

where i is an integer. It can be verified by differentiation and substitution that this sum still satisfies the partial differential equation and the first two boundary conditions.

The final step is to evaluate the constant which serves as a coefficient of each term in the series. This is done using the third boundary condition. Equation (12) becomes

$$1 = A_1 \cos\left(\frac{\pi}{2}\right) n + A_2 \cos\left(\frac{3\pi}{2}\right) n + A_3 \cos\left(\frac{5\pi}{2}\right) n + \cdots$$

$$+ A_i \cos\left(\frac{2i-1}{2}\right) \pi n + \cdots \quad (13)$$

Both sides of this equation are multiplied by $\cos\left[(2i-1)/2\right]\pi n\,dn$ and integrated over the range of 0 to 1. The left-hand side becomes

$$\int_0^1 \cos\left(\frac{2i-1}{2}\right)\pi n\,dn = \frac{2}{2i-1}\frac{1}{\pi}\left[\sin\left(\frac{2i-1}{2}\right)\pi n\right]_0^1$$

$$= -\frac{2}{2i-1}\frac{1}{\pi}(-1)^i$$

The first term on the right-hand side of the equation can be integrated with the aid of a table of integrals to give

$$\int_0^1 A_1 \cos\left(\frac{\pi}{2}\right) n \cos\left(\frac{2i-1}{2}\right)\pi n\,dn = A_1\left[\frac{\sin(i-1)\pi n}{(2i-2)\pi} + \frac{\sin i\pi n}{2i\pi}\right]_0^1$$

$$= A_1\left[\frac{\sin(i-1)\pi}{(2i-2)\pi} + \frac{\sin i\pi}{2i\pi}\right]$$

$$= 0$$

The integral is zero for all values of the integer i other than 1. The second term on the right-hand side vanishes in the same manner as the first, and so do all succeeding terms except the ith term. This becomes

$$A_i \int_0^1 \cos^2\left(\frac{2i-1}{2}\right)\pi n\,dn = A_i \frac{2}{2i-1}\frac{1}{\pi}\left[\frac{\pi}{2}\frac{2i-1}{2} n + \frac{1}{4}\sin(2\pi)\frac{2i-1}{2} n\right]_0^1$$

$$= A_i \frac{2}{2i-1}\frac{1}{\pi}\left(\frac{\pi}{2}\frac{2i-1}{2} + 0 - 0 - 0\right)$$

$$= \frac{A_i}{2}$$

Thus Eq. (13) reduces to

$$-\frac{2}{2i-1}\frac{1}{\pi}(-1)^i = \frac{A_i}{2}$$

from which

$$A_i = \frac{-4(-1)^i}{(2i-1)\pi}$$

(That is, $A_1 = \frac{4}{\pi}$, $A_2 = -\frac{4}{3\pi}$, $A_3 = \frac{4}{5\pi}$, etc.).

The general solution is therefore

$$Y = \frac{4}{\pi} e^{-(\pi/2)^2 \tau} \cos\left(\frac{\pi n}{2}\right) - \frac{4e^{-(3\pi/2)^2 \tau}}{3\pi} \cos\left(\frac{3\pi n}{2}\right)$$
$$+ \frac{4e^{-(5\pi/2)^2 \tau}}{5\pi} \cos\left(\frac{5\pi n}{2}\right) - \cdots \quad (14)$$

Equation (14) written in compact form is

$$Y = \sum_{i=1}^{i=\infty} \frac{-2(-1)^i}{[(2i-1)/2]\pi} e^{-[(2i-1)\pi/2]^2 \tau} \cos\left(\frac{2i-1}{2}\right)\pi n \quad (15)$$

Equation (15) is now applied to the specific example.

$$Y = \frac{292 - 290}{292 - 70} = 0.0090$$

$$n = 0$$

Therefore

$$0.0090 = \frac{4}{\pi} e^{-(\pi/2)^2 \tau} - \frac{4}{3\pi} e^{-(3\pi/2)^2 \tau} + \frac{4}{5\pi} e^{-(5\pi/2)^2 \tau} - \cdots$$

The solution for τ (which contains the time variable θ) must be obtained by trial and error. As a first approximation, only the first term on the right-hand side will be considered. This gives

$$\tau = -\left(\frac{2}{\pi}\right)^2 \ln \frac{(\pi)(0.0090)}{4}$$

$$= 2.01$$

$$\theta = \frac{C_p \rho}{k} x_o^2 \tau$$

$$= \frac{2.01}{(0.0028)(48)^2}$$

$$= 0.313 \text{ hr (18.7 min)}$$

It is necessary to check the relative magnitude of the terms in the series solution to see if all terms other than the first one are negligible.

When $\tau = 2.01$, the series becomes

$$Y = \frac{4}{\pi} e^{-4.97} - \frac{4}{3\pi} e^{-44.8} + \frac{4}{5\pi} e^{-124} - \cdots$$

$$= (1.27)(0.00708) - (0.423)(3.55 \times 10^{-20}) + \cdots$$

The validity of the approximation which employed only the first term of the series is apparent. Although not all series solutions converge so rapidly as in the example shown here, they frequently do so. This can often be established by a visual inspection of the exponents in the series (as in this case).

The temperature at any point in the rubber sheet at any instant can be determined by substitution of the appropriate values for n and τ in Eq. (15). Table 21-1 was prepared to show the development of the temperature profiles as heating proceeds. It is apparent that the results are contradictory at the surface at zero time. This is a result of the boundary conditions imposed on the mathematical solution.

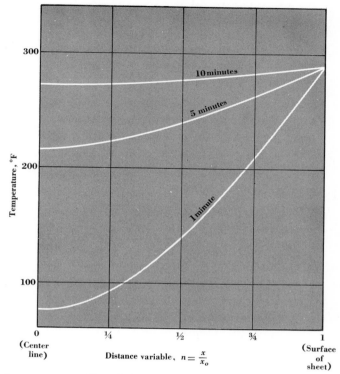

Fig. 21-2.   *Illustration of temperature profiles calculated in*
Example 21-2.

The results are illustrated graphically in Fig. 21-2.   At the center the temperature gradient is zero since the slab is being heated uniformly from both sides.   The same condition would result if a sheet of half the thickness of the sheet in the example were heated from one side only, while the other side was covered with a layer of perfect insulation.

Although the preceding example is rather lengthy, it is a typical illustration of the application of the technique of separation of variables to a problem in unsteady-state heat transfer.   The mathematical manipulations were shown to be rather elementary.   Actually, the student who has studied the use of Fourier series will recognize that the constant A_i, which was determined rather laboriously in the example, is a Fourier constant and can be found with much less effort when the appropriate mathematical techniques are known.

Solutions to unsteady-state conduction problems involving flat, parallel surfaces usually contain series of sine or cosine terms.   On the other hand, systems with cylindrical boundaries generally give rise to expressions which are known as Bessel functions (called in German *Zylinderfunktionen*). These functions are available in tabulated form.[1]

Table 21-1.   Temperature Distribution in Rubber Sheet
            (Example 21-2)

Time elapsed, min	$\frac{4}{\pi} e^{-(\pi/2)^2 \tau}$	$n = 0$ $\cos \frac{n\pi}{2}$ $= 1$ (center line)	$n = \frac{1}{4}$ $\cos \frac{n\pi}{2}$ $= 0.924$	$n = \frac{1}{2}$ $\cos \frac{n\pi}{2}$ $= 0.707$	$n = \frac{3}{4}$ $\cos \frac{n\pi}{2}$ $= 0.383$	$n = 1$ $\cos \frac{n\pi}{2}$ $= 0$ (surface)
				Temperature in sheet, °F		
0	1	70	70	70	70	
1	9.76×10^{-1}	75	92	139	209	292
5	3.37×10^{-1}	217	223	239	263	292
10	9.02×10^{-2}	272	273	278	284.3	292
20	6.37×10^{-3}	290.6	290.7	291	291.5	292
30	4.52×10^{-4}	291.9	291.9	291.9	292	292
40	3.19×10^{-5}	292	292	292	292	292

If a solid cylinder of length sufficient to eliminate end effects receives heat uniformly from its surface, which is held at constant temperature, the differential equation relating temperature, time, and radial position derived from Eq. (21-3) is

$$\frac{\partial t}{\partial \theta} = \frac{k}{\rho C_p} \left(\frac{\partial^2 t}{\partial r^2} + \frac{1}{r} \frac{\partial t}{\partial r} \right) \tag{21-4}$$

This equation, when treated in the manner outlined in Example 21-2, gives rise to two solutions, one containing an exponential time variable and the other a Bessel function in which the argument contains the radius variable. After these solutions have been combined, the general solution takes the form of an infinite series in order to satisfy the boundary conditions.

$$\frac{t_s - t}{t_s - t_o} = \frac{2}{R} \sum_{i=1}^{i=\infty} \frac{e^{-a_i^2 k\theta/\rho C_p}}{a_i J_1(a_i R)} J_0(a_i r) \tag{21-5}$$

J_0 and J_1 are Bessel functions of the first kind (zero and first order, respectively), and a_i is the ith root of $J_0(a_i R) = 0$. The initial temperature is t_o, the surface temperature (constant) is t_s, and the radius of the rod is R.

The solutions to many common problems in heat conduction have been

[1] E. Jahnke and F. Emde, "Tables of Functions," Dover Publications, New York, 1945; W. Flügge, "Four-place Tables of Transcendental Functions," McGraw-Hill Book Company, Inc., New York, 1954.

presented graphically.[1] Examination of these plots reveals the presence of the same groups used in the solutions given above. The ordinate is usually the fractional unaccomplished temperature change, $(t_s - t)/(t_s - t_o)$; the abscissa is related to the exponential group containing time as a variable. The distance variable n is a parameter within a family of curves on each plot, whereas each family of curves is determined by the boundary conditions, i.e., whether or not a convective resistance (represented by a heat-transfer coefficient h) exists at the surface.

Example 21-3

Find the solution to the problem given in Example 21-2 using Perry, p. 462, fig. 4. Using the nomenclature in Perry's Handbook,

$$X = \frac{k\theta}{\rho C_p r_m{}^2} = \frac{0.0028\theta}{(\frac{1}{48})^2} = 6.44\theta$$

$$Y = \frac{292 - 290}{292 - 70}$$

$$= 0.0090$$

$$m = \frac{k}{h_T r_m} = 0 \qquad \text{surface temperature is assumed constant, implying that surface resistance is negligible and heat-transfer coefficient } h_T \text{ is infinite}$$

$$n = \frac{r}{r_m} = 0$$

Using the appropriate values of Y, m, and n, we find from the chart that $X = 2.1$. Therefore $\theta = 2.1/6.44 = 0.33$ hr, or about 20 min.

Newman's Rule

The solutions discussed to this point have been solutions to differential equations containing three variables. Obviously, not all cylinders and plates encountered in industry have sufficient length-thickness ratios so that they can be treated as infinitely wide or long. Fortunately, the technique for solving many problems of systems with finite dimensions in all directions is rather simple. This technique is often called Newman's rule. Newman has shown[2] that if a brick-shaped object is heated or cooled, the general solution describing temperature as a function of time θ and three distance variables x, y, and z can be written as

$$Y = Y_x Y_y Y_z$$

where $Y_x = f_1(x,\theta)$ is the equation already derived for one-dimensional unsteady-state conduction in Example 21-2. $Y_y = f_2(y,\theta)$ and $Y_z = f_3(z,\theta)$

[1] See Perry, p. 462.
[2] A. B. Newman, *Trans. AIChE*, **27**:310 (1931); H. S. Carslaw and J. C. Jaeger, "Conduction of Heat in Solids," 2d ed., Oxford University Press, London, 1959.

are equations for conduction in the y and z directions, respectively, and are identical with Y_x in all respects, except that the term representing one-half the thickness in the x direction is replaced by the half-slab thickness in the y and z directions.

Example 21-4

Find the time for the temperature at the center of a cube of rubber (½-in. side) to reach 290°F under the same conditions as Examples 21-2 and 21-3.

Since the dimensions are the same in all directions, $Y_x = Y_y = Y_z$. Therefore $Y = Y_z{}^3$.

Since

$$Y = 0.0090$$
$$Y_z = 0.208$$

As before,

$$m = n = 0$$

From Perry, fig. 4, p. 462,

$$X = 0.75$$
$$= 6.44\theta$$
$$\theta = 0.116 \text{ hr (7 min)}$$

Newman's rule can be applied equally well to cylinders. In these circumstances a combination of charts is used (Perry, p. 462, figs. 2 and 4). The unaccomplished temperature change is

$$Y = Y_x Y_r$$

where

$$Y_x = f_1(x,\theta)$$

and

$$Y_r = f_2(r,\theta)$$

and Y_x and Y_r are found from the two figures previously cited.

It should be noted in closing that the technique of Newman is not an approximation but is mathematically rigorous. Furthermore, it applies to problems where there is a finite surface resistance to heat transfer.

PROBLEMS

21-1. A solid, steel cylinder 2 in. in diameter is at an initial temperature of 1400°F throughout when it is suddenly quenched in water at 100°F. If the surface of the steel is assumed to fall immediately to 100°F, find the time (in seconds) required for the temperature at the center of the cylinder to reach 400°F. The cylinder can be assumed to have a large ratio of length to diameter.

21-2. A cylinder of the same dimensions as that in Prob. 21-1 is quenched under the same conditions. However, the resistance to heat transfer at the surface is to be accounted for by using an average surface heat-transfer coefficient of 1250 Btu/(hr)(sq ft)(°F).   Find the time for the center of the cylinder to reach 400°F.

21-3. A concrete beam (8 by 12 in.) is exposed to a temperature of 1500°F in a burning building.   Determine the exposure time required for the temperature at the center of the beam to reach 600°F if the beam is at an initial temperature of 70°F.   The thermal diffusivity of concrete can be taken as 0.022 sq ft/hr.

NUMERICAL, GRAPHICAL, AND ANALOG METHODS IN THE ANALYSIS OF HEAT CONDUCTION

Many problems in steady- and unsteady-state conduction are difficult to solve analytically. The differential equations, based on the differential energy balance, can be written readily enough. However, the mathematical boundary conditions are difficult to apply when the physical boundaries of the object are complex and when the temperatures at these boundaries are not uniform. In general, few analytical solutions exist for heat-transfer systems which do not possess some elements of symmetry in both shape and temperature.

When the analytical solutions cannot be obtained, the engineer may resort to an alternative method such as numerical or graphical analysis, or he may construct an electrical or hydraulic analog of the system and make direct measurements of its performance. In this chapter, we shall examine several numerical and graphical methods and, at the end of the chapter, we shall discuss briefly the use of analogs.

It should not be assumed that the numerical and graphical solutions are necessarily less accurate than the analytical solutions. In fact, many (though not all) of them can be made as accurate as desired by mere repetition of routine steps which, if performed an infinite number of times, would give an exact solution. This characteristic is often an advantage, because the accuracy required of a solution is usually known beforehand, and the solution can be stopped when this is reached. An analytical solu-

Fig. **22-1.**   *Relaxation technique applied to one-dimensional conduction.*

tion, on the other hand, must usually be carried out to the end before any answer whatsoever is obtained.

The principal disadvantage of numerical methods is that they are tedious to perform, but with the use of a high-speed digital computer, this disadvantage is overcome. Sometimes numerical procedures, however, do not readily converge to the correct result, no matter how many iterations are performed.

Steady-state Conduction

A number of methods of solving steady-state conduction problems are described by Jakob.[1] We shall consider only the relaxation technique, which is a simple but powerful tool. There are applications of this method in many branches of engineering and science,[2] but we shall restrict our discussion to its use in solving heat-conduction problems.

We shall consider first the application of the relaxation technique in one-dimensional heat flow. The system shown in Fig. 22-1 is a solid of uniform thermal conductivity, insulated on four sides so that heat is conducted in only the x direction. A square grid is drawn on the figure which represents the solid. The sides of the squares, Δy and Δx, are equal; a thickness Δz in the z direction will be assumed. As the heat in the element surrounding point 1 flows into the block surrounding point 2, the rate of heat flow will be

[1] M. Jakob, "Heat Transfer," vol. 1, John Wiley & Sons, Inc., New York, 1949.
[2] R. V. Southwell, "Relaxation Methods in Engineering Science," Oxford University Press, London, 1940.

$$q_{12} = k \, \Delta z \, \Delta y \, \frac{t_1 - t_2}{\Delta x} \tag{22-1}$$

The rate of heat flow from the block of solid around point 2 to the block around point 3 will be

$$q_{23} = k \, \Delta z \, \Delta y \, \frac{t_2 - t_3}{\Delta x} \tag{22-2}$$

The rate at which heat accumulates at point 2 is

$$q_{12} - q_{23} = k \, \Delta z \, (t_1 + t_3 - 2t_2) \tag{22-3}$$

since $\Delta y = \Delta x$. Equation (22-3) can also be written as

$$\frac{q_{12} - q_{23}}{k \, \Delta z} = t_1 + t_3 - 2t_2 \tag{22-4}$$

If the system is at steady state, q_{12} equals q_{23}, and Eq. (22-4) can be rearranged to give

$$t_2 = \frac{t_1 + t_3}{2} \tag{22-5}$$

If an arbitrary temperature distribution is chosen for all the points in the system, it can be tested for correctness using Eq. (22-5). If the temperature t_2 is in error, it may be revised by adding or subtracting $\frac{1}{2}$ $[(q_{12} - q_{23})/k \, \Delta z]$ [as found from Eq. (22-4) with the initial values of t_1, t_2, and t_3] to the temperature t_2. The quantity $(q_{12} - q_{23})/(k \, \Delta z)$ has the dimension of temperature, and the addition of the amount indicated will, of necessity, make Eq. (22-5) valid at that point. If all but one of the temperatures at the nodes of the grid are correct, then alterations at this point will, of course, destroy the consistency among the temperatures at the remaining points. However, the magnitude of the correction diminishes by halves with succeeding points and, if not too great initially, soon vanishes as a significant quantity. The relaxation technique is illustrated in Example 22-1.

Example 22-1

A solid rod conducts heat from a heat source at 800°F to a heat sink at 200°F. The sides of the rod are insulated as shown in Fig. 22-2. Find the temperature distribution in the rod.

We know by the use of Fourier's heat-conduction equation that the temperature distribution in the rod will be a linear function of position. However, we shall assume for the purposes of illustrating the technique that the temperature at point 2 is 700°F and at point 3 is 300°F. The calculation can be made as shown in Table 22-1. The quantity $(q_{12} - q_{23})/(k \, \Delta z)$ will be designated q_2' and, similarly, $(q_{23} - q_{34})/(k \, \Delta z)$ will be called q_3'. These quantities are sometimes referred to as "residuals."

Fig. 22-2.   *Relaxation model (Example 22-1).*

Using the initial temperature distribution (step 0) the quantity q'_2 is calculated using Eq. (22-4) and q'_3 is found from a similar expression.   Half of each of these quantities is then added or subtracted, as the sign indicates, to the respective temperatures t_2 and t_3 (step 1).   Using the new temperature distribution, new values of q'_2 and q'_3 are calculated and new values of t_2 and t_3 once more computed (step 2).   The repetition of this simple process gives figures nearly equal to the correct temperatures after eight steps.

Table 22-1.   *One-dimensional Relaxation*

Step	Point					
	1	2		3		4
	t_1	t_2	q'_2	t_3	q'_3	t_4
0	800	700		300		200
			-300		300	
1	800	550		450		200
			150		-150	
2	800	625		375		200
			-75		75	
3	800	587		413		200
			39		-39	
4	800	607		393		200
			-21		21	
5	800	596		404		200
			12		-12	
6	800	602		398		200
			-6		6	
7	800	599		401		200
			3		-3	
8	800	600.5	$\ldots$	399.5	$\ldots$	200

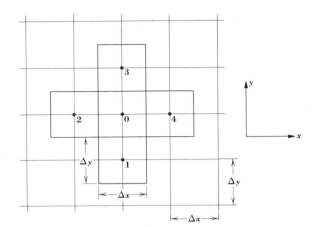

Fig. 22-3. Relaxation techniques applied to two-dimensional conduction.

The procedure shown in Example 22-1, although simple to describe, can be replaced by more sophisticated procedures[1] which can shorten the number of steps.   However, the principles are the same as illustrated in Table 22-1.

The use of relaxation in two-dimensional heat flow is illustrated with reference to Fig. 22-3.

We consider the solid to be conducting heat in the x and y directions but not in the z direction.   If the solid has a thickness Δz in the z direction, we can write

$$q_{10} = k \, \Delta z \, \Delta x \, \frac{t_1 - t_o}{\Delta y} \tag{22-6}$$

$$q_{20} = k \, \Delta z \, \Delta y \, \frac{t_2 - t_o}{\Delta x} \tag{22-7}$$

$$q_{03} = k \, \Delta z \, \Delta x \, \frac{t_o - t_3}{\Delta y} \tag{22-8}$$

$$q_{04} = k \, \Delta z \, \Delta y \, \frac{t_o - t_4}{\Delta x} \tag{22-9}$$

If we subtract Eqs. (22-8) and (22-9) from Eqs. (22-6) and (22-7), we obtain an equation for the net heat flux into the element.

$$q_{10} + q_{20} - q_{03} - q_{04} = k \, \Delta z (t_1 + t_2 + t_3 + t_4 - 4t_o) \tag{22-10}$$

As before, Δx equals Δy, so these quantities have been canceled.   We rearrange Eq. (22-10) and define a term q_o' as

[1] F. Kreith, "Principles of Heat Transfer," p. 89, International Textbook Company, Scranton, Pa., 1958.

Fig. 22-4. Relaxation model (Example 22-2).

$$q_o' = \frac{q_{10} + q_{20} - q_{03} - q_{04}}{k \, \Delta z} = t_1 + t_2 + t_3 + t_4 - 4t_o \qquad (22\text{-}11)$$

If the heat is being transferred at steady state, q_o' is zero and t_o is the arithmetic average of the temperatures at the four surrounding points.

Example 22-2

The wall of a furnace has an inside temperature of 400°F and an outside temperature of 100°F. Find the centerline temperature of the wall.

The wall is shown in Fig. 22-4 with a square grid with sides equal to half the wall thickness. Because of the plane of symmetry through the corner, the temperature at point 4 will be the same as at point $4a$. At a considerable distance from the corner the mid-wall temperature will obviously be 250°F. If we choose all the centerline temperatures as 250°F, we shall introduce some error, because the temperature at point 5 would seem to be lower. Therefore we choose $t_5 = 200°F$ and $t_1 = t_2 = t_3 = t_4 = 250°F$. The solution to the problem is shown in Table 22-2.

The procedure followed is to use the initial temperature distribution to calculate the q' values. For example, we find in step 0 that

$$q_5' = 250 + 100 + 100 + 250 - (4)(200)$$
$$= -100$$

and

$$q_4' = 250 + 100 + 200 + 400 - (4)(250)$$
$$= -50$$

and so on.

We then add or subtract one-fourth the value of q' to or from each corresponding temperature to obtain the new temperature profile, with which we repeat the calculations until the values of q' are negligible.

The accuracy of the temperatures found in Example 22-2 can be increased by use of a smaller grid. If the boundary of the system had been curved, a smaller grid would, in fact, have been necessary. However, the temperatures found with the large grid are a good basis for guessing the initial temperature distribution in the smaller grid. In Example 22-2 the

Table 22-2.   Two-dimensional Relaxation

Step	Point 1		Point 2		Point 3		Point 4		Point 5	
	t_1	q_1'	t_2	q_2'	t_3	q_3'	t_4	q_4'	t_5	q_5'
0	250		250		250		250		200	
		0		0		0		-50		-100
1	250		250		250		237		175	
		0		0		-13		-23		-26
2	250		250		247		231		168	
		0		-3		-7		-9		-10
3	250		249		245		229		165	
		-1		-1		-2		-6		-2
4	250		249		244		227		164	
		-1		-2		0		0		-2

calculations are simplified by the fact that although there is heat flow in two directions, the unknown temperatures extend only in one direction. With a smaller grid for this system, the temperatures would have to be "relaxed" in both directions.   In this case the tabular form for calculating the temperatures, shown in the example, would be rather cumbersome. A more convenient method would be to sketch the shape of the solid section on a large sheet of paper and to construct beside each point a table for calculations of t and q'.   The physical locations of the points thus are much more obvious in the calculations, and there is less chance for error. If any arithmetic error is discovered, the calculations need not be repeated but merely continued.   The error will eventually be eliminated, and the only penalty will be in the increased number of routine calculations that must be made.

Other factors affecting heat transfer can be treated by relaxation calculations.   For example, if heat is being generated in the solid at the rate of q_r Btu/(hr)(cu ft), the heat-balance equation, comparable with Eq. (22-11) for two-dimensional conduction, becomes

$$q_o' = t_1 + t_2 + t_3 + t_4 - 4t_o + \frac{q_r(\Delta x)^2}{k} \tag{22-12}$$

The initial temperature distribution is guessed and then relaxed by revising t_o values so that q_o' in Eq. (22-12) is zero.

Three-dimensional conduction can also be analyzed by relaxation techniques. A three-dimensional grid gives six points surrounding each interior nodal point. The relaxation equation (without generation) is

$$q'_o = t_1 + t_2 + t_3 + t_4 + t_5 + t_6 - 6t_o \tag{22-13}$$

In the cases we have chosen, the temperatures at the boundaries of the system have been known. If, however, the solid surfaces are in contact with a fluid, we are likely to know instead the temperature of the fluid. This type of problem can be solved by relaxation methods but requires the use of a coefficient of heat transfer, which we have not yet discussed. The procedure for doing this is rather simple, and it will be left to the student to derive the appropriate relaxation equation after he has learned something about convective coefficients.

Although a knowledge of the temperature distribution in a solid may be desired for some other purpose, it is frequently used to calculate the heat flux. This can be found from the temperature distribution by simply multiplying the temperature gradient normal to any isothermal plane in the solid by thermal conductivity, as indicated by the Fourier conduction equation.

Unsteady-state Conduction

Numerical methods have been developed for solving problems of unsteady-state heat conduction, and graphical techniques have been suggested which are equivalent to the numerical solutions. We shall consider only sufficient cases to make clear the methods employed; for the numerous specialized applications of the method, we refer the student to literature in this field.[1]

The numerical method suggested by Dusinberre will be applied to a slab having a uniform cross-sectional area A and a thickness L. The initial temperature profile for the system is illustrated in Fig. 22-5. The total thickness L is divided into a number of sections of equal thickness Δx.

At an instant of time the temperature profile is as shown by the line through temperatures t_o, t_1, t_2, etc. A heat balance is written for the shaded element of thickness Δx, which has plane 1 as its center. The temperature gradient at the left face of the element is taken as $(t_o - t_1)/\Delta x$; thus the rate of heat flow is $kA[(t_o - t_1)/\Delta x]$. The temperature gradient at the right side of the element is taken as $(t_1 - t_2)/\Delta x$, so that the rate of heat flow out is $kA[(t_1 - t_2)/\Delta x]$. The rate of accumulation of energy in

---

[1] G. M. Dusinberre, "Numerical Analysis of Heat Flow," McGraw-Hill Book Company, Inc., New York, 1949; G. A. Hawkins and J. T. Agnew, The Solution of Transient Heat Conduction Problems by Finite Differences, *Purdue Univ. Eng. Bull., Research Ser.*, no. 98, 1946.

Fig. 22-5.   *Unsteady-state heat conduction.*

the element, expressed in finite differences, is $[A \, \Delta x \, \rho C_p(t_1' - t_1)]/\Delta\theta$, in which $t_1' - t_1$ is the increase in the temperature of the element during time, $\Delta\theta$. These three terms can be written as an equation for the conservation of energy,

$$\frac{kA(t_o - t_1)}{\Delta x} - \frac{kA(t_1 - t_2)}{\Delta x} = \frac{A \, \Delta x \, \rho C_p(t_1' - t_1)}{\Delta\theta}$$

which simplifies to

$$t_1' - t_1 = \frac{k}{\rho C_p} \frac{\Delta\theta}{(\Delta x)^2} (t_o + t_2 - 2t_1) \tag{22-14}$$

Both Δx and $\Delta\theta$ can be chosen arbitrarily. The distance increment Δx is usually chosen to give some whole number of increments. The choice of $\Delta\theta$ remains. If the quantity $\dfrac{\rho C_p}{k} \dfrac{(\Delta x)^2}{\Delta\theta}$ is expressed by the symbol M, Eq. (22-14) becomes

$$t_1' = \frac{t_o + t_1(M - 2) + t_2}{M} \tag{22-15}$$

The choice of a number for the modulus M therefore fixes the increment of time $\Delta\theta$. If M is chosen as 2, Eq. (22-15) reduces to $t_1' = (t_o + t_2)/2$. In this case we have

$$\Delta\theta = \frac{\rho C_p}{k} \frac{(\Delta x)^2}{2} \tag{22-16}$$

If more accuracy is desired, a higher value of the modulus is chosen. However, the advantage of choosing $M = 2$ is that the calculations are reduced to the taking of arithmetic averages.

The graphical solution of a problem using $M = 2$ is known as the Schmidt method. A plot is made of initial temperature distribution, and the points two planes apart are joined in alternate steps. Both the numerical and graphical procedures are illustrated in Example 22-3.

Example 22-3

A system similar to that illustrated in Example 21-2 will be used to illustrate both the numerical and graphical procedures. A rubber sheet ½ in. thick, initially at 70°F, is heated by bringing both surfaces to a temperature of 292°F at the same instant and holding them at that temperature. The thermal diffusivity of rubber, $k/\rho C_p$, is 0.0028 sq ft/hr.

If $M = 2$ is chosen and the sheet is considered as six slabs, each of thickness 0.0833 in., the time increment is

$$\Delta\theta = \frac{(\Delta x)^2}{2}\frac{\rho C_p}{k}$$

$$= \frac{(0.0833/12)^2}{(2)(0.0028)}$$

$$= 0.00858 \text{ hr } (0.515 \text{ min})$$

If we carried the solution to the point of finding how long it took for the centerline temperature to reach 290°F (as in Example 21-2), the number of increments would be $18.7/0.515 = 36.3$ (the required time, as found in Example 21-2, was 18.7 min). This is such a large number of steps that the solution will not be carried to that extent. However, in the same example we see that the centerline temperature was 217°F after 5 min (8.7 increments), so the checking of this figure will be our present goal. The results are shown in Table 22-3.

Table 22-3.   *Numerical Analysis of Steady-state Conduction in a Rubber Sheet*

$\Delta\theta$	t_o	t_1	t_2	t_3	t_4	t_5	t_6
0	292	70	70	70	70	70	292
1	292	181	70	70	70	181	292
2	292	181	125	70	125	181	292
3	292	209	125	125	125	209	292
4	292	209	167	125	167	209	292
5	292	230	167	167	167	230	292
6	292	230	199	167	199	230	292
7	292	246	199	199	199	246	292
8	292	246	223	199	223	246	292
9	292	258	223	223	223	258	292
10	292	258	240	223	240	258	292

The results in Table 22-3 indicate that after $9(\Delta\theta)$ and $10(\Delta\theta)$ time increments the centerline temperature was 223°F. This checks approximately the analytical results of Example 21-2, in which the centerline temperature was found to be 217°F after 5

Fig. 22-6. *Graphical solution of heat-conduction problem (Example 22-3).*

min (9.70 $\Delta\theta$). If the results of Table 22-3 are plotted as centerline temperature versus time, a smooth curve drawn through the points will eliminate the stepwise character of the results and permit interpolation.

The graphical solution is shown in Fig. 22-6, and it coincides with the results of the numerical and analytical solutions.

Numerical and graphical solutions are available for systems in which there is unsteady-state heat transfer by two-dimensional conduction, conduction with convection at a surface, and conduction with heat generation in the solid. Solutions are also available for transient conduction in cylinders, composite slabs, and composite cylinders and spheres.

Analog Methods

Heat-conduction problems can often be solved by using systems which are analogs of the heat-transfer system. The criterion for two systems to be mathematical analogs is that they must be described by the same mathematical equations. For example, the two-dimensional Laplace equation, $\partial^2\phi/\partial x^2 + \partial^2\phi/\partial y^2 = 0$, can be written for steady-state heat conduction (ϕ is temperature), or for the voltage distribution in an electric conductor (ϕ is voltage), or for the flow field of an incompressible ideal fluid (ϕ is velocity potential).

The flow lines in a heat-conduction system can be obtained by constructing either a liquid-flow analog or an electric analog. The liquid-flow-analog system is obtained by constructing a plate of shape similar to a plane in the heat-transfer system. A sheet of glass is placed a very short distance (say $\frac{1}{16}$ in.) above and parallel to the plate. Liquid flows into the space between the plate and the glass at boundaries representing the heat source and out at other boundaries representing the heat sink. Insulated surfaces are represented by walls over which the fluid cannot flow. Before the glass is installed, soluble colored crystals (e.g., potassium permanganate) are sprinkled over the plate. When the flow (known as Hele-Shaw flow) begins, these give off streaks of colored fluid which indicate the flow lines in the system. Flow must, of course, be laminar and must fill the space between the plates. When the flow lines are fully established, the plate is photographed. The isotherms can then be drawn at right angles to the flow lines, and by using a technique known as the "method of curvilinear squares," the heat flux can be calculated.[1]

The flow lines can also be found by use of an electric-analog field plotter. In this method a thin sheet of electrically conducting paper is cut to the same shape as the heat-conduction system. Electrodes are attached to highly conductive wires at edges representing isothermal boundaries of the heat-transfer system. When the voltage is applied to these electrodes, the locations of constant-voltage lines on the paper are detected and plotted by means of a stylus attached to a voltage-detecting instrument. Perforations are made on the paper while tracing equipotential lines which are, of course, analogous to the isotherms in the heat-transfer system.

Unsteady-state conduction problems can be solved by electrical[2] and fluid-flow analogs. In both cases networks are set up which simulate the heat-conduction system. We have seen that the equation for unsteady-state conduction in one direction is

$$\frac{\partial t}{\partial \theta} = \alpha \frac{\partial^2 t}{\partial x^2} \tag{21-1}$$

The electric potential E in a small wire in which a current is flowing can be represented by

$$\frac{\partial E}{\partial \theta} = \frac{1}{RC} \frac{\partial^2 E}{\partial x^2} \tag{22-17}$$

where R = resistance per unit length
$\quad\quad C$ = capacitance per unit length
Self-inductance and leakage conductance are assumed to be negligible. In the electrical analog of the thermal system, voltage corresponds to

[1] An interesting discussion of liquid-flow analogs is given by A. D. Moore, *J. Appl. Phys.*, **20:**790 (1949).

[2] M. Jakob and G. A. Hawkins, "Elements of Heat Transfer," 3d ed., chap. 4, John Wiley & Sons, Inc., New York, 1957.

temperature difference, electric current corresponds to heat flow, electric resistance corresponds to thermal resistance, and electric capacitance corresponds to thermal capacitance.

The use of liquid-flow networks as analogs of heat-transfer systems has been less common than the use of the electrical networks, probably because of the greater ease of making electrical measurements. The hydraulic-analog method has been described by Juhasz.[1]

PROBLEMS

22-1. Using the conditions shown in Example 22-2, find the temperature on a grid of side length equal to one-quarter the furnace-wall thickness.

22-2. The furnace described in Example 22-2 has walls 2 in. thick and 2 ft square. If all six walls have a uniform temperature of 400°F inside and 100°F outside, find the total rate of heat loss from the furnace. The thermal conductivity of the wall is 0.58 Btu/(hr)(ft)(°F).

22-3. Devise a method of applying relaxation methods to steady-state, one-dimensional heat flow through a slab consisting of two layers of different thermal conductivity.

22-4. A fire started on the ground raises the surface temperature almost immediately to 1800°F. The initial temperature for a depth of several feet, however, is 60°F. If the fire maintains the temperature of 1800°F for an hour, find the temperature at a depth of 1 ft at the end of this time. The thermal diffusivity of the soil is 0.020 sq ft/hr.

22-5. A brick wall 1 ft thick is initially at 70°F. Suddenly the temperature at one side is raised to 400°F, and the temperature at the other side is raised at the same instant to 300°F. How long will it take the centerline temperature to read 200°F if the surface temperatures specified above are constant? The thermal diffusivity of the brick is 0.016 sq ft/hr.

[1] I. S. Juhasz, Hydraulic Analogy for Transient Cross-flow Heat-exchangers, Paper 57-A-125, New York meeting, American Society of Mechanical Engineers, December, 1957.

CONVECTIVE HEAT-TRANSFER COEFFICIENTS

23

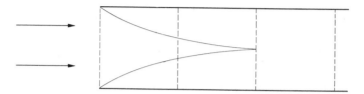

In most industrial processes heat transfer in fluids is accompanied by some form of fluid motion so that the heat transfer does not occur by conduction alone. The resulting transfer of heat by simultaneous conduction and fluid flow has been defined as forced convection when the motion arises principally from a pressure gradient caused by a pump or blower, and as natural convection when the motion arises only from the density differences associated with the temperature field.

Whether the heat-transfer mechanism is natural or forced convection, the fluid motion can be described by the equations of fluid mechanics. At low velocities the flow is laminar throughout the system; at high velocities it is generally thought to be laminar near the heating surface and turbulent some distance away. Although fluid velocities in natural convection are usually lower than in forced convection, it is incorrect to think of natural convection as causing only laminar flow; turbulence does occur when the critical Reynolds number for the system is exceeded.

All problems of convective heat transfer can be expressed in terms of the differential mass, energy, and momentum balances. However, the mathematical difficulties connected with the integration of these simultaneous nonlinear partial differential equations are such that analytical solutions exist only for simplified cases. High-speed electronic computers can often be used for the numerical solution of the equations, but even these powerful tools have so far permitted the solution of only relatively simple problems.

One of the problems simplest to deal with analytically is that of heat transfer between a fluid and a flat plate when the fluid is flowing parallel to the plate. Such a system is illustrated in Fig. 23-1. The fluid approaching the plate has a uniform temperature t_o, and the plate has a uniform temperature t_s; for this discussion we shall take t_o as being greater

283

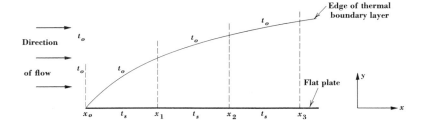

Fig. 23-1. *Development of a thermal boundary layer for flow over a flat plate.*

than t_s.   The fluid adjacent to the plate cools, and the zone of fluid in which the temperature lies between t_o and t_s is known as the thermal boundary layer.   Under special circumstances the boundaries of this region coincide with those of the velocity boundary layer; this matter is discussed at length in Chap. 24.

As the fluid moves by the plate and the distance from the leading edge of the plate increases, the thickness of the thermal boundary layer increases.   The temperature profiles at various cross sections normal to the plate also change.   A number of profiles are shown in Fig. 23-2.   These profiles depend on flow conditions as well as on the thermal properties of the fluid.   Regardless of these factors, however, the general shape of a developing thermal boundary on a flat plate is as shown in Fig. 23-1.

Another important heat-transfer system is one in which heat is transferred between a fluid and the wall of a pipe in which it is flowing.   If the fluid enters at a uniform temperature t_o and the pipe wall is at some lower temperature t_s, the development of a thermal boundary layer is as depicted in Fig. 23-3.   The thermal boundary layer thickens as the distance from the pipe inlet increases, and the layer finally comes together at the center of the pipe.   The axial distance from the pipe inlet to this point x_2 is known as the thermal-entrance length.   Beyond this point the temperature profile becomes flatter; if the pipe is long enough, the profile becomes com-

Fig. 23-2.   *Temperature profiles in a developing thermal boundary layer on a flat plate.*

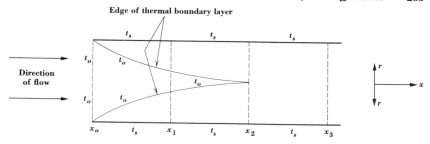

Fig. 23-3. *Development of a thermal boundary layer for flow in a pipe.*

pletely flat at a uniform temperature t_s. The temperature profiles near the entrance are depicted in Fig. 23-4.

As mentioned above, the temperature profile at a point in a flow system is influenced by the velocity profile. This influence is indicated by the presence of the velocity terms in the differential energy balance, Eq. (10-11). It is not so apparent, however, that the velocity profile is influenced by the temperature profile. The Navier-Stokes equations do not in fact contain temperature explicitly, but they do contain temperature-dependent terms, notably those including viscosity. Consequently, the velocity profile of an isothermal system may differ substantially from the velocity profile of a system in which heat is being transferred. It is this nonisothermal velocity profile, of course, that provides the velocity terms to be used in solving the differential momentum and energy balances for a nonisothermal system. Needless to say, this additional complication must frequently be overlooked to permit a solution to be obtained; this simplification, however, may introduce a serious error when the viscosity of the fluid is strongly dependent on temperature. Frequently the temperature gradient is greatest near the wall, and it is in this region that the velocity gradient is also greatest. The effect of temperature on the viscosity of the fluid at the wall may therefore have a pronounced effect on both the velocity and temperature profiles of the system.

Fig. 23-4. *Temperature profiles near the entrance of a pipe.*

Individual Heat-transfer Coefficients

Although the analysis is complicated for steady-state laminar-flow systems, even greater difficulties are encountered in systems with turbulent flow wherein the velocity and temperature at any point are functions of time.   In the study of the isothermal flow of fluids, the difficulties caused by the time-dependent nature of turbulent systems led to the use of dimensional analysis and the concept of the mixing length.   In order to get around the difficulties encountered in the solution of heat-transfer problems in turbulent systems, it is common practice in engineering to write the rate of heat transfer in terms of a heat-transfer coefficient h as

$$q = hA(t_s - t_m) \tag{23-1}$$

The surface temperature is t_s, and t_m represents the temperature of the fluid medium at some distance from the surface.   For this case t_s is greater than t_m; if t_m is greater than t_s, the positions of the two terms may be reversed to keep q positive.   The definitions of t_m for specific cases are set by convention and will be discussed presently.

Since h and t_s often vary from one point to another on the heat-transfer surface, Eq. (23-1) should be thought of as applying at a point on a surface and put in the form

$$dq = h(t_s - t_m)\, dA \tag{23-2}$$

Because the quantities h, $t_s - t_m$, and dq can often be expressed as functions of temperature, the integral form of Eq. (23-2) is written as

$$\int_0^q \frac{dq}{h(t_s - t_m)} = \int_0^A dA \tag{23-3}$$

In this chapter we shall not be concerned with the integration of Eq. (23-2); this subject will be considered in later discussions on applications, such as heat exchangers.   Although Eq. (23-1) will frequently be used in what follows in this chapter, the possible restriction of its application to a differential area if $h(t_s - t_m)$ varies should be kept in mind.

The concept of a heat-transfer coefficient is useful, but it does not really allow us to avoid the basically complicated nature of the problem.   The quantity h is a function of the properties of the fluid, the geometry and roughness of the surface, and the flow pattern of the fluid.   Several methods are available for evaluating h: analytical methods are used for laminar-flow systems; for turbulent systems we shall use integral methods, mixing-length theory, and dimensional analysis.

Another way of looking at convective heat transfer is to write the conduction equation for the fluid at the solid surface.   For convenience we shall use the system shown in Fig. 23-1, for which we write

$$q = kA \left(\frac{dt}{dy}\right)_{y=0} \tag{23-4}$$

Although we know k for the fluid, $(dt/dy)_{y=0}$ is unknown, so this equation is not directly useful for calculating q. In considering conduction in a solid, we were able to integrate the Fourier equation (20-1), but in the flowing fluid at values of $y > 0$, energy is also being carried by convective transport, so the energy balance on an element of fluid leads to the relatively complicated differential energy balance, Eq. (10-11), rather than the simple conduction equation (20-1).

It is of interest to combine Eq. (23-4) with a form of Eq. (23-1) applicable to the flat-plate problem of Fig. 23-1. This is written as

$$dq = k \, dA \left(\frac{dt}{dy}\right)_{y=0} = h(t_o - t_s) \, dA$$

which can be rearranged to give

$$h = \frac{k}{t_o - t_s} \left(\frac{dt}{dy}\right)_{y=0} \tag{23-5}$$

or in an equivalent form,

$$h = k \left\{ \frac{d[(t - t_s)/(t_o - t_s)]}{dy} \right\}_{y=0} \tag{23-6}$$

Equation (23-6) is written in terms of the dimensionless unaccomplished temperature change from the surface to the edge of the thermal boundary layer. It is apparent from these relations that any factor which would cause an increase in the temperature gradient at the wall, such as an increase in the velocity of flow past the heated surface, would also cause an increase in the value of the heat-transfer coefficient. Equation (23-6) also shows how the heat-transfer coefficient can vary with position. For both the flat plate and the heated pipe, if the wall temperature is constant at all points, the quantity $\{d[(t - t_s)/(t_o - t_s)]/dy\}_{y=0}$ is infinite at the leading edge so that the coefficient h is infinite at this point. As the thermal boundary layer thickens, both the gradient at the wall and the heat-transfer coefficient diminish. This behavior is illustrated by the curves of Figs. 23-2 and 23-4. In pipes the local, or point, heat-transfer coefficient approaches some constant value as the distance from the pipe inlet increases. For long pipes the contribution of the entrance effect is often small and is frequently neglected in engineering calculations.

Let us now complete the definition of h for some specific cases by defining t_m for some other situations. For flow through a heated conduit with a wall temperature t_s, we write

$$q = hA(t_s - t_b) \tag{23-7}$$

where t_b is the bulk (mixing-cup) temperature.[1]

For natural convection adjacent to a hot surface at t_s we set

$$q = hA(t_s - t_\infty) \tag{23-8}$$

where t_∞ is the temperature of the fluid far from the surface, i.e., at the edge of the thermal boundary layer.

The concept of the convective coefficient is also applied to heat transfer by boiling and condensation. Experimental evidence shows that when condensation of a pure vapor occurs on the exterior surface of a cold tube, almost the entire resistance to heat transfer outside the tube occurs in the film of condensate. This is the basis of an analytical model, which gives reasonably accurate results in many systems. The condensing coefficient is defined by the equation

$$q = hA(t_{sv} - t_s) \tag{23-9}$$

where t_{sv} = temperature of saturated vapor

t_s = temperature of tube surface

In this case, as in that illustrated by Fig. 23-1, the temperature difference in the defining equation for h is arbitrarily reversed to keep q positive.

For heat transfer to a boiling fluid the defining equation is

$$q = hA(t_s - t_{sl}) \tag{23-10}$$

where t_{sl} is the saturation-liquid temperature. The mechanism of boiling is believed to be by heat transfer from the solid to the liquid, then from the liquid to the interface of each growing bubble. The application of Eq. (23-10) is complicated by the very strong dependence (sometimes to the third power) of h on the temperature difference $t_s - t_{sl}$.

Finally, the concept of the heat-transfer coefficient has been extended to the design of systems where radiant-heat transfer is a contributing mechanism. The equation for radiant-heat transfer between two surfaces at t_{s1} and t_{s2} can be written as a pseudo-convection process by setting

$$q = h_r A(t_{s1} - t_{s2}) \tag{23-11}$$

where the subscript r is added to the coefficient to make its meaning clear. It will be shown later in the discussion of radiant-heat transfer that h_r can be calculated from fundamental considerations. Although it has a third-power dependence on temperature and is therefore variable with the temperature difference (as the boiling coefficient was), in many cases h_r can be assumed to be approximately constant at some average value throughout the system. This procedure often has the distinct advantage of preserving the linearity of a system of heat-transfer equations. As a result it is

---

[1] The mixing-cup temperature was defined in Chap. 4.

possible to obtain analytical solutions to problems which otherwise would have to be analyzed numerically.

The coefficient h is often called in the engineering literature the individual film coefficient. This expression is best understood with reference to heat transfer to a turbulent fluid flowing in a conduit. If the resistance to heat flow is thought of as existing only in a laminar film, the coefficient h is equivalent to $k/\Delta x_e$, where Δx_e is the equivalent thickness of a stationary film just thick enough to offer the resistance corresponding to the observed value of h. Since there is often an appreciable resistance in the turbulent core and since the stationary film has not even an approximate physical counterpart in laminar flow, boiling, and radiation, we shall refer in this book to h as an individual, or a convective, heat-transfer coefficient. However, it is not uncommon in engineering practice to use the term "film coefficient," and the fictitious nature of the film should be kept in mind.

Range of Individual Coefficients

It is of considerable value to acquire some notion of the magnitude of the various coefficients. Heat transfer is generally a process in which several mechanisms are combined in both series and parallel. Frequently, the magnitude of one or two resistances[1] is so much greater than those of the remainder of the process that an adequate analysis is obtained by neglecting all minor resistances. Table 23-1 is reproduced from McAdams[2] to indicate the relative magnitude of various types of convective coefficients.

Table 23-1. Approximate Range of Some Individual Coefficients

	h, $Btu/(hr)(sq\ ft)(°F)$
Steam, dropwise condensation	5000–20,000
Steam, film-type condensation	1000–3000
Water, boiling	300–9000
Organic vapors, condensing	200–400
Water, heating	50–3000
Oils, heating or cooling	10–300
Steam, superheating	5–20
Air, heating or cooling	0.2–10

As an example of the idea of a controlling resistance, if air were heated in a device in which condensing steam gave up heat on one side of a metal

---

[1] The thermal resistance in convection is $1/hA$, in accord with the discussion in Chap. 20.

[2] W. H. McAdams, "Heat Transmission," 3d ed., McGraw-Hill Book Company, Inc., New York, 1954.

Fig. 23-5.   Heat transfer through an insulated pipe.

surface and the air received the heat on the other side, it is apparent that the resistance due to the condensing steam would be negligible compared with the resistance of the air.

Over-all Heat-transfer Coefficients

The problem of conduction through a series of resistances has already been considered.   It is now appropriate to study systems in which heat is transferred by a series of conduction and convection mechanisms.

Figure 23-5 illustrates a system in which heat flows from a fluid at a bulk temperature t_1, through the pipe wall, through a layer of insulation, and finally into a fluid at bulk temperature t_5.   The interfacial temperatures t_2, t_3, and t_4 are as shown.

The heat-transfer coefficients h_i and h_o refer to the inside and outside coefficients, respectively.   The steady-state heat-flow rate is

$$q = h_i A_i (t_1 - t_2) = k_b A_{b,lm} \frac{t_2 - t_3}{\Delta r_b} = k_c A_{c,lm} \frac{t_3 - t_4}{\Delta r_c} = h_o A_o (t_4 - t_5)$$

$$(23\text{-}12)$$

The individual temperature drops can be found by rearranging (23-12).

$$t_1 - t_2 = q \frac{1}{h_i A_i}$$

$$t_2 - t_3 = q \frac{\Delta r_b}{k_b A_{b,lm}}$$

$$t_3 - t_4 = q \frac{\Delta r_c}{k_c A_{c,lm}}$$

$$t_4 - t_5 = q \frac{1}{h_o A_o}$$

These equations are added and rearranged to give

$$q = \frac{t_1 - t_5}{1/h_i A_i + \Delta r_b/k_b A_{b,lm} + \Delta r_c/k_c A_{c,lm} + 1/h_o A_o} \qquad (23\text{-}13)$$

Each term in the denominator can be considered as a resistance, so that Eq. (23-13) can be rewritten as

$$q = \frac{\Delta t_{\text{over-all}}}{\Sigma R} \qquad (23\text{-}14)$$

However, a more common procedure is to multiply the right-hand side of Eq. (23-13) by either A_i/A_i or A_o/A_o. Using the latter term, we obtain

$$q = \frac{A_o \Delta t_{\text{over-all}}}{A_o/h_i A_i + \Delta r_b A_o/k_b A_{b,lm} + \Delta r_c A_o/k_c A_{c,lm} + 1/h_o} \qquad (23\text{-}15)$$

The quantity

$$\frac{1}{A_o/h_i A_i + \Delta r_b A_o/k_b A_{b,lm} + \Delta r_c A_o/k_c A_{c,lm} + 1/h_o}$$

is called the over-all coefficient of heat transfer based on the outside area and is usually designated as U_o. If Eq. (23-13) had been multiplied by A_i/A_i, a quantity called U_i, the over-all coefficient of heat transfer based on the inside area, would have resulted. This quantity is defined as

$$U_i = \frac{1}{1/h_i + \Delta r_b A_i/k_b A_{b,lm} + \Delta r_c A_i/k_c A_{c,lm} + A_i/h_o A_o} \qquad (23\text{-}16)$$

The definitions of these quantities, U_o and U_i, make it possible to write

$$q = U_o A_o \Delta t_{\text{over-all}} \qquad (23\text{-}17)$$

$$q = U_i A_i \Delta t_{\text{over-all}} \qquad (23\text{-}18)$$

The ratios $A_i/A_{b,lm}$, A_o/A_i, A_i/A_o, etc., can be replaced by the ratios of radii $r_i/r_{b,lm}$, r_o/r_i, r_i/r_o. In many cases these ratios are nearly unity and can be taken as such. This is about the only basis for deciding whether to calculate an outside or an inside coefficient. For example, if the inside resistance is much greater than the other three resistances (as shown by h_i being much smaller than h_o, $k_b/\Delta r_b$, and $k_c/\Delta r_c$), one can write

$$U_i = \frac{1}{1/h_i + \Delta r_b/k_b + \Delta r_c/k_c + 1/h_o} \qquad (23\text{-}19)$$

as a satisfactory approximation. The basis for doing this is that the last three terms of the denominator are small in comparison with $1/h_i$, so that the ratios of radii would represent negligible corrections. In certain problems it is reasonable to assume that all the terms but one can be ignored, and we write $U_i = h_i$ or $U_o = h_o$, depending on which term remains.

The illustration chosen here contains four resistances in series. However, the over-all coefficient can be used to represent as many resistances in series as desired. Such cases can be analyzed using the procedures followed here, but the nature of additional terms in the over-all coefficient is rather obvious, so that these terms can be written by analogy with those given in Eqs. (23-15) and (23-16).

If the system is one of flat, parallel walls, the areas cancel, so that the expression

$$U_i = U_o = \frac{1}{1/h_i + \Delta x_b/k_b + \Delta x_c/k_c + 1/h_o} \qquad (23\text{-}20)$$

is rigorous.

The over-all coefficient could be defined in terms of one of the log mean areas, but this is seldom done. In fact, when tabulations of over-all coefficients are encountered, they frequently do not state whether the values given are for U_o or U_i because the uncertainty in the individual coefficients is somewhat greater than the effect of the area ratio. In such a case the over-all coefficient is usually assumed to be U_o.

Tabulations of over-all coefficients are given in Perry[1] and in Nelson.[2] The sample in Table 23-2 is taken from Perry.   Values such as those quoted

Table 23-2.   Over-all Coefficients of Heat Transfer

	U, $Btu/(hr)(sq\ ft)(°F)$
Stabilizer reflux condenser..................................	94
Oil preheater...	108
Reboiler (condensing steam to boiling water)..................	300–800
Air heater (molten salt to air)..............................	6
Steam-jacketed vessel evaporating milk.......................	500

in Table 23-2 are recommended only for preliminary design estimates, although it is not uncommon for information of this sort to be the only kind obtainable.

Fouling Coefficients

The tendency of certain fluids to form deposits on heat-transfer surfaces is a serious problem in the design of heat-exchange equipment. It can happen that the thermal resistance due to the deposit is greater than the sum of all the other resistances.

In some cases a hard scale is deposited on heat-transfer surfaces in a

[1] Pages 480–482.
[2] W. L. Nelson, "Petroleum Refinery Engineering," 4th ed., p. 522, McGraw-Hill Book Company, Inc., New York, 1949.

boiler or evaporator. Coke is often deposited inside the tubes of oil heaters in a refinery. The resistance of such layers can be represented using a heat-transfer coefficient equal to the thermal conductivity of the scale divided by its thickness. This type of scale can be removed by sand-blasting, by the use of pneumatic cleaning tools, and occasionally by pumping a chemical cleaning solution through the equipment.

Another type of fouling is the porous deposit formed from mud, soot, and even vegetable matter. The thermal conductivities of these materials may be high, but the fluid contained in the pores frequently has a much lower thermal conductivity. The effective thermal conductivity, therefore, may be almost as low as that of the fluid. These deposits can sometimes be removed by blowing with steam, air, or hot water. The growth of vegetable material in condensers is inhibited by chlorinating the water.

The presence of fouling deposits is anticipated in the design of heat exchangers by the use of a fouling coefficient which has the form of a heat-transfer coefficient. An equation for the heat flux through the scale is written

$$q = h_d A \, \Delta t_{\text{scale}} \tag{23-21}$$

If the fouling resistance is incorporated into the analysis of a series of resistances, the final equation for heat transfer is the same as Eqs. (23-17) and (23-18). However, the over-all coefficient contains an extra term and is written

$$U_o = \cfrac{1}{\cfrac{A_o}{h_i A_i} + \cfrac{A_o}{h_{di} A_i} + \cfrac{\Delta r_b}{k_b}\cfrac{A_o}{A_{b,lm}} + \cfrac{\Delta r_c}{k_c}\cfrac{A_o}{A_{c,lm}} + \cfrac{1}{h_o}} \tag{23-22}$$

The fouling coefficient for the inside surface is h_{di}. If fouling occurred simultaneously on the outer surface, the term $1/h_{do}$ would need to be added to the denominator.

Tabulations of fouling coefficients are given in many references, including Nelson,[1] The Standards of the Tubular Exchanger Manufacturers Association,[2] and Perry.[3] Nelson gives an interesting discussion of the problem. It should be noted, however, that he refers to the fouling coefficient in terms of the "fouling factor," which is $1000/h_d$. Both terms are in use in industry. Nelson shows that fouling is often as much dependent on the velocity of the fluid past the surface as it is on the nature of the fluid. A sample tabulation of fouling coefficients is given in Table 23-3.

It is apparent that the fouling resistance will usually increase with time

[1] *Ibid.*, pp. 489–492.

[2] Tubular Exchanger Manufacturers Association, New York, 1949.

[3] Page 464.

Table 23-3.   Fouling Coefficients

	h_d, $Btu/(hr)(sq\ ft)(°F)$
Overhead vapors from crude-oil distillation............................	1000
Dry crude oil (300–100°F):	
Velocity under 2 ft/sec	250
Velocity 2–4 ft/sec...	330
Velocity over 4 ft/sec......................................	500
Air..	500
Steam (non-oil-bearing)...	200
Water, Great Lakes, over 125°F..	500

until cleaning is necessary; however, there are some cases for which the resistance ceases to increase after some time because the rate of deposition is balanced by the rate of removal by scouring. No indication of the effect of time is given in Table 23-3; this omission is customary in published data because of the approximate nature of the figures available.

Example 23-1

A reflux condenser contains ¾-in., 16-gauge copper tubes in which cooling water circulates. Hydrocarbon vapors condense on the exterior surfaces of the tubes. Find the over-all heat-transfer coefficient U_o. The inside convective coefficient can be taken as 800 Btu/(hr)(sq ft)(°F), and the outside coefficient as 250 Btu/(hr)(sq ft)(°F).

Appropriate fouling coefficients from Table 23-3 are $h_{do} = 1000$ and $h_{di} = 500$. The following quantities can be calculated for use in Eq. (23-22):

$$\frac{1}{h_o} = \frac{1}{250} = 0.0040 \qquad \frac{1}{h_{do}} = \frac{1}{1000} = 0.0010$$

$$\frac{\Delta r}{k}\frac{r_o}{r_{lm}} = \left[\frac{0.065}{(12)(220)}\right]\left(\frac{0.75}{0.69}\right) = 0.000027$$

$$\frac{r_o}{h_i r_i} = \frac{0.75}{(800)(0.62)} = 0.0015$$

$$\frac{r_o}{h_{di} r_i} = \left(\frac{1}{500}\right)\left(\frac{0.75}{0.62}\right) = 0.0024$$

These quantities are substituted in Eq. (23-22) to give

$$U_o = \frac{1}{0.0024 + 0.0015 + 0.000027 + 0.0040 + 0.001}$$

$$= \frac{1}{0.0089} = 112\ Btu/(hr)(sq\ ft)(°F)$$

The fractional resistance due to fouling is 0.0034/0.0089 = 0.38; the resistance of the metal wall is negligible. U_i is easily calculated since $U_i A_i = U_o A_o$, giving $U_i = (112)(0.75/0.62) = 135$ Btu/(hr)(sq ft)(°F).

PROBLEMS

23-1. A jacketed kettle is used for removing 1500 lb/hr of water from an aqueous salt solution. Heat is supplied by steam condensing in the jacket at 250°F. The solution in the kettle boils at 220°F and has a latent heat of 965 Btu/lb. The heat-transfer surface has an area of 500 sq ft, is constructed of steel, and is ¼ in. thick. Calculate the increase in capacity that might be expected if the heat-transfer surface is replaced by one of copper and all other conditions are unchanged.

23-2. An experimental study of the effect of scale on heat flux was conducted using a 1-in., 18-gauge copper tube. Water flowed inside the tube, and steam condensed on the outside. The over-all coefficient U_o was determined over a wide range of water velocities for both clean and fouled tubes and was found to follow the equations

$$\frac{1}{U_o} = 0.00030 + \frac{1}{268u_b^{0.8}} \qquad \text{clean tube}$$

$$= 0.00080 + \frac{1}{268u_b^{0.8}} \qquad \text{fouled tube}$$

Find the fouling coefficient, the steam-side coefficient (assumed constant), and the water-side coefficient for a velocity $u_b = 2$ ft/sec.

23-3. Tallow is stored in a vertical tank 10 ft in diameter and 30 ft high. The tank is insulated with a 2-in. layer of 85 per cent magnesia. To prevent freezing, the tallow is maintained at a temperature of 115°F by a heating coil consisting of a 20-gauge, ¾-in. copper tube containing condensing steam at 5 psig. Assuming that the minimum outdoor temperature is 0°F and that the tallow is always at a uniform temperature, compute the length of copper tubing needed to maintain the tank at 115°F in coldest weather. Neglect heat losses from the top and bottom of the tank.

Heat-transfer coefficient	h, Btu/(hr)(sq ft)(°F)
Steam condensing inside coil............................	800
Tubing wall to molten tallow...........................	40
Molten tallow to tank wall.............................	40
Outer surface of insulation to surroundings...............	2

23-4. A single-effect evaporator is removing 5000 gal water/week from a colloidal suspension which deposits scale on the steam-heating chest. It operates continuously except for 6 hr, once a week, to clean the scale from the chest. Just before cleaning, the over-all heat-transfer coefficient was found to be 50, and 1 hr after resuming operation it was 230 Btu/(hr)(sq ft)(°F).

Assuming that none of the scale formed on the chest falls off during the run and that scale deposition is proportional to the total amount of heat transferred, calculate the length of a run for maximum capacity. What would this capacity be, expressed as gallons of water evaporated per week?

23-5. A rectangular metal fin 1 in. high and ⅛ in. thick has a thermal conductivity of 25 Btu/(hr)(ft)(°F) and a uniform base temperature of 250°F. It is exposed to an air stream at 70°F with a velocity past the fin such that the convective coefficient of heat transfer h is 15 Btu/(hr)(sq ft)(°F). Assuming that the temperature gradient parallel to the base of the fin is negligible, compute the temperature at the tip of the fin, the total heat flow from the fin, and the fin efficiency. The fin efficiency is defined as the actual heat flow from the fin divided by the heat flow if the fin were everywhere at the same temperature as at its base.

23-6. A 1-in.-diameter rod 2 ft long is supported by two brass plates maintained at 600 and 500°F. The rod is in an atmosphere at 100°F and loses heat under conditions such that the combined heat-transfer coefficient covering both convection and radiation from its surface is 4 Btu/(hr)(sq ft)(°F). Find the rate at which heat flows from the rod to the air in Btu/hr, making the following assumptions:

(1) The thermal conductivity of rod, k, is constant at 100 Btu/(hr)(ft)(°F).

(2) The radial-temperature variation in the rod is negligible.

23-7. One end of a ½-in.-diameter aluminum rod is being heated in a furnace which is at a uniform temperature of 600°F. The combined heat-transfer coefficient covering both convection and radiation from the furnace to the rod is 6 Btu/(hr)(sq ft)(°F). The rod extends into the furnace to a depth of 8 in. Outside the furnace the rod is exposed to air at a constant temperature of 80°F, and the combined heat-transfer coefficient here is 2 Btu/(hr)(sq ft)(°F). The rod is quite long, so its cold end may be assumed to be at room temperature. Find the temperature at the hot end of the rod assuming:

(1) Heat flow and temperature distribution are independent of time.

(2) The furnace wall is of zero thickness.

(3) Each heat-transfer coefficient given above is uniform over the entire surface of the section of the rod to which it applies.

(4) The radial-temperature gradient in the rod is zero.

(5) The thermal conductivity of aluminum is constant at $k = 120$ Btu/(hr)(sq ft)(°F).

HEAT TRANSFER WITH
LAMINAR FLOW
24

In this chapter we shall study some problems of heat transfer in a fluid in laminar flow. In Chap. 12 we saw that the equation of continuity could be combined with the Navier-Stokes equations to give solutions for problems of isothermal laminar flow in some important situations. To solve heat-transfer problems, the differential energy balance must be considered simultaneously. As before, we shall see that the problems involving laminar flow are easier to solve than problems with turbulent flow.

The heat-transfer problems in laminar flow of interest to engineers will be considered in two categories dependent on flow pattern:

1. The flow pattern varies with the distance from the leading edge of the system. This occurs with all external flow systems and also near the inlet of all internal flow systems.

2. The flow pattern is the same at all cross sections normal to flow. This is called "developed" flow and occurs only in internal flow systems far from the entrance.

All flow systems must have some entrance effect. Furthermore, the physical properties of all fluids are dependent on temperature and differ at all points in a nonisothermal system. Therefore, in a system transferring heat, a uniform flow pattern is never developed even at great distances from the entrance. From this we conclude that the concept of "developed" laminar flow with heat transfer is only an idealization. However, the solution of the differential balances when the physical properties vary throughout the system is quite difficult, so in our discussions we shall assume that these properties are constant. For these idealized systems developed flow is an attainable condition.

Most of our attention will be given in this chapter to one example of each class of problem cited above.   First, we shall consider heat transfer between a fluid and a flat plate.   From the differential energy balance we shall obtain a solution in which the temperature of the fluid is a function of such independent variables as position and free-stream velocity.   As a second example, we shall apply the differential energy balance (in cylindrical coordinates) to a fluid being heated in a pipe.   The solution for this system also gives the temperature as a function of position and velocity.

Although these solutions of the differential energy balance provide enough information to solve most practical problems, engineers prefer to work with heat-transfer coefficients.   As a result, it is customary to express heat-transfer performance, even for laminar flow, in terms of these coefficients.   The procedure for converting an equation expressing temperature as a function of position into an equation for the heat-transfer coefficient will be illustrated later in this chapter.   The heat-transfer coefficients for laminar flow have a strong dependence on position.   This is not usually the case for heat transfer with turbulent flow.

Heat Transfer with a Developing Velocity Distribution

Laminar Flow Parallel to a Flat Plate.   The problem of heat transfer to a fluid flowing in laminar motion parallel to a flat plate has been solved by Pohlhausen.[1]   His solution is based upon the differential balances of mass, energy, and momentum which were derived earlier in Chaps. 9 to 11. The application of the balances of mass and momentum to the problem of determining the velocity field for isothermal, laminar flow past a flat plate was described in Chap. 12.   To extend the discussion to include heat transfer from the flat plate to the fluid, we start by writing the differential energy balance for incompressible flow without heat generation.

$$u_x \frac{\partial t}{\partial x} + u_y \frac{\partial t}{\partial y} + u_z \frac{\partial t}{\partial z} + \frac{\partial t}{\partial \theta} = \frac{k}{\rho C_p} \left(\frac{\partial^2 t}{\partial x^2} + \frac{\partial^2 t}{\partial y^2} + \frac{\partial^2 t}{\partial z^2} \right) \qquad (10\text{-}11)$$

If the flow is two-dimensional, $u_z = 0$.   At steady state $\partial t/\partial \theta = 0$.   In addition, conduction is neglected in all directions except normal to the plate, so $\partial^2 t/\partial x^2 = \partial^2 t/\partial z^2 = 0$.   The resulting equation is

$$u_x \frac{\partial t}{\partial x} + u_y \frac{\partial t}{\partial y} = \frac{k}{\rho C_p} \frac{\partial^2 t}{\partial y^2} \qquad (24\text{-}1)$$

This equation is similar to the simplified momentum equation derived earlier,

[1] E. Pohlhausen, *Z. angew. Math.u. Mech.*, **1**:115 (1921).   See also J. G. Knudsen and D. L. Katz, "Fluid Dynamics and Heat Transfer," McGraw-Hill Book Company, Inc., New York, 1958.

$$u_x \frac{\partial u_x}{\partial x} + u_y \frac{\partial u_x}{\partial y} = \frac{\mu}{\rho} \frac{\partial^2 u_x}{\partial y^2} \tag{24-2}$$

When Eq. (24-2) was combined with the continuity equation (12-44), a solution was obtained for the velocity distribution in the laminar boundary layer. This is shown in Fig. 12-8, which presents the dimensionless velocity u_x/u_o as a function of $y\sqrt{u_o/\nu x}$ (designated as η).

If the fluid has a Prandtl number $C_p\mu/k$ of 1, then it can be seen that the thermal diffusivity $k/\rho C_p$ and the kinematic viscosity μ/ρ are equal. Furthermore, if the temperature t in Eq. (24-1) is replaced by a dimensionless variable $(t_s - t)/(t_s - t_o)$, it follows that Eqs. (24-1) and (24-2) have the same boundary conditions. We consider here only the case for which the plate is at a uniform temperature t_s; for convenience we choose t_s as greater than the fluid temperature t_o at the edge of the thermal boundary layer.

At $y = 0$ $\qquad \dfrac{t_s - t}{t_s - t_o} = 0, \dfrac{u_x}{u_o} = 0$

At $y = \infty$ $\qquad \dfrac{t_s - t}{t_s - t_o} = 1, \dfrac{u_x}{u_o} = 1$

At $x = 0$ $\qquad \dfrac{t_s - t}{t_s - t_o} = 1, \dfrac{u_x}{u_o} = 1$

We see that the differential equations for energy and momentum, (24-1) and (24-2), are identical when applied to fluids with a Prandtl number of 1. Therefore they have identical solutions; i.e., for any point (x,y) in the flow system, the dimensionless temperature and velocity variables $(t_s - t)/(t_s - t_o)$ and u_x/u_o are equal. Thus the velocity-profile solution shown in Fig. 12-8 is equally valid for the determination of temperature profiles. This implies that in this case the transfers of heat and momentum are directly analogous, and the thermal and hydrodynamic boundary layers are of equal thickness. These results are significant because many gases and some liquids (such as water at 350°F) have a Prandtl number of approximately 1. In general, however, liquids have Prandtl numbers in the range of 0.001 to 1000 and sometimes beyond. Pohlhausen extended the solution to cover fluids with a Prandtl number not equal to 1 by the procedure outlined below.

We use the variables defined in Chap. 12:

$$\eta = y\sqrt{\frac{u_o}{\nu x}} \tag{12-68}$$

$$f(\eta) = \frac{\psi}{\sqrt{x\nu u_o}} \tag{12-69}$$

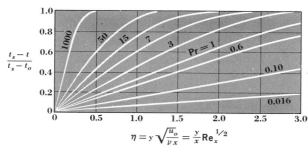

$$\eta = y \sqrt{\frac{u_o}{\nu x}} = \frac{y}{x} \mathbf{Re}_x^{1/2}$$

Fig. 24-1. *Temperatures for laminar flow past a flat plate at uniform temperature; Prandtl number range, 0.016 to 1000.*

$$u_x = \frac{\partial \psi}{\partial y} = u_o f'(\eta) \tag{12-72}$$

$$u_y = -\frac{\partial \psi}{\partial x} = \frac{1}{2} \sqrt{\frac{\nu u_o}{x}} \left[\eta f'(\eta) - f(\eta) \right] \tag{12-73}$$

and the dimensionless temperature $(t_s - t)/(t_s - t_o)$. The differential energy balance, Eq. (24-1), then reduces to the following equation:

$$\frac{d^2 \left(\dfrac{t_s - t}{t_s - t_o} \right)}{d\eta^2} + \frac{\mathbf{Pr}[f(\eta)]}{2} \frac{d \left(\dfrac{t_s - t}{t_s - t_o} \right)}{d\eta} = 0 \tag{24-3}$$

which can be integrated directly by the methods used for ordinary differential equations. The details of this solution are given by Knudsen and Katz.[1] The values of $f(\eta)$ which were determined for the isothermal-flow problem are represented by a series given earlier in this book [Eq. (12-74)]. They were used by Pohlhausen to obtain the temperature profiles for fluids with a wide range of Prandtl numbers. A number of such curves are shown in Fig. 24-1. The quantity η used in Fig. 24-1 can also be written as $(y/x)\sqrt{u_o x/\nu}$, in which two dimensionless groups, y/x and $u_o x/\nu$, can be discerned. The latter group is a local Reynolds number and is usually written $\mathbf{Re}_x$, indicating that it applies at a distance x from the leading edge of the plate.

The solution represented in Fig. 24-1 is valid for fluids with a wide range of Prandtl number. For fluids with the more limited range, $\mathbf{Pr} > 0.6$, the curves on Fig. 24-1 can be represented empirically by a single line relating the temperature variable $(t_s - t)/(t_s - t_o)$ to the quantity $(y/x) (\mathbf{Re}_x)^{1/2} \mathbf{Pr}^{1/3}$, as shown in Fig. 24-2. This procedure is based on the equation found by Pohlhausen for the ratio of the thickness of the hydrodynamic boundary layer δ to the thickness of the thermal boundary layer δ_{th}:

$$\frac{\delta}{\delta_{th}} = \mathbf{Pr}^{1/3} \tag{24-4}$$

[1] *Op. cit.*

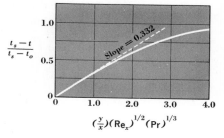

Fig. 24-2.   Temperatures for laminar flow past a flat plate at uniform temperature; Pr > 0.6.

This approximation is valid for $\mathbf{Pr} > 0.6$; the principal substances thus excluded are liquid metals.

We shall now use the relation shown in Fig. 24-2 to find the heat-transfer coefficient. This quantity was defined in the previous chapter by the equation

$$h = k \left\{ \frac{d[(t - t_s)/(t_o - t_s)]}{dy} \right\}_{y=0} \tag{23-6}$$

In view of the boundary conditions of this system, we rewrite Eq. (23-6) as

$$h = k \left\{ \frac{\partial[(t_s - t)/(t_s - t_o)]}{\partial y} \right\}_{y=0} \tag{24-5}$$

The quantity $\left\{ \dfrac{\partial[(t_s - t)/(t_s - t_o)]}{\partial y} \right\}_{y=0}$ can be obtained for fluids with $\mathbf{Pr} > 0.6$ by taking the slope of the curve in Fig. 24-2 at $(y/x)\,(\mathbf{Re}_x)^{1/2}\,\mathbf{Pr}^{1/3} = 0$. This slope is 0.332.

$$\left\{ \frac{\partial[(t_s - t)/(t_s - t_o)]}{\partial y} \right\}_{y=0} = \frac{0.332}{x}\,(\mathbf{Re}_x)^{1/2}\,\mathbf{Pr}^{1/3} \tag{24-6}$$

Consequently, the local heat-transfer coefficient h_x can be represented by the equation

$$h_x = \frac{0.332k}{x}\,(\mathbf{Re}_x)^{1/2}\,\mathbf{Pr}^{1/3} \tag{24-7}$$

The quantity $h_x x/k$ is an important dimensionless group in heat transfer, known as the Nusselt number. The quantity x is a characteristic length. When the Nusselt group contains a heat-transfer coefficient dependent on position h_x, then the Nusselt number is likewise dependent on position and is written $\mathbf{Nu}_x$. It is apparent, therefore, that Eq. (24-7) can be written entirely in terms of dimensionless groups.

$$\mathbf{Nu}_x = 0.332\,(\mathbf{Re}_x)^{1/2}\,\mathbf{Pr}^{1/3} \tag{24-8}$$

Equation (24-7) gives the local heat-transfer coefficient h_x at a distance x from the leading edge of the plate. If the effective mean coefficient h_m

for the entire section of the plate between the leading edge and point x is desired, this can be obtained as follows:

$$q = h_m A (t_s - t_o) = \int_0^L h_x(t_s - t_o)b \, dx \qquad (24\text{-}9)$$

where b is the width of the plate in the z direction. Since the plate is at a uniform temperature, $t_s - t_o$ is constant. We get, then,

$$h_m = \frac{b}{A} \int_0^L h_x \, dx$$

$$= \frac{0.332k}{L} \left(\frac{u_o}{\nu}\right)^{\frac{1}{2}} \left(\frac{C_p\mu}{k}\right)^{\frac{1}{3}} \int_0^L \frac{dx}{x^{\frac{1}{2}}} \qquad (24\text{-}10)$$

Therefore the equation for the mean coefficient h_m is

$$h_m = \frac{0.332k}{L} \left(\frac{u_o}{\nu}\right)^{\frac{1}{2}} \left(\frac{C_p\mu}{k}\right)^{\frac{1}{3}} (2L^{\frac{1}{2}})$$

$$= \frac{0.664k}{L} \left(\frac{u_o L}{\nu}\right)^{\frac{1}{2}} \left(\frac{C_p\mu}{k}\right)^{\frac{1}{3}} \qquad (24\text{-}11)$$

This may be written in terms of dimensionless numbers as

$$\mathbf{Nu}_m = 0.664 \, (\mathbf{Re}_L)^{\frac{1}{2}} \, \mathbf{Pr}^{\frac{1}{3}} \qquad (24\text{-}12)$$

The symbol $\mathbf{Re}_x$ is used in equations involving point coefficients. The symbol $\mathbf{Re}_L$ is used in equations involving average coefficients which apply over a surface of length L.

It was pointed out in Chap. 12 that the laminar boundary layer persists on smooth plates to a Reynolds number of approximately 5×10^5. Obviously, the analysis of heat transfer given in this chapter is governed by the same restrictions. Furthermore, it should not be forgotten that Eqs. (24-6) to (24-12) apply only for $\mathbf{Pr} > 0.6$.

Example 24-1

Air at 70°F with a uniform free-stream velocity of 50 ft/sec is moving parallel to a smooth flat plate heated to a uniform surface temperature of 212°F. Find the length of the laminar boundary layer on the plate, the thickness of the hydrodynamic and thermal boundary layers at the critical length, the local heat-transfer coefficient at the critical length, and the mean heat-transfer coefficient over the portion of the plate covered by the laminar boundary layer.

Air at 150°F has the following physical properties:[1]

$\nu = 0.21 \times 10^{-3}$ sq ft/sec
$k = 0.0164$ Btu/(hr)(ft)(°F)
$\mathbf{Pr} = 0.72$

[1] F. Kreith, "Principles of Heat Transfer," International Textbook Company, Scranton, Pa., 1958.

The length of laminar boundary layer is found by taking the critical Reynolds number $\mathbf{Re}_x$ as 5×10^5. Solving for x, we get

$$x = (5 \times 10^5) \frac{\nu}{u_o} = \frac{(5 \times 10^5)(0.21 \times 10^{-3})}{50}$$

$$= 2.1 \text{ ft}$$

The thickness of the hydrodynamic boundary layer can be found from Eq. (12-75).

$$\delta = 5.0 \sqrt{\frac{\nu x}{u_o}}$$

At $x = 2.1$ ft, we find

$$\delta = 5 \sqrt{\frac{(0.21 \times 10^{-3})(2.1)}{50}}$$

$$= 0.0148 \text{ ft}$$

The thermal-boundary-layer thickness at $x = 2.1$ ft is found from Eq. (24-4).

$$\frac{\delta}{\delta_{th}} = \mathbf{Pr}^{1/3}$$

$$\delta_{th} = \frac{0.0148}{(0.72)^{1/3}}$$

$$= \frac{0.0148}{0.895}$$

$$= 0.0165 \text{ ft}$$

The local heat-transfer coefficient at $x = 2.1$ ft is found from Eq. (24-7).

$$h_x = \frac{0.332k}{x} (\mathbf{Re}_x)^{1/2} \mathbf{Pr}^{1/3}$$

$$= \frac{(0.332)(0.0164)}{(2.1)} (5 \times 10^5)^{1/2} (0.72)^{1/3}$$

$$= 1.65 \text{ Btu/(hr)(sq ft)(°F)}$$

The mean effective heat-transfer coefficient for the section of the plate between the leading edge and the point where the laminar boundary layer breaks down ($x = 2.1$ ft) is twice the local coefficient at $x = 2.1$; thus $h_m = 2h_x = 3.3$ Btu/(hr)(sq ft)(°F).

Heat Transfer to a Fluid Entering a Pipe. A fluid usually enters a pipe with uniform velocity and temperature profiles. If the pipe wall is heated or cooled over its entire length, then both thermal and hydrodynamic velocity profiles begin developing at the pipe inlet. As in the case of flow parallel to a flat plate, the local coefficient of heat transfer has a value of infinity at the inlet and diminishes toward an asymptotic value far down the pipe.

The problem of the developing hydrodynamic boundary layer has been solved for isothermal flow and has already been discussed in Chap. 12. The problem in which the hydrodynamic and thermal boundary layers develop simultaneously has been studied by Kays.[1]   His approach was to combine Langhaar's results for the developing velocity profile with a numerical solution of the differential energy balance.   He obtained solutions, limited to fluids with $Pr = 0.7$, for boundary conditions of constant wall temperature, uniform heat flux from the wall, and constant temperature difference between the wall and the fluid.

Natural Convection from a Vertical Plate.   An important system to the engineer is that in which heat is transferred from a vertical plate to a fluid moving parallel to it by natural convection.   In any system in which the density of the fluid varies with position, natural convection is present. However, when the fluid is also moving as a result of forced convection, the natural-convection effects are not often important.   If the flow due to forced convection is reduced, a region is entered in which both mechanisms are important.   The example we shall consider in this section is the limiting case in which flow results entirely from heating.

This problem can be solved by using the energy and continuity equations given in the foregoing analysis for forced laminar flow past a heated plate. However, the differential momentum balance must include a body-force term due to the effect of gravity on the heated fluid.   The resulting momentum balance is written as

$$\rho \left(u_x \frac{\partial u_x}{\partial x} + u_y \frac{\partial u_x}{\partial y} \right) = g\rho\beta(t - t_\infty) + \mu \frac{\partial^2 u_x}{\partial y^2} \tag{24-13}$$

Although the body force caused by the variation of density is important in this equation, the effects of compressibility on the other terms in the differential balances are not important, so that they may be used with the assumption of constant physical properties.   This set of equations has been solved [2] for the case of natural-convection heating of ideal diatomic gases adjacent to a vertical plate at constant temperature.   The solution expressed in dimensionless groups is

$$Nu_m = 0.478 \, (Gr)^{1/4} \tag{24-14}$$

where mean Nusselt number $= Nu_m = h_m L/k$

Grashof number $= Gr = [gL^3(t_s - t_\infty)]/\nu^2 T$

The heat-transfer coefficient h_m is the mean coefficient applicable between the lower edge of the plate and any point at a distance L above the lower edge.   It is used with a temperature difference which is the wall temperature minus the fluid temperature outside the thermal boundary layer, t_∞ or t_o.   The temperature in the denominator of the Grashof number must be

[1] W. M. Kays, *Trans. ASME*, 77:1265 (1955).

[2] Pohlhausen's solution is outlined in standard references such as M. Jakob, "Heat Transfer," vol. 1, p. 444, John Wiley & Sons, Inc., New York, 1949.

expressed in absolute units because the analytical solution contains the assumption that the coefficient of volumetric expansion β is equal to the reciprocal of the absolute temperature T. This is true only for ideal gases. The Grashof number is found in most correlations of natural-convection heat transfer. Equation (24-14) is valid only for systems in which the flow is entirely laminar. Turbulent systems will be considered in Chaps. 25 and 26.

Other Systems. Engineers are interested in laminar flow in other heat-transfer systems with developing velocity profiles. One system is the flat plate, in which heating is begun at some distance from the leading edge. The hydrodynamic boundary layer in this case is already partially developed when the thermal boundary layer starts to develop.

The problem of flow normal to a heated cylinder or sphere is of considerable importance. At low Reynolds numbers, for which there is laminar flow with no separation, it is possible to obtain numerical solutions of the differential balances. However, for most practical cases the fluid separates from the sides of the cylinder, and empirical methods must be used. This problem will be considered more extensively in Chap. 25, Heat Transfer with Turbulent Flow.

Heat Transfer with a Developed Velocity Distribution in a Pipe

The heat-transfer problems most frequently encountered have to do with the heating and cooling of fluids in pipes. Although the entrance effects which we have just discussed affect over-all performance significantly in short pieces of equipment, we are often concerned with the performance of equipment in which the entrance effect is negligible.

The velocity profile in developed, isothermal, laminar flow has the shape of a parabola. The equation for this profile was derived first in this book in Chap. 7, from the over-all momentum balance, and subsequently in Chap. 12, from the differential mass and momentum balances. It is

$$u_x = 2u_b \left[1 - \left(\frac{r}{r_i} \right)^2 \right] \tag{24-15}$$

If the fluid is heated or cooled, the velocity profile can be greatly altered because of the effect of temperature on viscosity. The complications resulting in the heat-transfer problems are so great that only approximate solutions have been obtained. Graetz[1] has provided solutions for two cases. In one the distortion of the velocity profile is assumed to be negligible and the parabolic profile is maintained. In the other solution, the

---

[1] L. Graetz, *Ann. Physik*, N.F., **18**:79 (1883) and **25**:737 (1885).

distortion is assumed to be so great that the velocity profile is flat over the pipe cross section. This type of flow is called rodlike, or plug, flow. Such a condition might be approximately achieved if a liquid in laminar flow were heated from the pipe wall (Fig. 23-1). The two Graetz solutions are discussed below.

Parabolic Velocity Profile. This solution is obtained by making the assumption that Eq. (24-15) represents the axial fluid velocity at all points in the system. As boundary conditions, the wall temperature of the tube is assumed to be uniform and the inlet fluid temperature is assumed to be constant over the pipe cross section.

The differential energy balance, Eq. (10-11), can be expressed in cylindrical coordinates and, if applied to a steady-state system with axial symmetry, reduces to

$$u_x \frac{\partial t}{\partial x} = \alpha \left(\frac{\partial^2 t}{\partial r^2} + \frac{1}{r} \frac{\partial t}{\partial r} + \frac{\partial^2 t}{\partial x^2} \right) \tag{24-16}$$

If the further assumption is made that heat conduction in the direction of flow is negligible in comparison with the other transport terms, then $\partial^2 t / \partial x^2$ can be dropped from Eq. (24-16). If Eq. (24-15) is combined with this simplified energy equation, we obtain

$$\frac{\partial^2 t}{\partial r^2} + \frac{1}{r} \frac{\partial t}{\partial r} = \frac{2 u_b}{\alpha} \left[1 - \left(\frac{r}{r_i} \right)^2 \right] \frac{\partial t}{\partial x} \tag{24-17}$$

This partial differential equation can be solved by the technique of separation of variables, illustrated in Chap. 21. The temperature variable is assumed to be the product of two quantities, one of which is a function of radial distance r and the other a function of axial distance x. Two ordinary differential equations are obtained. The solution of the equation relating t and x is a simple exponential relation. The solution of the equation relating t and r is a series. The combined solutions give the equation

$$\frac{t_s - t}{t_s - t_o} = \sum_{n=0}^{n=\infty} B_n \phi_n e^{\beta_n{}^2 (x/r_i)/\text{Re Pr}} \tag{24-18}$$

The values of the constants B_n and β_n have been provided for the first 10 terms in the series by Sellars, Tribus, and Klein.[1] The same reference contains equations for determining values of ϕ_n, which is a function of r/r_i. Details of the Graetz solution are given by Drew[2] and by Jakob.[3] The bulk temperature of the fluid at any axial position can be obtained by combining Eq. (24-18), which defines temperature, and Eq. (24-15), for velocity, in the following expression:

[1] J. R. Sellars, M. Tribus, and J. S. Klein, *Trans. ASME*, **78**:441 (1956).
[2] T. B. Drew, *Trans. AIChE*, **26**:26 (1931).
[3] *Op. cit.*, p. 451.

$$t_b = \frac{1}{\pi r_i{}^2 u_b C_p \rho} \int_{r=0}^{r=r_i} (\rho C_p t u_x)(2\pi r)\ dr$$

which simplifies to

$$t_b = \frac{2}{r_i{}^2 u_b} \int_{r=0}^{r=r_i} t u_x r\ dr \qquad (24\text{-}19)$$

A brief discussion of the definition of the bulk, or mixing-cup, temperature appears in Example 4-2.

The local coefficient of heat transfer h_x can be found by writing a heat balance on a differential length of pipe dx.

$$h_x(\pi D\ dx)(t_s - t_b) = w C_p\ dt_b$$

This equation reduces to

$$h_x = \frac{w C_p}{\pi D} \frac{dt_b}{dx} \frac{1}{t_s - t_b} \qquad (24\text{-}20)$$

This expression for the local coefficient of heat transfer h_x is converted into an equation for the local Nusselt number $h_x D/k$ by multiplying both sides by D/k.

Thus the manipulation of Eqs. (24-18) to (24-20) will lead finally to a complicated equation expressing the group $\mathbf{Nu}_x$ as a function of $w C_p/kx$, which is known as the Graetz number. This can be expanded and written as $\mathbf{Pe}\ (\pi/4)(D/x)$, where the quantity $\mathbf{Pe}$, called the Peclet number, is the product $\mathbf{Re}\ \mathbf{Pr}$. The results of this analysis are shown in Fig. 24-3.

Flat Velocity Profile. If the flow is assumed to be rodlike, $u_x = u_b$ at all points and the combined mass, energy, and momentum equations simplify to

$$\frac{\partial^2 t}{\partial r^2} + \frac{1}{r}\frac{\partial t}{\partial r} = \frac{u_b}{\alpha}\frac{\partial t}{\partial x} \qquad (24\text{-}21)$$

The solution of this equation is somewhat simpler than the solution of the equation involving the parabolic profile. This occurs because the partial differential equation, when the variables are separated, gives two ordinary differential equations which can be solved by standard methods. One solution is a simple exponential equation, and the other involves a Bessel function. The final solution, when combined with the boundary conditions of uniform wall temperature and uniform inlet temperature, is as follows.

$$\frac{t_s - t}{t_s - t_o} = \sum_{n=1}^{n=\infty} \frac{2}{a_n J_1(a_n)} J_0\left(\frac{a_n r}{r_i}\right) e^{-2a_n{}^2(x/r_i)/\mathbf{Re}\ \mathbf{Pr}} \qquad (24\text{-}22)$$

The quantity a_n is the nth root of the expression $J_0(a_n) = 0$. J_0 and J_1 are Bessel functions of zero and first order, which can be found in standard

Fig. 24-3.   *Local Nusselt number for developed laminar flow in a pipe.*
a.   Rodlike flow, uniform heat flux.
b.   Rodlike flow, uniform wall temperature.
c.   Parabolic flow, uniform heat flux.
d.   Parabolic flow, uniform wall temperature.

$$\frac{w C_p}{k x} = (\tfrac{\pi}{4})(\tfrac{D}{x}) \text{Re} \, \text{Pr}$$

tabulations.   Details of this solution are given in the references previously cited for the problem of flow with a parabolic profile.

The equation for the bulk temperature, Eq. (24-19), is simplified when applied to rodlike flow because $u_x = u_b$.   This gives

$$t_b = \frac{2}{r_i{}^2} \int_{r=0}^{r=r_i} t r \, dr \tag{24-23}$$

The local coefficient of heat transfer h_x can be found from t_b by employing Eq. (24-20).   This coefficient is then used to calculate the local Nusselt number $h_x D/k$.   The equation for this useful group is

$$\frac{h_x D}{k} = \frac{\displaystyle\sum_{n=1}^{n=\infty} e^{-2 a_n{}^2 (x/r_i)/\text{Re} \, \text{Pr}}}{\displaystyle\sum_{n=1}^{n=\infty} a_n{}^{-2} e^{-2 a_n{}^2 (x/r_i)/\text{Re} \, \text{Pr}}} \tag{24-24}$$

This relation is shown graphically in Fig. 24-3.

Uniform Heat Flux.   Both flow systems assumed in the preceding pages give different solutions if the boundary condition of constant wall temperature is replaced with the condition of uniform heat flux from the wall. The behavior of the local Nusselt number with this boundary condition is shown in Fig. 24-3.

The local Nusselt number can be seen to approach asymptotic values for long tubes for all cases shown in Fig. 24-3.   The asymptotic values, in the case of uniform heat flux, can be predicted without the complete solution of the partial differential equations, as illustrated in Example 24-2.

Example 24-2

Show that the local Nusselt number for uniform heat flux to a fluid in rodlike flow approaches a value of 8 for long pipes.

The combined mass, energy, and momentum equations for this system reduce to

$$\frac{\partial^2 t}{\partial r^2} + \frac{1}{r}\frac{\partial t}{\partial r} = \frac{u_b}{\alpha}\frac{\partial t}{\partial x} \tag{24-21}$$

If heat is added at a constant rate per unit length of pipe, the temperature profile will approach some constant shape at great distances from the pipe inlet. In this region $\partial t/\partial x$ is constant at all radial and axial points, so that Eq. (24-21) can be written as

$$\frac{\partial^2 t}{\partial r^2} + \frac{1}{r}\frac{\partial t}{\partial r} = \frac{u_b}{\alpha}\frac{\partial t}{\partial x} = a \tag{1}$$

in which a is a constant.

Because the flow is rodlike,

$$\frac{\partial t}{\partial x} = \frac{dt_b}{dx} = \frac{a\alpha}{u_b} \tag{2}$$

From Eq. (24-20),

$$h_x = \frac{wC_p}{\pi D}\frac{a\alpha}{u_b}\frac{1}{t_s - t_b} \tag{3}$$

The flow rate w is

$$w = \rho u_b \frac{\pi D^2}{4}$$

We substitute this in Eq. (3) to get

$$h_x = \rho u_b \frac{\pi D^2}{4}\frac{C_p}{\pi D}\frac{ak}{\rho C_p u_b}\frac{1}{t_s - t_b}$$

$$= \frac{akD}{4(t_s - t_b)}$$

This is rearranged to give the local Nusselt number:

$$\frac{h_x D}{k} = \frac{aD^2}{4(t_s - t_b)} \tag{4}$$

The temperature at any radial point can be found in terms of the constant a by integrating Eq. (1). This is done by the standard method of substituting a new variable for $\partial t/\partial r$ and reducing Eq. (1) to a first-order equation, which can then be integrated directly. The integrated equation for temperature is

$$t = \frac{ar^2}{4} + C_1 \ln r + C_2 \tag{5}$$

The boundary conditions $\partial t/\partial r = 0$ at $r = 0$, and $t = t_s$ at $r = D/2$, are substituted to obtain values for the arbitrary constants C_1 and C_2.

The solution is

$$t = a\left(\frac{r^2}{4} - \frac{D^2}{16}\right) + t_s \tag{6}$$

In Eq. (6) t_s is a function of x, so that $t = f(r,x)$.

When this equation is integrated according to Eq. (24-23), the bulk temperature is found to be

$$t_b = -\frac{aD^2}{32} + t_s \tag{7}$$

This is rearranged to give the temperature difference

$$t_s - t_b = \frac{aD^2}{32}$$

which is substituted in Eq. (4) to give

$$\frac{h_x D}{k} = \frac{aD^2}{4} \frac{32}{aD^2} = 8 \tag{8}$$

Average Coefficients.   It is convenient for design purposes to know the average heat-transfer coefficient for an entire length of pipe.   If the surface temperature t_s is constant and t_{b2} represents the bulk temperature at the pipe discharge, an arithmetic average coefficient h_a over the area A can be defined by the following equation:

$$q = h_a A \frac{(t_s - t_o) + (t_s - t_{b2})}{2} = h_a A (t_s - t_b)_a \tag{24-25}$$

Two of the quantities in this equation are

$$q = wC_p(t_{b2} - t_o)$$

and

$$A = \pi D L$$

We substitute these in Eq. (24-25) and rearrange to get the Nusselt number based on the arithmetic average temperature difference.

$$\frac{h_a D}{k} = \frac{2wC_p}{\pi k L} \frac{t_{b2} - t_o}{(t_s - t_o) + (t_s - t_{b2})} \tag{24-26}$$

A value of t_{b2} can be obtained by substituting in Eq. (24-19) the results of one of the solutions for t as a function of x and r [Eq. (24-18) or (24-22)]. This value of t_{b2} can then be put into Eq. (24-26) in order to calculate $h_a D/k$.   Some results of this procedure are shown in Fig. 24-4.   An equivalent way of defining h_a is to write an equation similar to (24-9):

$$\frac{q}{b} = h_a L(t_s - t_b)_a = \int_0^L h_x(t_s - t_b) \, dx \tag{24-27}$$

This would give the same results as Eq. (24-26).

For long pipes and low flow rates the discharge bulk temperature t_{b2} is approximately equal to the surface temperature t_s, so that Eq. (24-26) simplifies to

$$\frac{h_a D}{k} = \frac{2wC_p}{\pi k L} \tag{24-28}$$

This simplification applies to both rodlike and parabolic flow.   The result is that curves b and c in Fig. 24-4 merge for low values of wC_p/kL and have a slope of 1.

Frequently, an equation similar to (24-25) is written with the driving

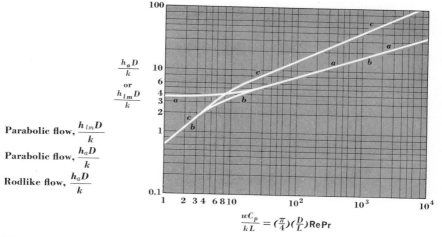

$h_a D / k$

or

$h_{lm} D / k$

a. **Parabolic flow,** $\dfrac{h_{lm} D}{k}$

b. **Parabolic flow,** $\dfrac{h_a D}{k}$

c. **Rodlike flow,** $\dfrac{h_a D}{k}$

$$\frac{wC_p}{kL} = (\tfrac{\pi}{4})(\tfrac{D}{L})\,\mathrm{Re\,Pr}$$

Fig. 24-4. Average Nusselt number for developed laminar flow in a pipe with uniform wall temperature.

force as the logarithmic mean of $t_s - t_o$ and $t_s - t_{b2}$. The behavior of the two kinds of mean Nusselt number $h_a D/k$ and $h_{lm}D/k$ as functions of wC_p/kL is shown in Fig. 24-4.

At values of $wC_p/kL > 10$, the parabolic-flow equation for the average Nusselt number $h_a D/k$ can be represented adequately by the empirical expression

$$\frac{h_a D}{k} = 1.62 \left(\frac{4wC_p}{\pi kL}\right)^{\!\frac13} \tag{24-29}$$

The quantity $4wC_p/\pi kL$ is equal to $\dfrac{Du_b\rho}{\mu}\dfrac{C_p\mu}{k}\dfrac{D}{L}$, so that Eq. (24-29) can be written as

$$\mathbf{Nu}_a = 1.62\,\mathbf{Re}^{\frac13}\,\mathbf{Pr}^{\frac13}\left(\frac{D}{L}\right)^{\!\frac13} \tag{24-30}$$

This equation is the basis of the well-known heat-transfer correlation of Sieder and Tate,[1] who proposed the following equation:

$$\mathbf{Nu}_a = 1.86\,\mathbf{Re}^{\frac13}\,\mathbf{Pr}^{\frac13}\left(\frac{D}{L}\right)^{\!\frac13}\left(\frac{\mu}{\mu_s}\right)^{\!0.14} \tag{24-31}$$

where μ = fluid viscosity at average bulk temperature

μ_s = viscosity at wall temperature

The term μ/μ_s is an empirical correction for the distortion of the velocity profile which results from the effect of temperature on viscosity.

[1] E. N. Sieder and G. E. Tate, *Ind. Eng. Chem.*, **28**:1929 (1936).

Another representation found quite commonly is obtained by dividing both sides of Eq. (24-31) by the product **Re Pr**. This gives

$$\frac{h_a}{C_p G}\left(\frac{C_p \mu}{k}\right)^{2/3}\left(\frac{\mu_s}{\mu}\right)^{0.14} = 1.86\left(\frac{D u_b \rho}{\mu}\right)^{-2/3}\left(\frac{D}{L}\right)^{1/3} \qquad (24\text{-}32)$$

The reliability of this equation is discussed by McAdams,[1] who points out that some experimental data deviate as much as 250 per cent above the values predicted by Eq. (24-32). One probable reason for this is that the equation is derived from an approximation which assumes developed flow in short tubes, and in short tubes the entrance effects which we have discussed earlier may be quite significant. Fortunately for the designer, the assumption of developed flow gives lower heat-transfer coefficients than those actually obtained with entrance effects, so that designs based on developed flow are likely to have an extra margin of safety.

PROBLEMS

24-1. Lubricating oil is being heated in a double-pipe heat exchanger. The oil enters a 1-in., schedule-40 inner steel pipe with a velocity of 1 ft/sec at a temperature of 100°F. It leaves at 160°F. The annular space between the pipes contains steam condensing at 220°F. The heat-transfer coefficient for the condensing steam is 2000 Btu/(hr)(sq ft)(°F). Find the length of pipe required for the exchanger. The oil has the following average physical properties: density, 56 lb/cu ft; specific heat, 0.47 Btu/(lb)(°F); thermal conductivity, 0.070 Btu/(hr)(ft)(°F).

24-2. A modification of the problem of heat transfer to a fluid in laminar flow in a pipe with constant wall temperature has been solved by Lévêque.[2] The parabolic profile is assumed to be completely developed before the fluid enters a section of pipe where heating from the wall begins. A thermal boundary layer then develops, superimposed on the already developed parabolic velocity profile.

The following equation was obtained by Lévêque for the local coefficient of heat transfer h_x, which can be combined with the driving force $t_s - t_o$ to give the local heat flux:

$$\mathbf{Nu}_x = 1.077\left(\frac{D}{x}\right)^{1/3}\mathbf{Re}^{1/3}\,\mathbf{Pr}^{1/3}$$

This equation gives the same value for the Nusselt number in the region **Re Pr** $(D/x) >$ 100 as is obtained from the more complicated Graetz solution for developed parabolic flow shown in Fig. 24-3. Since the Lévêque equation is not valid beyond the length where the thermal boundary layer reaches the center of the pipe, the region in which it coincides with the general solution by Graetz is a measure of the length of the thermal boundary layer or thermal entrance effect. Calculate this length in terms of pipe diameters for Reynolds numbers of 100, 1000, and 2000 for air, water, light oil, and mercury at 200°F.

[1] W. H. McAdams, "Heat Transmission," 3d ed., p. 237, McGraw-Hill Book Company, Inc., New York, 1954.

[2] J. Lévêque, *Ann. mines*, **13**(12):201, 305, 381 (1928). See also Knudsen and Katz, *op. cit.*, p. 262.

Fluid	Pr
Air..........................	0.72
Water......................	1.88
Light oil...................	62
Mercury...................	0.016

24-3. Equation (24-8) does not apply for fluids with a Prandtl number less than 0.6. Find the heat-transfer coefficient at the critical Reynolds number $\mathbf{Re}_x = 500,000$ for mercury flowing past a flat horizontal plate at 200°F. At this temperature the Prandtl number for mercury is 0.016.

24-4. The partial differential equation describing the temperature distribution in a fluid being heated while flowing in parabolic laminar flow is given earlier in the chapter as Eq. (24-17). Show by a procedure similar to that used in Example 24-2 that for a very long pipe with uniform heat flux the local Nusselt number has an asymptotic value of $^{48}\!/_{11}$.

24-5. A fluid with uniform inlet temperature t_o is flowing at a steady mass velocity G lb/(hr)(sq ft) in laminar motion through a closed duct of rectangular cross section, the surfaces of which are kept at a uniform temperature t_s at all points. Because of the effect of temperature on the viscosity of the fluid, the velocity profile may be assumed to be flat as in plug-type flow. The width of the duct is much greater than the depth, so that heat transfer at the vertical sides may be neglected. Longitudinal conduction is also negligible, and the thermal properties of the fluid can be assumed constant.

Derive an expression for the mixing-cup, or bulk, temperature of the liquid in terms of the dimensions of the system, the physical properties of the liquid, and the distance x from the inlet. Similarities between this problem and Example 21-2 which illustrated unsteady-state heat conduction should be noted.

HEAT TRANSFER WITH TURBULENT FLOW

Forced-convection heat transfer to a fluid flowing in turbulent motion in a pipe may be the commonest heat-transfer system in industry. Although forced convection may be associated with laminar flow and natural convection with turbulent flow, these are cases of secondary importance. Heat-transfer coefficients are higher with turbulent flow than with laminar flow, and heat-transfer equipment is usually designed to take advantage of this fact.

The state of knowledge concerning heat transfer with turbulent flow is necessarily limited by our knowledge of isothermal turbulent flow. We saw in Chap. 13 that the use of the Navier-Stokes equations in the analysis of isothermal turbulent flow is complicated because of the fluctuations in the velocity components. The use of the differential energy balance in the analysis of nonisothermal turbulent flow is difficult for the same reason. Heat is transferred in most turbulent streams primarily by the movement of numerous macroscopic elements of fluid (eddies) between regions at different temperatures. We cannot predict the behavior of these eddies with time, but even if we could, the expressions describing this behavior would probably be so complicated that the combined solution of the equations of energy and momentum would not be possible. Nevertheless, answers must be found to these problems. In this chapter, we consider some theoretical developments in turbulent heat transfer which are of use to the engineer, and in the next chapter we shall examine some design equations. The theory tells us why the design equations work and what some of their limitations are.

Entrance Effects

In the preceding chapter on heat transfer with laminar flow, the first part of the discussion was concerned with heat transfer in developing flow and the latter part with heat transfer in developed flow. Entrance effects which are associated with developing flow exist also in turbulent systems and may have a significant effect on over-all performance in flow through short pipes ($L/D < 60$). Once this entrance region has been passed, the heat-transfer coefficients in developed turbulent flow remain essentially constant. We have seen that this is not true for laminar flow.

Entrance Effects in a Pipe. Numerous possible combinations of thermal and hydrodynamic entrance conditions exist. In the following examples we assume that the fluid enters with a uniform temperature and that the pipe wall is at some uniform temperature higher than that of the entering fluid. Certain flow conditions at the entrance will be considered, and their effects on the local heat-transfer coefficients deduced qualitatively from the knowledge we have gained thus far of hydrodynamic and heat-transfer theory.

1. The fluid enters the pipe with a uniform velocity profile at a rate such that $\mathbf{Re} < 2100$. Under these conditions a laminar boundary layer will build up, starting from the leading edge, until it fills the pipe at some distance downstream. The heat-transfer coefficient will be infinite at the inlet but will continue to diminish even after the point of developed flow has been reached. This case was considered in the previous chapter.

2. The fluid enters the pipe in laminar flow with a uniform velocity profile at a rate such that $\mathbf{Re} > 2100$. This condition can be achieved with a rounded entrance. At the leading edge a laminar boundary layer develops which, at a critical distance, breaks down into a turbulent boundary layer in a manner already described in Chap. 12 with reference to flow past a flat plate. This turbulent boundary layer increases in thickness with increasing downstream distance until it fills the pipe with a turbulent core and a laminar sublayer at the wall. Downstream from this point the system is identical in all respects with the system that would develop if the flow had been turbulent from the entrance. This flow behavior is reflected in the values of the local heat-transfer coefficient, which decrease from infinity at the inlet to some minimum value at the critical point where the laminar boundary layer changes into a turbulent boundary layer. Near this point the heat-transfer coefficient increases in magnitude for a short distance, but then continues to decrease downstream until the turbulent boundary layers meet at the center of the pipe. Experimental values of h_x are shown in Fig. 25-1 for air flowing into a tube with a bellmouth entrance. The

Fig. 25-1. Local coefficients of heat transfer near the inlet of a tube with a bellmouth entrance. (From L. M. K. Boelter, G. Young, and H. W. Iverson, NACA Tech. Mem.1451,1948.)

point of minimum h_x moves toward the entrance with increasing values of **Re**.

3. The fluid enters the pipe in a state of turbulence with a nonuniform velocity profile at a rate such that **Re** > 2100. The velocity profile at the entrance may be caused by the presence of a sudden contraction or a pipe bend immediately upstream. A thermal boundary layer will build up, starting from the beginning of the heated length, and will fill the pipe at some downstream point. However, this entrance length for nonuniform turbulent flow usually does not have any significant effect on the local heat-transfer coefficients beyond 10 pipe diameters, whereas entrance effects in laminar flow often persist for 50 or more pipe diameters. The local heat-transfer coefficient at the beginning of the heated length is infinite in turbulent flow because of the temperature discontinuity, just as it is for laminar flow. However, it quickly falls to some constant value, as described above.

Boelter, Young, and Iverson[1] measured heat-transfer coefficients for air flowing into a pipe (1.785 in. ID) and correlated the average coefficient h_m in terms of the coefficient far downstream h_∞ by the equation

$$h_m = h_\infty \left(1 + \frac{K}{L/D}\right) \tag{25-1}$$

Values of K depend on the entrance condition as shown in Table 25-1. At

[1] L. M. K. Boelter, G. Young, and H. W. Iverson, *NACA Tech. Mem.* 1451, 1948.

distances less than 5 pipe diameters from the inlet, the results could not be correlated.

Table 25-1.   Values of K for Eq. (25-1)

Type of entrance	K
Bellmouth...	0.7
Bellmouth with one screen...	1.2
Short calming section ($L/D = 2.8$) with sharp-edged entrance...........	$\sim$3
Long calming section ($L/D = 11.2$) with sharp-edged entrance...........	1.4
45° angle-bend entrance..	$\sim$5
90° angle-bend entrance..	$\sim$7
1-in. square-edged orifice, located 1 in. upstream from entrance...........	$\sim$16
1.4-in. square-edged orifice, located 1 in. upstream from entrance...........	$\sim$7

The experiments with entrances equipped with orifices (and for a simple sharp-edged entrance as well) showed that peaks existed in plots h_x versus L/D at values of L/D between 1 and 3. These are caused by the turbulence surrounding the vena contracta.

Turbulent Flow Parallel to a Flat Plate. Heat-transfer coefficients in the region of the laminar boundary layer on a flat plate were analyzed in the previous chapter, starting with the basic differential balances. The problem could also have been solved in a semiempirical fashion by what is known as the von Kármán integral method. In this chapter we are dealing with turbulent flow and are unable to use the Navier-Stokes equations, so we shall use the integral method to obtain an approximate solution to the problem.

The use of the integral method for isothermal flow has already been illustrated in Chap. 13. An empirical equation was written for the velocity distribution in the boundary layer, and a force-momentum balance made on a segment of the layer. This subsequently yielded an equation for the drag coefficient at the surface of the plate. The equation for the velocity distribution was

$$\frac{u_x}{u_o} = \left(\frac{y}{\delta}\right)^{\frac{1}{7}} \tag{13-95}$$

In this problem we shall assume that a similar equation describes the temperature distribution.

$$\frac{t_s - t}{t_s - t_o} = \left(\frac{y}{\delta_{th}}\right)^{\frac{1}{7}} \tag{25-2}$$

The Prandtl number is assumed to be 1, so that $\delta = \delta_{th}$; the boundary of the control volume shown in Fig. 25-2 is the boundary of both the

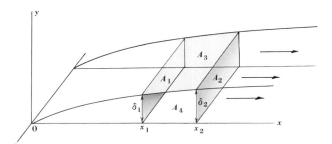

Fig. 25-2.   Control volume for analysis of heat transfer in a turbulent boundary layer.

hydrodynamic and thermal boundary layers.   Viscous dissipation and conduction in the x and z directions are neglected.

Heat is carried into this system by fluid transport through faces A_1 and A_3 and out through face A_2.   It is also conducted into the system from the section of the plate of area A_4.

The over-all energy balance, Eq. (4-6), is written for the control volume shown in Fig. 25-2.   We neglect the variation of the kinetic energy $u^2/2g_c$ and the potential energy gz/g_c.   The enthalpy H is represented by $C_p t$; the flow is steady, so $d\check{E}/d\theta$ is zero; and no shaft work is done, $\dot{W}_s = 0$. The heat-conduction rate into the control volume through A_4 is written as

$$q = \iint\limits_{A_4} h_x(t_s - t_o)\, dA$$

Thus the over-all energy balance becomes

$$\iint\limits_{A_1} \rho C_p t u \cos \alpha\, dA + \iint\limits_{A_2} \rho C_p t u \cos \alpha\, dA + \iint\limits_{A_3} \rho C_p t u \cos \alpha\, dA$$

$$= \iint\limits_{A_4} h_x(t_s - t_o)\, dA \quad (25\text{-}3)$$

At face A_1, $u \cos \alpha = -u_x$, and at face A_2, $u \cos \alpha = u_x$, so we can write

$$\iint\limits_{A_2} \rho C_p t u_x\, dA - \iint\limits_{A_1} \rho C_p t u_x\, dA + \iint\limits_{A_3} \rho C_p t u \cos \alpha\, dA$$

$$= \iint\limits_{A_4} h_x(t_s - t_o)\, dA \quad (25\text{-}4)$$

As a further simplification, the mass flow through face A_3 is related to the mass flow through faces A_1 and A_2 by the following equation, derived in Chap. 13 for an incompressible fluid:

$$\iint\limits_{A_3} \rho u \cos \alpha\, dA = - \iint\limits_{A_2} \rho u_x\, dA + \iint\limits_{A_1} \rho u_x\, dA \quad (13\text{-}81)$$

Since the temperature of the fluid at the upper edge of the boundary layer (face A_3) is constant at the free-stream temperature t_o, we multiply Eq. (13-81) by t_o and substitute in Eq. (25-4) for the integral over A_3 to get

$$\iint_{A_2} \rho C_p(t - t_o)u_x \, dA - \iint_{A_1} \rho C_p(t - t_o)u_x \, dA = \iint_{A_4} h_x(t_s - t_o) \, dA$$

$$(25\text{-}5)$$

Because all the areas have the same width and there is no variation of any quantity in the z direction, we can write Eq. (25-5) with single integrals and insert suitable limits of integration.

$$\int_0^{\delta_2} \rho C_p(t - t_o)u_x \, dy - \int_0^{\delta_1} \rho C_p(t - t_o)u_x \, dy = \int_{x_1}^{x_2} h_x(t_s - t_o) \, dx \qquad (25\text{-}6)$$

If we now consider the length $x_2 - x_1$ to approach zero, the left-hand side of Eq. (25-6) becomes a differential quantity and the right-hand side becomes the heat-transfer rate from a segment of finite width but differential length. Therefore we have

$$d \left[\int_0^{\delta} \rho C_p(t - t_o)u_x \, dy \right] = h_x(t_s - t_o) \, dx \qquad (25\text{-}7)$$

from which we obtain

$$h_x = \rho C_p \frac{d}{dx} \left(\int_0^{\delta} \frac{t - t_o}{t_s - t_o} u_x \, dy \right) \qquad (25\text{-}8)$$

The dimensionless temperature function under the integral sign can be rearranged to give

$$\frac{t - t_o}{t_s - t_o} = 1 - \frac{t_s - t}{t_s - t_o}$$

$$= 1 - \left(\frac{y}{\delta}\right)^{1/7} \qquad (25\text{-}9)$$

Furthermore, we have

$$u_x = u_o \left(\frac{y}{\delta}\right)^{1/7} \qquad (25\text{-}10)$$

We substitute Eqs. (25-9) and (25-10) in (25-8), change the variable y in the differential to y/δ, and rewrite the upper limit of integration to get

$$h_x = \rho C_p u_o \frac{d}{dx} \left\{ \delta \int_0^1 \left[1 - \left(\frac{y}{\delta}\right)^{1/7} \right] \left(\frac{y}{\delta}\right)^{1/7} d\frac{y}{\delta} \right\} \qquad (25\text{-}11)$$

The integral can be obtained directly; it has a numerical value of $7/72$. Therefore the local coefficient of heat transfer is

$$h_x = \rho C_p u_o \frac{7}{72} \frac{d\delta}{dx} \qquad (25\text{-}12)$$

The thickness of the boundary layer δ was found in Chap. 13 to be represented by the equation

$$\frac{\delta}{x} = 0.376 \ (\mathbf{Re}_x)^{-\frac{1}{5}} \qquad (13\text{-}102)$$

Differentiating this equation, we get

$$\frac{d\delta}{dx} = 0.376 \left(\frac{\mu}{u_o\rho}\right)^{\frac{1}{5}} \left(\frac{4}{5}\right) x^{-\frac{1}{5}}$$

$$= 0.301 \ (\mathbf{Re}_x)^{-\frac{1}{5}} \qquad (25\text{-}13)$$

The derivative is substituted in Eq. (25-12) to give

$$\frac{h_x}{\rho C_p u_o} = 0.0292 \ (\mathbf{Re}_x)^{-\frac{1}{5}} \qquad (25\text{-}14)$$

If both sides of this equation are multiplied by $xu_o\rho/\mu$ and $C_p\mu/k$, we get the equation in terms of the local Nusselt number $h_x x/k$,

$$\mathbf{Nu}_x = 0.0292 \ (\mathbf{Re}_x)^{\frac{4}{5}} \ \mathbf{Pr}$$

Since $\mathbf{Pr} = 1$, the final form of the equation is

$$\mathbf{Nu}_x = 0.0292 \ (\mathbf{Re}_x)^{\frac{4}{5}} \qquad (25\text{-}15)$$

If the expression for h_x is integrated from the leading edge of the plate to a distance $x = L$, as was illustrated in Chap. 24, we obtain the mean Nusselt number,

$$\mathbf{Nu}_m = 0.0365 \ (\mathbf{Re}_L)^{\frac{4}{5}} \qquad (25\text{-}16)$$

This derivation for $\mathbf{Nu}_m$ has been based on the assumption that the turbulent boundary layer starts at the leading edge. However, a laminar boundary layer precedes the turbulent boundary layer, which commences at a critical value of approximately $\mathbf{Re}_x = 500,000$. The local coefficients can be found by applying Eq. (24-8) from the leading edge to the critical distance and Eq. (25-15) from the critical point downstream. In this method of using this equation, x must always be the distance from the leading edge of the plate, not the distance from the point where turbulence starts. The direct use of Eq. (25-16) to obtain the mean coefficient when a significant portion of the plate is covered by a laminar boundary is wrong. Instead, the mean coefficient is found by integrating, using Eq. (24-8) from $x = 0$ to the end of the laminar zone, and further integration from this point to the end of the plate, using Eq. (25-15).

The Analogy between Momentum Transfer and Heat Transfer

The similarity of heat and momentum transport was noted by Osborne Reynolds in 1874; his work has led to useful, simple equations relating the friction factor, the heat-transfer coefficient, and the mass-transfer coefficient. Improvements were made in these equations by Prandtl (1910) and Taylor (1916); we shall study a derivation which leads to the Prandtl-Taylor equation. Murphree (1932) and von Kármán (1939) extended this work still further; an equation bears von Kármán's name. In recent years, further modifications have been made, including work by Reichardt (1940), Boelter, Martinelli, and Jonassen (1941), Martinelli (1947), Lyon (1951), and Deissler (1954).[1]

In this book we shall not consider in detail derivations of equations more complex than the Prandtl-Taylor equation. The equations for heat transfer can be extended easily to cover mass transfer; this is done in Chap. 35, which is devoted to mass transfer in turbulent systems.

Reynolds Analogy. Reynolds stated that in the transport of heat or momentum between a fluid and a solid surface, two mechanisms contributed to the transport process:

"1. The natural internal diffusion of the fluid when at rest.

"2. The eddies caused by visible motion which mixes the fluid up and continually brings fresh particles into contact with the surface."[2]

The first cause he recognized to be dependent on the nature of the fluid, and the second cause to be a function of the velocity of the fluid past the surface. The combined effects of these causes led to a heat-transfer equation, which he wrote as

$$H = At + B\rho vt$$

where t = difference in temperature between surface and fluid

ρ = density

v = bulk velocity

A and B = constants

H = heat transmitted per unit of area of surface per unit of time

The resistance R to motion offered by friction in the fluid he wrote as

$$R = A'v + B'\rho v^2$$

in which A' and B' are also constants. Various considerations, which he did not name specifically, led to the supposition that A and B were proportional to A' and B'. In our present nomenclature we recognize that the

[1] These equations are discussed by M. Jakob, "Heat Transfer," vol. 1, chap. 24, John Wiley & Sons, Inc., New York, 1949; and by J. G. Knudsen and D. L. Katz, "Fluid Dynamics and Heat Transfer," chap. 15, McGraw-Hill Book Company, Inc., New York, 1958.

[2] O. Reynolds, *Proc. Manchester Lit. Phil. Soc.*, **14**:7 (1874). See also O. Reynolds, "Papers on the Mechanical and Physical Subjects," vol. 1, p. 81, Cambridge University Press, London, 1900.

quantity Reynolds wrote as $B\rho v$ is equivalent for highly turbulent systems to the coefficient of heat transfer h, and the quantity B' is proportional to the friction factor f. Thus Reynolds said, in effect, that h was proportional to f.

Reynolds' ideas have been extended by others and placed in mathematical terms to give an equation relating h and f. We shall consider two principal methods of doing this, one based on a proportionality and the other on equations of flux of heat and momentum.

The proportionality of heat and momentum transfer can be stated in terms of four quantities, which we shall define with reference to a fluid at a bulk temperature t_b flowing through a pipe and losing heat to the wall of the pipe, which is at temperature t_s. The four quantities are:

(a) The heat flux from the fluid to the pipe wall, $h(t_b - t_s)$ Btu/(hr)(sq ft)

(b) The momentum flux at the wall, $\tau_s g_c$ (lb)(ft/hr)/(hr)(sq ft)

(c) The rate at which energy available for transfer as heat is transported parallel to the pipe wall, $wC_p(t_b - t_s)$ Btu/hr

(d) The rate at which momentum is transported parallel to the pipe wall, wu_b (lb)(ft/hr)/hr

It is then postulated that these four quantities can be described by the following proportionality:

$$\frac{(a)}{(c)} = \frac{(b)}{(d)}$$

From this the heat-transfer coefficient can be found as

$$h = \frac{\tau_s g_c C_p}{u_b} \tag{25-17}$$

It has been shown in Chap. 13 that the shear stress at the wall τ_s is related to the friction factor by the equation

$$\tau_s g_c = \frac{f u_b{}^2 \rho}{2} \tag{25-18}$$

Therefore we combine Eqs. (25-17) and (25-18) to obtain an equation which, though not actually derived by Reynolds, is known as the Reynolds analogy:

$$h = \frac{f u_b \rho C_p}{2} \tag{25-19}$$

The second method of deriving the equation has a semitheoretical basis and will be examined after we have discussed the application of mixing-length theory in the next section.

Eddy Thermal Diffusivity and Mixing Length.   In Chap. 13 on turbulent

Fig. 25-3.   Effect of Prandtl mixing length in the transport of heat in a turbulent stream.

flow, we wrote Eq. (13-37), relating total shear stress $\bar{\tau}_{yx}{}^t$ to velocity gradient $d\bar{u}_x/dy$:

$$\bar{\tau}_{yx}{}^t = \frac{\rho}{g_c}\,(\nu + \nu_e)\,\frac{d\bar{u}_x}{dy} \tag{13-37}$$

In this equation ν, the kinematic viscosity, depends only on the molecular properties of the fluid, whereas ν_e, the eddy kinematic viscosity, depends on the motion of the fluid.   The quantity ν_e was shown to be related to the Prandtl mixing length ℓ and the velocity gradient by the equation

$$\nu_e = \ell^2 \left|\frac{d\bar{u}_x}{dy}\right| \tag{13-39}$$

A similar quantity known as the eddy thermal diffusivity can be derived. Consider a fluid flowing under the conditions represented in Fig. 25-3. Velocities and temperatures are shown at two planes separated by a distance equal to the Prandtl mixing length ℓ.   Fluid is assumed to be transported between the planes with a velocity equal to the time-average magnitude of the fluctuating velocity component $\overline{|u_y'|}$.   Energy is transported with the packets of fluid at a rate per unit area which equals the mass flux times the product of specific heat and temperature difference, $\overline{|u_y'|}\rho C_p[\ell(d\bar{t}/dy)]$. In Chap. 13 it was indicated that the fluctuating velocity components at a point u_y' and u_x' had the same time-average magnitude, and a relation was given for these quantities in terms of the Prandtl mixing length:

$$\overline{|u_y'|} = \overline{|u_x'|} = \ell \left|\frac{d\bar{u}_x}{dy}\right| \tag{13-40}$$

Therefore the heat flux due to the turbulent motion of the fluid becomes $\rho C_p \ell^2 \left|\dfrac{d\bar{u}_x}{dy}\right| \dfrac{d\bar{t}}{dy}$.   This expression contains the quantity $\ell^2|d\bar{u}_x/dy|$, which was defined as the eddy kinematic viscosity ν_e in Eq. (13-39).   When the same group appears in an equation for turbulent heat transfer it is referred to as the eddy thermal diffusivity and will be written as α_e.

The turbulent heat flux can therefore be written $\rho C_p \alpha_e (d\bar{t}/dy)$. The Fourier equation for heat conduction, Eq. (19-1), could have been written in terms of molecular thermal diffusivity:

$$\frac{q}{A} = -\rho C_p \alpha \frac{d\bar{t}}{dy} \tag{25-20}$$

If an equation is written to represent heat transferred in a fluid by the combined mechanisms of conduction and turbulent diffusion, we obtain

$$\frac{q}{A} = -\rho C_p (\alpha + \alpha_e) \frac{d\bar{t}}{dy} \tag{25-21}$$

which is similar to Eq. (13-37) given above.

On the basis of our derivations, the eddy kinematic viscosity ν_e and the eddy thermal diffusivity α_e are equal. Although experimental evidence indicates that this is only approximately true, the assumption of equality is often made in theoretical work. Derivations for both terms are based on the assumption that packets of fluid travel a distance equal to the Prandtl mixing length and then give up their excess heat and axially directed momentum. This is most unlikely to occur in practice, but it is not unreasonable to suppose that the actual transport of heat and momentum differs from the idealized representation by about the same amount.

Although the subject of mass transfer will be considered later, it is appropriate at this point to write an equation for mass transfer of a component A in a binary-flow system:

$$J_A = -(D_{AB} + D_{ABe}) \frac{d\bar{\rho}_A}{dy} \tag{25-22}$$

This equation contains the molecular diffusivity D_{AB} and the eddy diffusivity D_{ABe}. A derivation similar to that outlined above for α_e will be given later to show that $D_{ABe} = \ell^2 |d\bar{u}_x/dy|$. Thus D_{ABe}, α_e, and ν_e are equal, according to the mixing-length theory.

Derivation of Reynolds Analogy from Eddy Transport Theory. Equation (25-19) relating h and f was derived from a proportionality based on intuition. It can also be derived from the equations of turbulent flux of heat and momentum, and this derivation is, perhaps, more revealing because the assumptions that will have to be made reveal the shortcomings of the final equation.

Equation (25-21) is written for a fluid being cooled in a pipe with heat being transferred radially. The distance y is measured from the wall, so Eq. (25-21) becomes

$$\frac{q}{A} = \rho C_p (\alpha + \alpha_e) \frac{dt}{dy} \tag{25-23}$$

All the quantities in this equation are on a time mean basis, and a similar equation is written for momentum flux, in which only time mean quantities are referred to. Total shear on the face of a cylindrical element in the x direction is

$$\tau g_c = \rho(\nu + \nu_e) \frac{du}{dy} \qquad (25\text{-}24)$$

If the molecular transport coefficients α and ν are assumed to be negligible when compared with the turbulent transport coefficients, Eqs. (25-23) and (25-24) can be written in terms of dy.

$$dy = \frac{\rho C_p \alpha_e \, dt}{q/A} = \frac{\rho \nu_e \, du}{\tau g_c}$$

If α_e and ν_e are assumed to be identical, this expression may be written

$$du = \frac{C_p \tau g_c}{q/A} \, dt \qquad (25\text{-}25)$$

The variation of τ with radial position has already been shown for both laminar and turbulent flow to follow the relation

$$\frac{\tau}{\tau_s} = 1 - \frac{y}{r_i}$$

If heat flux in a turbulent system is analogous to momentum flux, then it is assumed to follow a similar equation.

$$\frac{q/A}{(q/A)_s} = 1 - \frac{y}{r_i} \qquad (25\text{-}26)$$

From these two equations we see that $\tau g_c/(q/A)$ is constant for all radial positions. It is most convenient to write it at the wall, so we shall designate it $\tau_s g_c/[(q/A)_s]$, although in most convection equations the quantity q/A is implicitly understood as referring to flux at the wall. Because the ratio is constant, Eq. (25-25) can be integrated with $C_p \tau_s g_c/[(q/A)_s]$ outside the integral sign. We integrate between conditions at the wall and at some radial position in the fluid at which the local time mean velocity is the same as the bulk velocity and assume that the fluid temperature at this point is the same as the bulk, or mixing-cup, temperature.

$$u_b - u_s = \frac{C_p \tau_s g_c}{(q/A)_s} (t_b - t_s)$$

We know that the velocity at the wall u_s is zero. Furthermore, we have

$$\left(\frac{q}{A}\right)_s = h(t_b - t_s)$$

and

$$\tau_s g_c = \frac{f u_b^2 \rho}{2}$$

Fig. 25-4.   *Ratio of turbulent transport coefficients for mercury in a vertical tube. (From S. E. Isakoff and T. B. Drew, "Proceedings of the General Discussion on Heat Transfer," p. 479, Inst. of Mech. Engrs. and Am. Soc. of Mech. Engrs., New York, 1951.)*

a.   Re = 400,000.
b.   Re = 200,000.
c.   Re = 100,000.
d.   Re = 50,000.

Therefore we get

$$u_b = C_p \frac{f u_b^2 \rho}{2} \frac{t_b - t_s}{h(t_b - t_s)} \tag{25-27}$$

which reduces to

$$h = \frac{f u_b \rho C_p}{2} \tag{25-19}$$

One of the major assumptions in this derivation was that α and ν were negligible compared with α_e and ν_e. The ratio ν/α is equal to the Prandtl number, so for fluids with Pr = 1, $\nu = \alpha$. Therefore, in this special case, $\nu + \nu_e = \alpha + \alpha_e$, and Eq. (25-19) can be obtained without disregarding the molecular transport terms. It is significant that Eq. (25-19) gives best results when applied to gases, for which, as we know, Pr $\sim$ 1.

The equality of α_e and ν_e has been challenged by many investigators. These quantities can be calculated from measurements of temperature and velocity profiles. Most results indicate that $0.5 < \alpha_e/\nu_e < 2$. The variation of this ratio with distance from the wall and with Re is shown in Fig. 25-4.

The Prandtl-Taylor Analysis. One of the deficiencies of the Reynolds analogy was that, for fluids with Prandtl numbers other than unity, the molecular coefficients of thermal diffusivity and kinematic viscosity were neglected. This is often a valid assumption in the turbulent core of fluid in a pipe. However, the laminar sublayer has an important effect on heat

Fig. 25-5.   *Flow model for the derivation of the Prandtl-Taylor equation.*

transfer, and in this region, where the eddy coefficients diminish to zero, the molecular coefficients α and ν cannot be discarded.

The Prandtl-Taylor analysis is an attempt to overcome this shortcoming. Basically, the method employed is to write a conduction equation for the laminar sublayer and a Reynolds-analogy equation for the turbulent core. These equations are then combined in the customary method of combining resistances in series to produce a single equation for the over-all resistance.

A flow system in a circular pipe is represented in Fig. 25-5.   The fluid is considered to be in only two states of motion, as indicated.

In the laminar sublayer the velocity is assumed to be so small that all the heat which enters from the turbulent zone is conducted to the wall. Thus the heat flux in this layer is

$$\frac{q}{A} = \frac{k(t_i - t_s)}{L} \tag{25-28}$$

The momentum flux in the layer is

$$\tau g_c = \mu \frac{du}{dy} \tag{25-29}$$

The shear-stress distribution in a circular pipe is

$$\tau = \tau_s \left(1 - \frac{y}{r_i}\right)$$

In the laminar sublayer, which is extremely thin, $y/r_i \ll 1$ and $\tau \sim \tau_s$. Therefore we rewrite Eq. (25-29) as

$$du = \frac{\tau_s g_c}{\mu} \, dy$$

which can be integrated over the thickness L of the sublayer to give

$$u_i = \frac{\tau_s g_c}{\mu} L$$

which determines the thickness of the layer as

$$L = \frac{\mu u_i}{\tau_s g_c} \tag{25-30}$$

This is combined with Eq. (25-18) to eliminate τ_s in favor of f.

$$L = \frac{2\mu u_i}{f u_b{}^2 \rho}$$

This expression for L is substituted in Eq. (25-28) to give an equation for the heat flux in the sublayer.

$$\frac{q}{A} = \frac{k f u_b{}^2 \rho}{2\mu u_i} (t_i - t_s) \tag{25-31}$$

Heat and momentum transfer in the core are assumed to follow the Reynolds analogy. The rate at which momentum is transported parallel to the pipe wall is $w u_b$ when the turbulent zone extends to the wall, as in the derivation which led to Eq. (25-19). However, if a laminar sublayer surrounds the core, the rate at which momentum is transported parallel to the edge of the turbulent core is $w(u_b - u_i)$. Very little fluid is flowing in the laminar sublayer, so that the bulk velocity u_b and mass-flow rate w in the core are very nearly the same as the total bulk velocity and mass-flow rate. The heat-transfer coefficient h in Eq. (25-19) becomes the heat-transfer coefficient for only the turbulent core and will be designated as h'. Thus the proportionality which leads to a relation for h' becomes

$$\frac{h'(t_b - t_i)}{w C_p (t_b - t_i)} = \frac{\tau_s g_c}{w(u_b - u_i)} \tag{25-32}$$

from which we get

$$h' = \frac{\tau_s g_c C_p}{u_b - u_i}$$

and, substituting for $\tau_s g_c$ with Eq. (25-18), we obtain

$$h' = \frac{f u_b{}^2 \rho C_p}{2(u_b - u_i)} \tag{25-33}$$

Therefore the heat flux

$$\frac{q}{A} = h'(t_b - t_i)$$

becomes

$$\frac{q}{A} = \frac{f u_b{}^2 \rho C_p}{2(u_b - u_i)} (t_b - t_i) \tag{25-34}$$

Equations (25-31) and (25-34) are next arranged in terms of driving force.

$$t_i - t_s = \frac{q}{A} \frac{2\mu u_i}{k f u_b{}^2 \rho}$$

$$t_b - t_i = \frac{q}{A} \frac{2(u_b - u_i)}{f u_b{}^2 \rho C_p}$$

These are added to give

$$t_b - t_s = \frac{q}{A}\left[\frac{2\mu u_i}{kfu_b^2\rho} + \frac{2(u_b - u_i)}{fu_b^2\rho C_p}\right] \tag{25-35}$$

Since the conventional equation for convection is

$$\frac{q}{A} = h(t_b - t_s)$$

we see that an equation for h can be written as

$$h = \frac{1}{2\mu u_i/kfu_b^2\rho + [2(u_b - u_i)]/fu_b^2\rho C_p} \tag{25-36}$$

If the right-hand side of this equation is multiplied by $fu_bC_p\rho/2$ in both the numerator and denominator, we obtain

$$h = \frac{fu_b\rho C_p/2}{\dfrac{u_i}{u_b}\dfrac{C_p\mu}{k} + 1 - \dfrac{u_i}{u_b}} \tag{25-37}$$

For fluids with $\mathsf{Pr} = 1$, this equation reduces to Eq. (25-19).

In our discussions of the universal velocity profile in Chap. 13 we learned that for the laminar sublayer the dimensionless velocity and distance variables u^+ and y^+ are equal. This equality can be seen in Fig. 13-6. It persists up to $u^+ = y^+ = 5$ and provides a basis for determining the velocity u_i in Eq. (25-37). The relation between u and u^+ was shown to be

$$u^+ = \frac{u}{u^*} \tag{13-46}$$

The term u^* was shown to be related to the friction factor as follows:

$$u^* = u_b\sqrt{\frac{f}{2}} \tag{13-68}$$

Therefore we can write

$$u = u^+ u_b\sqrt{\frac{f}{2}}$$

and at the edge of the laminar sublayer, where $u^+ = 5$, we have

$$u_i = 5u_b\sqrt{\frac{f}{2}} \tag{25-38}$$

which can be substituted in Eq. (25-37) to give

$$h = \frac{fu_b\rho C_p/2}{1 + 5\sqrt{f/2}(\mathsf{Pr} - 1)} \tag{25-39}$$

This may also be written in terms of the Nusselt number if we multiply both sides by D/k to give

$$\mathbf{Nu} = \frac{\mathbf{Re}\,\mathbf{Pr}\,(f/2)}{1 + 5\sqrt{f/2}(\mathbf{Pr} - 1)} \qquad (25\text{-}40)$$

Several other expressions have been offered for u_i/u_b in place of the quantity $5\sqrt{f/2}$ shown above. The difference is due to the presence of a buffer region between the laminar sublayer and the turbulent core, as shown in Fig. 13-6. If the equations representing the laminar sublayer and the turbulent core are extrapolated, they meet in the buffer region at $u^+ = y^+ = 11.6$. This quantity is therefore suggested by some authors in place of the quantity 5 in the denominator of Eq. (25-40).

Other Analogies. A major improvement in the Prandtl-Taylor equation was made by von Kármán, who considered the resistance to heat transfer to be composed of three parts. These correspond to the laminar sublayer, the buffer zone, and the turbulent core and are shown in the plot of the universal velocity profile, Fig. 13-6.

The derivation of von Kármán's equation is similar to the Prandtl-Taylor analysis. Equations are written for the laminar sublayer ($y^+ \leqq 5$), in which the molecular thermal diffusivity and kinematic viscosity are considered but the eddy terms are neglected. This leads to an expression for the temperature drop over this layer. In the analysis of the buffer layer ($5 \leqq y^+ \leqq 30$), both the molecular and eddy transport terms are considered. An empirical equation [$u^+ = 5 + 5 \ln (y^+/5)$], representing the velocity in the buffer layer, is used to obtain an equation for the eddy kinematic viscosity, which is then substituted for the eddy thermal diffusivity in the heat-flux equation. Integration of this equation with both eddy and molecular thermal diffusivities gives an equation for the temperature drop over the buffer layer. Finally, the Reynolds analogy is applied to the turbulent core ($y^+ \geqq 30$) to supply an equation for the temperature drop over this resistance. The three temperature drops are then added, as in the Prandtl-Taylor analysis, to give an equation for the over-all temperature drop. The heat flux q/A divided by the over-all temperature drop gives the heat-transfer coefficient shown in the following equation:

$$h = \frac{f u_b \rho C_p / 2}{1 + 5\sqrt{f/2}\{\mathbf{Pr} - 1 + \ln\left[(1 + 5\,\mathbf{Pr})/6\right]\}} \qquad (25\text{-}41)$$

Like the Prandtl-Taylor equation, this also reduces to Reynolds analogy, Eq. (25-19), for fluids with $\mathbf{Pr} = 1$.

The results of most analogies can be put in general form, as illustrated in Eqs. (25-39) and (25-41), in which the numerator of the right-hand side is the simple Reynolds analogy, Eq. (25-19), and the denominator is a complex group of terms which serves as a correction. Some modifications include terms which account for the difference between bulk velocity and centerline velocity; others correct for the variation of $\tau g_c/(q/A)$ with radial position. In the work of Deissler, the variation of viscosity with temperature is taken into account.

No further discussion of the theoretical analogies will be given. The references mentioned earlier in this chapter contain summaries of most of the important equations and references to others. One final analogy worth discussing, however, is the empirical j-factor relation proposed by Colburn.[1] This analogy may be obtained by replacing the entire denominator in either Eq. (25-39) or (25-41) by the expression $\text{Pr}^{2/3}$. The equation is then rearranged to present it in its customary form.

$$\frac{h}{u_b \rho C_p}\, \text{Pr}^{2/3} = \frac{f}{2} = j_H \tag{25-42}$$

The term j_H is called the j factor for heat transfer. As with the other analogies, the j-factor equation reduces to Reynolds analogy for fluids with $\text{Pr} = 1$.

We shall see that a similar expression exists for mass-transfer coefficients, in which the Reynolds analogy for mass transfer is altered in the same way as for heat transfer; however, the Schmidt number replaces the Prandtl number. The j factor obtained for mass transfer is written j_M.

The j-factor relation has been shown experimentally to have considerable merit in correlating heat- and mass-transfer data. It has been used for many systems other than pipes and flat plates. In general, it has been found that $j_H = j_M$. However, in systems in which the fluid flows around spheres and other bluff objects, the frictional loss is often due more to form drag than to frictional drag. In these cases j_H still equals j_M but neither is equal to $f/2$, which is usually determined from over-all pressure-loss measurements. In systems in which form drag is absent, e.g., pipes and flat plates, the relation $j_H = j_M = f/2$ holds.

Equations for Heat-transfer Coefficients Based on the Analogies

Equations for the prediction of friction factors can be combined with the analogy equations to provide a direct method of predicting heat-transfer coefficients. For example, Reynolds analogy gives the equation

$$h = \frac{f u_b \rho C_p}{2} \tag{25-19}$$

which can be expressed as

$$\text{Nu} = \frac{f}{2}\, \text{Re}\, \text{Pr} \tag{25-43}$$

[1] A. P. Colburn, *Trans. AIChE*, **29**:174 (1933).

In Chap. 13 we saw that a convenient empirical equation for the friction factor for flow in a pipe was

$$f = 0.046 \, \mathbf{Re}^{-0.2} \tag{13-72}$$

Equations (25-43) and (13-72) can be combined to give

$$\mathbf{Nu} = 0.023 \, \mathbf{Re}^{0.8} \, \mathbf{Pr} \tag{25-44}$$

Because this equation is based on (25-19), which applies only when $\mathbf{Pr} = 1$, we write Eq. (25-44) as

$$\mathbf{Nu} = 0.023 \, \mathbf{Re}^{0.8} \tag{25-45}$$

This, as we shall see, is identical with the well-known Dittus-Boelter equation when that equation is used for fluids with $\mathbf{Pr} = 1$. The Prandtl-Taylor analogy and the von Kármán analogy can be combined with equations for the friction factor to produce equations for the Nusselt number as a function of $\mathbf{Re}$ and $\mathbf{Pr}$. The empirical *j*-factor analogy of Colburn can also be used. If the form of the Colburn analogy used in Eq. (25-42) is rearranged in terms of dimensionless groups, we obtain

$$j_H = \frac{f}{2} = \frac{\mathbf{Nu}}{\mathbf{Re} \, \mathbf{Pr}} \, \mathbf{Pr}^{0.67} \tag{25-46}$$

Equation (13-72) is substituted for f, and Eq. (25-46) reduces to

$$0.023 \, \mathbf{Re}^{-0.2} = \frac{\mathbf{Nu}}{\mathbf{Re} \, \mathbf{Pr}^{0.33}}$$

or

$$\mathbf{Nu} = 0.023 \, \mathbf{Re}^{0.8} \, \mathbf{Pr}^{0.33} \tag{25-47}$$

which is a common form.

PROBLEMS

25-1. Air is heated by passing it through a series of short sections of straight steel pipe which extend through a rectangular tank containing hot water. The pipe is 1-in., schedule-40, and the immersed lengths are 2 ft long. The return bends are outside the water tank. The bulk air velocity is 50 ft/sec, and the air pressure can be assumed to be constant at 1 atm. If the air enters at 60°F, find its exit temperature. The inside-pipe-wall temperature can be assumed to be constant at the temperature of the water, which is 210°F.

25-2. Derive Eq. (25-16) for the average Nusselt number for a plate of length L from Eq. (25-15) for the local Nusselt number for turbulent flow.

25-3. Air at 60°F is moving with a free-stream velocity of 100 ft/sec across a flat horizontal plate with a uniform surface temperature of 200°F. The plate is 2 ft wide and 4 ft long. Find the total heat-transfer rate in both the portion of the plate covered by the laminar boundary layer and the portion covered by the turbulent boundary layer.

25-4. Derive an equation for flow in a pipe relating the heat-transfer coefficient h and the friction factor f for the case where $\alpha_e \ll \alpha$ and $\nu_e \ll \nu$.

25-5. Derive the Prandtl-Taylor equation by integrating the flux equations (25-23) and (25-24).

SOME DESIGN EQUATIONS FOR
CONVECTIVE HEAT TRANSFER

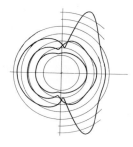

The Application of Dimensional Analysis to Heat Transfer

In the preceding chapters we examined three methods of obtaining equations for predicting heat-transfer coefficients in laminar- and turbulent-flow systems. The use of the combined momentum, energy, and continuity equations gave solutions to heat-transfer problems in laminar flow but not in turbulent flow. A second method, the von Kármán integral method, was used to obtain heat-transfer coefficients for turbulent flow over a flat plate. The third method, based on the analogy between heat and momentum transfer, gave solutions to heat-transfer problems with turbulent flow in a pipe.

A fourth method of obtaining heat-transfer equations, for either laminar or turbulent flow, is the use of dimensional analysis. As an illustration, we shall apply this procedure, outlined in Chap. 14, to a problem of natural-convection heat transfer. Natural-convection heat transfer from a plate to a fluid has already been discussed briefly in the chapter on laminar flow. However, laminar flow persists only to a certain point above the leading edge and then breaks down into turbulence. The answer obtained by dimensional analysis is not limited to one type of flow.

Example 26-1

It will be assumed that the heat-transfer coefficient in natural convection in a heated pipe can be related in a dimensionless equation to the physical variables which are listed below. Find the dimensionless groups which form the basis of such an equation.

Six fundamental dimensions are chosen: length $[L]$, mass $[M]$, time $[\theta]$, temperature $[T]$, heat $[H]$, and force $[F]$. Because heat and force are capable of being expressed in terms of the other four dimensions, we include in our list of variables two dimensional constants, the proportionality factor g_c from Newton's second law, and the mechanical equivalent of heat J.

Variable	Symbol	Dimension
Length of heated section......................	L	$[L]$
Fluid density................................	ρ	$[M/L^3]$
Fluid viscosity..............................	μ	$[M/L\theta]$
Fluid thermal conductivity....................	k	$[H/L\theta T]$
Dimensional constant........................	g_c	$[ML/F\theta^2]$
	J	$[FL/H]$
Mean heat-transfer coefficient.................	h_m	$[H/\theta T L^2]$
Temperature difference, $t_s - t_o$...............	Δt	$[T]$
Coefficient of thermal expansion...............	β	$[T^{-1}]$
Specific heat of fluid.........................	C_p	$[H/MT]$
Gravitational acceleration....................	g	$[L/\theta^2]$
Bulk velocity of fluid.........................	u_b	$[L/\theta]$
Diameter of pipe............................	D	$[L]$

The total number of variables is 13, and we have chosen to express these in terms of six dimensions. As is often the case, the maximum number of variables which will not form a dimensionless group is equal to the number of fundamental dimensions. Thus, according to Buckingham's theorem, we should obtain seven dimensionless groups. The variables which we choose to be common to all groups are the first six in the table above. Each of the remaining seven variables will, in turn, be added to the first six, to give the seven groups. The first group is

$$\pi_1 = L^a \rho^b \mu^c k^d g_c{}^e J^f h_m{}^g$$

We substitute the dimensions and obtain

$$[1] = [L]^a \left[\frac{M}{L^3}\right]^b \left[\frac{M}{L\theta}\right]^c \left[\frac{H}{L\theta T}\right]^d \left[\frac{ML}{F\theta^2}\right]^e \left[\frac{FL}{H}\right]^f \left[\frac{H}{\theta T L^2}\right]^g$$

which yields the following simultaneous equations:

$$
\begin{array}{ll}
[L] & 0 = a - 3b - c - d + e + f - 2g \\
[M] & 0 = b + c + e \\
[\theta] & 0 = -c - d - 2e - g \\
[T] & 0 = -d - g \\
[H] & 0 = d - f + g \\
[F] & 0 = -e + f
\end{array}
$$

These can be solved to give $b = c = e = f = 0$, $a = g$, and $d = -g$. Therefore π_1 reduces to $(h_m L/k)^g$. The exponent g is of no significance and could have been assumed to be unity throughout the analysis.

The second group, π_2, is found in a similar fashion. The first six variables are combined with the variable Δt, which represents the temperature-difference driving force.

$$\pi_2 = L^a \rho^b \mu^c k^d g_c{}^e J^f (\Delta t)^g$$

which gives

$$1 = [L]^a \left[\frac{M}{L^3}\right]^b \left[\frac{M}{L\theta}\right]^c \left[\frac{H}{L\theta T}\right]^d \left[\frac{ML}{F\theta^2}\right]^e \left[\frac{FL}{H}\right]^f [T]^g$$

from which we obtain the equations

$[L]$	$0 = a - 3b - c - d + e + f$
$[M]$	$0 = b + c + e$
$[\theta]$	$0 = -c - d - 2e$
$[T]$	$0 = -d + g$
$[H]$	$0 = d - f$
$[F]$	$0 = -e + f$

These equations can be solved to give $a = b = 2g$, $c = -3g$, and $d = e = f = g$. Taking the exponent g as unity, the group becomes

$$\pi_2 = \frac{L^2 \rho^2 k g_c J \, \Delta t}{\mu^3}$$

In the analysis for π_3, the additional variable is β, replacing Δt. Because β has the reciprocal of the dimension possessed by Δt, the analysis for π_3 will yield

$$\pi_3 = \frac{\mu^3 \beta}{L^2 \rho^2 k g_c J}$$

The remaining groups, obtained by the procedures already illustrated, are

$$\pi_4 = \frac{C_p \mu}{k}$$

$$\pi_5 = \frac{L^3 \rho^2 g}{\mu^2}$$

$$\pi_6 = \frac{l \rho u_b}{\mu}$$

$$\pi_7 = \frac{D}{L}$$

The seven groups obtained in Example 26-1 can be used to correlate the results of experiments in natural convection. One common way of doing this is to write an equation of the form

$$\pi_1 = \alpha \pi_2{}^\beta \pi_3{}^\gamma \pi_4{}^\delta \pi_5{}^\epsilon \pi_6{}^\zeta \pi_7{}^\eta \tag{26-1}$$

The constants represented by the Greek letters can be determined by a statistical analysis of the experimental results, often the least-squares method. Groups which have no effect on h_m can easily be located because the exponents on these groups will be very small. Two groups may have the same exponent, indicating that the variables they contain may be combined in a single group. As an example, if the analysis of Example 26-1 is used as a basis for correlating natural-convection heat transfer from a flat, vertical plate (i.e., a tube of infinite diameter), it is found that the combined groups, $\pi_2 \pi_3 \pi_5$, give a single dimensionless group, $L^3 \rho^2 g \beta \, \Delta t / \mu^2$, known as the Grashof number, which together with π_1, the Nusselt number, and π_4, the Prandtl number, are adequate to correlate the results. The groups

π_6 and π_7 are meaningless in this analysis because $u_b = 0$ and $D = \infty$. The correlating equation is

$$\pi_1 = \alpha(\pi_2\pi_3\pi_5)^\beta(\pi_4)^\delta \tag{26-2}$$

The problem of natural-convection heat transfer with laminar flow of gases has been seen in a previous chapter to be represented by the expression

$$\frac{h_m L}{k} = 0.478 \left(\frac{L^3\rho^2 g\,\Delta t}{\mu^2 T}\right)^{0.25} \tag{24-14}$$

The Prandtl number is approximately constant at unity for most gases, so the absence of that group would be expected. The Grashof group in Eq. (24-14) differs from the product $\pi_2\pi_3\pi_5$ only in that for an ideal gas, β equals $1/T$, where T is the absolute temperature. Equation (26-2) is the basis of a number of correlations for natural-convection heat transfer from a flat plate for gases and liquids in both laminar and turbulent systems.

Equation (26-1) can also serve as the basis for the analysis of forced-convection heat transfer. If the flow is turbulent, the length of the pipe has little effect on the heat-transfer coefficient ($h_m \approx h$), so groups π_1 and π_7 are combined to give the Nusselt number hD/k. Groups π_2, π_3, and π_5, which have to do with gravitational forces in a variable-density field, have negligible effects; π_4, the Prandtl number, remains, and π_6 and π_7 combine to give the Reynolds number $Du_b\rho/\mu$. Thus an equation is obtained of the form

$$\frac{hD}{k} = \alpha\left(\frac{Du_b\rho}{\mu}\right)^\beta\left(\frac{C_p\mu}{k}\right)^\gamma \tag{26-3}$$

Although most equations which are obtained by the procedures of dimensional analysis are of the form $\pi_1 = \alpha\pi_2{}^\beta\pi_3{}^\gamma \cdots$, there is no necessity that this be so. In fact we shall see shortly that heat-transfer coefficients from spheres may be correlated by an equation of the general form $\pi_1 = \alpha + \beta\pi_2{}^\gamma\pi_3{}^\delta$.

Summary of Equations Used
for Predicting Convective Heat-transfer Coefficients

The equations used by engineers for predicting heat-transfer coefficients have various origins, ranging from fundamental derivations to empirical correlations of dimensionless groups. The fact that most equations are expressed in terms of dimensionless groups should not be taken to mean that they all have their origin in dimensional analysis. We have seen that such common groups as the Nusselt, Reynolds, Prandtl, and Grashof numbers also occur in equations obtained analytically.

The equations presented below have been obtained from a variety of sources. Since most of them have been reprinted in numerous textbooks, we shall not attempt to give the original references.[1]

Convection in Circular Pipes

Laminar Flow. The theoretical equations proposed in the chapter on heat transfer with laminar flow have been used with success where the temperature gradient has not been so large as to affect fluid properties significantly. The results of these derivations have been plotted (Fig. 24-3) in terms of the local Nusselt number $\mathbf{Nu}_x$, which contains the local heat-transfer coefficient h_x. Mean heat-transfer coefficients based on arithmetic and logarithmic mean temperature-difference driving force have been calculated from the local coefficients and are plotted in Fig. 24-4. For the case of constant wall temperature, if the Graetz number wC_p/kL is less than 5 (perhaps as a result of a low flow rate or a long pipe), the Nusselt number h_aD/k is approximately equal to $\dfrac{2}{\pi}\dfrac{wC_p}{kL}$. This approximation is equivalent to assuming that the fluid is leaving at the wall temperature. If wC_p/kL is greater than 10, the Nusselt number can be approximated by the equation

$$\frac{h_aD}{k} = 1.62 \left(\frac{4wC_p}{\pi kL}\right)^{\frac{1}{3}} \tag{24-29}$$

Sieder and Tate proposed a modification of Eq. (24-29) which accounts for the effect of temperature on viscosity by the use of a factor $(\mu/\mu_s)^{0.14}$. The quantity μ_s is the viscosity at the wall temperature. The other properties, including μ, are evaluated at the arithmetic average bulk temperature. The Sieder and Tate equation expressed in dimensionless groups is

$$\mathbf{Nu}_a = 1.86 \, \mathbf{Re}^{\frac{1}{3}} \, \mathbf{Pr}^{\frac{1}{3}} \left(\frac{D}{L}\right)^{\frac{1}{3}} \left(\frac{\mu}{\mu_s}\right)^{0.14} \tag{24-30}$$

which is limited by the same restrictions as Eq. (24-29).

The equations given above apply when the pipe-wall temperature is uniform. This condition is often approximately achieved in condensers. In Chap. 24 we saw that laminar-flow systems with uniform heat flux at the wall have also been analyzed. This condition may be achieved in heat exchangers when the over-all temperature difference is constant along the exchanger. The data in Fig. 24-3 can be used for this case.

Turbulent Flow. Three well-known equations for correlating heat-trans-

---

[1] An excellent source of heat-transfer equations and data is the textbook by W. H. McAdams, "Heat Transmission," 3d ed., McGraw-Hill Book Company, Inc., New York, 1954.

fer data are presented.   All apply to the fully developed turbulent flow of fluids for which $\mathbf{Pr} > 0.7$.   In pipes for which $L/D > 60$, the entrance effects are negligible.   The equations can, however, be used for shorter pipes if the entrance region is treated separately by the use of Eq. (25-1) and Table 25-1.

The first equation considered is that of Dittus and Boelter, for which all fluid properties are evaluated at the arithmetic-mean bulk temperature.

$$\frac{hD}{k} = 0.023 \left(\frac{Du_b\rho}{\mu}\right)^{0.8} \left(\frac{C_p\mu}{k}\right)^{0.3 \text{ or } 0.4} \tag{26-4}$$

This equation correlates data for heating of the fluid when the exponent on the Prandtl number is 0.4 and for cooling of the fluid when the exponent is 0.3.   The difference appears to be the result of temperature effects on viscosity in the laminar sublayer.   Equation (25-30) shows that the thickness of this layer is proportional to fluid viscosity.   If two turbulent systems of the same fluid at the same bulk temperature are compared in heating and cooling experiments, the system being heated will have a higher temperature in the laminar sublayer than the system being cooled.   Consequently, if the fluid is a liquid, the sublayer of the heated system will be thinner, and the heat-transfer coefficient will therefore be higher than for the system being cooled.   Since the Prandtl number is greater than 1 for most liquids, raising the exponent in Eq. (26-4) has the effect of raising h. For most gases the Prandtl number is near unity and approximately independent of temperature, so that the value of the exponent on $\mathbf{Pr}$ is of minor consequence.   An understanding of this lack of effect for gases may be gained from the fact that viscosity and thermal conductivity increase at almost the same rate with temperature, so that the thermal resistance of the sublayer is approximately constant.

Another well-known equation is that of Colburn.   If the exponent on the Prandtl number in Eq. (26-4) is taken as 0.33, the equation can be rearranged by dividing both sides by $\mathbf{Pr}\,\mathbf{Re}$ to read

$$\frac{h}{u_b\rho C_p} \left(\frac{C_p\mu}{k}\right)^{\frac{2}{3}} = 0.023 \left(\frac{Du_b\rho}{\mu}\right)^{-0.2} \tag{26-5}$$

Each side of this equation is equal to the quantity previously defined as j_H.   The fluid properties are evaluated at the arithmetic mean of the wall and bulk fluid temperatures.

Sieder and Tate have presented an equation for turbulent-flow heat-transfer coefficients which has a viscosity correction similar to the correction they proposed for laminar-flow coefficients.   Because it takes account of the effect of temperature on viscosity more directly than either the Dittus-

Boelter or Colburn equations, it is valid for fluids whose Prandtl numbers are as high as 10^4. It is written

$$\frac{h}{u_b \rho C_p} \left(\frac{C_p \mu}{k}\right)^{\frac{2}{3}} \left(\frac{\mu_s}{\mu}\right)^{0.14} = 0.023 \left(\frac{D u_b \rho}{\mu}\right)^{-0.2} \tag{26-6}$$

All fluid properties are evaluated at the arithmetic average bulk temperature except the quantity μ_s, which is evaluated at the average wall temperature.

Example 26-2

In a heat exchanger water flows through a long 1-in., 16-gauge copper tube at a bulk velocity of 7 ft/sec and is heated by steam condensing at 300°F on the outside of the tube. The water enters at 60°F and leaves at 140°F. Find the heat-transfer coefficient for the water.

The physical properties of water at 100°F are

$\rho = 62.0$ lb/cu ft
$C_p = 0.998$ Btu/(lb)(°F)
$\mu = 0.000458$ lb/(ft)(sec)
$k = 0.364$ Btu/(hr)(ft)(°F)

The ID of the tubing is 0.870 in.

$$\mathbf{Re} = \frac{(0.870/12)(7)(62.0)}{0.000458}$$

$$= 68{,}600$$

$$\mathbf{Pr} = \frac{(0.998)(0.000458)(3600)}{0.364}$$

$$= 4.53$$

Because the flow is turbulent and the tube is quite long, we have a choice of calculating the heat-transfer coefficient from any one of the three standard equations (26-4) to (26-6).

(a) Using the Dittus-Boelter equation (26-4), we get

$$h = \frac{(0.023)(0.364)}{(0.870/12)} (68{,}600)^{0.8} (4.53)^{0.4}$$

$$= 1560$$

The exponent on $\mathbf{Pr}$ is 0.4 because the fluid is being heated.

(b) In the Colburn equation (26-5), the physical properties must be evaluated at the arithmetic mean of the wall and bulk-fluid temperatures. The arithmetic mean bulk temperature is 100°F. The temperature of the condensing steam is 300°F. To calculate the wall temperature we need to know the coefficient of heat transfer for the condensing steam. The calculation of coefficients for condensation will be explained in a later chapter. For the present problem we assume that the average coefficient for condensation is of the same magnitude as the heat-transfer coefficient for water. If we neglect the temperature drop over the copper wall, the average wall temperature is 200°F. Therefore, to use the Colburn equation, we must know the physical properties of water at 150°F. These are

$$\rho = 61.2 \text{ lb/cu ft}$$
$$C_p = 1.00 \text{ Btu/(lb)(°F)}$$
$$\mu = 0.000292 \text{ lb/(ft)(sec)}$$
$$k = 0.384 \text{ Btu/(hr)(ft)(°F)}$$

$$\text{Re} = \frac{(0.870/12)(7)(61.2)}{0.000292}$$

$$= 107,000$$

$$\text{Pr} = \frac{(1.00)(0.000292)(3600)}{0.384}$$

$$= 2.73$$

Substituting these values in Eq. (26-5) gives

$$h = (0.023)(7)(3600)(61.2)(1.0)(107,000)^{-0.2}(2.73)^{-\frac{2}{3}}$$

$$= \frac{35,600}{(10.1)(1.95)}$$

$$= 1800 \text{ Btu/(hr)(sq ft)(°F)}$$

(c) The Sieder-Tate equation (26-6) contains the physical properties evaluated at the bulk temperature. It can be rearranged to read

$$\frac{hD}{k} = 0.023 \text{ Re}^{0.8} \text{ Pr}^{0.33} \left(\frac{\mu}{\mu_s}\right)^{0.14}$$

$\text{Re} = 68,000$, and $\text{Pr} = 4.53$ as in part (a); $\mu = 0.000458 \text{ lb/(ft)(sec)}$; μ_s is the viscosity at the average wall temperature, which we have already estimated to be 200°F, so that $\mu_s = 0.000205 \text{ lb/(ft)(sec)}$. Therefore we get

$$h = \frac{(0.023)(0.364)}{(0.870/12)} (68,600)^{0.80}(4.53)^{0.33} \left(\frac{0.000458}{0.000205}\right)^{0.14}$$

$$= (0.115)(7400)(1.65)(1.12)$$
$$= 1580 \text{ Btu/(hr)(sq ft)(°F)}$$

Convection in Noncircular Conduits

A heat-transfer system which is commonly encountered is that in which fluids at different temperatures flow in concentric pipes. The heat-transfer coefficient of the fluid in the annular space can be predicted from equations similar to those which apply for circular pipes; however, the equivalent diameter, as defined in Chap. 15, must be used. For the annular space this equivalent diameter D_{eq} is the ID of the outer pipe D_2 minus the OD of the inner pipe D_1. Wiegand has proposed an equation for the heat-transfer coefficient on the outer wall of the inner pipe, which is

$$\frac{hD_{eq}}{k} = 0.023 \left(\frac{D_{eq}u_b\rho}{\mu}\right)^{0.8} \left(\frac{C_p\mu}{k}\right)^{0.4} \left(\frac{D_2}{D_1}\right)^{0.45} \tag{26-7}$$

For the inner wall of the outer pipe, Eq. (26-6) is recommended, with the substitution of D_{eq} for D.

The use of the equivalent diameter in conventional heat-transfer equations has been found to be valid for other configurations, such as triangular and rectangular ducts. Equations (26-4) to (26-6), when used with D_{eq}, give reasonably reliable results.

Convection Normal to a Cylinder

Numerous investigations have been made of heat transfer between a cylinder and a fluid flowing normal to the axis of the cylinder. For Reynolds numbers less than 1.0, the equations of continuity, energy, and momentum have been solved numerically to yield local heat-transfer coefficients. At higher flow rates experimental investigations have provided information on local heat-transfer coefficients. Figure 26-1 shows measured values of the local Nusselt number plotted as a function of angular position at various values of **Re**. High heat-transfer coefficients occur at the forward stagnation point and decrease as the laminar boundary layer thickens. At values of **Re** from 10^3 to 10^5 separation of the laminar boundary layer occurs at slightly more than 80° from the stagnation point. The velocity gradient at the cylinder surface at this point is nearly zero, and the heat-transfer coefficient has a minimum value, as shown on the curve for **Re** = 39,800 in Fig. 26-1. Beyond this separation point the surface is exposed to a turbulent wake, which causes the heat-transfer coefficient to increase.

At higher values of **Re** the boundary layer changes from laminar to turbulent at approximately 95°. When this happens in flow over a flat plate or inside a tube near the entrance, a minimum occurs, followed by a sudden increase of the heat-transfer coefficient, as we have already seen. Thus a minimum heat-transfer coefficient is observed at the transition point of 95° for a cylinder, followed by a sharp increase in the heat-transfer coefficient for that portion of the surface covered by the turbulent boundary layer. The turbulent boundary layer then separates from the cylinder at a position between 130 and 150° from the stagnation point, causing a second minimum to occur in the curve for the heat-transfer coefficient. This behavior is seen in the curve for **Re** = 426,000 in Fig. 26-1. The values of the local heat-transfer coefficients and the location of the minima are strongly dependent on the intensity of turbulence in the free stream.

Average coefficients for the entire surface of the cylinder can be determined from plots of local coefficients, but are more often found from correlations of average coefficients. Most writers recommend an equation of the type

$$\frac{hD}{k} = b \left(\frac{D u_0 \rho}{\mu} \right)^n \tag{26-8}$$

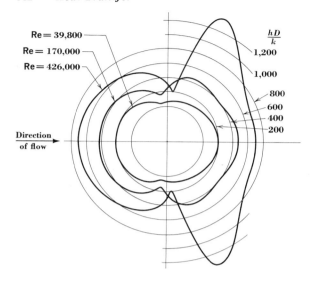

Re = 39,800
Re = 170,000
Re = 426,000

$\frac{hD}{k}$

1,200
1,000
800
600
400
200

Direction
of flow

Fig. 26-1. *Local values of Nusselt number for air flow normal to a cylinder. [From E. Schmidt and K. Wenner, Forsch. Gebiete Ingenieurw.,* 12:65 *(1933).]*

in which the constants b and n depend on **Re**, as shown in Table 26-1. The values in this table are for the calculation of the heat-transfer coefficients of gases. For liquids the same constants are used, but in addition the right-hand side of Eq. (26-8) must be multiplied by 1.1 $\mathbf{Pr}^{1/3}$. All fluid

Table 26-1.   Constants† for Use in Eq. (26-8)

$Du_o\rho/\mu$	n	b
1–4	0.330	0.891
4–40	0.385	0.821
40–4000	0.466	0.615
4000–40,000	0.618	0.174
40,000–250,000	0.805	0.0239

† Taken from W. H. McAdams, "Heat Transmission," 3d ed., p. 260, McGraw-Hill Book Company, Inc., New York, 1954.

properties are evaluated at the arithmetic mean of the surface and free-stream temperatures.

Data on natural convection from horizontal cylinders are of value in estimating heat losses from pipes. A suitable correlation for the average Nusselt number for a single horizontal cylinder when the product **Pr Gr** ranges from 10^3 to 10^9 is

$$\frac{hD}{k} = 0.53 \left(\frac{D^3\rho^2 g\beta\,\Delta t}{\mu^2}\right)^{1/4} \left(\frac{C_p\mu}{k}\right)^{1/4} \tag{26-9}$$

The presence of the Grashof number $D^3\rho^2 g\beta\,\Delta t/\mu^2$ would be expected in any correlation of natural-convection heat transfer, as was pointed out earlier in this chapter. The physical properties are evaluated at the arithmetic average of the surface temperature and the temperature of the fluid outside the thermal boundary layer.

Example 26-3

A pipe contains steam at a temperature such that the temperature of the outer surface of the insulation around the pipe is 130°F. The OD of the insulation is 4 in., and the line is in a room in which the air is at a temperature of 70°F. Find the convective heat-transfer coefficient between the surface of the insulation and the air.

Equation (26-9) is used, so the physical properties must be evaluated at 100°F. They are

$k = 0.0154$ Btu/(hr)(ft)(°F)
$\rho = 0.071$ lb/cu ft
$\beta = 0.00179$(°F)$^{-1}$
$\mu = 1.29 \times 10^{-5}$ lb/(ft)(sec)
$C_p = 0.240$ Btu/(lb)(°F)

$$\mathsf{Gr} = \frac{(\frac{4}{12})^3(0.071)^2(32.2)(0.00179)(60)}{(1.29 \times 10^{-5})^2}$$

$$= 387 \times 10^4$$

$$\mathsf{Pr} = \frac{(0.240)(1.29 \times 10^{-5})(3600)}{0.0154}$$

$$= 0.720$$

Therefore, using Eq. (26-9), we get

$$h = \frac{(0.53)(0.0154)}{\frac{4}{12}}(387 \times 10^4)^{1/4}(0.720)^{1/4}$$

$$= 1.01 \text{ Btu/(hr)(sq ft)(°F)}$$

The product $\mathsf{Pr}\,\mathsf{Gr}$ is obviously within 10^3 to 10^9, the range of applicability of the equation.

Convection Normal to a Bank of Circular Tubes

The effect of one tube on another is to increase the heat-transfer coefficient of the downstream tube. Numerous correlations have been proposed for heat-transfer coefficients of a fluid flowing across a bundle of tubes. One of the best-known correlations is that of Grimison, who wrote a conventional equation for gases,

$$\frac{hD}{k} = b\left(\frac{DG_{max}}{\mu}\right)^n \tag{26-10}$$

and supplied values of the constants b and n, from which mean coefficients can be obtained for banks of tubes 10 or more rows deep. $G_{\max}$ is the product of density times the velocity at the minimum cross section. Fluid properties are evaluated at the arithmetic mean of the air and tube-wall temperatures, as recommended for Eq. (26-8). A table of the constants b and n is given by McAdams.[1] As an example, tubes spaced in a pattern of equilateral triangles in which the center-to-center distance between tubes is twice the tube diameter are represented by the values $b = 0.482$ and $n = 0.556$. When the tubes are located on a square grid with the same center-to-center spacing, $b = 0.229, n = 0.632$. When used for fluids other than gases, the right-hand side of Eq. (26-10) should be multiplied by $1.1\ \mathsf{Pr}^{\frac{1}{3}}$.

For tube bundles less than 10 rows deep, the average heat-transfer coefficient for the bundle can be calculated from Eq. (26-10) and the ratios given in Table 26-2.

Table 26-2.   *Ratio of Mean Heat-transfer Coefficient for Bank of Tubes N Rows Deep to the Coefficient for Tubes in a Single Row*

					N					
	1	2	3	4	5	6	7	8	9	10
Triangular grid........	1	1.10	1.22	1.31	1.35	1.40	1.42	1.44	1.46	1.47
Square grid........	1	1.25	1.36	1.41	1.44	1.47	1.50	1.53	1.55	1.56

Example 26-4

Air is being heated by blowing it over a bank of five rows of 1-in., 14-gauge copper tubes 4 ft long. The tubes are spaced with their centers at the corners of equilateral triangles; the center-to-center distance is 2 tube diameters. There are five tubes per row, and there is a space of $\frac{1}{2}$ in. between the outside tubes and the duct. Steam is condensing at 227°F inside the tubes, and the resistance to heat transfer of the condensing steam and the tube walls can be neglected. If 500 cu ft/min of air enters the heater at 1 atm pressure and 60°F, find the mean heat-transfer coefficient for the air. Assume that the exit air temperature is 100°F.

The mean heat-transfer coefficient for the tube bank will be found using Grimison's equation (26-10).

The exit temperature of the air is 100°F, so the mean air temperature is 80°F. The physical properties of air will be taken at $(80 + 227)/2 = 153$°F. They are $k = 0.0164$ Btu/(hr)(ft)(°F), and $\mu = 1.36 \times 10^{-5}$ lb/(ft)(sec). The mass velocity is based on air at 60°F. Thus we use $\rho_{60°F} = 0.076$ lb/cu ft.

The minimum free-cross-sectional area for flow in the heater is $(4)(4)(\frac{1}{12}) + (2)(4)(0.5/12) = 1.667$ sq ft. Therefore the maximum mass velocity is

[1] *Ibid.*

$$G_{max} = \frac{(500)(0.076)}{(1.667)(60)}$$

$$= 0.380 \text{ lb/(sec)(sq ft)}$$

and

$$\frac{DG_{max}}{\mu} = \frac{(\frac{1}{12})(0.380)}{1.36 \times 10^{-5}}$$

$$= 2330$$

From the discussion following Eq. (26-10), we obtain the constants for this system, which are $b = 0.482$, $n = 0.556$. Thus

$$h = \frac{(0.482)(0.0164)}{\frac{1}{12}} (2330)^{0.556}$$

$$= 7.1 \text{ Btu/(hr)(sq ft)(°F)}$$

Grimison's equation applies to banks of 10 rows of tubes or more. In this problem the bank contains only 5 rows. From Table 26-2 we see that the ratio of the mean coefficient for a bank of 5 rows to the mean coefficient for a bank of 10 rows is $1.35/1.47$. Therefore, for the bank of 5 rows, the mean heat-transfer coefficient is

$$h = (7.1)(1.35/1.47)$$

$$= 6.5 \text{ Btu/(hr)(sq ft)(°F)}$$

Convection from Spheres

Both local and average heat-transfer coefficients have been measured for single spheres. In a qualitative way the local coefficients behave in the same manner for spheres as for cylinders. Heat-transfer coefficients diminish from the forward stagnation point to the point of separation of the laminar boundary layer and then increase. When the transition to a turbulent boundary layer is followed by separation, the two points are indicated by sudden trends of increasing h_x in the region 90 to 120° from stagnation.

Many of the data used for predicting average heat-transfer coefficients for spheres have been obtained by measurements of mass-transfer rates. A generally accepted correlation is that of Froessling, which is written

$$\frac{hD}{k} = 2.0 + 0.6 \left(\frac{C_p\mu}{k}\right)^{\frac{1}{3}} \left(\frac{Du_o\rho}{\mu}\right)^{\frac{1}{2}} \tag{26-11}$$

The quantity 2.0 is the value obtained for the Nusselt number for heat transfer by conduction from a sphere of diameter D in an infinite stagnant medium. This constant can be obtained by writing an equation for steady-state, spherical conduction as follows:

$$q = (k)(4\pi r^2) \frac{dt}{dr} = \text{const} \tag{26-12}$$

We integrate this equation from the surface of the sphere ($r = D/2$, $t = t_s$)

to some point a great distance away ($r = \infty$, $t = t_o$). The heat-transfer rate q is constant not only with time, but also with radial position. Equation (26-12) is therefore written as

$$\frac{q}{4\pi k} \int_{D/2}^{\infty} \frac{dr}{r^2} = \int_{t_s}^{t_o} dt \tag{26-13}$$

which gives

$$\frac{q}{4\pi k} \left(-\frac{1}{\infty} + \frac{1}{D/2} \right) = t_o - t_s \tag{26-14}$$

This equation is rearranged to give

$$q = 2\pi D k (t_s - t_o) \tag{26-15}$$

However, we write by convention

$$q = (h)(\pi D^2)(t_s - t_o) \tag{26-16}$$

Thus, combining Eqs. (26-15) and (26-16), we obtain

$$\frac{hD}{k} = 2 \tag{26-17}$$

Convective Heat Transfer between a Fluid and a Packed Bed

One method of solution of this problem has been suggested by Ranz.[1] Although the particles of a bed may not be spherical, an analysis based on flow in a regularly packed bed of spheres gives a good approximation for the heat-transfer coefficient.

The spheres are assumed to be packed in the closest possible arrangement, called rhombohedral packing. The bed consists of parallel layers of spheres in planes normal to the direction of flow. The spheres in successive layers are directly centered over the orifices formed by the openings between the spheres in the previous layer. The spheres in any layer are centered directly above those in the third layer below. In this arrangement, the centers of any four adjacent spheres are at the corners of a tetrahedron.

The method is based on the assumption that the heat-transfer coefficient for any sphere in the bed is the same as it would be for flow past a single sphere at the velocity through one of the orifices between the spheres. The jet from any orifice impinges directly on the sphere in the next layer.

It remains to calculate the relation of the velocity through the space shown in Fig. 26-2 to the superficial velocity. The ratio of the total bed cross-sectional area to the area of the openings must be found. If the diameter of the spheres is small compared with the over-all width or diameter of the bed, the ratio desired is equal to the ratio of area of the triangle

[1] W. E. Ranz, *Chem. Eng. Progr.*, **48**:247 (1952).

Fig. 26-2. *Section through a packed bed of spheres.*

shown in Fig. 26-2 to the area of the opening between the arcs of the circles in one triangle. The side of the equilateral triangle is D, so the area is $\sqrt{3}(D^2/4)$. The area of the sum of the three sectors is $\pi D^2/8$, so the ratio of the area of the triangle to the area of the orifice is $2\sqrt{3}/(2\sqrt{3} - \pi)$, or 10.73.

The method is reduced to the simple procedure of multiplying the superficial velocity by 10.73 and substituting the result for u_o in Eq. (26-11). The coefficients predicted by this method are about 10 per cent higher than those measured for a bed of randomly packed, nearly spherical particles. The empirical correlation of such data usually consists of an equation relating the j factor to the Reynolds number for a certain range of **Re**.

Convection from a Plane Surface

Heat transfer between plane surfaces and a fluid in forced convection has been discussed in the two preceding chapters on laminar and turbulent flow. A laminar boundary layer builds up, starting from the leading edge of the plate, and extends a distance limited by the critical Reynolds number, which is approximately $\mathbf{Re}_x = 500{,}000$. Beyond this point the boundary layer is turbulent. Equations (24-8) and (25-15) can be used to predict local heat-transfer coefficients in the two zones. An over-all average coefficient can be obtained by integrating $h_x\,dx$ over the entire length of the plate.

If the fluid is moving past the plate as the result of natural convection, the heat-transfer coefficients are still dependent on whether the boundary layer is laminar or turbulent. It was pointed out in the section on dimensional analysis earlier in this chapter that correlations of natural-convection heat-transfer coefficients usually involve the Grashof number, $(L^3\rho^2 g\beta\,\Delta t)/\mu^2$.

Equation (24-14) for ideal gases heated by laminar natural convection from a vertical plate contains the Grashof number:

$$\mathsf{Nu}_m = 0.478 \; \mathsf{Gr}^{1/4} \qquad\qquad (24\text{-}14)$$

McAdams gives a more general equation for laminar natural convection,

$$\mathsf{Nu}_m = 0.59 \; \mathsf{Gr}^{1/4} \, \mathsf{Pr}^{1/4} \qquad\qquad (26\text{-}18)$$

and for combined laminar and turbulent natural convection,

$$\mathsf{Nu}_m = 0.13 \; \mathsf{Gr}^{1/3} \, \mathsf{Pr}^{1/3} \qquad\qquad (26\text{-}19)$$

Equation (26-18) applies when the product $\mathsf{Gr}\,\mathsf{Pr}$ lies between 10^4 and 10^9, and Eq. (26-19) applies for $\mathsf{Gr}\,\mathsf{Pr} > 10^9$. The fluid properties are evaluated at the arithmetic average temperature $(t_s + t_o)/2$.

Heat Transfer to Liquid Metals

The use of liquid metals as heat-transfer fluids is common in the field of nuclear engineering. Liquid metals can be heated over a wide range of temperature without the necessity of keeping the system under great pressure. However, a disadvantage is that they are often somewhat dangerous to handle.

Another advantage of the use of liquid metals is that they have high heat-transfer coefficients compared with many liquids and, in addition, have high heat capacities per unit volume. These properties make them useful for removing heat from nuclear reactors, where large amounts of heat must be removed quickly and economically.

Although liquid metals have about the same viscosity as many liquids, they have thermal conductivities about 100 times greater, and hence have Prandtl numbers much smaller than 1. Because of the high thermal conductivity, the ratio of the heat-transfer rate by the molecular mechanism to the rate by the eddy mechanism is much larger than for most other fluids. As a result, most standard correlations of heat-transfer coefficients cannot be applied to liquid metals, and separate correlations have been developed.

The equations derived by Lyon and by Martinelli using the analogy between heat and momentum transfer have been mentioned in the previous chapter. Their results indicate that molecular conduction of heat is significant in the core of a turbulent stream as well as in the laminar sublayer. Lyon[1] employed velocity-distribution data in his equation to obtain values for the Nusselt number for liquid metals. His results can be represented by the following approximate equation, which gives the average heat-transfer coefficient for circular pipes for which $L/D > 60$.

[1] R. N. Lyon, *Chem. Eng. Progr.*, **47**:75 (1951).

$$\frac{hD}{k} = 7 + 0.025 \left(\frac{Du_b\rho}{\mu}\right)^{0.8} \left(\frac{C_p\mu}{k}\right)^{0.8} \tag{26-20}$$

In this equation, which applies where there is uniform heat flux from the wall, the physical properties are evaluated at the bulk temperature of the fluid.

Seban and Shimazaki[1] have proposed a similar equation for liquid metals in circular tubes with a constant wall temperature. It differs from Eq. (26-20) only in that the constant 7 is replaced by 5. Both equations apply when **Re Pr** is greater than 100 and, obviously, become identical at high values of **Re Pr**.

Boundary-layer flow of liquid metals on flat plates has been considered by Grosh and Cess.[2] They suggested that, because liquid metals have a much thicker thermal boundary layer than momentum boundary layer, the free-stream velocity can be assumed to represent the actual velocity at all values of y in the temperature field. This simplifies the differential energy balance to

$$u_o \frac{\partial t}{\partial x} = \alpha \frac{\partial^2 t}{\partial y^2} \tag{26-21}$$

This partial differential equation was solved to give the temperature distribution and the local heat-transfer coefficient for constant wall temperature. The results expressed in dimensionless numbers are as follows:

$$\mathbf{Nu}_x = \sqrt{\frac{\mathbf{Re}_x\,\mathbf{Pr}}{\pi}} \tag{26-22}$$

This equation was checked with numerical solutions of the differential energy balance and found to give values approximately 10 per cent too low in the range $0.005 < \mathbf{Pr} < 0.025$.

Effect of Surface Roughness on Heat-transfer Coefficients

Surface roughness has an effect on the friction factor in turbulent flow, as has been seen in Chaps. 13 and 15. However, in laminar flow the effect is negligible. A similar situation exists in heat transfer. Except for a slight increase in the heat-transfer area, the roughness found on commercial heat-transfer surfaces has little effect on heat transfer with laminar flow. When the flow is turbulent, the roughness may or may not have a significant effect. If the roughness elements do not protrude from the laminar sublayer, then the heat-transfer coefficient will not be affected. On the other hand, protuberances that extend into the buffer zone or the turbulent core

[1] R. A. Seban and T. T. Shimazaki, *Trans. ASME*, **73**:803 (1951).
[2] R. J. Grosh and R. D. Cess, *Trans. ASME*, **80**:667 (1958).

will cause an increase both in the loss of energy due to friction and in the heat-transfer coefficient.

It has been known for some time that if surfaces with transverse fins are used, the increases in the heat-transfer area and in the heat-transfer coefficient are usually offset by an increase in the power required to pump the fluid past the heat-transfer surface.

In a study of the effect of roughness on both the friction factor and the heat-transfer coefficient, Brouillette[1] cut V-shaped grooves in thick-walled copper tubing and measured both heat-transfer and pressure-drop data for water. He found that a roughness ratio of 0.05 (protuberance height/tubing diameter) caused the heat-transfer coefficient to double; however, this effect was accompanied by a fourfold increase in the friction factor. The inside heat-transfer area was increased by the presence of the grooves, but even the combined effects of increased h and A were not generally sufficient to give as high a ratio of heat flux to pumping power as was obtained for a smooth tube.

The disproportionate increase in friction factor is probably caused by a substantial contribution of form drag to the total frictional loss. With flow past plates and through smooth pipes, in which form drag is absent, the analogy between heat and momentum transfer is quite good. However, with flow across cylinders, form drag constitutes a major portion of the total resistance to flow, and the friction factor (as calculated from total pressure drop) is no longer related to the heat-transfer coefficient by a direct proportionality such as the j-factor relationship. The same situation seems to exist in flow systems in which the roughness elements on a solid surface extend beyond the laminar sublayer into the turbulent core.

PROBLEMS

26-1. A horizontal schedule-40, 2-in. steel pipe is carrying water at a bulk velocity of 5 ft/sec at an average temperature of 200°F. The pipe is insulated with a layer of 85 per cent magnesia 1 in. thick. The air surrounding the insulation is at 90°F. Find the temperature at the outer surfaces of the insulation and the pipe and the heat loss by convection in Btu/(hr)(lin ft). Neglect radiation loss.

26-2. Air at 96°F flows at a velocity of 18 ft/sec normal to a schedule-40, 1½-in. steel pipe. The pipe contains saturated steam at 275°F and is 10 ft long. Assuming that the resistance to heat transfer in the condensing steam and in the steel pipe is negligible compared with the resistance of the air, find the heat loss from the pipe.

26-3. It is necessary to heat 14,300 lb/hr of oil from 95 to 190°F in a 1-in., schedule-40 steel pipe jacketed by a second pipe in which steam is condensing at 10 psig. The oil has an average specific heat of 0.46 Btu/(lb)(°F), a specific gravity of 0.82, and a thermal

[1] E. C. Brouillette, M.S. thesis in chemical engineering, Purdue University, Lafayette, Ind., 1955.

conductivity of 0.073 Btu/(hr)(ft)(°F). The following table shows the viscosity of the oil as a function of temperature:

Temperature, °F.............	95	110	130	160	190
Viscosity, cp.................	13.5	10.8	8.1	5.5	4.8

The heat-transfer coefficient for the condensing steam can be taken as 1500 Btu/(hr)(sq ft)(°F). Find the length of pipe required and discuss the assumptions made in your solution.

26-4. The inside vertical wall of a furnace 8 ft high and 8 ft wide has a surface temperature of 2000°F. The wall is composed of 4 in. of firebrick, 4 in. of Silocel brick, and 8 in. of building brick. The atmospheric temperature outside the furnace is 70°F. Find the heat loss from this surface in Btu/(hr) by convection.

26-5. A steel ball ½ in. in diameter is quenched from 800°F by dropping it in a stream of oil moving past the ball with a velocity of 5 ft/sec. Because the resistance to conduction within the ball is much less than the resistance to heat transfer in the oil, the ball can be assumed to be at a uniform temperature at any instant. Find the time for the ball to cool to 200°F. The average physical properties of the oil are $k = 0.073$ Btu/(hr)(ft)(°F); $\rho = 52$ lb/cu ft; $C_p = 0.54$ Btu/(lb)(°F); $\mu = 0.00083$ lb/(ft)(sec).

26-6. A spherical drop of water is moving through air with a constant velocity of 80 ft/sec. The air temperature is 80°F, and the drop temperature is constant at the wet-bulb temperature of 63°F. If the drop has an initial diameter of ¼ in., find the time for it to evaporate completely.

26-7. An electric conductor, which is a solid cylindrical copper wire, is covered by a layer of insulation. The copper wire has a diameter of 0.01 ft. The insulation, which has maximum permissible temperature of 200°F, has a thermal conductivity $k = 0.04$ Btu/(hr)(ft)(°F). The air around the wire has a bulk temperature of 100°F.

The addition of insulation to a cylinder usually decreases the heat loss. However, for very small cylinders, the addition of insulation may increase the heat loss, and this is of considerable importance in the design of electrical systems where heat dissipation is desired.

For the system described above, find the thickness of insulation which would assure a maximum heat loss.

BOILING AND CONDENSATION
27

The transfer of heat which accompanies a change of phase is often distinguished by high rates. Heat flux as high as 50 million Btu/(hr)(sq ft) has been obtained in boiling systems. This mechanism of transferring heat has become of importance in rocket technology and nuclear-reactor design, where large quantities of heat are produced in small spaces. Although condensation rates have not reached a similar magnitude, coefficients of heat transfer for condensation as high as 20,000 Btu/(hr)(sq ft)(°F) have been reported. Condensing coefficients in ordinary commercial equipment are generally higher than in systems where a change of phase does not occur.

BOILING

Mechanisms

Among the various heat-transfer mechanisms, boiling is perhaps the most complex. In the quenching of very hot metals in liquids, the heat-transfer rate often increases as the temperature difference between the metal and liquid decreases. A similar occurrence, known as the Leidenfrost phenomenon, is observed when drops of liquid fall on a very hot surface. Although the drops bounce vigorously on the surface, they may take several seconds to evaporate. However, when drops fall on a much cooler surface of the same material, the bouncing does not occur. Instead, the drops wet the surface, spread out, and evaporate in a second or less. The explanation for both the paradoxical quenching behavior and the Leidenfrost phenomenon lies in the fact that boiling heat transfer occurs by several different mechanisms and that the mechanism is often more important in determining heat flux than the temperature-difference driving force.

Fig. 27-1.   Boiling regimes for water at atmospheric pressure.

An early investigation of these mechanisms was made by Nukiyama[1] in 1934.   He immersed a platinum wire in water at 212°F and heated the wire electrically.   The heat flux from the wire was calculated from the power input, and the temperature of the wire was determined from its electric resistance.   His results and those of subsequent investigators were of the form shown in Fig. 27-1.

Nukiyama found that as the temperature of the wire increased above 212°F, the rate of heat transfer increased smoothly, until at 300°F the temperature of the wire suddenly jumped to about 1800°F.   However, further increases in the power input caused only regular increases in the wire temperature.   A decrease in the power input from this point caused the wire temperature to decrease, as shown by the smooth curve below 1800 down to 570°F, whereupon the temperature dropped to below 300°F. Below this point, it followed the curve already established for increasing heat flux.

Nukiyama concluded that at least three types of boiling existed, and subsequent work has proved him correct.   The first mechanism encountered is now known as nucleate boiling.   At surface temperatures only a few degrees above 212°F, bubbles form and rise in columns from discrete places on the heater surface.   As the temperature difference is increased, more sites on the surface begin producing bubbles, so that more columns

[1] Shiro Nukiyama, Maximum and Minimum Values of Heat Transmitted from Metal to Boiling Water under Atmospheric Pressure, *J. Soc. Mech. Eng., Japan*, **37**(206):367–374 (1934).

of bubbles are available for removing heat from the surface.   If the temperature difference becomes sufficiently high, the concentration of bubble columns reaches some maximum, indicated as point B on Fig. 27-1, at which liquid can no longer reach the heater surface at a sufficient rate to form the required amount of vapor.   At this point the mechanism changes to what is known as film boiling, and the temperature of the wire rises (even though the heat flux remains constant) to the value corresponding to point D.   The name film boiling applies because the heater surface is now in contact with only the vapor phase, which exists as a film between the heater and the liquid.   Vaporization of liquid takes place at the liquid-vapor interface, causing the film thickness to increase until the vapor breaks off from the film in irregularly shaped bubbles at random locations. The wire melts if the point D occurs at such a high temperature that the metal is above its melting point.   Nukiyama found this burnout to occur with copper wires, but not with platinum wires, which have a much higher melting point.

Film boiling may be stable at points both above and below D.   However, if the heat flux is lowered sufficiently, the film breaks down in the vicinity of point C.   The mechanism of nucleate boiling is reestablished at the same heat flux but on the segment of the curve between A and B.

The transition zone from B to C has received only minor attention. Because of the difficulty of controlling the temperature of the wire, electric heaters are of little use for experimental work in this region.   With all heaters the surface is partially blanketed with vapor in the transition zone, but the thickness of the vapor varies greatly.   Because of the instability of operation in this region and because increases in the driving force cause a decrease in heat flux, this mechanism is of little interest at present in industrial operations.

The portion of the curve to the left of point A on Fig. 27-1 does not represent boiling, but rather heating by natural convection.   The fluid may be at its boiling point, but if the heater surface is no more than a few degrees hotter, no bubbles appear on the surface.   The portion of the curve near point A is a region in which the first few bubble columns have formed; the heat load is shared between the mechanisms of nucleate boiling and natural convection.

Nucleate Boiling

No very satisfactory mechanism has yet been proposed for nucleate boiling.   Early experimental work was largely devoted to measuring boiling performance; the results were correlated using empirical equations composed of dimensionless groups. However, contradictions in the experimental results of the different investigators have brought most of their equations into disrepute. Recently, equations based partly on mechanistic concepts have been proposed and will be discussed later in this section. Many aspects of boiling are still unexplained, and predictions of boiling coefficients without reference to experimental data may easily be in error by 100 per cent.

Nucleation. It is observed in chemistry laboratories that liquids in glass containers often do not begin to boil at the saturation temperature corresponding to atmospheric pressure. In fact, superheating in excess of 100°F can be obtained if care is taken to use pure liquids and clean glassware. However, this state of supersaturation can be quickly ended, and violent ebullition of vapor occurs if impurities are added to the system.

Although the phenomenon of superheating is most spectacularly demonstrated in the nonboiling, unstable system described above, it also occurs in all boiling systems. The temperature of a boiling liquid, measured some distance from the heated surface, is often as much as a degree higher than the temperature of the vapor above the liquid; the vapor is at the saturation temperature. Adjacent to the heated surface the liquid superheat may be as high as 30 to 50°F. This zone is extremely thin; most of the temperature drop usually occurs less than 1 mm from the heater.

The explanation for the presence of superheat in boiling systems is that the saturation temperatures and pressures ordinarily used by engineers (e.g., as found in steam tables) apply to equilibrium at a flat interface between vapor and liquid. However, if a force balance is written at the equator of a spherical vapor bubble of radius r, the internal pressure p_g exceeds the surrounding liquid pressure p_ℓ by an amount equal to the effect of the surface force, which tends to contract the bubble. Thus we write

$$p_g(\pi r^2) = p_\ell(\pi r^2) + 2\pi r\sigma \tag{27-1}$$

from which we get

$$p_g - p_\ell = \frac{2\sigma}{r} \tag{27-2}$$

To achieve the excess pressure $p_g - p_\ell$, which may be very high in small bubbles, the liquid which forms the vapor nucleus must be at a temperature much higher than the flat-surface saturation temperature. If nuclei with large radii of curvature are available, the required excess pressure will be smaller and boiling will commence at a lower superheat. A perfectly pure liquid in contact with a flat heated surface would, in theory, require an infinite amount of superheat. A liquid is not, however, a continuum, and clusters of molecules could serve as nuclei. Furthermore, the conditions

Boiling coefficient h, Btu/(hr)(sq ft)(°F)

$t_s - t_{sl}$, °F

Emery paper

○ 4–0
□ 0
▽ 2 (roughest)

Fig. 27-2.   Coefficients of heat transfer for n-hexane boiling on a flat plate polished with three grades of emery paper. [From AIChE Journal, 6(1):83 (1960).]

of perfect purity and flatness are unobtainable, so that the highest super-heats recorded are of the order of 100 to 200°F. The effect of solid impurities in preventing bumping can be explained on the basis of the probable large radius of curvature of the nuclei they provide. However, it is likely that boiling does not require the presence of foreign matter, but can be initiated on the heating surface. Numerous experiments have shown that metal surfaces polished with emery paper have higher coefficients of heat transfer when rough paper is used to polish the surface than when fine paper is used. Sample results are shown in Fig. 27-2.

One way in which surface conditions are believed to affect boiling is by the trapping of vapor in surface cavities before boiling begins. The pits on the heater surface may contain air when boiling begins, but after a short time all the air is dissipated and only molecules of the substance being boiled remain in the vapor space. If the pits are round-bottomed, the liquid will fill them completely when boiling stops, and they will not serve as sources of bubbles when boiling is resumed. However, if the pits have angular bottoms and the liquid-vapor system has a sufficiently large contact angle, the liquid will not completely fill the pits when boiling stops. The liquid-vapor interface will bulge downward into the pit, but in this case the surface forces act with the pressure in the vapor space to balance the liquid pressure. The liquid advances only until the radius of curvature of the interface is small enough so that $p_g + 2\sigma/r$ is equal to p_ℓ and a stable gas pocket remains. Upon further heating, bubbles are once again emitted from this site.

Bubble Behavior. The formation, growth, and release of bubbles is an extremely rapid sequence of events. Photographic studies have shown that the total time between the release of successive bubbles is often only a few hundredths of a second. The rapid growth and departure of vapor bubbles causes great turbulence in the liquid, especially in the zone of high superheat near the heater surface. This turbulence assists in the transport of heat from the heater surface to the liquid evaporating at the bubble surface. The rapid growth of the bubble and the turbulence in the liquid assist each other, and this mechanism probably accounts for the high heat-transfer coefficients encountered in boiling systems.

Experiments have shown that the heat-transfer coefficient is proportional to some power of the concentration of active centers ranging from 0.25 to 0.46, although no theoretical reasons for this relation are known. The number of active centers on a heater surface increases with an increase of superheat, but little is known about this relationship other than that it probably depends on the roughness of the surface and the physical properties of the boiling fluid. The accurate prediction of boiling coefficients may be possible when these two mechanisms are understood.

Correlations of Nucleate-boiling Heat-transfer Coefficients. Two recent correlations by Rohsenow[1] and by Forster and Zuber[2] have met with some success in the correlation of boiling coefficients. Both correlations have some basis in theory, but in the end resort to a combination of dimensionless groups for which no mechanistic explanation is offered. Both equations are of the form

$$\mathbf{Nu} = a\,\mathbf{Re}^b\,\mathbf{Pr}^c \tag{27-3}$$

The characteristic velocity used by Rohsenow in $\mathbf{Re}$ is fnV_b, where f is the frequency of bubble formation at a site (bubbles per second), n is the number of active sites per unit area, and V_b is the volume of a bubble. The quantity fnV_b can be seen to have the units of velocity. The Forster and Zuber correlation, on the other hand, employs a velocity which is the radial velocity of the interface of the growing bubble. They found that the product of radial velocity and bubble radius is independent of time; thus the Reynolds number, which contains this product, is also independent of time and can be calculated from the properties of the system.

Although the two equations discussed above seem to have firmer bases than the many completely empirical correlations which preceded them,

[1] W. M. Rohsenow, *Trans. ASME,* **74:**969 (1952).

[2] H. K. Forster and N. Zuber, *AIChE Journal,* **1:**531 (1955).

they do not offer entirely reliable methods of predicting boiling coefficients. One difficulty is that the effects of none of the individual variables are known. In boiling from electrically heated wires, the wire diameter seems to be a variable. In boiling from horizontal tubes, the average boiling coefficient varies with tube size while the local boiling coefficient may vary as much as 100 per cent from the bottom to the top of the tube.

The effect of surface tension on boiling coefficients is unknown. Westwater,[1] in a thorough review of the state of knowledge of boiling, shows that if the effect of surface tension on the boiling coefficient were represented by the equation

$$h = \text{const } \sigma^n \tag{27-4}$$

the values predicted by various experimenters for the exponent n would range from -2.5 to 1.275.

The effect of degree of superheat on the boiling coefficient is variable. Many commercial surfaces give data which can be represented approximately by the equation[2]

$$h = \text{const } (\Delta t)^{2.5} \tag{27-5}$$

However, values of the exponent as low as 1.4 have been reported on copper tubes, whereas flat surfaces polished with coarse emery paper may give values as high as 25.

The conclusion that one must draw from the present state of knowledge of nucleate boiling is that although we have some understanding of boiling performance, we are unable to predict reliable values for the boiling coefficients of heat transfer at the present time. In these circumstances the engineer has no alternative but to obtain experimental data.

Maximum Heat Flux

As the superheat of a boiling liquid is increased, the concentration of active centers on the heating surface increases and the heat flux also increases. The mass rate of the vapor rising from the surface must at steady state be equal to the mass rate of liquid proceeding toward the surface. As the boiling rate increases, the rate of liquid influx must increase; since the area available for liquid flow decreases with increasing number of bubble

[1] J. W. Westwater, "Advances in Chemical Engineering," vol. 1, chap. 1, Academic Press, Inc., New York, 1956.

[2] The temperature-difference driving force is defined by some writers as the temperature of the heater surface minus the bulk temperature of the liquid. Others employ the temperature of the heater surface minus the saturation temperature of the liquid. The latter definition gives slightly greater values of Δt than the former and appears to be in more general use.

columns, the liquid velocity must increase very sharply. A limiting condition is reached because the drag exerted by each phase on the other prevents indefinite increases in velocity. At this limiting condition, the liquid flow toward the heated surface cannot increase and the surface becomes largely blanketed with vapor. If the heat input to the surface is held constant (as with electrical heating), the surface temperature will rise quickly to some much higher value, at which heat is transmitted to the fluid by the mechanism of film boiling. If the heat input is a variable and the surface temperature is slowly increased (as in the case of boiling on steam-heated tubes), the boiling mechanism enters the transition zone between nucleate and film boiling.

The maximum heat flux at which nucleate boiling occurs is of considerable importance in industrial operations. Film boiling has few advantages; the superheat at which the maximum flux occurs with nucleate boiling is generally regarded as a limiting operating condition.

Film Boiling

Film boiling occurs when the superheat is sufficiently high to keep the heater surface completely blanketed with vapor. Heat is transmitted through the gas film by conduction, convection, and radiation. High heat fluxes are often obtained with film boiling at high surface temperatures because of the contribution of radiation. In addition, high heat fluxes are obtained if the vapor in the film is turbulent, as, for example, in film boiling from a long vertical surface.

Film boiling is important in rocket technology when liquefied gases such as hydrogen and oxygen are used to cool the rocket engine. Extremely high superheats occur in these systems, causing heat to be transferred by film boiling.

CONDENSATION

Mechanisms

Heat transfer by the condensation of vapors on a cold surface is a common industrial process. Condensation occurs usually on the outer surfaces of tubes in a shell-and-tube heat exchanger, and in most condensers the liquid inside the tubes which receives the heat is water.

The vapor being condensed may consist of only one substance, as in the case of steam being condensed in a power plant, or it may be a mixture of substances. The mixture may consist of some substances which are condensable and some which are not, as in the condensation of moisture from air in a dehumidifier. Finally, the mixture may consist of substances which are all condensable at the temperature of the cold surface, as in the case of vapor from a distillation column. In this chapter we shall consider primarily the problem of the condensation of a pure substance.

Vapor-liquid equilibrium is influenced by pressure as well as by temperature, so the pressure in a condensing system is an important variable. Because the cooling fluid in large condensers is usually water at near-atmospheric temperature, the approximate surface temperature of the condenser is usually fixed within a fairly narrow range. Condensation of the vapors is then made to occur by the choice of a suitable operating pressure. It is in this manner that the operating pressure is determined for many industrial separations.

Condensation on solid surfaces occurs by two methods. One is known as film condensation. If the condensate wets the surface readily, a liquid film forms on which further condensation occurs. The latent heat of condensation is transferred through the liquid film to the surface. When a vapor consisting of a single component condenses in this fashion, nearly the entire resistance to heat transfer from the vapor to the surface is found in the liquid film. The second kind of condensation, known as dropwise condensation, occurs when the liquid wets the surface sparingly so that the condensate coalesces into discrete drops attached to the surface. The drops grow by further condensation on their surfaces and by coalescing with adjacent drops. If the solid surface is not horizontal, the drops grow until they reach a sufficient size to cause them to run down the surface to its lowest point and fall off. In flowing downward, the drops sweep clear a path, so that a substantial portion of the surface is free from condensate at all times. This unwetted surface offers no resistance to heat transfer, and for this reason coefficients for dropwise condensation reach extremely high values. McAdams[1] reports values of h_m measured by various workers which range from 4000 to 75,000 Btu/(hr)(sq ft)(°F). Unfortunately, dropwise condensation appears to be possible only when the surface is coated with a "promoter"—for example, benzyl mercaptan, which prevents wetting of the surface. A condenser when treated with this material will give dropwise condensation for only a short time, because the promoter is dissipated. For this reason industrial condensers are designed on the assumption of film condensation, and we shall consider only this mechanism in the remainder of this chapter.

The local heat-transfer coefficient for condensation usually varies with

[1] W. H. McAdams, "Heat Transmission," 3d ed., chap. 13, McGraw-Hill Book Company, Inc., New York, 1954.

position; it varies along the length of a vertical tube and around the perimeter of a horizontal tube. The derivation we shall examine in the next section is for a mean condensing coefficient with a constant temperature difference. This temperature difference, as was mentioned earlier in Chap. 23, serves in part to define the heat-transfer coefficient. In condensing it is taken as the temperature at the vapor-liquid interface minus the temperature at the liquid-solid interface. If the vapor is a pure substance, its saturation temperature will be the temperature at the vapor-liquid interface. If the vapor is superheated or is a mixture, its temperature will not be the same as the vapor-liquid interface temperature. Nevertheless, this interface temperature minus the liquid-solid interface temperature is the driving force used in defining condensing coefficients.

Condensation on Vertical Tubes

Nusselt[1] in 1916 presented theoretical relations for the mean coefficient of heat transfer for a pure saturated vapor condensing on vertical and horizontal tubes. It was assumed in both cases that the flow of liquid was entirely viscous, that there was negligible drag at the vapor-liquid interface, and that the contribution of inertia forces to the downward flow of liquid was negligible. It has been shown since that the last two assumptions are usually valid but that in many situations the liquid flow is turbulent. This usually occurs with condensation on a long vertical tube. Near the top of the tube the flow is laminar, but when the condensate film attains a certain thickness, the flow becomes turbulent and Nusselt's equation no longer applies. The criterion for transition between the two types of flow is the value of Reynolds number $\mathbf{Re}_L$. For a film of thickness x_e flowing down a vertical tube of diameter D with a bulk velocity u_b, the hydraulic radius is found by its customary definition to be simply x_e. Thus, at any distance L from the top of the tube where the film thickness is x_e, we write

$$\mathbf{Re}_L = \frac{4x_e u_b \rho}{\mu} \tag{27-6}$$

The mass-flow rate is $x_e u_b \rho \pi D$, and the mass flow per unit of tube perimeter is $x_e u_b \rho$. This quantity, designated as Γ, increases from a value of zero at the top of the tube to a maximum at the bottom. Using it in the Reynolds number, we obtain

$$\mathbf{Re}_L = \frac{4\Gamma}{\mu} \tag{27-7}$$

Laminar flow exists when the Reynolds number is less than 2000, and

[1] W. Nusselt, *Z. deut. Ing.*, **60**:541, 569 (1916).

turbulent flow when it is greater. This is therefore a limitation on the validity of the Nusselt equation.

The tube diameter is usually much greater than the thickness of the film, so the cylindrical system may be represented approximately by a rectangular coordinate system. The origin is at the top of the tube, with the x axis directed outward normal to the tube surface and the y axis directed downward.

The following Navier-Stokes equation is the basis of the hydrodynamic analysis, which, as usual, precedes the heat-transfer analysis.

$$u_x \frac{\partial u_y}{\partial x} + u_y \frac{\partial u_y}{\partial y} + u_z \frac{\partial u_y}{\partial z} + \frac{\partial u_y}{\partial \theta} = g_c Y - \frac{g_c}{\rho} \frac{\partial p}{\partial y}$$

$$+ \nu \left(\frac{\partial^2 u_y}{\partial x^2} + \frac{\partial^2 u_y}{\partial y^2} + \frac{\partial^2 u_y}{\partial z^2} \right) \quad (11\text{-}53)$$

The left side of this equation is zero because the flow is steady, and u_x, u_z, and $\partial u_y / \partial y$ are assumed to be zero. On the right side, $\partial p / \partial y$ is zero, and the variation of u_y in both y and z directions is neglected, so that Eq. (11-53) becomes

$$\frac{d^2 u_y}{dx^2} = \frac{-g_c Y}{\nu} \quad (27\text{-}8)$$

The body force Y reduces to g/g_c, because the y axis is vertical, so that Eq. (27-8) becomes

$$\frac{d^2 u_y}{dx^2} = \frac{-g}{\nu} \quad (27\text{-}9)$$

Equation (27-9) is integrated twice to give

$$u_y = \frac{-gx^2}{2\nu} + C_1 x + C_2 \quad (27\text{-}10)$$

The two arbitrary constants are found by the application of two boundary conditions: $u_y = 0$ at $x = 0$, and $du_y/dx = 0$ at the vapor-liquid interface, where $x = x_e$. This latter condition is true if drag at the vapor-liquid interface is negligible. The use of these values gives

$$u_y = \frac{g}{\nu} \left(x_e x - \frac{x^2}{2} \right) \quad (27\text{-}11)$$

The mass rate can be found by integrating over the film thickness. Neglecting the change in perimeter with increase in x, we obtain

$$w = \int_0^{x_e} \frac{g}{\nu} \left(x_e x - \frac{x^2}{2} \right) \rho \pi D \, dx = \frac{\rho \pi D g}{\nu} \frac{x_e^3}{3} \quad (27\text{-}12)$$

From this we see that the mass rate per unit of tube perimeter, which we defined earlier as Γ, is

$$\Gamma = \frac{\rho g x_e{}^3}{3\nu} \tag{27-13}$$

To find the mean heat-transfer coefficient, a heat balance is written for a differential length of tube dy located at a distance y from the top of the tube. The heat-flow rate is

$$dq = h\pi D \, dy \, (t_{sv} - t_s) \tag{27-14}$$

The temperature gradient in the y direction is assumed to be negligible, so all the heat of condensation released at the vapor-liquid interface is conducted horizontally to the tube surface. If the film has a thickness x_e, we can write

$$dq = k\pi D \, dy \, \frac{t_{sv} - t_s}{x_e} \tag{27-15}$$

Combining Eqs. (27-14) and (27-15), we obtain

$$h = \frac{k}{x_e} \tag{27-16}$$

By definition, the local heat-transfer coefficient is

$$h = \frac{dq}{dA \, (t_{sv} - t_s)}$$

$$= \frac{\lambda \, dw}{dA \, (t_{sv} - t_s)} \tag{27-17}$$

where dw = condensation rate, lb/hr, at the differential section
$\quad\quad \lambda$ = latent heat of vaporization

However, the local condensation rate can also be written as

$$\frac{dw}{dA} = \frac{dw}{\pi D \, dy} = \frac{d\Gamma}{dy} \tag{27-18}$$

Combining Eqs. (27-16) to (27-18) gives

$$h = \frac{k}{x_e} = \frac{\lambda}{t_{sv} - t_s} \frac{d\Gamma}{dy} \tag{27-19}$$

or

$$t_{sv} - t_s = \frac{x_e \lambda}{k} \frac{d\Gamma}{dy} \tag{27-20}$$

For the entire length L of the tube on which laminar flow exists, we write

$$q = h_m A(t_{sv} - t_s) = \lambda w_L \tag{27-21}$$

This equation is solved for the temperature difference

$$t_{sv} - t_s = \frac{\lambda w_L}{h_m A} = \frac{\lambda \Gamma_L}{h_m L} \tag{27-22}$$

which is substituted in Eq. (27-20) and rearranged to give

$$dy = \frac{x_e h_m L}{k \Gamma_L} d\Gamma \tag{27-23}$$

From Eq. (27-13) the film thickness is

$$x_e = \left(\frac{3\nu \Gamma}{\rho g}\right)^{\frac{1}{3}} \tag{27-24}$$

This result is substituted in Eq. (27-23):

$$dy = \frac{h_m L}{k \Gamma_L} \left(\frac{3\nu}{\rho g}\right)^{\frac{1}{3}} \Gamma^{\frac{1}{3}} d\Gamma \tag{27-25}$$

This equation is integrated from $y = 0$ to $y = L$ and from $\Gamma = 0$ to $\Gamma = \Gamma_L$ and rearranged to give the mean heat-transfer coefficient for the entire laminar region

$$
\begin{aligned}
h_m &= \tfrac{4}{3} k \left(\frac{\rho g}{3 \nu \Gamma_L}\right)^{\frac{1}{3}} \\
&= 0.925 \left(\frac{k^3 \rho g}{\nu \Gamma_L}\right)^{\frac{1}{3}}
\end{aligned} \tag{27-26}
$$

If Eq. (27-22) is rearranged, the quantity Γ_L can be expressed as

$$\Gamma_L = \frac{h_m L (t_{sv} - t_s)}{\lambda} \tag{27-27}$$

Substituting Eq. (27-27) in Eq. (27-26), we obtain

$$h_m = 0.925 \left[\frac{k^3 \rho g \lambda}{h_m L (t_{sv} - t_s)}\right]^{\frac{1}{3}} \tag{27-28}$$

The mean heat-transfer coefficient can be readily extracted by cubing both sides of Eq. (27-28), solving for h_m, and taking the fourth root. This procedure gives

$$h_m = 0.942 \left[\frac{k^3 \rho g \lambda}{\nu L (t_{sv} - t_s)}\right]^{\frac{1}{4}} \tag{27-29}$$

The mean coefficient can also be expressed in terms of $\mathbf{Re}_L$, as defined in Eq. (27-7). To achieve this result we rearrange Eq. (27-26) to give

$$
\begin{aligned}
h_m \left(\frac{\nu^2}{k^3 g}\right)^{\frac{1}{3}} &= 1.47 \left(\frac{4 \Gamma_L}{\mu}\right)^{-\frac{1}{3}} \\
&= 1.47 \, (\mathbf{Re}_L)^{-\frac{1}{3}}
\end{aligned} \tag{27-30}
$$

in which $\mathbf{Re}_L$ is the Reynolds number at the bottom of the laminar-flow region on the tube.

Equation (27-29) shows a dependence of h_m on the temperature drop over the condensate film. In the operation of a condenser the cold fluid flowing through the inside of the tube increases in temperature, so that

$$h_m\left(\frac{\nu^2}{k^3 g}\right)^{1/3}$$

Recommended

Theoretical

$$\frac{4\Gamma_L}{\mu}$$

Fig. 27-3. *Condensing coefficients on a vertical tube. (From W. H. McAdams, "Heat Transmission," 3d ed., p. 335, McGraw-Hill Book Company, Inc., New York, 1954.)*

the assumption that $t_{sv} - t_s$ is constant is not valid. Nevertheless, the relation between temperature drop and h_m is only by the power of $\frac{1}{4}$, so the variation of h_m because of this is usually small.

The physical properties of the condensate vary with temperature, but the only property affected significantly is the viscosity. It has been shown that the viscosity should be evaluated at a temperature equal to the temperature of the saturated vapor minus $\frac{3}{4}$ $(t_{sv} - t_s)$. The other properties can also be used at this temperature. A minor correction may also be made to the latent heat λ, because the total heat flux is actually the sum of the latent heat plus the sensible heat given up by subcooling the liquid in the condensate film. An accepted procedure is to multiply λ by the factor $\left[1 + \dfrac{0.4 C_p(t_{sv} - t_s)}{\lambda}\right]^2$ before using it in Eq. (27-29).

Equation (27-29) has been compared with experimental data and found to be generally too conservative. It has been suggested that this is because ripples on the surface of the condensate film give a certain amount of mixing. Experimental values of h_m range as high as 50 per cent greater than the values predicted by Eq. (27-29). Consequently, the recommended procedure is to multiply the theoretical values of h_m obtained from Eq. (27-29) by a factor of 1.2. Both the theoretical and recommended relations are shown in Fig. 27-3.

If the tube is sufficiently long, the film thickness increases and the flow becomes turbulent. A theoretical solution is not available for this situation. However, the mean coefficient has been measured experimentally in numerous investigations. McAdams[1] recommends the following empirical correlation:

[1] *Loc. cit.*

$$h_m \left(\frac{\nu^2}{k^3 g}\right)^{\frac{1}{3}} = 0.0077 \left(\frac{4\Gamma_L}{\mu}\right)^{0.4} \tag{27-31}$$

This relation, which is recommended for values of the Reynolds number $4\Gamma_L/\mu$ greater than 2000, is shown in Fig. 27-3, in addition to the curves for laminar flow. The mean coefficient obtained from Eq. (27-31) applies to the entire tube, i.e., both the laminar and turbulent portions.

Condensation on Horizontal Tubes

The local coefficient of heat transfer for a vapor condensing on a horizontal tube is a function of position, just as it is for a vertical tube. However, for a horizontal tube the variation occurs around the periphery of the tube rather than along the axis. The highest coefficient is on the top of the tube, where the condensate film is thinnest, and the lowest is on the underside.

Nusselt's derivation for condensation on a horizontal tube is similar to that for a vertical tube and will not be given here. It leads to the following equation for the mean heat-transfer coefficient:

$$h_m = 0.725 \left[\frac{k^3 \rho g \lambda}{\nu D (t_{sv} - t_s)}\right]^{\frac{1}{4}} \tag{27-32}$$

This expression, which is similar to Eq. (27-29) for the vertical tube, can be rearranged, using the substitutions shown below, to give h_m as a function of $\mathbf{Re}_L$.

$$h_m \left(\frac{\nu^2}{k^3 g}\right)^{\frac{1}{3}} = 1.20 \, (\mathbf{Re}_L)^{-\frac{1}{3}} \tag{27-33}$$

As before, the Reynolds number is expressed as

$$\mathbf{Re} = \frac{(4)(\text{hydraulic radius})(u_b \rho)}{\mu} \tag{27-34}$$

The hydraulic radius is found by the customary procedure and is equal to the thickness of the film x_e at any point. The quantity $x_e u_b \rho$ is the mass rate of condensate per lineal foot of tubing at a certain peripheral position on each side of the tube. Thus Eq. (27-34) can be written as follows:

$$\mathbf{Re} = \frac{4 x_e u_b \rho}{\mu} \tag{27-35}$$

The Reynolds number at the base of the tube, which we shall write as $\mathbf{Re}_L$, is the one used for defining h_m in Eq. (27-33). It can be written in terms of the total mass rate per foot of tubing as

$$\mathbf{Re}_L = \frac{4}{\mu}\frac{\Gamma_L}{2} = \frac{2\Gamma_L}{\mu} \tag{27-36}$$

where Γ_L is total rate of condensate formation on the tube per foot of length, and $\Gamma_L/2$, the rate for each side, is the mass rate just before the streams of condensate join at the bottom of the tube. Equation (27-36) therefore defines $\mathbf{Re}_L$ as used in going from Eq. (27-32) to Eq. (27-33).

If a number of horizontal tubes are arranged in a vertical row so that all the condensate from each tube falls on the tube beneath, the mean coefficients on successive tubes diminish. The derivation which leads to Eq. (27-32) can be extended theoretically[1] to include the effect of N tubes in a vertical row to give a mean coefficient for the entire bank of tubes as

$$(h_m)_N = 0.725 \left[\frac{k^3\rho g\lambda}{\nu N D(t_{sv} - t_s)}\right]^{\frac{1}{4}} \tag{27-37}$$

This equation has been found to give satisfactory predictions of mean coefficients for banks of tubes, provided the mass-flow rate of condensate on the lowest tube is such that $\mathbf{Re}_L < 2000$. There will, of course, always be a certain amount of turbulence on any tube below the top, because of the condensate dripping from the tube above. This has the effect of increasing $(h_m)_N$. On a single horizontal tube it is unlikely that condensation will occur at a sufficient rate to cause turbulent flow. However, the flow of vapor over the condensing film may cause ripples to occur, with the result that the coefficients will be higher than those predicted from Eq. (27-32).

Superheated Vapors

If the vapor being condensed enters the condenser in a superheated condition, this superheat must be removed along with the latent heat by the cooler fluid inside the tubes. The mechanism of condensation is coupled with desuperheating so that an analysis of the process might be expected to require the consideration of both steps. It has been found experimentally, however, that the resistance offered by desuperheating is negligible. Even with superheat the temperature of the liquid at the vapor-liquid interface is the saturation temperature, so that the usual condensing coefficient is employed with the driving force $t_{sv} - t_s$, as in the case of a saturated vapor. The extremely small resistance for desuperheating will be more readily understood when we have considered simultaneous heat and mass transfer in Chap. 38.

[1] M. Jakob, "Heat Transfer," vol. 1, chap. 30, John Wiley & Sons, Inc., New York, 1949.

Effect of Noncondensable Gases

This phenomenon is familiar in the form of condensation of atmospheric moisture to give dew. It also occurs in industrial equipment in which liquids containing dissolved air are boiled and later condensed.

Condensation of a constituent will occur only if the partial pressure of that constituent in the gas exceeds the vapor pressure at the temperature of the cold surface. If this partial-pressure difference exists, the condensable constituents will diffuse through the gas phase to the cold surface and condense there. In addition to the latent heat given up by condensation at the surface, sensible heat will be transferred by conduction or convection to the interface from the bulk of the gas phase.

This situation, like the condensation of superheated vapor, is a coupled process. However, in this case the diffusion step is not usually negligible; in fact, the rate of diffusion may be so low as to become the controlling step. The analysis of this process requires the simultaneous application of equations for heat and mass transfer and will not be discussed at this point.

In some processes the gas contains only a small portion of condensable material and flows through the condenser continuously. In others, however, the gas entering the condenser is nearly all condensable. These total condensers must contain provision for continuous or periodic venting; otherwise the noncondensable gases will accumulate and the capacity of the condenser will diminish to zero.

Condensation of Mixtures

Condensers for the condensation of mixtures may operate in a variety of ways. If all the vapor entering is to be condensed and opportunity is provided for the establishment of equilibrium conditions, the bulk of the vapor phase in the condenser at any instant will acquire an equilibrium composition different from that of the liquid. The liquid which leaves must necessarily have the same composition as the vapor entering, but the bulk vapor phase will be richer than either of these in the most volatile components. This is illustrated in Fig. 27-4, which shows the vapor-liquid equilibrium for a binary system of components A and B at constant pressure. A saturated vapor of composition x_1 enters the condenser continuously at temperature t_1. The liquid leaving is of the same composition but is assumed to be at the liquid-saturation temperature t_2. The bulk of the vapor in the condenser is at the same temperature as the liquid t_2 but is of a different composition x_2.

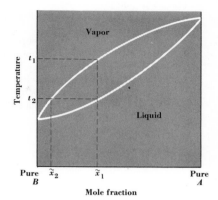

Fig. 27-4.   Vapor-liquid equilibrium diagram illustrating equilibrium in condensation of mixtures.

The determination of the heat load in a condenser is rather simple under these conditions. The vapor-liquid interface temperature is merely the saturation temperature t_2 of the liquid at the condenser pressure. The equations derived for predicting condensing coefficients for pure substances are used with the physical properties of the liquid condensate. The temperature difference is, as before, the vapor-liquid interface temperature minus the solid-liquid interface temperature.

The assumptions made above regarding equilibrium between the bulk gas phase and the liquid are not always valid. Another way of analyzing the problem would be to assume that the bulk gas phase in the condenser has the same composition as the entering gas. Under these conditions, the vapor-liquid interfacial temperature and the liquid interfacial composition are determined by trial-and-error procedures and are functions of the solid-liquid interfacial temperature.

PROBLEMS

27-1. A shell-and-tube condenser contains four rows with four copper tubes per row, arranged in square pitch. The tubes are ¾-in. 16 BWG and are 3 ft long. Water is flowing through the tubes at a rate such that the convection heat-transfer coefficient for the water is $h = 1000$ Btu/(hr)(sq ft)(°F). The water rises only slightly in temperature and may be assumed to be at a constant temperature of 60°F. Pure, saturated steam at 5 psig is condensing on the shell side. Determine the capacity of the condenser in Btu/hr under these conditions when it is (*a*) in a vertical position, and (*b*) in a horizontal position.

27-2. A condenser contains horizontal, finned tubes which are ½-in.-OD copper tubes to which a continuous spiral fin is attached. The fin has an over-all diameter of 1½ in., a thickness of 0.02 in., and a pitch such that it spirals around the tube 16 times per inch of tube length. Estimate the condensing coefficient for the top tube in the condenser in Btu/(hr)(°F)(sq ft of total condensing area).   Assume that the metal surface is at 140° at all points and that the condensing vapor is saturated steam at 210°F.   The fins may be considered to have an effective height equal to the area of a fin face divided by the outside fin diameter.

27-3. The condensation of a superheated vapor is a coupled process of desuperheating and condensation.   If no condensation occurs, the desuperheating process has a resistance to heat transfer which may be 100 times greater than the resistance offered when condensation occurs.   Nevertheless, when desuperheating and condensation are combined, the resistance of the desuperheating step is negligible compared with the condensing resistance.   Explain this paradox.

RADIANT HEAT TRANSFER

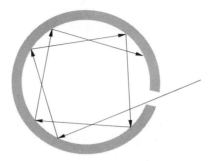

The Nature of Thermal Radiation

Radiant energy of the form called thermal radiation is emitted by every body having a temperature greater than absolute zero. This does not mean, however, that the amount of thermal radiation emitted is always significant. Its importance in a heat-transfer process depends on the amount of heat being transferred simultaneously by other mechanisms. In systems at or below room temperature thermal radiation is likely to be negligible. However, at temperatures of "red heat" ($\sim$1000°F) and higher, radiant transmission is often the principal mechanism of heat transfer.

Bodies may emit radiant energy of other forms in addition to thermal radiation. Bombardment of a substance by electrons produces radiation which we call X rays. Exposure to one form of radiation often causes a body to emit another, or secondary, radiation; e.g., certain minerals fluoresce under ultraviolet light. In fact, there is a whole spectrum of electromagnetic radiation in which the various arbitrary divisions are referred to by names reflecting the method of origin or some characteristic quality. All forms have the same velocity of propagation but differ in wavelength and origin. All forms produce heat when absorbed. Nevertheless, it is only the electromagnetic radiation produced by virtue of the temperature of the emitter that we call thermal radiation. Some of this thermal radiation we also call visible light. Most of it, however, falls outside the spectrum of visible light and is ordinarily included in what we call infrared radiation. Table 28-1 gives the approximate ranges of wavelength of some forms of radiation.

Table 28-1. Characteristic Wavelengths of Radiation

	Wavelength range, cm
Gamma rays...............	0.01–0.15 ($\times 10^{-8}$)
X rays....................	0.06–1000 ($\times 10^{-8}$)
Ultraviolet.................	100–3500 ($\times 10^{-8}$)
Visible....................	3500–7800 ($\times 10^{-8}$)
Infrared...................	7800 $\times 10^{-8}$–0.04
Radio.....................	0.04–10^7

The amount of thermal radiation emitted by a body depends on its temperature and surface condition. At any temperature the radiation emitted extends over a spectrum, as shown in Fig. 28-1. As the temperature changes, both the total emissive power and the distribution of energy change. It can be seen that the wavelength at which the maximum emissive power occurs decreases as the temperature of the emitter increases. The spectrum of visible light occurs on the low-wavelength side of the thermal-radiation spectrum, so increasing the temperature causes increasing amounts of the thermal energy to appear as light. In addition, the distribution of the energy in the visible range alters. At low temperatures, where visible light is just emitted (e.g., 1000°F), the light is red because of the encroachment of the thermal spectrum onto the visible spectrum from

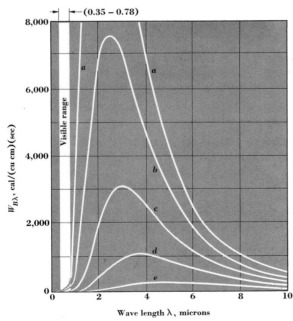

Fig. 28-1. *Spectral distribution of total energy emitted by a black body. (From M. Jakob, "Heat Transfer," vol. I, John Wiley & Sons, Inc., New York, 1950.)*

a. $T = 1400°$K.
b. 1200°K.
c. 1000°K.
d. 800°K.
e. 600°K.

$W_{B\lambda}$, cal/(cu cm)(sec)

Wave length λ, microns

the red side. As the temperature increases, more energy is emitted at the lower wavelengths and the light becomes more nearly white.

The sun emits energy at 10,000°F, so we might expect another object at the same temperature to emit light of the same quality as sunlight. However, surface conditions also affect the emission at particular wavelengths, so both surface conditions and temperature would need to be duplicated. Furthermore, the light we receive from the sun has passed through the earth's atmosphere, which absorbs some energy and thus affects the quality of the light as we receive it. That this happens is evident in the changing character of sunlight as the length of its path through the atmosphere changes with time of day and with changing amounts of atmospheric pollution.

Absorption, Reflection, and Transmission

Radiant energy striking matter may be absorbed, transmitted, or reflected. The fraction of the total energy which is absorbed is called the absorptivity α; the fraction transmitted is the transmissivity τ; and the fraction reflected is the reflectivity ρ. These definitions lead to the equation

$$\alpha + \tau + \rho = 1 \qquad (28\text{-}1)$$

A body having an absorptivity of unity is called a black body. If absorptivity plus reflectivity equals 1 for a substance, it is said to be opaque. Certain solids are only partially opaque in very thin sections, but the absorption of energy in most opaque solids is accomplished essentially at the surface. Some solids, of course, are nearly transparent, as are most liquids and gases.

Absorption does not occur equally for radiation of all wavelengths; since the spectral distribution of energy is a function of the temperature of the emitter, the absorptivity of a receiver depends on the temperature of the emitter. The variation of absorptivity of a solid with wavelength is shown in Fig. 28-2. Selective absorption is especially significant in absorption by gases, which are transparent to radiation of some wavelengths but highly absorbent for others. The absorptivity of a material also depends on its own temperature, although any variation because of this effect is usually less significant than the variation resulting from temperature changes of the emitter. Thus the specification of α for a particular surface requires the designation of two temperatures. In solving many problems, however, it is necessary to assume that the absorptivity of a surface is not a function of the spectral distribution; the surface in these circumstances is spoken of as a "gray" surface.

Fig. 28-2.   *Variation of absorptivity and emissivity with wavelength. [From W. Sieber, Z. tech. Physik, 22:130 (1941).]*

    a.   White fireclay.
    b.   Polished copper.

Reflectivity and transmissivity are characteristics which we experience in the everyday world. The criteria for predicting these quantities for visible light also apply to thermal radiation. Polished metallic surfaces have high reflectivities, and granular surfaces have low reflectivities. Gases and liquids usually transmit most of the radiation incident upon them, although liquids are capable of reflecting substantial amounts of energy. Because of the relation between α, τ, and ρ in Eq. (28-1), the remarks made above concerning variation of absorptivity with temperature obviously apply also to the sum of transmissivity and reflectivity.

Reflection from a macroscopic section of surface depends greatly on the character of the surface. If the surface is very smooth, the angles of incidence and reflection are the same. However, most surfaces encountered in engineering are sufficiently rough so that some reflection occurs in all directions. If the total reflection is independent of the angle of incidence, it is said to be "diffuse." This assumption is made in solving most engineering problems.

Emissivity

If one or more small non-heat-generating bodies are contained within a large evacuated enclosure, they will eventually reach a state of thermal equilibrium at which each receives radiant heat at the same rate at which it loses it. If W_1 is the total rate of emission of energy per unit area for a body of area A_1, W_o is the flux of radiant energy from the enclosure which strikes area A_1, and α_1 is the absorptivity of surface A_1, then we can write

$$W_1 A_1 = W_o \alpha_1 A_1 \qquad (28\text{-}2)$$

from which

$$\frac{W_1}{\alpha_1} = W_o \qquad (28\text{-}3)$$

For additional small bodies W_o will remain constant, so we can write

$$\frac{W_1}{\alpha_1} = \frac{W_2}{\alpha_2} = \cdots = \frac{W_n}{\alpha_n} \qquad (28\text{-}4)$$

Thus in a system at thermal equilibrium, all bodies will have the same temperature and all bodies will have the same ratio of total emissive power to absorptivity. This principle is called Kirchhoff's law.

If one of the surfaces in the enclosure absorbs all the radiation incident upon it, it has an absorptivity of 1 and, as mentioned earlier, is referred to as a black body. Because W/α is fixed, this places an upper limit on the emissive power of that surface, or any other at the same temperature, so that a black body is referred to as an ideal emitter as well as a perfect absorber. Thus the emissive power of a black body [in Btu/(hr)(sq ft of surface area)] is a function only of its own temperature. By definition, the emissivity of a real surface is the ratio of its emissive power W_1 to that of a black body W_2 at the same temperature. This emissivity is designated as ϵ_1. If we rewrite Eq. (28-4) to include this definition, we have

$$\frac{W_1}{W_2} = \frac{\alpha_1}{\alpha_2} = \epsilon_1$$

in which object 2 is chosen to be a black body. Because α_2 is unity, we obtain for the nonblack body the relation

$$\alpha_1 = \epsilon_1 \qquad (28\text{-}5)$$

To generalize, we may state that in a system at thermal equilibrium the emissivity of any object in the system is the same as its absorptivity. In a system where various portions are at different temperatures, this is not true, but is often assumed to be true so that a solution can be obtained to a problem. As mentioned earlier, the absorptivity of a surface actually varies with the wavelength of the incident radiation; sometimes, however, the surface is assumed to be "gray," and α is assumed to be constant. In these circumstances, α for a surface is evaluated by determining the emissivity, not at the actual surface temperature, but rather at the temperature of the source of the radiation, because this is the temperature the absorbing surface would have if it were at thermal equilibrium with the emitter. It is a fact that the temperature of the absorber has some effect on absorptivity as well, but the effect of the temperature of the emitter is usually more important.

Emissivity, like absorptivity, is low for polished metal surfaces and is moderately high for oxidized metal surfaces. It is also high for most nonmetallic substances. Table 28-2 contains some typical values of emissivity. Emissivity, like absorptivity, varies with wavelength and also with the angle between the emitted beam and the emitting surface. The variation with wavelength is shown in Fig. 28-2. The values in Table

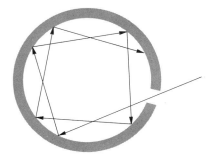

Fig. 28-3. *Absorption of radiation in a hollow container.*

28-2 are for the total emissivity, which includes radiation of all wavelengths normal to the emitting surface.   The variation of emissivity with angle often is not large; in such circumstances the variation is neglected and the values of Table 28-2 are taken as being total hemispherical emissivities.

Table 28-2.   Total Emissivities of Some Surfaces†

Surface	Temperature, °F	Emissivity
Polished aluminum...............	73	0.040
Polished copper..................	242	0.023
Polished iron....................	800–1800	0.144–0.377
Cast iron, newly turned..........	72	0.435
Oxidized iron....................	212	0.736
Asbestos board..................	74	0.96
Red brick.......................	70	0.93
Sixteen different oil paints, all colors...............	212	0.92–0.96
Water...........................	32–212	0.95–0.963

† J. H. Perry, "Chemical Engineers' Handbook," 3d ed., p. 484, McGraw-Hill Book Company, Inc., New York, 1950.

Some of the values in this table are so close to unity that the surfaces may be considered to be black bodies.

One way of achieving nearly perfect black-body conditions is by absorbing or emitting radiation through a small hole in a hollow object. This is illustrated in Fig. 28-3.   Radiation entering the hole is likely to be reflected numerous times before finally being reflected out of the hole by which it entered.   Each time it impinges on the surface, a fraction α is absorbed, so that after a few reflections, nearly all the radiation which entered is absorbed.   In effect, the hole in the container is equivalent to a surface of the same area with an absorptivity of 1.   Similarly, in its emissive characteristics, the effect of the hole is that of a black body of the same area at a temperature equal to the temperature of the enclosure.

This principle is employed when making temperature measurements by a method which requires that the emitting surface have an emissivity of 1. The instrument, a pyrometer, is sighted on a cavity or wedge-shaped hole in the walls of the system.

The Stefan-Boltzmann Law

It can be shown from thermodynamic considerations that the total emissive power of a black body is proportional to the fourth power of the absolute temperature. This relation, known as the Stefan-Boltzmann law, applies to the total radiant energy of all wavelengths emitted in all directions and is written[1]

$$W_B = \sigma T^4 \tag{28-6}$$

The quantity σ, known as the Stefan-Boltzmann constant, has a value of 0.1714×10^{-8} Btu/(hr)(sq ft)($^\circ$R)^4. If the emissivity of a real surface is expressed as a total emissivity ϵ, the total emissive power of the real body in Btu/(hr)(sq ft) is

$$W = \epsilon \sigma T^4 \tag{28-7}$$

An expression for the monochromatic emissive power of a black body $W_{B\lambda}$ as a function of the wavelength was derived from quantum theory by Planck in 1900. The equation,[2] known as Planck's law, is

$$W_{B\lambda} = \frac{C_1 \lambda^{-5}}{e^{C_2/\lambda T} - 1} \tag{28-8}$$

The term $W_{B\lambda}$ has the dimensions of energy/(area)(time)(unit increment of wavelength). It is expressed in units of ergs/(sec)(cu cm) when the constants C_1 and C_2 are 3.74×10^{-5} (erg)(sq cm)/sec and 2.59 (cm)($^\circ$R), respectively. This function is plotted in Fig. 28-1. It can be differentiated to obtain $dW_{B\lambda}/d\lambda$, and if this derivative is equated to zero, it yields the following expression for the wavelength at which the maximum emission of energy occurs:

$$5\lambda T(1 - e^{C_2/\lambda T}) = C_2 \tag{28-9}$$

This equation can be solved by trial and error for λT to give

$$\lambda_{\text{max}} = \frac{0.5216}{T} \tag{28-10}$$

[1] We use T to indicate absolute temperature (degrees Kelvin or degrees Rankine) in this book and t for degrees Fahrenheit or degrees centigrade.

[2] Another common form of Planck's law gives the intensity of the monochromatic radiation *normal* to the radiating surface. Equation (28-8), however, gives the monochromatic emissive power, which represents all the energy of wavelength λ emitted through a *hemispherical* solid angle. This is obtained by multiplying the normal intensity by a factor π.

in which the constant 0.5216 has units of (cm)(°R). Equation (28-10) is known as Wien's displacement law; it predicts a decreasing wavelength at peak emissive power for increasing temperature. It is of interest that the radiation from the sun has a maximum intensity at a wavelength of approximately 5×10^{-5} cm. According to Eq. (28-10), the surface temperature of the sun is 10,400°R.

Equation (28-8) for the monochromatic emissive power can be integrated over the entire spectrum to give the total emissive power. Thus the Stefan-Boltzmann constant from Eq. (28-6) becomes

$$\sigma = \frac{1}{T^4} \int_0^\infty W_{B\lambda}\, d\lambda \tag{28-11}$$

Substituting Planck's law, Eq. (28-8), in Eq. (28-11) yields

$$\sigma = \frac{C_1}{T^4} \int_0^\infty \frac{\lambda^{-5}}{e^{C_2/\lambda T} - 1}\, d\lambda$$

or

$$\sigma = \frac{C_1}{C_2{}^4} \int_0^\infty \frac{(C_2/\lambda T)^5}{e^{C_2/\lambda T} - 1}\, d\frac{\lambda T}{C_2}$$

which is rearranged to give

$$\sigma = \frac{C_1}{C_2{}^4} \int_0^\infty \frac{(C_2/\lambda T)^3}{e^{C_2/\lambda T} - 1}\, d\frac{C_2}{\lambda T} \tag{28-12}$$

The value of σ obtained by integrating Eq. (28-12) is $\dfrac{C_1}{15}\left(\dfrac{\pi}{C_2}\right)^4$. If the values of C_1 and C_2 given above are substituted in the expression and the answer converted to engineering units, we obtain a numerical value for σ of 0.1714×10^{-8} Btu/(hr)(sq ft)(°R)⁴. According to Jakob,[1] this value is about 1½ per cent smaller than the best experimental measurements.

Radiant Heat Exchange between Black Surfaces

If two surfaces at different temperatures are arranged so that radiant energy can be exchanged between them, a net flow of heat will occur from the hotter to the colder surface. Perhaps the simplest system to consider is one in which the surfaces are flat, parallel planes of infinite length and breadth. Most systems, however, do not have simple geometry, and the net heat-flow rate depends on the spatial arrangement of the two (or more) surfaces. To simplify the discussion, we shall assume in this section that we are dealing only with black surfaces, so that all the energy incident upon any surface is absorbed. We consider a system in which radiant energy

---

[1] M. Jakob, "Heat Transfer," vol. 1, p. 39, John Wiley & Sons, Inc., New York, 1949.

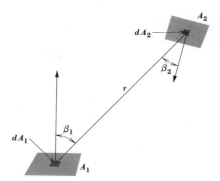

Fig. 28-4. *Radiant heat exchange between two area elements.*

is exchanged between two elements, 1 and 2, with areas dA_1 and dA_2 shown in Fig. 28-4. The line joining these elements has a length r, and the angles between this line and normals to the two surfaces are β_1 and β_2. The rate of transfer of radiant heat from 1 to 2 is proportional to the product of the apparent areas of the elements and inversely proportional to the square of the distance between them. The apparent areas, i.e., the areas normal to a beam of radiation, are $dA_1 \cos \beta_1$ and $dA_2 \cos \beta_2$, so that the rate of radiation from 1 to 2 is

$$dq_{1 \to 2} = \frac{I_1 \, dA_1 \cos \beta_1 \, dA_2 \cos \beta_2}{r^2} \tag{28-13}$$

The quantity I_1 is a proportionality constant called the intensity of radiation from surface 1. We use the following procedure to relate it to the total emissive power of surface 1, which we have seen to be $\sigma T_1^4 \, dA_1$. The quantity $dA_2 \cos \beta_2 / r^2$ is the differential solid angle subtended from the center of 1 to the boundaries of 2 and is written $d\omega$. We integrate[1] Eq. (28-13) over the entire hemispherical angle 2π.

---

[1] The integration may be illustrated with reference to the accompanying diagram, Fig. 28-5. The apparent area of dA_2, which is the differential area normal to the beam, is $dA_2 \cos \beta_2$. It is shown here as a portion of the surface of a hemisphere which has dA_1 at the center. The circumference of the segment is $2\pi r \sin \beta_1$, and the width is $r \, d\beta_1$. The normal area of the circumferential segment, therefore, is $2\pi r^2 \sin \beta_1 \, d\beta_1$. We integrate, starting with the general form, Eq. (28-13).

$$dq_{1 \to 2} = I_1 \, dA_1 \int_0^{\pi/2} \frac{\cos \beta_1 \cos \beta_2 \, dA_2}{r^2}$$

We substitute in this for $\cos \beta_2 \, dA_2$ and get

$$dq_{1 \to 2} = I_1 \, dA_1 \int_0^{\pi/2} \frac{(\cos \beta_1)(2\pi r^2 \sin \beta_1 \, d\beta_1)}{r^2}$$

$$= 2\pi I_1 \, dA_1 \int_0^{\pi/2} \cos \beta_1 \sin \beta_1 \, d\beta_1$$

$$= \pi I_1 \, dA_1$$

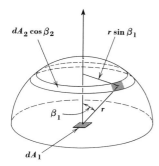

$dA_2 \cos \beta_2$ $r \sin \beta_1$

β_1 r

dA_1

Fig. 28-5.   Hemispherical model for determining   intensity of radiation.

$$dq_{1\to2} = I_1 \, dA_1 \int_0^{2\pi} \cos \beta_1 \, d\omega$$

$$= \pi I_1 \, dA_1$$

By equating this quantity with the result from the Stefan-Boltzmann equation we see that the intensity I_1 of radiation from surface 1 is $\sigma T_1^4/\pi$. Thus we rewrite Eq. (28-13) as

$$dq_{1\to2} = \frac{\sigma T_1^4 \, dA_1 \cos \beta_1 \, dA_2 \cos \beta_2}{\pi r^2} \tag{28-14}$$

A consideration of radiant-heat flow from surface 2 to surface 1 leads to a similar expression.

$$dq_{2\to1} = \frac{\sigma T_2^4 \, dA_1 \cos \beta_1 \, dA_2 \cos \beta_2}{\pi r^2} \tag{28-15}$$

The net flow of heat is found by taking the difference

$$dq_{12} = \frac{\sigma \, dA_1 \cos \beta_1 \, dA_2 \cos \beta_2}{\pi r^2} (T_1^4 - T_2^4) \tag{28-16}$$

If the two surfaces have finite areas, A_1 and A_2, Eqs. (28-14) and (28-15) are evaluated by performing the indicated double integrations in each case.

In engineering it is convenient to use simpler formulas to represent heat flow, so the integrated form of Eq. (28-14) is represented as

$$q_{1\to2} = \sigma A_1 F_{12} T_1^4 \tag{28-17}$$

and Eq. (28-15) as

$$q_{2\to1} = \sigma A_2 F_{21} T_2^4 \tag{28-18}$$

The quantity F_{12} designates the fraction of the total radiation leaving surface 1 which strikes surface 2, and the quantity F_{21} represents the fractional impingement of radiation from 2 on 1. F_{12} and F_{21} are known as "view factors." If the two surfaces are at the same temperature, $q_{1\to2}$ and

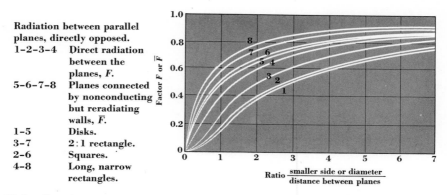

Fig. 28-6. *View factor F and interchange factor $\bar{F}$ for opposed parallel disks, squares, and rectangles. (From W. H. McAdams, "Heat Transmission," 3d ed., p. 69, McGraw-Hill Book Company, Inc., New York, 1954.)*

$q_{2\to1}$ must be equal, from which it follows that $A_1F_{12} = A_2F_{21}$. Therefore we can write either of the following equations for the net flux between surfaces 1 and 2 even when T_1 and T_2 are not equal, because A_1F_{12} and A_2F_{21} depend only on the geometry of the system.

$$q_{12} = \sigma A_1 F_{12}(T_1{}^4 - T_2{}^4) \tag{28-19}$$

$$q_{12} = \sigma A_2 F_{21}(T_1{}^4 - T_2{}^4) \tag{28-20}$$

Although the equality of A_1F_{12} and A_2F_{21} was established considering black surfaces, it is equally valid for nonblack surfaces.

The view factor F_{12} can be evaluated by combining Eq. (28-17) with the integrated form of Eq. (28-14). By this procedure it is found that

$$F_{12} = \frac{1}{A_1} \int_{A_2}\!\!\int_{A_1} \frac{dA_1 \cos\beta_1\, dA_2 \cos\beta_2}{\pi r^2} \tag{28-21}$$

Values of the view factor have been calculated for a number of spatial arrangements shown in Fig. 28-6. Other values are given in Perry, sec. 6. The method of determining these factors is illustrated in Example 28-1.

Example 28-1

Determine the view factor for radiant-heat transfer between a small disk of area A_1 and a parallel large disk of area A_2. The disks are assumed to be directly opposed; i.e., a line joining their centers is normal to both disks. The large disk has a radius a, and the distance between centers is r_o. This system is shown in Fig. 28-7. Equation (28-21) is

$$F_{12} = \frac{1}{A_1} \int_{A_2}\!\!\int_{A_1} \frac{dA_1 \cos\beta_1\, dA_2 \cos\beta_2}{\pi r^2}$$

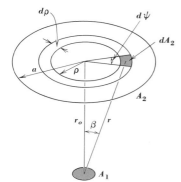

Fig. 28-7.   Parallel disks (Example 28-1).

In this problem A_1 is small compared with A_2, so for the integration over A_1, the other quantities under the integral sign can be considered constant. In addition, the angles β_1 and β_2 are equal; they will be designated simply as β. Therefore the equation for the view factor reduces to

$$F_{12} = \int_{A_2} \frac{\cos^2 \beta \, dA_2}{\pi r^2}$$

The differential element dA_2 is shown in the figure. The area of the element is

$$dA_2 = \rho \, d\psi \, d\rho$$

It can also be seen from the construction that $\cos \beta = r_o/r$. Thus the view factor may be written as

$$F_{12} = \int_0^a \int_0^{2\pi} \frac{r_o{}^2}{\pi r^4} \rho \, d\psi \, d\rho$$

The system is symmetrical, so the first integration produces the result

$$F_{12} = \int_0^a \frac{2r_o{}^2}{r^4} \rho \, d\rho$$

The quantity r is a function of ρ as follows:

$$r^2 = \rho^2 + r_o{}^2$$

Thus we have

$$F_{12} = \int_0^a \frac{2r_o{}^2 \rho \, d\rho}{(\rho^2 + r_o{}^2)^2}$$

$$= \int_0^a \frac{r_o{}^2 \, d\rho^2}{(\rho^2 + r_o{}^2)^2}$$

which, upon integration, yields

$$F_{12} = \frac{a^2}{a^2 + r_o{}^2}$$

Multiple Surfaces. In a system enclosed by i surfaces, it follows that

$$F_{11} + F_{12} + F_{13} + \cdots + F_{1i} = 1 \tag{28-22}$$

If surface 1 cannot "see" itself, $F_{11} = 0$. If the surfaces are all black, the net heat flow between surface 1 and all other surfaces is

$$q_{1,\text{net}} = \sigma A_1 F_{12} T_1{}^4 - \sigma A_2 F_{21} T_2{}^4 + \sigma A_1 F_{13} T_1{}^4 - \sigma A_3 F_{31} T_3{}^4 + \cdots \tag{28-23}$$

The terms containing $\sigma A_1 T_1{}^4$ can be collected and expressed as a single term using the summation expressed in Eq. (28-22). Equation (28-23) can then be written as

$$q_{1,\text{net}} = \sigma A_1 T_1{}^4 - \sigma(A_2 F_{21} T_2{}^4 + A_3 F_{31} T_3{}^4 + \cdots + A_i F_{i1} T_i{}^4) \tag{28-24}$$

Refractory Surfaces. In many heat-transfer systems the high- and low-temperature surfaces which serve as "source" and "sink" for radiant heat are connected by a wall of some refractory material through which only a negligible amount of heat flows. Radiant energy is absorbed by these refractory surfaces, but at steady operation it is emitted at the same rate if there is no heat loss through the refractory. Hence there is no net heat flux associated with the radiant interchange at the refractory surfaces.

If we consider two black surfaces 1 and 2 connected by a refractory surface R, the heat transfer from surface 1 to surface 2 must include not only the direct transfer represented by the view factor F_{12}, but also the energy from surface 1 which is absorbed by the refractory surface and reradiated to surface 2. A factor $\overline{F}_{12}$, called the interchange factor, is defined to represent the sum of these two effects. The refractory surface radiates energy[1] to both surfaces 1 and 2 (F_{R1} and F_{R2}) and also to itself, if it can see itself (F_{RR}). However, all the energy radiated to itself is ultimately reradiated to surface 1 or surface 2, and the fraction reradiated to surface 2 is $F_{R2}/(F_{R1} + F_{R2})$. The interchange factor, therefore, is the sum of the fraction radiated directly plus the fraction reradiated.

$$\overline{F}_{12} = F_{12} + F_{1R} \frac{F_{R2}}{F_{R1} + F_{R2}} \tag{28-25}$$

If both sides of Eq. (28-25) are multiplied by A_1 and the right side rearranged, we obtain

$$A_1 \overline{F}_{12} = A_1 F_{12} + \frac{1}{F_{R1}/A_1 F_{1R} F_{R2} + 1/A_1 F_{1R}}$$

For any two surfaces, even if one is a refractory, the relations $A_1 F_{1R} = A_R F_{R1}$ and $A_R F_{R2} = A_2 F_{2R}$ are valid, since they depend only on spatial considerations. We then use these two relations to obtain

---

[1] It is assumed that this reradiation (plus any reflection) is equal in all directions, or "diffuse," and is therefore independent of the direction from which it arrived.

$$A_1\overline{F}_{12} = A_1F_{12} + \frac{1}{1/A_2F_{2R} + 1/A_1F_{1R}} \tag{28-26}$$

Therefore, from a knowledge of A_1, A_2, and the view factors F_{12}, F_{1R}, and F_{2R}, the interchange factor $\overline{F}_{12}$ can be calculated. The interchange factors for a number of geometrical arrangements are shown in Fig. 28-6.

The net radiant exchange between two surfaces which are connected by refractory reradiating surfaces is given by the equation

$$q_{12} = \sigma A_1\overline{F}_{12}T_1{}^4 - \sigma A_2\overline{F}_{21}T_2{}^4 \tag{28-27}$$

If this equation is applied to two surfaces at the same temperature, it follows that the quantities $A_1\overline{F}_{12}$ and $A_2\overline{F}_{21}$ must be equal. Since they depend entirely on geometric considerations, it follows that they are equal when not at the same temperature. Thus we rewrite Eq. (28-27) as

$$q_{12} = \sigma A_1\overline{F}_{12}(T_1{}^4 - T_2{}^4) \tag{28-28}$$

Gray Surfaces

If the surfaces from which there is a net heat flux are not black bodies, the emissive power of each of the surfaces is determined by using the Stefan-Boltzmann equation multiplied by the emissivity. Furthermore, the absorption of energy on each surface is not complete, but equals the amount of energy incident on the surface multiplied by the absorptivity. These two factors make an accurate analysis of radiant transfer between real surfaces much more complicated than between black bodies. To simplify the problem, it is often assumed that the surfaces are gray. As mentioned earlier, this assumption is equivalent to assuming that absorptivity is independent of the wavelength of the incident radiation, and thus of the temperature and other characteristics of the emitter. In effect, the emissivity and absorptivity of a surface are assumed to be the same. Hottel[1] has shown that for the case of two surfaces 1 and 2, between which there is net heat flux, connected by any number of refractory reradiating zones, the net flux can be represented by the equation

$$q_{12} = \sigma A_1\mathfrak{F}_{12}(T_1{}^4 - T_2{}^4) \tag{28-29}$$

in which the factor $\mathfrak{F}_{12}$ is

$$\mathfrak{F}_{12} = \frac{1}{(1/\overline{F}_{12}) + (1/\epsilon_1 - 1) + (A_1/A_2)(1/\epsilon_2 - 1)} \tag{28-30}$$

The derivation of this equation is rather complex; for details, the reader is referred to the work of Hottel. Equation (28-30) is readily applied to a

[1] H. C. Hottel, chap. 4 in W. H. McAdams, "Heat Transmission," 3d ed., McGraw-Hill Book Company, Inc., New York, 1954.

number of simple but useful systems. For the case of a small body 1 in a large enclosure 2, e.g., a pipe in a room, $\overline{F}_{12} = 1$ and $A_1/A_2 = 0$. Therefore $\mathcal{F}_{12} = \epsilon_1$. When radiant energy is exchanged between two large parallel planes, the interchange factor $\overline{F}_{12}$ is unity and the areas are equal, so we get

$$\mathcal{F}_{12} = \frac{1}{1/\epsilon_1 + 1/\epsilon_2 - 1} \tag{28-31}$$

These two systems can be analyzed directly without the aid of Eq. (28-30); the same results as shown above are obtained.

The Radiation Heat-transfer Coefficient

Unless radiation from a surface occurs in a vacuum, it is usually accompanied by convective heat transfer. If the radiating surfaces are at uniform temperatures, we calculate the heat transfer by convection by the usual methods. The heat transfer by radiation is computed from the Stefan-Boltzmann equation with the appropriate coefficients. The total rate of heat transfer is the sum of the contributions of the two mechanisms. However, in dealing with both mechanisms simultaneously, it is often convenient to define a heat-transfer coefficient for radiation in the manner of a convective coefficient. This matter has already been discussed in Chap. 23, and a coefficient defined by the following equation:

$$q = h_r A (t_{s1} - t_{s2}) \tag{23-11}$$

The temperatures t_{s1} and t_{s2} are the surface temperatures of the source and sink, respectively. To obtain an expression for h_r, we write Eq. (23-11) in terms of the absolute temperatures of the surfaces:

$$q = h_r A (T_1 - T_2) \tag{28-32}$$

The equation for radiant-heat flux between black surfaces with a view factor of 1 is

$$q = \sigma A (T_1^4 - T_2^4) \tag{28-33}$$

By combining Eqs. (28-32) and (28-33), we obtain the definition of h_r:

$$h_r = \sigma \frac{T_1^4 - T_2^4}{T_1 - T_2} \tag{28-34}$$

The strong dependence of h_r on temperature is seen in this equation. Nevertheless, the use of h_r is as rigorous as the use of the Stefan-Boltzmann equation, provided this variation in h_r is taken into account. Values of h_r calculated from Eq. (28-34) are shown in Fig. 28-8. The ratio in Eq. (28-34), if divided out, gives the definition of h_r as

$$h_r = \sigma(T_1^3 + T_1^2 T_2 + T_1 T_2^2 + T_2^3) \tag{28-35}$$

Fig. 28-8.   The radiant-heat-transfer coefficient.
Temperature of other surface:

a.	1000°F.
b.	800°F.
c.	600°F.
d.	400°F.
e.	200°F.
f.	0°F.

It is evidently of no importance in the determination of h_r which subscript, 1 or 2, represents the source and the sink.

In radiation between gray surfaces or between surfaces with view factors other than 1, it is necessary to modify Eq. (28-32) by multiplying the right-hand side by $\mathfrak{F}_{12}$, just as would be done with Eq. (28-33).

Thermocouple Errors

A thermocouple used to measure a fluid temperature in a container may give a reading significantly different from the fluid temperature if the walls are at some other temperature.   This difference occurs because the thermocouple tip maintains its temperature constant by exchanging heat with the fluid by convection and with the walls by radiation.

If the wall temperature t_s is higher than the gas temperature t_g, the thermocouple indicates some intermediate temperature t_c.   The heat-flow equations are

$$q = h_r A_c \mathfrak{F}_{cs}(t_s - t_c)$$
$$= h A_c(t_c - t_g)$$

These equations can be solved for the gas temperature to give

$$t_g = t_c - \frac{h_r \mathfrak{F}_{cs}}{h}(t_s - t_c) \tag{28-36}$$

A calculation showing the magnitude of this effect is given in Example 28-2.

Example 28-2

A glass thermometer ($\epsilon = 0.96$) is inserted in a large circular duct at right angles to the wall.   The thermometer bulb, ¼ in. in diameter, is at the center of the duct.   Air flows through the duct at a rate such that the convective heat-transfer coefficient between the thermometer and the air is 17.7 Btu/(hr)(sq ft)(°F).

(a) If the walls of the duct are at 800°F and the thermometer reads 300°F, what is the temperature of the air in the duct?

(b) If silver foil ($\epsilon = 0.03$) is wrapped around the thermometer, what will be the new thermometer reading?

(a) The thermometer can see only the duct, so its view factor is unity. The area of the thermometer is so much less than the area of the duct that $(A_c/A_s)(1/\epsilon_s - 1)$ is negligible compared with the other terms in the denominator of Eq. (28-30). Hence, for this problem, Eq. (28-30) becomes

$$\mathfrak{F}_{cs} = \frac{1}{\frac{1}{1} + (1/\epsilon_c - 1) + 0} = \epsilon_c = 0.96$$

The radiation heat-transfer coefficient is found from Fig. 28-8 to be 7.6 Btu/(hr)(sq ft)(°F). The gas temperature is found using Eq. (28-36).

$$t_g = 300 - \frac{(7.6)(0.96)(800 - 300)}{17.7} = 94\,°F$$

(b) The thermometer reading is now found by trial and error from Eq. (28-36).

$$94 = t_c - \frac{(h_r)(0.03)}{17.7}(800 - t_c)$$

Assume $t_c = 100°F$; from Fig. 28-8, $h_r = 6.0$.

$$94 = 100 - \frac{(6.0)(0.03)(700)}{17.7}$$

$$= 100 - 7.1$$
$$= 93$$

It is evident that the thermometer would read approximately 101°F.

Example 28-2 shows that the error in a temperature reading caused by radiation can be reduced by covering the surface of the temperature-sensing device with some material which has a low emissivity and absorptivity. The error can also be reduced by enclosing the device in a shield such as a hollow tube. The gas is free to pass between the thermocouple and the tube, but the thermocouple can see little more than the shield. In these circumstances the shield exchanges heat primarily with the gas and the duct and is at some intermediate temperature. The thermocouple, however, exchanges heat with the shield and the gas and is at some temperature closer to the gas temperature than it would have been if the shield were not used.

Two other factors may affect the reading of a thermocouple in low-velocity gas systems. If the gas is air, it neither emits nor absorbs important amounts of radiation itself, but has merely the convective effect already discussed. However, if the gas contains appreciable quantities of triatomic or higher polyatomic molecules, these constituents absorb and emit significant amounts of radiation. This radiant transfer with the gas affects the thermocouple reading but causes the thermocouple to give a more nearly correct reading. A fourth mechanism results from the fact that the thermocouple is probably at the wall temperature at the point where it emerges from the duct. The resulting gradient between the temperature at the wall and that at the tip affects the heat balance on the tip and may give rise to significant errors if the thermocouple is short.

Radiation from Gases

Although solids and liquids emit radiation over a continuous spectrum, gases do not. In fact, most monatomic and diatomic gases, like those contained in air, emit scarcely any radiation. Other gases such as water vapor and carbon dioxide emit radiation only within certain spectral bands. The general rule is that only triatomic and higher polyatomic gases emit radiation in significant amounts. The gases which radiate energy also absorb it, but only within the same bands in which it is emitted. Gases which do not emit radiation do not absorb it.

The width of the emission (or absorption) bands for a particular gas depends on both temperature and pressure. Furthermore, the intensity of emission at any one set of conditions varies with wavelength over the bandwidth. An approximate representation for water vapor gives bands from 2.2 to 3.3, 4.8 to 8.5, and 12 to 25 μ. For carbon dioxide the bands are from 2.4 to 3.0, 4.0 to 4.8, and 12.5 to 16.5 μ. The higher-wavelength bands are usually not of great significance in absorption because only a small fraction of the total thermal radiation from solids falls in these ranges. Visible light (0.35 to 0.78 μ) is not absorbed by either water vapor or carbon dioxide.

The absorption of radiant energy for a particular gas depends on the number of molecules in the path of the beam. The extent of absorption in a gaseous medium can be increased by increasing the length of the path or by increasing the partial pressure of the absorbing constituent. Let us call $I_{\lambda L}$ the intensity of radiation at a particular wavelength after having passed through a thickness L of gas, and $I_{\lambda o}$ the intensity of the radiation at the same wavelength before it enters the gas. These intensities are related by the exponential equation

$$I_{\lambda L} = I_{\lambda o} e^{-m_\lambda L} \qquad (28\text{-}37)$$

The quantity m_λ is a characteristic of the particular gas, its partial pressure, and the wavelength of the radiation considered. It can be seen from Eq. (28-37) that if a gas layer is infinitely thick, the absorption will be complete at wavelengths for which m_λ is greater than zero, i.e., within the bands characteristic of that gas.   Since m_λ is a function of wavelength, the absorptivity of a finite thickness of gas will vary with λ.

The rigorous treatment of problems of gas radiation is complex even when the geometrical shapes are simple.   Consequently, the total emission or absorption of radiation associated with a gaseous mass of finite dimensions is usually analyzed by the approximate methods of Hottel,[1] which yield results of engineering value.   Hottel has determined for a number of gases what is known as the emissivity as a function of temperature and pressure by considering a hemispherical mass of gas of radius L radiating to the mid-point of the base of the hemisphere.   From the mid-point the beam length is the same in all directions.   The gas emissivity ϵ_g is defined as the ratio of the energy radiated from the hemispherical body of gas to an element of surface at the mid-point divided by the energy radiated to the same element by a black hemispherical surface at the gas temperature. The rate of radiation from the gas is therefore $\sigma \epsilon_g T_g{}^4$ per unit area of receiving surface.   If the surface element at the mid-point is radiating heat back to the gas, the absorption rate by the gas will be $\sigma \alpha_g T_1{}^4$, in which α_g is the absorptivity of the gas for black-body radiation from a surface at T_1.   The net rate of radiant heat transfer is the difference, $\sigma(\epsilon_g T_g{}^4 - \alpha_g T_1{}^4)$. Values of the emissivity are plotted in a series of graphs, such as Fig. 28-9, for carbon dioxide in a system at a total pressure of 1 atm.   Absorptivities are obtained using the same charts.

Table 28-3.   *Equivalent Beam Lengths for Gas Radiation*†

Shape	Equivalent beam length L
Sphere.....................................	$0.60 \times$ diameter
Cylinder of infinite length.....................	$0.90 \times$ diameter
Space between infinite parallel planes...........	$2.0 \times$ distance between planes
Space outside an infinite bank of tubes with centers on equilateral triangles; tube diameter equals clearance..............	$2.8 \times$ clearance

† From H. C. Hottel, chap. 4 in W. H. McAdams, "Heat Transmission," 3d ed., McGraw-Hill Book Company, Inc., New York, 1954.

The parameter in Fig. 28-9 is PL, in which P is the partial pressure of carbon dioxide in atmospheres and L is the beam length in feet.   Shapes other than hemispheres can be analyzed by employing the beam length of a hemisphere giving an equivalent amount of radiation.   Table 28-3 gives these lengths for a number of systems.

[1] *Ibid.*

Fig. 28-9. *Total emissivity of carbon dioxide. (From W. H. McAdams, "Heat Transmission," 3d ed., p. 83, McGraw-Hill Book Company, Inc., New York, 1954.)*

The radiant transfer between a gas at temperature T_g and a black surface of finite area A at temperature T_1 is found from the equation

$$q = \sigma A (\epsilon_g T_g{}^4 - \alpha_g T_1{}^4) \tag{28-38}$$

The emissivity of the gas ϵ_g is evaluated at the temperature of the gas. The absorptivity of the gas is evaluated at the temperature of the surface. As empirical corrections to α_g, the parameter PLT_1/T_g is used in place of PL in finding a value on the ordinate axis; this value is multiplied by $(T_g/T_1)^{0.65}$ to give α_g. The procedures are outlined in the following example.

Example 28-3

A stack 3 ft in diameter contains a gas with 5 per cent CO_2 at 2000°F and 1 atm total pressure. The flow of gas past the surface of the stack is at rate such that the convective heat-transfer coefficient from the gas to the refractory is 1.5 Btu/(hr)(sq ft)(°F). If the refractory surface is at 1900°F and has an emissivity of 1.0, calculate the amounts of heat transferred from the gas by radiation and convection.

To find the heat flux due to radiation we first find the parameter PL to be used in determining absorptivity and emissivity. The mean beam length L is found using Table 28-3.

$$PL = (0.05)(0.90)(3)$$
$$= 0.135$$

The gas temperature T_g is 2460°R. Therefore we find, from Fig. 28-9, that the gas emissivity ϵ_g is 0.07.

The parameter for finding gas absorptivity is

$$\frac{PLT_1}{T_g} = 0.135(2360/2460)$$

$$= 0.130$$

The ordinate value on Fig. 28-9 at this value of the parameter and at $T = 2360$ is 0.072, which we use in calculating the value of α_g.

$$\alpha_g = 0.072(2460/2360)^{0.65}$$
$$= 0.074$$

The net radiant transfer of energy is

$$\frac{q}{A} = 0.171 \left[0.070(2460/100)^4 - 0.074 \, (2360/100)^4 \right]$$

$$= 0.171(25,700 - 22,900)$$
$$= 480 \text{ Btu/(hr)(sq ft)}$$

The heat flux by convection is

$$\frac{q}{A} = (1.5)(100)$$

$$= 150 \text{ Btu/(hr)(sq ft)}$$

If the enclosure is not black, some of the radiation striking it is reflected back into the gas and to other walls. It has been found that if the emissivity of the enclosure is greater than 0.7, it is usually sufficiently accurate to use an effective emissivity ϵ', which is equal to $(\epsilon + 1)/2$, in which ϵ is the actual emissivity of the enclosure. Equation (28-38) is therefore modified empirically to give

$$q = \sigma A \epsilon'(\epsilon_g T_g^4 - \alpha_g T_1^4) \tag{28-39}$$

For systems containing water vapor, the methods are similar to those outlined above for carbon dioxide. For mixtures of water vapor and carbon dioxide, there is a slight overlap of the emission bands, so the emissivities are not additive. The reader is referred to the work of Hottel mentioned above for methods of solving problems involving water vapor, mixtures of emitting gases, and gases containing suspended luminous particles.

Solar Radiation

Solar radiation is responsible for the maintenance of the surface temperature on the earth. The solar constant of 442 Btu/(hr)(sq ft) represents the rate at which solar energy reaches the earth's atmosphere per square foot of area normal to the beam. If this rate is multiplied by the normal receiving area of the earth, $\pi D^2/4$, in which D is the earth's diameter, we obtain the total rate of receipt of solar energy. This rate may be equated to $\sigma \pi D^2 T_m{}^4$, which represents the total emission rate from the earth at some mean surface temperature T_m, assuming an emissivity of 1.0. This calculation gives an approximate mean surface temperature of 504°R, or 44°F. The rate of conduction from the earth's core as mentioned in Chap. 18 is approximately 0.01 Btu/(hr)(sq ft) and is obviously negligible compared with the radiant flux.

It is evident that the energy reaching the surface of the earth is somewhat depleted, from having passed through the atmosphere—a thickness of roughly 90 miles of air, dust, water vapor, and carbon dioxide. The dust, water vapor, and carbon dioxide are all capable of absorbing radiant energy, and some of this energy is reradiated directly back into space instead of to the earth. However, the absorptive effect of the gases is diminished by the fact that most of the solar radiation, emitted at 10,000°F, is at wavelengths below the absorptive bands of carbon dioxide and water, so that the gases of the atmosphere are nearly transparent to solar radiation. Radiation emitted from the earth is affected, however. The emission temperatures for this terrestrial radiation are much lower than the sun's temperature, so terrestrial radiation is emitted at higher wavelengths. These overlap the absorption bands of carbon dioxide and water vapor, so that much of the terrestrial radiation is absorbed by the atmosphere and reradiated to the earth. This phenomenon is referred to as a "greenhouse" effect, because the transmission of solar energy through glass and subsequent trapping by the glass of reradiation from within the greenhouse assist in keeping a greenhouse at the proper temperature in cold weather.

The atmospheric effects depend on the concentration of the absorbing gases in the atmosphere. It has been suggested that the increasing concentration of carbon dioxide in the atmosphere in the last two centuries as the result of combustion may upset the balance between rates at which radiation is received and emitted by the earth. Any such change would be a decrease in the rate at which energy is lost from the earth, with the result that the mean temperature of the earth's surface and its atmosphere would rise.

We are often made aware of the effects of nocturnal radiation, as in the formation of frost. When the sun is down, some thermal radiation is still received on the earth's surface from space, but the amount is small. Consequently, there is a net loss of radiant energy from the ground at night. This loss may be offset by convection from the earth's atmosphere, but if the air is very still, the surface temperature may drop below 32°F. Thus frost will form, even though the air temperature is above freezing. It is well known that frost is avoided in such circumstances either by a slight breeze or by cloud cover. Loss by radiation is sometimes reduced artificially by the creation of smoke clouds; the prevention of freezing is effected more by the reduction of radiant-energy loss and by convective mixing than by the heat of combustion released in forming the smoke.

PROBLEMS

28-1. A blackened ball of iron with a diameter of 1 in. is cooling in a large evacuated enclosure whose walls are maintained at 60°F. How long will be required for the temperature of the ball to change from 300 to 299°F? How long will it take to change from 300 to 100°F? Assume the ball is at a uniform internal temperature at all times.

28-2. A 2-in., schedule-40 steel pipe ($\epsilon = 0.66$) containing steam is in a room at 60°F. The pipe is not insulated, and its outer surface is at 210°F. Find the heat loss per foot of pipe by natural convection and by radiation.

28-3. A 6-in., schedule-40 steel pipe is carrying oil at 750°F. The pipe is insulated with a 1-in. layer of magnesia which has an emissivity of 0.90. The surrounding air and objects are at 80°F. Find the heat loss per hour per foot of pipe. The convective heat-transfer coefficient from the insulation to the air in the room is 0.97 Btu/(hr)(sq ft)(°F), and the coefficient from the oil to the inside pipe wall is 100 Btu/(hr)(sq ft)(°F).

28-4. Three parallel aluminum sheets, each with an emissivity of 0.2, are large enough so that they may be assumed to be infinite in extent. The outer sheets are held at temperatures of 2000 and 1000°F. Find the temperature of the center sheet and the heat flow through the system in Btu/(hr)(sq ft). Each sheet may be assumed to be at a uniform temperature throughout, and the space between the sheets may be considered to be a vacuum.

28-5. Air is flowing through a duct in which the walls have an inside temperature of 500°F. A thermocouple housed in a rusted steel well ($\epsilon = 0.9$), inserted at right angles to the air stream, indicates a temperature of 300°F. The mass velocity of the air is 3600 lb/(hr)(sq ft), and the OD of the well is ½ in. Estimate the true temperature of the air in the duct.

Assume the thermocouple and well to be at the same temperature. For air flow at right angles to a cylinder between temperatures of 100 and 300°F, the convective coefficient of heat transfer may be obtained from the following dimensional equation:

$$h = 0.026 \frac{G^{0.6}}{D^{0.4}}$$

where h = convective coefficient, Btu/(hr)(sq ft)(°F)
  G = mass velocity of air, lb/(hr)(sq ft)
  D = outside diameter of cylinder, ft

28-6. Two parallel disks of 6 and 8 in. diameter are 6 in. apart and oriented so as to be on a common axis. The smaller disk is at 500°F, and the larger at 200°F. Find the rate of transfer of energy by radiation from each disk to the other, assuming both to be black bodies.

28-7. The asphalt-covered roof of a house (ϵ = 0.90) is at an angle such that it is approximately normal to the sun's rays. The roof is insulated on its lower side and comes to thermal equilibrium with the air above it, which is at 20°F. Find the equilibrium temperature at some point on the roof which sees only the sky. The coefficient of heat transfer for natural convection between the roof and the air is 1.5 Btu/(hr)(sq ft)(°F). It can be assumed that the transmissivity of solar energy by the earth's atmosphere is 0.70 on this particular day.

28-8. A furnace stack 6 ft in diameter contains hot gas at 2000°F. The stack has brick walls 6 in. thick. The gas in the stack is at 1 atm pressure and contains 10 per cent by volume of carbon dioxide; the remainder is oxygen and nitrogen. The bulk velocity of the gases is such that the convective coefficient of heat transfer inside the stack is 5 Btu/(hr)(sq ft)(°F). Find the heat flux through the walls of the stack in Btu/(hr)(sq ft). The thermal conductivity of the brick is 0.7 Btu/(hr)(ft)(°F), and its emissivity is 0.90. The atmospheric temperature is 70°F, and the mean convective coefficient of heat transfer outside the stack is 2 Btu/(hr)(sq ft)(°F).

HEAT-EXCHANGE EQUIPMENT

In this chapter we shall consider the application of heat-transfer theory to the design and operation of certain types of heat-exchange equipment. We have covered a number of such applications in previous chapters, but the following topics are best discussed after all the principal mechanisms of heat transfer have been studied.

HEAT EXCHANGERS

General Remarks

The determination of the required heat-transfer area is one of the principal objectives in the design of heat exchangers. The basic equation for determining the area was introduced in Chap. 23.

$$\int_0^q \frac{dq}{h(t_s - t_m)} = \int_0^A dA \tag{23-3}$$

Although the integration of this equation is a valid method of determining the area A, it is more common to write Eq. (23-17) for a differential segment of the exchanger for which the outside tube area is dA_o and integrate as follows:

$$\int_0^q \frac{dq}{U_o \, \Delta t_{\text{over-all}}} = \int_0^{A_o} dA_o \tag{29-1}$$

This equation contains the over-all coefficient of heat transfer U_o, based on the outside tube area A_o, and the difference between the mixing-cup temperatures of the hot and cold fluids, Δt.† The reason for not using Eq. (23-17) directly is that both Δt and U_o may vary from one end of the exchanger to the other. Equation (23-18), which defined U_i in terms of A_i,

† To simplify the notation, Δt, as defined by Eq. (29-2), is used in this chapter to designate $\Delta t_{\text{overall}}$.

Fig. 29-1.   *Double-pipe heat exchanger.*

can also be expressed in differential form and integrated in the manner shown above.   We shall limit our subsequent analysis to equations based on the outside area; however, it should be remembered that a similar treatment exists in terms of A_i and U_i.

Under steady conditions the mixing-cup temperatures of the hot and cold fluids in a heat exchanger are assumed to be fixed at any cross section normal to the flow.   If we designate these temperatures as t_h and t_c, the over-all temperature difference in Eq. (29-1) is $t_h - t_c$.   For convenience, this quantity will be written as

$$\Delta t = t_h - t_c \tag{29-2}$$

Double-pipe Heat Exchangers

The simplest kind of heat exchanger consists of two concentric tubes through which the hot and cold fluids flow in the same or in opposite directions.   These two types of flow are called concurrent and countercurrent flow.   This device, called a double-pipe heat exchanger, can be made either from a pair of single lengths of pipe with appropriate fittings at the ends or from a number of lengths arranged in a vertical row with the sections connected at alternate ends, as shown in Fig. 29-1.

The exchanger shown in Fig. 29-1 could be regarded as one long run of two concentric pipes, except for the end effects.   The analysis below will be based on this simplification.   Two fluids with constant but different inlet temperatures enter opposite ends of the exchanger shown in Fig. 29-2. In this system, the hot fluid enters the inner pipe at a constant rate of w_h lb/hr and the cold fluid enters the annulus at a constant rate of w_c lb/hr.   The choice of path for each fluid depends on considerations such as corrosion, fluid pressure, and permissible pressure drop.   The tempera-

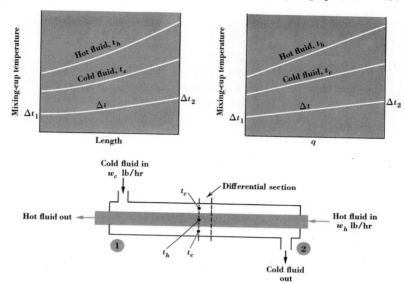

Fig. 29-2.   Temperature distribution in a double-pipe heat exchanger.

tures of the fluids as a function of length are shown in Fig. 29-2.   The fluid temperatures usually do not vary linearly with distance from the inlet.

A heat balance can be written for the differential section of the exchanger shown in Fig. 29-2.

$$dq = w_c C_{pc}\, dt_c = w_h C_{ph}\, dt_h = U_o(t_h - t_c).dA_o \tag{29-3}$$

Equation (29-3) shows that if the specific heats are constant, the individual mixing-cup temperatures are linear with respect to q, as illustrated in Fig. 29-2.   The difference between the mixing-cup temperatures, Δt, is also linear with respect to q.   Consequently, we can express the derivative of Δt with respect to q in terms of the over-all change in Δt and the total heat-transfer rate q in the exchanger.   The derivative can be written as

$$\frac{d(\Delta t)}{dq} = \frac{\Delta t_2 - \Delta t_1}{q} \tag{29-4}$$

From Eq. (29-3) we obtain an expression for dq in terms of the over-all coefficient and substitute it in Eq. (29-4) to give

$$\frac{d(\Delta t)}{U_o\, \Delta t\, dA_o} = \frac{\Delta t_2 - \Delta t_1}{q} \tag{29-5}$$

This equation is rearranged to give

$$\int_{\Delta t_1}^{\Delta t_2} \frac{d(\Delta t)}{U_o\, \Delta t} = \frac{\Delta t_2 - \Delta t_1}{q} \int_0^{A_o} dA_o \tag{29-6}$$

If U_o is assumed to be constant, we get

$$q = U_o A_o \left[\frac{\Delta t_2 - \Delta t_1}{\ln (\Delta t_2 / \Delta t_1)} \right] \tag{29-7}$$

The quantity in brackets is the logarithmic mean temperature difference.

The same equation would have been obtained if the flow of the two streams in Fig. 29-2 had been concurrent. If $w_c C_{pc}$ and $w_h C_{ph}$ are equal, Eq. (29-3) shows that any change in temperature of the hot fluid along the exchanger is accompanied by equal change in the temperature of the cold fluid. In such a case, with countercurrent flow, Δt is the same at all cross sections in the exchanger, so that Δt_2 and Δt_1 are equal, making the right-hand side of Eq. (29-7) indeterminate. This presents no problem, however, because if Δt and U_o are both constant, Eq. (29-3) can be integrated directly and gives for the whole exchanger

$$q = U_o A_o \Delta t \tag{23-17}$$

If the over-all coefficient varies within the exchanger, Eq. (29-7) is not rigorous, although it is often used as an approximation. In some circumstances the convective coefficient of one of the fluids can be expressed as a linear function of the mixing-cup temperature of the fluid. If this fluid offers the major resistance to heat transfer, the over-all coefficient is approximately equal to the convective coefficient (as was shown in Chap. 23), so that U_o is a linear function of the mixing-cup temperature of that fluid. Since the temperature of each fluid and the temperature difference Δt are linear functions of q, it can be shown algebraically that Δt is a linear function of each temperature. Under these circumstances the over-all coefficient is a linear function of Δt. If we substitute the expression

$$U_o = a + b \, \Delta t$$

in Eq. (29-6), we obtain

$$\int_{\Delta t_1}^{\Delta t_2} \frac{d(\Delta t)}{\Delta t (a + b \, \Delta t)} = \frac{\Delta t_2 - \Delta t_1}{q} \int_0^{A_o} dA_o \tag{29-8}$$

The integration of the left-hand side yields

$$\left[\frac{1}{a} \ln \frac{\Delta t}{a + b \, \Delta t} \right]_{\Delta t_1}^{\Delta t_2} = \left[\frac{1}{a} \ln \frac{\Delta t}{U_o} \right]_{(\Delta t/U_o)_1}^{(\Delta t/U_o)_2} = \frac{1}{a} \ln \frac{U_{o1} \Delta t_2}{U_{o2} \Delta t_1} \tag{29-9}$$

The constant a may be found by algebraic manipulation of the definition of U_o as a linear function to give

$$a = \frac{U_{o1} \Delta t_2 - U_{o2} \Delta t_1}{\Delta t_2 - \Delta t_1} \tag{29-10}$$

We substitute this expression for the constant a in Eq. (29-9) and write the integrated form of Eq. (29-8),

$$\frac{\Delta t_2 - \Delta t_1}{U_{o1}\,\Delta t_2 - U_{o2}\,\Delta t_1} \ln \frac{U_{o1}\,\Delta t_2}{U_{o2}\,\Delta t_1} = \frac{\Delta t_2 - \Delta t_1}{q}\,A_o \qquad (29\text{-}11)$$

which is rearranged to give

$$q = \frac{U_{o1}\,\Delta t_2 - U_{o2}\,\Delta t_1}{\ln\,(U_{o1}\,\Delta t_2 / U_{o2}\,\Delta t_1)}\,A_o \qquad (29\text{-}12)$$

Thus it is not necessary to know the constants of the linear relation between the quantities U_o and Δt, but merely the terminal values of these quantities. If U_o is constant, Eq. (29-12) reduces to Eq. (29-7).

If the variation of U_o is so great that it cannot be represented adequately by a linear function of Δt, it is necessary to integrate Eq. (29-1) graphically or numerically. The quantity dq is replaced by either $w_h C_{ph}\,dt_h$ or $w_c C_{pc}\,dt_c$, and the equation becomes

$$w_h C_{ph} \int_{t_{h1}}^{t_{h2}} \frac{dt_h}{U_o(t_h - t_c)} = \int_0^{A_o} dA_o \qquad (29\text{-}13)$$

A relation between t_h and t_c at any cross section of the exchanger can be found by writing an enthalpy balance to include both fluids between that cross section and either end of the exchanger. This, in effect, is an integration of the middle terms of Eq. (29-3). The quantity U_o is calculated at that cross section from the individual coefficients expressed as resistances in the manner shown in Chap. 23.

Shell-and-Tube Heat Exchangers

The heat exchangers found most commonly in industry contain a number of parallel tubes enclosed in a single shell and for that reason are called shell-and-tube exchangers. They are used when large quantities of fluid must be heated or cooled and double-pipe exchangers of sufficient capacity would be too bulky and expensive. As in the case of double-pipe exchangers, the fluid streams may be flowing in the same or opposite directions. In Fig. 29-3, the hot fluid enters the tubes from a header and, leaving the tubes, flows into another header from which it leaves the unit. The cold fluid flows countercurrently through the shell side.

The temperature behavior of the fluids in the exchanger shown in Fig. 29-3 is analogous to that in the double-pipe exchanger shown in Fig. 29-2. Furthermore, the equations for determining the heat-transfer area in the two cases are identical; A_o is the total outside area of all the tubes in the analysis for the shell-and-tube exchanger.

If the exchanger shown in Fig. 29-3 were quite short, it is evident that the assumption of fluids flowing in parallel concurrent or countercurrent flow would not be realized. Instead, the principal path of the fluid in the

Hot fluid
out

Cold fluid
in

Cold fluid
out

Hot fluid
in

Fig. 29-3.   Single-pass shell-and-tube heat exchanger.

shell would be normal to the tube bundle. In these circumstances the analogy with the double-pipe exchanger breaks down. An analysis assuming complete cross flow has been carried out by Bowman, Mueller, and Nagle, who integrated the theoretical equations for this system. They compared their equation for q with a modified form of Eq. (29-7).

$$q = U_o A_o Y \frac{\Delta t_2 - \Delta t_1}{\ln (\Delta t_2 / \Delta t_1)} \tag{29-14}$$

in which Δt_1 and Δt_2 are the terminal temperature differences taken as if the fluids in the cross-flow exchanger were in countercurrent flow. The factor Y was then obtained by equating the two expressions. In designing cross-flow exchangers, values of the factor Y may be read from Fig. 29-4 and used with the terminal temperature differences for counterflow to obtain A_o.

Multipass Heat Exchangers

Shell-and-tube heat exchangers are sometimes modified by putting a partition in one of the headers so that the tube-side fluid makes two passes through the shell. This arrangement is shown schematically in Fig. 29-5.

In part of the exchanger the fluids in both the tube and shell sides are in concurrent flow, but in the remainder of the exchanger counterflow exists. This case has also been analyzed by Bowman, Mueller, and Nagle, and the necessity of using a cumbersome equation has been eliminated by providing a chart of values for Y to be used in conjunction with Eq. (29-14). As before, the values of Δt in Eq. (29-14) are taken as though counterflow existed in the entire exchanger.

Many other combinations have been analyzed, including systems with more than one shell pass. Multiple passes on the shell side are achieved

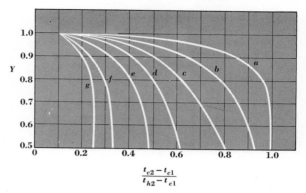

Fig. 29-4.
Correction factor for a cross-flow heat exchanger. [From R. W. Bowman, A. C. Mueller, and W. M. Nagle, Trans. ASME, 62:283 (1940).]

$$Z$$

$Z = \dfrac{t_{h2} - t_{h1}}{t_{c2} - t_{c1}}$

	Z
a.	0.2.
b.	0.6.
c.	1.0.
d.	1.5.
e.	2.0.
f.	3.0.
g.	4.0.

$\dfrac{t_{c2} - t_{c1}}{t_{h2} - t_{c1}}$

by placing partitions in the shell. Heat-transfer areas are calculated for these systems by the use of a correction factor as applied to Eq. (29-14) in the same manner as those already discussed. A number of charts for determining these factors are given in Perry's Handbook, sec. 6. Figure 29-6 gives correction factors for a shell-and-tube exchanger with one shell pass and two, four, six, eight, etc., tube passes.

In all systems it is assumed in the analysis that the fluid in any one pass of the shell of the exchanger is completely mixed at any cross section normal to flow. This is not actually achieved in the shell, but is often approached because of baffles in the shell, which cause mixing at various positions along the axis of the exchanger.

Fig. 29-5. *Heat exchanger with one shell pass and two tube passes.*

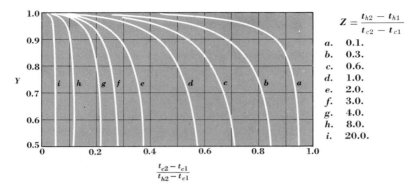

$$Z = \frac{t_{h2} - t_{h1}}{t_{c2} - t_{c1}}$$

a.	**0.1.**
b.	**0.3.**
c.	**0.6.**
d.	**1.0.**
e.	**2.0.**
f.	**3.0.**
g.	**4.0.**
h.	**8.0.**
i.	**20.0.**

Fig. 29-6.   *Correction factor for a shell-and-tube heat exchanger with one shell pass and an even number of tube passes. (From Tubular Exchanger Manufacturers Association.)*

In some heat exchangers the temperature of the shell-side fluid is constant throughout the exchanger.   For these systems, the correction factor Y has a value of unity and the unadorned logarithmic mean temperature difference is used, as in Eq. (29-7).

Example 29-1

Crude oil flows at the rate of 2000 lb/hr through the inside pipe of a double-pipe heat exchanger and is heated from 90 to 200°F.   The heat is supplied by kerosene, initially at 450°F, flowing through the annular space.   If the temperature of approach (minimum temperature difference between fluids) is 20°F, determine the heat-transfer area and the required kerosene flow rate for (*a*) concurrent flow and (*b*) countercurrent flow.

Data: Over-all coefficient U_o = 80 Btu/(hr)(sq ft)(°F)
      Specific heat of crude oil = 0.56 Btu/(lb)(°F)
      Specific heat of kerosene = 0.60 Btu/(lb)(°F)

The total heat load is

$$q = (2000)(0.56)(200 - 90)$$
$$= 132,000 \text{ Btu/hr}$$

(*a*) *Concurrent flow.*   The temperature distribution is represented in Fig. 29-7.   The exit temperature of kerosene is 220°F.   The kerosene flow rate is

$$w_h = \frac{132,000}{(0.60)(450 - 220)}$$
$$= 893 \text{ lb/hr}$$

The terminal temperature differences are $\Delta t_1 = 20°$ and $\Delta t_2 = 360°$.   The tube area is found from Eq. (29-7).

$$A_o = \frac{132,000}{80[(360 - 20)/\ln{(360/20)}]}$$
$$= 13.1 \text{ sq ft}$$

Fig. 29-7.   *Temperature distribution in a heat exchanger with concurrent flow (Example 29-1, part a).*

Fig. 29-8.   *Temperature distribution in a heat exchanger with countercurrent flow (Example 29-1, part b).*

(*b*) *Countercurrent flow.* The temperature distribution is shown in Fig. 29-8.   The exit temperature of kerosene in this case is 110°F, and the kerosene-flow rate is

$$w_h = \frac{132,000}{(0.60)(450 - 110)}$$

$$= 604 \text{ lb/hr}$$

The terminal temperature differences are $\Delta t_1 = 20°$ and $\Delta t_2 = 250°$.   The tube area is

$$A_o = \frac{132,000}{80[(250 - 20)/\ln{(250/20)}]}$$

$$= 16.9 \text{ sq ft}$$

Example 29-2

In a tubular heater with eight tube passes and a single shell pass, hot gas flows through the shell side and a liquid flows through the tubes.   The gas enters at 160°F and leaves at 102°F; the liquid enters at 52°F and leaves at 87°F.   If the over-all coefficient of heat transfer U_o is 5.5 Btu/(hr)(sq ft)(°F) and the total heat-transfer rate is 100,000 Btu/hr, find the total heat-transfer area.

The flow arrangement, if represented as counterflow, is as follows:

The parameters for determining the factor Y are

$$\frac{t_{c2} - t_{c1}}{t_{h2} - t_{c1}} = \frac{87 - 52}{160 - 52} = 0.32$$

$$Z = \frac{t_{h2} - t_{h1}}{t_{c2} - t_{c1}} = \frac{160 - 102}{87 - 52} = 1.66$$

From Fig. 29-6, $Y = 0.89$. The terminal temperature differences for counterflow are $\Delta t_1 = 50°$ and $\Delta t_2 = 73°$. The total heat-transfer area is

$$A_o = \frac{100{,}000}{(5.5)(0.89)[(73 - 50)/\ln(^{73}\!/_{50})]}$$

$$= 336 \text{ sq ft}$$

Extended Surfaces

The use of extended surfaces, often called fins, to give high heat-transfer rates in heat-exchange devices has been common for many years. An automobile radiator consists of a bank of tubes through which hot water from the engine circulates and loses heat to the surrounding air. The tubes are inserted through holes in a series of parallel plates which receive heat from the tube walls and transmit it to the air by the mechanism of forced convection. Some heat flows directly through the tube walls to the air, but most of it is dissipated through the plates. The amount dissipated by radiation is a small fraction of the total heat loss, so the name "radiator" is not descriptive of the device.

Other forms of extended surfaces attached to tubes are circular or spiral ribbon-type fins; longitudinal fins, which are plates attached to the outer surface running lengthwise along the tube; and pin fins, which are small pins or strips attached by one end to the outer surface of the tube in the manner of bristles. Fins may be welded or brazed to the tube and may be of the same or a different kind of metal. Some fins are formed directly from the metal of a thick-walled tube. Fins on tubes are usually found only on the outer surface.

Extended surfaces do not increase the heat-transfer rate significantly in all circumstances. This can be shown by the following considerations. The sum of the resistances to heat transfer is equal to the reciprocal of the product of area and the over-all coefficient of heat transfer defined in Chap. 23. In a system with two fluid resistances and a metal-wall resistance, the relation is

$$\frac{1}{U_o A_o} = \Sigma R = \frac{1}{h_o A_o} + \left(\frac{\Delta r}{k A_{lm}}\right)_{\text{metal}} + \frac{1}{h_i A_i} \qquad (29\text{-}15)$$

The quantity A_{lm} in the metal-resistance term is valid only for concentric, cylindrical surfaces; however, the metal resistance is usually not great and for the moment will be ignored. It can be seen that the effect of the presence of the fins on the outer surface will be to increase A_o and consequently to reduce the heat-transfer resistance $1/h_o A_o$ of the fluid outside the tube.

If the outside coefficient of heat transfer h_o is so small that the outside resistance is much greater than either the metal resistance or the inside resistance, the over-all resistance will be reduced almost in proportion to the amount by which A_o is increased. Thus it is possible to double the outside heat-transfer area by the use of fins and reduce the total resistance by almost one-half. An example of an application of this principle is the condensation of steam inside a copper tube as air is heated in passing over the finned outer surface. Conversely, if the coefficient of heat transfer on the outer surface h_o is high and the coefficient on the inner surface h_i is low, the outer resistance will constitute a small part of the total resistance. The effect of doubling the outside area is merely to cut in half an already negligible resistance so that the over-all resistance is reduced only slightly. This would be the situation if the foregoing system were reversed so that steam condensed on the outer, finned surfaces of tubes while air or some other gas passed through the tube. An analysis of these two situations is shown in Example 29-3.

If fouling of a tube surface occurs, the use of fins would not appear to be beneficial because of the possibility of trapping foreign particles between the fins. However, flow between fins is often at a fairly high velocity, and if the deposit is not likely to plug the space between the fins entirely, their presence may still be beneficial. The fouling resistance is $1/h_d A_o$, and if h_d is small compared with the other coefficients in the system, any increase in the surface area A_o on which fouling occurs cuts down the total resistance by a significant amount.

Example 29-3

Air is to be heated by the condensation of steam in a heat exchanger where the heat-transfer coefficient of the air is 10 Btu/(hr)(sq ft)(°F) and the coefficient for the condensing steam is 1000 Btu/(hr)(sq ft)(°F). Find the heat-transfer rate in Btu/(hr)(lin ft of tubing) for the following systems:

(a) Steam is condensing inside ¾-in., 18-gauge copper tubing, and air is flowing over the outside. The tubes are not finned.

(b) Same as (a), except that the outer surfaces of the tubes are finned.

(c) Steam is condensing on the outside of the finned tubes, and air is passing through the inside.

We shall assume that the over-all temperature difference is fixed at 100°F and that the resistance of the metal wall to heat transfer is negligible for all three systems. The outside area of the smooth tube is 0.196 sq ft/lin ft, and the inside area is 0.171 sq ft/lin ft. The finned tube has 16 circular fins per inch, of 0.052 in. height. The total outside area of tubing and fins is 0.539 sq ft/ft. The heat-transfer coefficients given above will be assumed to be constant for each fluid in all systems.

(a) Smooth tubing; steam inside, air outside:

$$\text{Steam resistance} = \frac{1}{(1000)(0.171)} = 0.00585 \text{ (hr)(°F)/Btu}$$

$$\text{Air resistance} = \frac{1}{(10)(0.196)} = 0.510 \text{ (hr)(°F)/Btu}$$

$$\Sigma R = 0.516 \text{ (hr)(°F)/Btu}$$

$$q = \frac{\Delta t}{\Sigma R} = \frac{100}{0.516} = 194 \text{ Btu/hr}$$

(b) Finned tubing; steam inside, air outside:

$$\text{Steam resistance} = 0.00585 \text{ (hr)(°F)/Btu}$$

$$\text{Air resistance} = \frac{1}{(10)(0.539)} = 0.185 \text{ (hr)(°F)/Btu}$$

$$\Sigma R = 0.191 \text{ (hr)(°F)/Btu}$$

$$q = \frac{100}{0.191} = 524 \text{ Btu/hr}$$

(c) Finned tubing; air inside, steam outside:

$$\text{Steam resistance} = \frac{1}{(1000)(0.539)} = 0.00185 \text{ (hr)(°F)/Btu}$$

$$\text{Air resistance} = \frac{1}{(10)(0.171)} = 0.585 \text{ (hr)(°F)/Btu}$$

$$\Sigma R = 0.587 \text{ (hr)(°F)/Btu}$$

$$q = \frac{100}{0.587} = 171 \text{ Btu/hr}$$

In system (b) the effect of the fins in reducing the major resistance is to cause a significant increase in the heat-transfer rate over the rate in system (a). In system (c), however, the effect of the fins is merely to reduce further the resistance of the steam, which was negligible even on an unfinned surface. The major resistance, which is that of the air stream, is at the inside of the tube, which is smaller in area than the outside of the smooth tube. Thus the total resistance in system (c) with the finned tubes is greater than in system (a), when smooth tubes were used.

Fin Efficiencies. Although the resistance to heat transfer of the metal wall was neglected in Example 29-3, this procedure is not always justifiable. Fins as high as 1 in. and only a few hundredths of an inch in thickness are not uncommon, and even when made of copper, such fins may offer a significant resistance to heat transfer. This resistance is, of course, more likely to be significant when the fluid resistances are small.

A quantitative method of describing the effect of the fin resistance is by the use of fin efficiency. This quantity is defined as the actual heat-transfer rate from a fin divided by the rate that would be obtained if the entire fin were at the temperature of the base of the fin, i.e., the outer cylindrical

Fig. 29-9. Efficiency of circular fins of constant thickness. [From K. A. Gardner, Trans. ASME, 67:621 (1945).]

    a. $r_o/r_b = 1.0.$
    b. $r_o/r_b = 1.4.$
    c. $r_o/r_b = 1.6.$
    d. $r_o/r_b = 1.8.$
    e. $r_o/r_b = 2.0.$
    f. $r_o/r_b = 3.0.$
    g. $r_o/r_b = 4.0.$

surface of the tube. The fin efficiency can be predicted mathematically, as shown in Example 29-4.

The heat flow from a tube surface to a fluid can be written as

$$q = hA_f \eta_f \, \Delta t + hA_t \, \Delta t \qquad (29\text{-}16)$$

where A_f = fin area

    A_t = area of tube surface between fins

    η_f = fin efficiency

    h = heat-transfer coefficient, assumed constant at all points on fin and tube surface

    Δt = temperature difference between base of fin and bulk-fluid phase

When written in Ohm's law form, Eq. (29-16) becomes

$$q = \frac{\Delta t}{1/[h(A_f \eta_f + A_t)]} \qquad (29\text{-}17)$$

in which the denominator has the dimensions of resistance. When an overall coefficient of heat transfer U_o based on the outside area is written, the term $1/h_o$, which appears in Eq. (23-15), is replaced by $A_o/h_o(A_f \eta_f + A_t)$, where A_o is the sum of A_f and A_t.

Fin efficiencies have been calculated for a number of configurations. A simple system is examined in Example 29-4, and a chart for determining the efficiency of a circular fin is given in Fig. 29-9.

Example 29-4

A longitudinal steel fin 1 in. high and ⅛ in. thick is exposed to an air stream at 70°F. The air moving past the fin has a uniform convection coefficient $h = 15$

Btu/(hr)(sq ft)(°F).   The fin has a thermal conductivity of 25 Btu/(hr)(ft)(°F) and a base temperature of 250°F.   Calculate the fin efficiency and the heat flow per lineal foot assuming that all temperature gradients in planes parallel to the base of the fin are negligible.   A section of the fin is shown in Fig. 29-10.

First a heat balance will be written for the differential element of width w ($\frac{1}{96}$ ft), height dx, and length 1 ft.

$$\text{Rate of heat conduction in} = -kw\,\frac{dt}{dx} \tag{1}$$

$$\text{Rate of heat conduction out} = -kw\left(\frac{dt}{dx} + \frac{d^2t}{dx^2}\,dx\right) \tag{2}$$

$$\text{Rate of heat convection out} = h(2\,dx)(t - 70) \tag{3}$$

At steady state, (1) = (2) + (3), which reduces to the following differential equation:

$$\frac{d^2t}{dx^2} - \frac{2h}{kw}\,(t - 70) = 0 \tag{4}$$

The solution of Eq. (4), which can be written down directly for this linear equation with constant coefficients, is

$$t - 70 = C_1 e^{\alpha x} + C_2 e^{-\alpha x} \tag{5}$$

in which α is substituted for $\sqrt{2h/kw}$ as a convenience, and C_1 and C_2 are arbitrary constants.   These constants are evaluated from a knowledge of two boundary conditions.   One is that at $x = 0$, $t = 250$°F.   Therefore

$$180 = C_1 + C_2 \tag{6}$$

The other boundary condition is that at the top of the fin ($x = \frac{1}{12}$ ft) the conduction rate to the surface equals the convection rate away from the surface.   This equality is written as

$$-kw\left(\frac{dt}{dx}\right)_{x=\frac{1}{12}} = hw\,(t_{x=\frac{1}{12}} - 70) \tag{7}$$

Substituting the proper values from Eq. (5) into Eq. (7) gives

$$-k(C_1\alpha e^{\alpha x} - C_2\alpha e^{-\alpha x}) = h(C_1 e^{\alpha x} + C_2 e^{-\alpha x})$$

The constant α is

$$\alpha = \left[\frac{(2)(15)}{(25)(\frac{1}{96})}\right]^{\frac{1}{2}} = 10.7 \text{ ft}^{-1}$$

At $x = \frac{1}{12}$, $\alpha x = 0.895$.

The second equation for C_1 and C_2 is thus

$$-(25)(10.7)(C_1 e^{0.895} - C_2 e^{-0.895}) = 15(C_1 e^{0.895} + C_2 e^{-0.895}) \tag{8}$$

Equations (6) and (8) are solved to give

$$C_1 = 23.4$$
$$C_2 = 156.6$$

The heat flow from the fin may be found by combining Eqs. (3) and (5) to obtain an equation for the heat loss from a differential area and integrating over the entire fin area. It is easier, however, to find the rate of heat conduction into the fin at the base, which is also equal to the total heat loss. Thus the total heat loss is

$$q = -kA \left(\frac{dt}{dx} \right)_{x=0}$$
$$= -(25)(\tfrac{1}{96})(10.7)(23.4 - 156.6)$$
$$= 370 \text{ Btu/(hr)(lin ft)}$$

The total heat loss if the fin were at 250°F throughout would be

$$q = hA(250 - 70)$$
$$= (15) \frac{1 + \tfrac{1}{8} + 1}{12} (250 - 70)$$
$$= 478 \text{ Btu/(hr)(lin ft)}$$

The fin efficiency η_f is thus $\frac{370}{478}$, or 0.78. The temperature at the top of the fin may be found by substituting $x = \frac{1}{12}$ in Eq. (5); it is 191°F.

Wilson's Method of Analysis

A useful method of determining the individual convective heat-transfer coefficients in a heat exchanger is that of Wilson.[1] If a single-phase fluid is flowing in developed turbulent flow inside the tubes of an exchanger, the convective coefficient h_i can be estimated by the Dittus-Boelter equation

$$\frac{h_i D}{k} = 0.023 \left(\frac{D u_b \rho}{\mu} \right)^{0.8} \left(\frac{C_p \mu}{k} \right)^{0.3} \tag{26-4}$$

This equation shows that h_i is proportional to $u_b{}^{0.8}$ if everything else is held constant. However, we shall find it desirable to change the average temperature of the fluid as u_b changes; the effect of the temperature if the fluid is water is represented by the term $1 + 0.011t$ in the equation

$$h_i = a u_b{}^{0.8}(1 + 0.011t) \tag{29-18}$$

The constant a could be calculated by equating (26-4) and (29-18), but it is usually determined from the results of the Wilson-line experiment described below. The temperature t is the average water temperature in degrees Fahrenheit.

[1] E. E. Wilson, *Trans. ASME*, **37**:47 (1915).

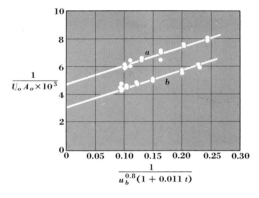

Fig. 29-11.   Wilson plot for boiling methanol on a 1¼-in. tube. [From AIChE Journal, 4:75 (1958).]

a. $\Delta t_o = 50°$F.
b. $\Delta t_o = 70°$F.

If a series of runs is conducted in which the velocity of the water in the tubes is varied, the over-all coefficient can be represented by the equation

$$\frac{1}{U_o A_o} = \frac{1}{h_o A_o} + \frac{\Delta r}{kA_{lm}} + \frac{1}{a u_b^{0.8}(1 + 0.011t)A_i} \qquad (29\text{-}19)$$

The first two terms on the right-hand side are the resistances of the outside fluid and the tube wall, respectively. If they are held constant for all runs, a linear relation exists between $1/U_o A_o$ and $1/u_b^{0.8}(1 + 0.011t)$. Such a plot is shown in Fig. 29-11, in which the over-all coefficients are for the boiling of methanol outside a 1¼-in. copper tube through which hot water is flowing. It can be seen in Fig. 29-11 that the predicted linear form is realized.

If the straight lines through the points are extrapolated to the ordinate at which $1/u_b^{0.8}(1 + 0.011t)$ equals zero, the velocity u_b at this point is infinite, and the resistance of the fluid inside the tube to heat transfer is zero. Therefore the intercepts of the straight lines on the ordinate axis of Fig. 29-11 give values of $1/U_o A_o$ equal to the sum of the tube wall and outside fluid resistances.

$$\left(\frac{1}{U_o A_o}\right)_{u_b = \infty} = \frac{1}{h_o A_o} + \frac{\Delta r}{kA_{lm}} \qquad (29\text{-}20)$$

The quantity $\Delta r/kA_{lm}$ can be readily calculated, and the value of the convective coefficient for the outside fluid h_o obtained.

It is essential that all resistances other than the inside resistance be held as nearly constant as possible during runs at different velocities. This means that the outside coefficient h_o must be held constant. Because h_o is a function of temperature drop for such systems as boiling, condensation, and natural convection, care must be taken that the temperature drop over the fluid outside the tube is held constant for successive runs. This is achieved by altering the temperature level of the fluid inside the tube each time its velocity is changed, so that the inclusion of the factor $(1 + 0.011t)$ is essential. Conditions are usually chosen so that the temperature change of the water is small from inlet to outlet.

Fouling coefficients can be estimated by the Wilson method if the outside fluid coefficient h_o can be predicted or is negligible. The fouling resistance $1/h_{do}A_o$ is a part of the intercept value.

In some pieces of equipment the value of the exponent on u_b in Eq. (29-18) may not be known. Upstream disturbances may cause it to differ from the value of 0.8 used for developed turbulent flow in circular pipes. If an incorrect exponent is used in the plot (for example, 0.8 when it should be 0.7), the experimental data should still extrapolate to the proper value of the ordinate representing all the other resistances. However, the line will no longer be quite straight, and extrapolation is more difficult. Nevertheless, the curvature is often not great enough to cause serious errors, and the method remains, in spite of this deficiency, a useful technique.

EVAPORATION

Equipment Types

The vaporization of a liquid for the purpose of concentrating a solution is a common step in chemical processing and is done in many ways. The simplest device is an open pan or kettle which receives heat from a coil or jacket or by direct firing underneath the pan. A somewhat more complicated apparatus is the horizontal-tube evaporator in which a liquid in the shell side of a closed, vertical, cylindrical vessel is evaporated by passing steam or other hot gas through a bundle of horizontal tubes contained in the lower part of the vessel. In both devices nucleate boiling occurs in the solution at the heated surface, and any circulation of the liquid that occurs is a result of the heating. The liquid level in the horizontal-tube evaporator is usually at less than half the height of the vessel; the empty space permits disengagement of entrained liquid from the vapor passing overhead.

A more efficient device is the vertical-tube evaporator. This consists of a vertical, cylindrical vessel with a bundle of vertical, steam-heated tubes at the base of the vessel. However, the bundle of tubes operates with steam around the tubes and the liquid to be evaporated within the tubes. Essentially, the bundle acts as a vertical shell-and-tube heat exchanger in which steam is admitted to the shell side and the evaporating liquid is on the tube side. Boiling within the tubes causes upward flow of the liquid-vapor mixture. After disengagement, the vapor is removed from the top of the vessel and the liquid remaining flows down in an annular space between the tube bundle and the wall of the vessel to the space beneath the tube bundle, where it begins the cycle once again. These evaporators are fed continuously, and the concentrated liquor is removed continuously from the bottom of the vessel. The apparatus described above is often referred to as a short-vertical-tube, basket-type evaporator and is one of the most common types. The flow is caused entirely by natural convection.

An evaporator which works in similar fashion is the long-tube, natural-circulation evaporator. Operating on somewhat the same principle as a smokestack, the long-tube evaporator gives higher fluid velocities than the short-tube evaporator. This high velocity is desirable because it promotes higher heat-transfer coefficients between the evaporating fluid and the tube walls. The method of operation is shown schematically in Fig. 29-12. A further improvement is sometimes made by pumping the circulating liquid around to give even higher velocities and higher heat-transfer coefficients than can be obtained by natural convection. These forced-circulation evaporators are especially useful for evaporating viscous liquids for which natural-circulation rates would be low.

Diagrams of various types of evaporator are given in Perry, sec. 7. Among the most important of recent designs is the falling-film evaporator, in which a film of solution flows down the surface of a tube and receives heat through the tube wall. The short exposure time in the falling-film evaporator makes it useful for concentrating solutions of heat-sensitive materials. Long-tube evaporators, in which the tubes are filled with liquid, may also be used for heat-sensitive solutions by not permitting recirculation. This type is sometimes referred to as a Kestner evaporator.

Evaporator Operation. The evaporator is merely a special kind of heat exchanger, and the heat-transfer rate is predicted from the equation

$$q = UA \, \Delta t \tag{29-21}$$

The area in Eq. (29-21) may be either the area on which steam is condensing or the area of the surface adjacent to the liquid solution. The reciprocal of the product of the over-all coefficient and the area, $1/UA$, is equal to the sum of the individual resistances of the condensing steam, the tube wall, the boiling fluid, and any fouling present. The resistances of both the condensing steam and the boiling fluid vary with position, so that $1/UA$ also varies.

In the vertical-tube evaporator the condensing coefficient is infinite at the top of the tube and decreases as the condensate film thickness increases down the tube. The heat-transfer coefficient for the evaporating solution also changes with position along the tube. At the bottom of the tube

Fig. 29-12. *Long-tube, natural circulation evaporator. (Swenson Evaporator Co.)*

the fluid is a single phase, and if the fluid is not at the saturation temperature, the heat-transfer coefficient is predictable from the usual equations describing heat transfer in circular tubes. When boiling begins, however, the heat-transfer coefficient increases because of the contribution of the growing bubbles to turbulence in the laminar sublayer. In addition, the presence of the vapor bubbles decreases the bulk density of the fluid in the tube and causes an increase in velocity in accordance with the continuity equation. This effect further increases the heat-transfer coefficient and causes more rapid vapor formation. The effect is autocatalytic and gives a marked increase in the heat-transfer coefficient at successively higher positions. If sufficient vapor is formed, however, the heat-transfer coefficient is adversely affected because parts of the walls are in contact with only vapor.

As a result of the variation of both the condensing and boiling heat-transfer coefficients, it can be seen that the determination of the over-all coefficient U from the individual resistances is likely to be extremely difficult,

a.	99.9.
b.	99.5.
c.	99.0.
d.	98.0.
e.	95.0.
f.	90.0.
g.	85.0.
h.	80.0.
i.	70.0.
j.	60.0.
k.	50.0.
l.	40.0.
m.	20.0.
n.	0.

Fig. 29-13. Boiling points of solutions of sodium hydroxide (per cent by weight of NaOH). (From G. G. Brown et al., "Unit Operations," John Wiley & Sons, Inc., New York, 1950.)

if not impossible. In fact, over-all coefficients for evaporators are usually predicted from the performance of other evaporators operating under conditions as nearly similar as possible.

A further difficulty encountered in the prediction of evaporator performance is the choice of a significant over-all temperature difference. The temperature of the liquid entering an evaporator tube may be below the saturation temperature for the pressure at that point. As the fluid moves up the tube, its temperature increases because of heating and its pressure decreases as in any fluid flowing in a tube of constant cross section. Thus the approach to saturation temperature is rapid. When boiling begins, the decreasing hydrostatic head and the increase in velocity as a result of vapor formation are additional factors causing a rapid decrease of pressure, so that the saturation temperature decreases markedly along the tube. Consequently, the local value of the over-all temperature difference between the condensing steam and the boiling fluid is most difficult to predict. Although recent work has been done to provide a more rigorous approach

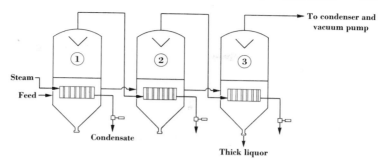

Fig. 29-14.   Forward feeding of multiple-effect evaporator battery.

to the problem, most evaporator design is done with an over-all temperature difference which is the temperature of the saturated steam minus the saturation temperature of the strong solution at the pressure existing in the vapor space of the evaporator.   Over-all coefficients are computed from evaporator performance using this Δt, and the same method of defining the temperature difference is employed for the design of other systems.

The boiling point of a solution at a certain pressure is a function of the concentration of the solution.   The calculation of the boiling-point rise due to dissolved solids is discussed in most textbooks of physical chemistry. In the design of evaporators it is common practice to use a representation known as a Dühring plot for calculating the boiling point of solutions. Such a plot is shown in Fig. 29-13.   The boiling point of pure water at the pressure in the vapor space of the evaporator is determined using steam tables.   The boiling point of the solution is then found on the Dühring plot using the appropriate value of the concentration parameter.

Multiple-effect Operation

One of the principal costs of evaporation is the cost of steam for heating. A considerable reduction in operating costs is achieved by operating a battery of evaporators in which the overhead vapor from one evaporator (or "effect") is condensed in the steam chest of the next evaporator, thus saving both the cost of condensing the vapor from the first unit and supplying heat for the second.   Several evaporators may operate in a battery in this fashion.   If the vapor from one unit is to heat an adjacent unit, it must condense at a higher temperature than the boiling liquid in that effect. This temperature difference is achieved by operating succeeding units at lower pressures.   The vapor from the last unit is usually sent to a condenser operating under a vacuum.

The method of operation shown in Fig. 29-14 is called forward feeding.

By this method the dilute feed solution is supplied to the same effect that receives the high-pressure steam. Subsequent effects are at successively lower pressures. Another method of operation is known as backward feeding. With this system the high-pressure steam is supplied to the effect receiving the most concentrated liquid, whereas the dilute feed enters the effect supplied with steam at the lowest pressure in the entire battery. An advantage of backward feeding is that the most concentrated liquor is at the highest temperature, tending to give a more equal distribution of heat-transfer coefficients in the various effects. However, interstage pumps are required in this system and add to equipment costs. Other methods of operation include parallel feeding, in which fresh feed enters each effect of the system.

The Calculation of the Performance of Multiple-effect Evaporator Systems

The precise solution of the theoretical equations for the design of an evaporator system is limited by the accuracy of the predicted values of the over-all heat-transfer coefficients. However, it is necessary to estimate the heat-transfer area, the operating conditions of each unit, and the steam consumption. One basic consideration is that the areas are usually required to be identical in all effects of a battery, so as to simplify operation and reduce capital costs.

The largest items by far in an enthalpy balance around a single effect are the latent heat terms for the condensing steam and boiling liquid. The contributions to the enthalpy balance from the sensible heat of the feed, the thick liquor, and the condensate are much smaller, and if the differences between effects resulting from these liquid streams are neglected, the heat load on all effects is the same. Therefore we can write

$$U_1 \Delta t_1 = U_2 \Delta t_2 = U_3 \Delta t_3 \tag{29-22}$$

This equation serves as a basis for estimating the temperature drop over each effect.

If the over-all coefficients for the various effects are identical, we find

$$q = UA(\Delta t_1 + \Delta t_2 + \Delta t_3) \tag{29-23}$$

which shows that the total rate of evaporation from the multiple-effect system is no greater than the rate that would be obtained from a single effect operating with a temperature difference equal to $\Delta t_1 + \Delta t_2 + \Delta t_3$. Thus it is evident that the advantage of multiple-effect operation is not in increasing capacity, but rather in steam and cooling-water economy.

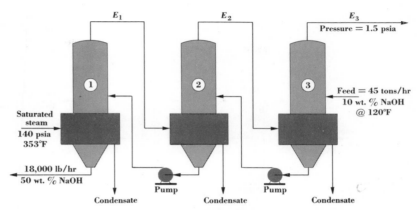

Fig. 29-15.   *Evaporator battery with backward feed (Example 29-5).*

Example 29-5

A triple-effect evaporator operating with backward feed is to be used to concentrate 45 tons/hr of a solution of 10 mass per cent NaOH in water to 50 mass per cent. Saturated steam at 140 psia is supplied to the steam chest of the first effect, and a pressure of 1.5 psia is to be maintained in the vapor space of the last effect. The feed is supplied at 120°F. The over-all heat-transfer coefficient for each effect is estimated to be 500 Btu/(hr)(sq ft)(°F). Find the heat-transfer area of each effect.

The system is shown schematically in Fig. 29-15. First, some elements of the material balance are considered:

$$\text{Amount of concentrated liquor from effect 1} = \frac{(45)(2000)(0.10)}{0.50}$$

$$= 18,000 \text{ lb/hr}$$

$$\text{Total evaporation rate} = 90,000 - 18,000$$
$$= 72,000 \text{ lb/hr}$$

If equal evaporation rates are assumed for each effect, we have

$$E_1 = E_2 = E_3 = 24,000 \text{ lb/hr}$$

The amount and concentration of the thick-liquor stream from each effect are found by a material balance. For example, considering effect 3:

$$\text{Amount of thick liquor} = 90,000 - 24,000$$
$$= 66,000$$

$$\text{Concentration of thick liquor} = \frac{(90,000)(0.10)}{66,000}$$

$$= 0.136$$

From Fig. 29-13 the boiling-point rise due to the dissolved sodium hydroxide in an aqueous solution of 13.6 mass per cent concentration is 7°F at a pressure of 1.5 psia (boiling point of pure water equal to 115°F). The material balances for each of the three effects yield the information in the following table. The boiling-point rises for

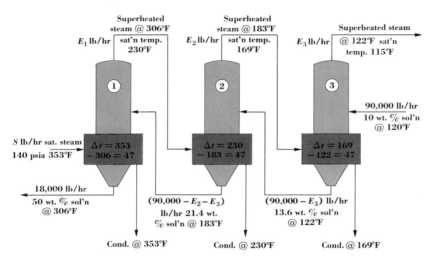

Fig. 29-16. *Temperatures and flow rates, first trial (Example 29-5).*

effects 1 and 2 depend slightly on pressure. Rough guesses of these pressures are sufficiently accurate at this point.

Thick liquor	Amount, lb/hr	Concentration, mass % NaOH	BP rise, °F
From effect 1..............	18,000	50	76
From effect 2..............	42,000	21.4	14
From effect 3..............	66,000	13.6	7

At 1.5 psia, the pressure in effect 3, the temperature of saturated water vapor is 115°F. The temperature of the steam supplied to the first effect is 353°F. If the solution in each effect were not subject to a boiling-point rise due to the dissolved NaOH, the over-all temperature-difference driving force to be shared between the three effects would be $353 - 115 = 238$°F. However, effect of the dissolved solid is to cause a series of boiling-point rises of $76 + 14 + 7 = 97$°F. As we have seen in Chap. 27, the superheat in a vapor stream does not contribute to the over-all temperature-difference driving force. Thus 97° must be subtracted from the total of 238° to obtain the sum of effective Δt's in the three evaporators. This gives

$$\Sigma \, \Delta t = 238 - 97$$
$$= 141$$

Assuming $q_1 = q_2 = q_3$, $U_1 = U_2 = U_3$, and $A_1 = A_2 = A_3$, we obtain $\Delta t_1 = \Delta t_2 = \Delta t_3$; hence $\Delta t = {}^{141}\!/_3 = 47$°F for each effect. We can now specify the temperatures of all the streams, as shown in Fig. 29-16.

Initially, we assumed that $E_1 = E_2 = E_3 = 24{,}000$ lb/hr, and this has permitted us to estimate roughly the temperatures and compositions of all streams. Using this information, shown in Fig. 29-16, we write enthalpy balances around each effect, using enthalpy information from the accompanying enthalpy chart, Fig. 29-17, for NaOH solutions, and from the steam tables.

Fig. 29-17. *Enthalpy-concentration diagram for aqueous solutions of NaOH. (From G. G. Brown et al., "Unit Operations," John Wiley & Sons, Inc., New York, 1950.)*

Enthalpy balances:

For effect 1 $(1193.0 - 324.8)S + 130(90,000 - E_2 - E_3)$
$$= 1194E_1 + (305)(18,000)$$

For effect 2 $(1194 - 199)E_1 + 78(90,000 - E_3)$
$$= 1140E_2 + 130(90,000 - E_2 - E_3)$$

For effect 3 $(1140 - 137)E_2 + 78(90,000) = 1115E_3 + 78(90,000 - E_3)$

In addition,

$$E_1 + E_2 + E_3 = 72,000$$

These four equations contain four unknown quantities E_1, E_2, E_3, and S and may be solved simultaneously to give

$$E_1 = 26{,}200 \text{ lb/hr}$$
$$E_2 = 23{,}100 \text{ lb/hr}$$
$$E_3 = 22{,}700 \text{ lb/hr}$$
$$S = 35{,}400 \text{ lb/hr}$$

The areas of the effects can now be calculated, taking q as the total enthalpy change of the condensing vapor in each effect.

$$A_1 = \frac{(35{,}400)(1194.1 - 330.5)}{(500)(47)}$$

$$= 1300 \text{ sq ft}$$

$$A_2 = \frac{(26{,}200)(1194 - 199)}{(500)(47)}$$

$$= 1110 \text{ sq ft}$$

$$A_3 = \frac{(23{,}100)(1140 - 137)}{(500)(47)}$$

$$= 987 \text{ sq ft}$$

The arithmetic average area is 1130 sq ft. In view of the accuracy of U, this is probably an adequate answer. However, the calculations can be refined by modifying each value of Δt by the ratio of the calculated area to the average area as follows:

$$\Delta t_1 = \frac{(47)(1300)}{1130} = 54$$

$$\Delta t_2 = \frac{(47)(1110)}{1130} = 46$$

$$\Delta t_3 = \frac{(47)(987)}{1130} = 41$$

With these figures the temperature distribution previously estimated can be revised and the four enthalpy balances solved once more for E_1, E_2, E_3, and S. The results are

$$E_1 = 26{,}100 \text{ lb/hr}$$
$$E_2 = 23{,}200 \text{ lb/hr}$$
$$E_3 = 22{,}700 \text{ lb/hr}$$
$$S = 33{,}000 \text{ lb/hr}$$

from which we recalculate the areas and obtain

$$A_1 = 1080 \text{ sq ft}$$
$$A_2 = 1140 \text{ sq ft}$$
$$A_3 = 1120 \text{ sq ft}$$

The arithmetic average area is 1110 sq ft. The total rate of evaporation expressed as pounds of vapor removed from the feed solution per pound of steam supplied to effect 1 is 72,000/33,000, or 2.2. This ratio is known as the steam economy. For a triple-effect evaporator battery it might be expected to be roughly $\frac{3}{1}$. However, a large amount of heat is lost in the concentrated solution from the first effect, and only 26,100 lb/hr of vapor is produced from 33,000 lb/hr of steam. In subsequent effects the ratio is more nearly unity.

PROBLEMS

29-1. A double-pipe heat exchanger is constructed of 200 ft of 2-in., schedule-40 steel pipe jacketed with 3-in., schedule-40 steel pipe. Hot water at the rate of 30,000 lb/hr under pressure enters the inside pipe at a temperature of 300°F, and 22,300 lb/hr of cold water enters the jacket at 60°F. Calculate the temperatures of the two streams leaving the exchanger and the total heat-transfer rates when the streams are counter-current and when they are concurrent. The convective coefficients of heat transfer inside and outside the clean tube may be taken as 1200 and 1175, respectively.

29-2. A multipass heat exchanger has two passes on the shell side and six passes on the tube side. It is cooling a petroleum oil inside the tubes from 275 to 125°F. Water is the coolant in the shell, with inlet and outlet temperatures of 55 and 88°F. The individual heat-transfer coefficients are h (oil) = 48, h (water) = 170, h (scale on water side) = 500. Neglect the metal-wall resistance. The exchanger has 120 1-in.-OD, 16 BWG tubes, each 6 ft long. Calculate the heat-transfer rate in Btu/hr.

29-3. A lubricating oil is being heated in a concentric-pipe heat exchanger. The oil enters the inner pipe with a velocity of 6.5 ft/sec at a temperature of 100°F. The inner pipe is a 1-in., schedule-40 steel pipe. The oil leaves at a temperature of 160°F. The annular space between the inner and outer pipes contains steam condensing at a uniform temperature of 220°F. The steam-side coefficient is 2000 Btu/(hr)(sq ft)(°F). Calculate the length of the heat exchanger, assuming that the heat-transfer coefficient for the oil is constant at the arithmetic average temperature. The oil has the following properties at 130°F: viscosity, 17.0 cp; specific heat, 0.47 Btu/(lb)(°F); density, 55.9 lb/cu ft; thermal conductivity, 0.070 Btu/(hr)(ft)(°F). The viscosity of the oil at 220°F is 4.2 cp.

29-4. Ten thousand pounds per hour of an organic liquid is heated from 60 to 140°F in a concentric-pipe heat exchanger. Saturated steam at a uniform temperature of 340°F is condensing in the outer pipe, which is 8-in., schedule-40 steel pipe. The exchanger is 40 ft long, and the inner section is 4-in., schedule-40 steel pipe.

If the inside pipe is replaced by a 6-in., schedule-40 pipe, calculate the length of exchanger required to give the same exit temperature of 140°F.

Additional data:

(1) Specific heat of organic liquid = 0.5 Btu/(lb)(°F).
(2) Condensing steam coefficient = 1500 Btu/(hr)(sq ft)(°F)—assume constant.
(3) Developed turbulent flow may be assumed to exist in the inside pipe under both sets of conditions.
(4) The steam condensate leaves the exchanger as a saturated liquid.
(5) The pipe-wall resistance to heat transfer may be assumed to be negligible.

29-5. Air at 60°F is being heated by blowing it over a bank of five rows of 1-in., 14-gauge vertical copper tubes 4 ft high. The tubes are staggered and spaced on equilateral triangles 2 tube diameters on a side; there is $\frac{1}{2}$ in. between the side tubes and the duct. There are five tubes per row. Steam at 5 psig is condensing inside the tubes; the condensate is not subcooled. The steam-side heat-transfer coefficient may be taken as 2000 Btu/(hr)(sq ft)(°F), and the resistance of the tube wall may be neglected.

It is desired to heat 500 cu ft/min of air measured at 1 atm and 60°F. What will be the air temperature at the discharge end of the exchanger?

29-6. Seven thousand pounds per hour of an organic liquid at 60°F is being heated on the tube side of a single-pass shell-and-tube heat exchanger by saturated steam condensing at 230°F on the shell side. The condensate is not subcooled. The exchanger consists of twenty $\frac{3}{8}$-in., 20-gauge copper tubes, each 20 ft long. When the exchanger is first placed in operation, it is found that the organic liquid is heated to 190°F as it leaves the exchanger. After a certain period of operation, it is found that the liquid exit temperature is 170°F.

(a) What is the fouling coefficient under these conditions?

(b) At what temperature must saturated steam now be used to heat 7000 lb of liquid per hour to 190°F?

Assume that the effect of temperature on the inside heat-transfer coefficient can be neglected and that the resistances of the tube wall and the condensing steam are small compared with the convective resistance of the organic liquid. The specific heat of the organic liquid is 0.55 Btu/(lb)(°F).

29-7. A heat exchanger for chilling water is to be designed using ¾-in., 18-gauge copper tubes. Water at the rate of 40 gal/min is to enter the tube side of the single-pass shell-and-tube exchanger at 70°F and is to be cooled to 50°F. Heat is removed on the shell side by Freon-12 boiling at 47°F. A bulk water velocity of 5 ft/sec in the tubes will be adequate, and under these circumstances the average inside heat-transfer coefficient h is 980 Btu/(hr)(sq ft)(°F). The boiling coefficient is not constant, but is a function of the temperature difference over the boiling film. Boiling coefficients may be obtained by plotting the data given below on a log-log plot of h versus Δt. Determine the total length of tubing, the number of tubes required, and the length per tube, by the following methods:

(a) Assume U is constant at the value obtained for that point in the exchanger where the water is at 60°F.

(b) Assume U is a linear function of Δt.

(c) Use the function U actually obtained from the data.

Data:

Boiling coefficient, h Btu/(hr)(sq ft)(°F).........	400	600	800	1000	1400
Temperature drop over boiling film, Δt°F.........	6.8	8.6	10.5	12.2	14.9

29-8. Find the fin efficiency of a pin fin attached by one end to a tube surface which is at 200°F. Air flowing past the fin is at 60°F and has a convective coefficient $h = 10$ Btu/(hr)(sq ft)(°F), which may be assumed to be constant at all points on the fin. The fin is a solid steel cylinder ⅛ in. in diameter and 1 in. high. Temperature gradients parallel to the base of the fin may be neglected.

29-9. A spiral-finned tube heats air by condensing steam inside the tube. A copper fin 0.03 in. thick, 1 in. deep, is wound on the outside of 0.75-in.-OD copper tubing. In a certain part of the heater the air temperature is 60°F, the steam temperature is 200°F, and the convective coefficient of heat transfer for the air is 20 Btu/(hr)(sq ft)(°F). Calculate the fin efficiency and the heat loss per fin. Each 360° turn of a spiral fin may be considered simply as an annular circular section of OD 2.75 in. and ID 0.75 in. The condensing steam and the tube wall offer so little resistance to heat transfer compared with the resistance of the air that the base of the fin may be assumed to be at 200°F.

29-10. An evaporator is supplied with an aqueous feed solution containing 5 mass per cent solids at a rate of 40,000 lb/hr and a temperature of 200°F. The thick liquor leaves the evaporator at a temperature of 150°F, containing 45 mass per cent solids. The saturation temperature of the vapor from the evaporator is 125°F. Saturated steam at 250°F is condensed in the steam chest and leaves as condensate at the same temperature. Assuming the specific heats of all solutions are equal to 1 Btu/(lb)(°F) and the over-all coefficient of heat transfer is 635 Btu/(hr)(sq ft)(°F), find the heat-transfer area and the steam economy.

29-11. An aqueous glue solution is to be concentrated from 4 to 50 wt per cent solids in a double-effect evaporator. Twenty tons of feed enters the system per hour, preheated to the boiling point of the effect into which it is introduced. Steam is available at 10 psig, and condenser facilities are capable of producing an absolute pressure of 4 in. Hg in the last effect. Assume that there is no rise in boiling point due to dissolved solids and that the specific heats of all solutions are constant at 1.2 Btu/(lb)(°F). All condensate streams leave at the condensing temperatures.

(a) Using forward feed, calculate the area of the heating surface required, the steam consumption, and the steam economy for each effect. The areas in each effect are to be equal. The over-all heat-transfer coefficients are $U_1 = 400$ and $U_2 = 350$ Btu/(hr)(sq ft)(°F).

(b) Repeat part (a), using backward feed and the coefficients given.

(c) Repeat part (a), using parallel feed and the coefficients given.

29-12. The tubes on which the data of Fig. 29-11 were taken had an OD of 1.25 in., a wall thickness of 0.065 in., and a length of 25 in. Find the boiling coefficient of heat transfer for each set of runs, assuming that no fouling was present.

PART

3

MASS TRANSFER

INTRODUCTION TO MASS TRANSFER
30

General Remarks

Some of the most typical chemical-engineering problems lie in the field of mass transfer. As mentioned at the beginning of this book, a distinguishing mark of the chemical engineer is his ability to design and operate equipment in which reactants are prepared, chemical reactions take place, and separations of the resulting products are made. This ability rests largely on a proficiency in the science of mass transfer. Applications of the principles of momentum and heat transfer are common in many branches of engineering, but the application of mass transfer has traditionally been largely limited to chemical engineering. Other important applications occur in metallurgical processes and, more recently, in problems of high-speed flight.

By mass transfer is meant the tendency of a component in a mixture to travel from a region of high concentration to one of low concentration. For example, if an open test tube with some water in the bottom is placed in a room in which the air is relatively dry, water vapor will diffuse out through the column of air in the test tube. There is a mass transfer of water from a place where its concentration is high (just above the liquid surface) to a place where its concentration is low (at the outlet of the tube). If the gas mixture in the tube is stagnant, the transfer occurs by molecular diffusion. If there is a bulk mixing of the layers of gas in the tube by mechanical stirring or because of a density gradient, mass transfer occurs primarily by the mechanism of forced or natural convection. These

427

mechanisms are analogous to the transfer of heat by conduction and by convection; there is, however, no counterpart in mass transfer for thermal radiation.

The analogy between momentum and energy transfer has already been studied in some detail, and it is now possible to extend the analogy to include mass transfer. This matter has been mentioned in earlier chapters and will be studied in detail in the chapters to follow.

In discussing the fundamentals of mass transfer we shall consider mainly binary mixtures, although multicomponent mixtures are important in industrial applications. Some of these more complicated situations will be discussed after the basic principles have been illustrated in terms of binary mixtures.

Molecular Diffusion

Molecular diffusion occurs in a gas as a result of the random motion of the molecules. This motion is sometimes referred to as a random walk. Across a plane normal to the direction of the concentration gradient (or any other plane), there are fluxes of molecules in both directions. The direction of movement for any one molecule is independent of the concentration in dilute solutions. Consequently, in a system in which there is a concentration gradient, the fraction of molecules of a particular species (referred to as species A) which will move across a plane normal to the gradient is the same for both the high- and low-concentration sides of the plane. Because the total number of molecules of A on the high-concentration side is greater than on the low-concentration side, there is therefore a net movement of A in the direction in which the concentration of A is lower. If there are no counteracting effects, the concentrations throughout the mixture tend to become the same. In the analogous transfer of heat in a gas by conduction, the distribution of hotter molecules (those which have a higher degree of random molecular motion) tends to be evened out by random mixing on a molecular scale. Similarly, if there is a gradient of directed velocity (as distinguished from random velocity) across the plane, the velocity distribution tends toward uniformity as a result of the random molecular mixing. There is a transfer of momentum, which is proportional to the viscosity of the gas.

The above remarks apply only in an approximate and qualitative way. The quantitative prediction of the diffusivity, thermal conductivity, and viscosity of a gas from a knowledge of molecular properties can be quite complicated. The consideration of such relations forms an important part of the subject of statistical mechanics.

Molecular diffusion also occurs in liquids and solids. Crystals in an unsaturated solution dissolve, with subsequent diffusion away from the solid-liquid interface. Diffusion in solids is of importance in metallurgical operations. When iron which is unsaturated with respect to carbon is heated in a bed of coke, the concentration of the carbon near the surface is increased by inward diffusion of carbon atoms.

Eddy Diffusion

Just as momentum and energy can be transferred by the motion of finite parcels of fluid, so mass can be transferred. We have seen that the rate of these transfer operations, caused by bulk mixing in a fluid, can be expressed in terms of the eddy kinematic viscosity, the eddy thermal diffusivity, and the eddy diffusivity. This latter quantity can be related to a mixing length which is the same as that defined in connection with momentum and energy transfer. In fact, the analogy between heat and mass transfer is so straightforward that equations developed for the former are often found to apply to the latter by a mere change in the meaning of the symbols. The reader is referred to the discussions in Chaps. 7 and 25.

Eddy diffusion is apparent in the dissipation of smoke from a smokestack. Turbulence causes mixing and transfer of the smoke to the surrounding atmosphere. In certain locations where atmospheric turbulence is lacking, smoke originating at the surface of the earth is dissipated largely by molecular diffusion. This causes serious pollution problems because mass is transferred less rapidly by molecular diffusion than by eddy diffusion.

Convective Mass-transfer Coefficients

In the study of heat transfer we found that the solution of the differential energy balance was sometimes cumbersome or impossible, and it was convenient to express the rate of heat flow in terms of a convective heat-transfer coefficient by an equation like

$$\frac{q}{A} = h(t_s - t_m) \tag{23-1}$$

The analogous situation in mass transfer is handled by an equation of the form

$$N_A = k_\rho(\rho_{As} - \rho_{Am}) \tag{30-1}$$

The mass flux N_A is measured relative to a set of axes fixed in space. The driving force is the difference between the concentration at the phase boundary (a solid surface or a fluid interface) and the concentration at some arbitrarily defined point in the fluid medium. The convective coefficient k_ρ may apply to forced or natural convection; there are no mass-transfer counterparts for boiling, condensation, or radiation heat-transfer coefficients. The value of k_ρ is a function of the geometry of the system and the velocity and properties of the fluid, just as was the coefficient h.

Separation Operations

The size of separation equipment depends on the rate at which a component is transferred from one phase to another, and this rate is in turn dependent on how fast the component is transferred to the interphase boundary. As the two individual heat-transfer coefficients influence the size of a heat exchanger, so the gas- and liquid-phase mass-transfer coefficients affect the size of a gas-absorption column.

For instance, ammonia can be separated from a mixture with air by passing the gas up through an absorption tower. Water is fed to the top of the tower and flows downward countercurrent to the rising gas in such a way that there is a large area of interphase contact. At any point in the tower the concentration of ammonia in the gas phase exceeds the concentration which would be in equilibrium with the water phase. As a result, the ammonia travels through the gas toward the surface of the water, is absorbed, and travels away from the interface into the interior of the water phase. The height of the tower is largely determined by the rate of mass transfer of ammonia from one phase to the other, and this rate will be expressed in terms of concentration differences and mass-transfer coefficients.

If the tower is sufficiently high, almost all the ammonia is removed from the air before it leaves at the top. To separate the ammonia from the water, the solution leaving the bottom of the tower is subjected to fractional distillation.

Although the rate of mass transfer is the dominant factor in the design of a gas-absorption tower or other separation device, the over-all mass and energy balances must also be satisfied. The capacity of a tower is determined by its diameter, and this dimension is calculated by the use of the principles of fluid dynamics to compute the permissible velocities of the fluid phases in the tower. The principles of thermodynamics assist in the prediction of the phase-equilibrium relations which govern the maximum driving forces available.

In the rest of this book we shall study, first, the principles of mass transfer through a single phase by the several possible mechanisms, and then we shall apply the results to interphase transfer as encountered in some of the common separation operations.

MOLECULAR DIFFUSION AND
DIFFUSIVITY
31

Fick's Law

The rate of mass transfer is given by Fick's (first) law as

$$\tilde{I}_A = -D_{AB}\frac{d\tilde{\rho}_A}{dy} \tag{31-1}$$

for ordinary molecular diffusion in the y direction at constant molal density. The quantity $\tilde{I}_A$ is the flux of constituent A, measured in lb moles/(hr)(sq ft), and $d\tilde{\rho}_A/dy$ is the gradient of concentration, in lb moles/(cu ft)(ft), which acts as a driving force. The symbol D_{AB} represents the diffusivity, or coefficient of diffusion, for a binary mixture of species A and B. Equation (31-1) is similar to Eqs. (7-19) and (9-19), but it is expressed in terms of pound moles rather than pounds. The distinction between the flux J_A used in these equations and the flux $\tilde{I}_A$ used above will be explained in Chap. 32.

Equation (31-1), as well as the analogous equations for heat and momentum transfer [Eqs. (7-18) and (7-21), for instance], rests on an essentially empirical basis. It is observed that for ideal gases and dilute liquids, D_{AB} is almost constant for a given pressure, temperature, and pair of substances; the diffusivity is almost independent of concentration. However, for most concentrated liquid solutions, for many solid systems, and for nonideal gases, it is observed that D_{AB} is a function of composition. This behavior is similar to the way the thermal conductivity is affected by temperature. For moderate variations in temperature, the thermal conductivity varies little, but for many substances a change of several hundred

431

degrees does cause an appreciable variation in the thermal conductivity.

In general, the viscosity and the thermal conductivity of a system are dependent on temperature, pressure, and composition, and so is the diffusivity. It is possible to define a diffusivity which is less dependent on concentration for certain nonideal systems than that defined by Eq. (31-1).

In momentum transfer the shear stress approaches zero as the velocity gradient decreases, and two parts of a system come to thermal equilibrium ($q/A = 0$) when the temperatures in the two parts become equal. Thus it is logical to assume that the chemical potential is the driving force in mass transfer, since a system comes to chemical or composition equilibrium as the chemical potential of each component becomes equal throughout the system. It can be shown that the mass flux is given by

$$\tilde{I}_A = -\frac{D'_{AB}\tilde{\rho}_A}{RT}\frac{d\mu_A}{dy} \tag{31-2}$$

This equation, which states that the flux is proportional to the gradient of chemical potential, defines a diffusivity D'_{AB}.

The two diffusivities can be related by expressing Eq. (31-2) in terms of concentrations. From thermodynamics, the chemical potential is related to the activity by

$$d\mu_A = RT\, d\ln a_A \tag{31-3}$$

The activity is in turn related to the mole fraction $\tilde{x}_A$ by

$$a_A = \frac{\gamma_A \tilde{\rho}_A}{\tilde{\rho}} = \gamma_A \tilde{x}_A \tag{31-4}$$

in which γ_A is called the activity coefficient. The standard state, for which the activity is unity, is here chosen as pure A ($\tilde{x}_A = 1.0$). The activity coefficient with this standard state always approaches unity as the mole fraction approaches unity, and for ideal solutions, γ_A is unity for all values of $\tilde{x}_A$.

Equations (31-3) and (31-4) may be used to express the gradient of chemical potential as

$$\frac{d\mu_A}{dy} = RT\left(\frac{d\ln \gamma_A}{dy} + \frac{d\ln \tilde{x}_A}{dy}\right) \tag{31-5}$$

or

$$\frac{d\mu_A}{dy} = \frac{RT}{\tilde{x}_A}\left(\tilde{x}_A \frac{d\ln \gamma_A}{d\tilde{x}_A} + 1\right)\frac{d\tilde{x}_A}{dy} \tag{31-6}$$

When Eq. (31-6) is substituted in Eq. (31-2), we get

$$\tilde{I}_A = -D'_{AB}\tilde{\rho}\frac{d\tilde{x}_A}{dy}\left(\tilde{x}_A \frac{d\ln \gamma_A}{d\tilde{x}_A} + 1\right) \tag{31-7}$$

Since the relation between γ_A and $\bar{x}_A$ can be found for a nonideal system by the usual methods of classical thermodynamics, the quantity in parentheses in Eq. (31-7) can be evaluated as a function of composition at a given pressure and temperature. Experiments have shown that the diffusivity D'_{AB} is much less dependent on concentration than D_{AB} in nonideal systems.

In ideal systems $d \ln \gamma_A / d\bar{x}_A$ is always zero; thus Eq. (31-7) becomes

$$\bar{I}_A = -D'_{AB}\bar{\rho}\frac{d\bar{x}_A}{dy} \tag{31-8}$$

This equation is correct when the molal density $\bar{\rho}$ is a function of composition, and thus of position. If $\bar{\rho}$ is constant, Eq. (31-8) can be written as

$$\bar{I}_A = -D'_{AB}\frac{d\bar{\rho}_A}{dy} \tag{31-9}$$

For this situation, the coefficients D'_{AB} and D_{AB} are identical. In other words, Eq. (31-1) should be used only for ideal systems for which the molal density is constant. Such a system is a mixture of ideal gases. If the molal density is a function of composition, Eq. (31-8) can be used for ideal systems. However, for many liquids, the density is about constant, and it is convenient to use

$$J_A = -D_{AB}\frac{d\rho_A}{dy} \tag{7-19}$$

rather than Eq. (31-8). The application of Eqs. (31-9) and (7-19) to some commonly encountered situations will be discussed in Chap. 32.

The combination of Eqs. (31-1) and (31-7) shows that

$$D_{AB} = D'_{AB}\frac{\bar{x}_A[(d \ln \gamma_A)/d\bar{x}_A] + 1}{\bar{x}_A[(d \ln \bar{\rho})/d\bar{x}_A] + 1} \tag{31-10}$$

The coefficient D'_{AB} has come into use only recently; most of the data in the literature are given in terms of D_{AB}, which is a function of composition for nonideal systems. We shall limit the remainder of our treatment to the use of D_{AB}.

The flux $\bar{I}_A$ is measured across a plane which moves with the molal average velocity of the mixture; for the equimolal counterdiffusion of two ideal gases in a closed container, the plane is stationary in space. The flux J_A is measured across a plane which moves with the mass average velocity; for the interdiffusion of two fluids of equal density in a closed container, the plane is stationary in space. For most other situations there is an additional flux because of bulk flow with respect to a plane fixed in space. This matter will be discussed in detail in Chap. 32.

Diffusivities

Solids. One component in a solid will diffuse through the other at a measurable rate if there is a suitable concentration gradient and the temperature is high enough. The effects of diffusion in solids are very important in metallurgy. As mentioned earlier, the depth to which carbon will penetrate in a given time from the surface of steel being carburized (case-hardened) is governed by the laws of diffusion. The rate of reaction in some chemical processes is determined by solid diffusion, but the number of applications of importance to the chemical engineer is much less than the number concerned with diffusion in liquids and gases. Diffusivities for a few solid systems are given in Table 31-1. The magnitude of the diffusivity varies widely from one system to another. The coefficient D_{AB} is strongly affected by concentration for many systems.

Table 31-1. Diffusivities in Solids†

System	D_{AB}, sq cm/sec
H_2 in SiO_2	$0.01–0.1 \times 10^{-6}$
He in SiO_2	$0.02–0.05 \times 10^{-8}$
H_2 in Ni	$1.0–10.0 \times 10^{-8}$
Bi in Pb	7.7×10^{-3}
Hg in Pb	3.6×10^{-1}
Sb in Ag	5.3×10^{-5}
Al in Cu	1.2×10^{-2}
Cd in Cu	3.5×10^{-9}

† From R. M. Barrer, "Diffusion in and through Solids," pp. 141, 275, The Macmillan Company, New York, 1941.

The coefficient of diffusion for a pair of solids cannot be accurately predicted from theory. A qualitative estimate can be made by using the theory of Eyring, in which diffusion is postulated to be an activated process. An interchange of atoms in the structure of a solid occurs as the atoms at a given plane vibrate about their equilibrium positions. A statistical fraction of the atoms vibrate with an energy greater than the activation energy, so that they jump to new equilibrium positions or adjacent "holes" in the lattice structure. The rate of mass transfer is proportional to exp $(-\Delta U/RT)$, so that the diffusivity increases rapidly with temperature; ΔU is the activation energy.

For details on the theory of diffusion in solids, the reader is referred to books by Barrer[1] and by Glasstone, Laidler, and Eyring[2] and reviews by LeClaire[3] and Birchenall.[4]

Liquids. Diffusion in liquids is important in many separation operations, notably liquid-liquid extraction, gas absorption, and distillation. An inspection of Table 31-2 shows that for all the systems listed, the values of D_{AB} are in the general range 10^{-5} to 10^{-6} sq cm/sec. The diffusivity is a function of composition.

Table 31-2.   Diffusivities in Liquids†
[Substance B (solvent) = water]

Solute A	Temperature, °C	Concentration	$D_{AB} \times 10^5$, sq cm/sec
Acetic acid..........	12.5	0.01 M	0.91
Carbon dioxide.......	18.0	0	1.71
Chlorine.............	18.0	0.1 M	1.40
Glycerol.............	10.0	0.125 M	0.63
Hydrogen............	25.0	0	3.36
Nitrogen.............	22.0	0	2.02
Oxygen..............	25.0	0	2.60
Ethanol.............	25.0	$\bar{x}_A = 0.05$	1.13
		0.10	0.90
		0.275	0.41
		0.50	0.90
		0.70	1.40
		0.95	2.20
n-Butanol............	30	$\bar{x}_A = 0.446$	0.267
		0.546	0.437
		0.642	0.560
		0.778	0.920
		0.869	1.24

† From R. C. Reid and T. K. Sherwood, "The Properties of Gases and Liquids," p. 288, McGraw-Hill Book Company, Inc., New York, 1958; and P. A. Johnson and A. L. Babb, *Chem. Revs.*, **56**:387–453 (1956).

There are two prominent theories for the prediction of approximate diffusivities in liquids. In the Eyring theory the molecules of a liquid are pictured as forming a quasi-crystalline lattice and the analysis is performed more or less as it was for diffusion in a solid. In the hydrodynamical

[1] R. M. Barrer, "Diffusion in and through solids," The Macmillan Company, New York, 1941.

[2] S. Glasstone, K. J. Laidler, and H. Eyring, "Theory of Rate Processes," chap. 9, McGraw-Hill Book Company, Inc., New York, 1941.

[3] A. D. LeClaire, Diffusion in Metals, *Progr. in Metal Phys.*, **4**:265–332 (1953).

[4] C. E. Birchenall, The Mechanics of Diffusion in the Solid State, *Met. Revs.*, **3**:235–277 (1958).

theory the diffusivity is first related to the force which acts on a sphere moving in a continuum. This force can be evaluated in terms of Stokes' law, and the resulting expression is called the Stokes-Einstein equation. The results of both theories can be put into the form

$$\frac{D_{AB}\mu}{T} = F(V) \tag{31-11}$$

in which $F(V)$ represents a function which depends on the molecular volume V of the mixture.

Equation (31-11) has been used by Wilke[1] as the basis of a method for the prediction of liquid diffusivities. According to Sherwood and Pigford,[2] the graph given by Wilke for $F(V)$ can be represented approximately by the following equation:

$$\frac{D_{AB}\mu}{T} = F(V) = \frac{4.0 \times 10^{-7}}{V_A^{1/3} - k_2} \tag{31-12}$$

in which $F(V)$ has the units $(lb)(ft)/(hr^2)(°R)$. Values of V_A can be obtained from several references,[2] and k_2 is a constant having values of 2.0, 2.46, and 2.84 for dilute solutions of water, methanol, and benzene, respectively.

Gases. Experimental values of the diffusivity of a number of binary gaseous systems are given in Table 31-3. The values fall approximately in the range 0.1 to 1.0 sq cm/sec. The diffusivities can be considered independent of concentration for gases at pressures near 1 atm.

Table 31-3. *Diffusivities in Gases*†
(Pressure about 1 atm)

System	Temperature, °C	D_{AB}, sq cm/sec
Air-ammonia...............	0	0.198
Air-benzene................	25	0.0962
Air–carbon dioxide...........	0	0.136
Air-chlorine................	0	0.124
Air-ethanol.................	25	0.132
Air-oxygen.................	0	0.175
Air-water..................	25	0.260

† From R. C. Reid and T. K. Sherwood, "The Properties of Gases and Liquids," p. 274, McGraw-Hill Book Company, Inc., New York, 1958.

The theory for the transport properties is understood better for the gaseous than for the liquid or solid states. From the kinetic theory, for nonpolar gases, the following formula gives good results:

[1] C. R. Wilke, *Chem. Eng. Progr.*, **45**:218 (1949).
[2] T. K. Sherwood and R. L. Pigford, 2d ed., "Absorption and Extraction," chap. 1, McGraw-Hill Book Company, Inc., New York, 1952.

$$D_{AB} = \frac{1.858 \times 10^{-3}T^{3/2}}{p\sigma^2_{AB}\Omega_D} \left(\frac{1}{M_A} + \frac{1}{M_B}\right)^{1/2} \tag{31-13}$$

in which M_A and M_B are molecular weights, T is in degrees Kelvin, p is in atmospheres, and D_{AB} is in square centimeters per second. To convert D_{AB} to square feet per hour, multiply by 3.87. The function Ω_D is determined by the temperature and two parameters σ_{AB} and ϵ_{AB}, which are characteristic of the potential energy of interaction between molecules of A and B. Methods of estimating the parameters σ_{AB} and ϵ_{AB} for various substances and a table of the function Ω_D are given by Bird, Stewart, and Lightfoot.[1]

We have given here only a qualitative description of the theories for the diffusivities of gases and liquids. A good introduction to the theoretical procedures to be used in estimating the diffusivities in gases and liquids is given by Bird, Stewart, and Lightfoot; more empirically oriented discussions are given by Treybal.[2] Perry's Handbook contains experimental data; Reid and Sherwood [3] contains experimental data and a review of the methods for predicting the diffusivity.

Diffusion in Porous Solids

In some chemical operations, such as heterogeneous catalysis, an important factor affecting the rate of reaction is the diffusion of a gaseous component through a porous solid. The effective diffusivity in the solid is reduced below what it would be in a free fluid, for two reasons. First, the tortuous nature of the path increases the distance which a molecule must travel to advance a given distance in the solid. Second, the free cross-sectional area is restricted. For many catalyst pellets, the effective diffusivity of a gaseous component is of the order of a tenth of its value in a free gas.

If the pressure is low enough and the pores are small enough, the mechanism of diffusion is basically changed; there exists what is called Knudsen diffusion. This type of diffusion occurs when the size of the pores approaches the mean free path of the gaseous molecules. A typical molecule now collides predominantly with the walls of the pores rather than with other molecules.

[1] R. B. Bird, W. E. Stewart, and E. N. Lightfoot, "Transport Phenomena," sec. 16.4, John Wiley & Sons, Inc., New York, 1961.

[2] R. E. Treybal, "Mass Transfer Operations," chap. 2, McGraw-Hill Book Company, Inc., New York, 1955; "Liquid Extraction," chap. 5, McGraw-Hill Book Company, Inc., New York, 1951.

[3] R. C. Reid and T. K. Sherwood, "The Properties of Gases and Liquids," chap. 8, McGraw-Hill Book Company, Inc., New York, 1958.

DIFFUSION IN BINARY MIXTURES
32

Basic Definitions

In Chap. 31 we mentioned two forms of Fick's law, one for a molal flux with respect to the molal average velocity [Eq. (31-1)] and one for a mass flux with respect to the mass average velocity [Eq. (7-19)]. Furthermore, in many problems we wish to know the flux with respect to axes fixed in space. In what follows we develop the relations among the various fluxes. Let us recall, first, the relations between mole fraction and mass fraction:

$$x_A = \frac{\rho_A}{\rho} = \frac{\tilde{x}_A M_A}{\tilde{x}_A M_A + \tilde{x}_B M_B} \tag{32-1}$$

$$\tilde{x}_A = \frac{\tilde{\rho}_A}{\tilde{\rho}} = \frac{x_A/M_A}{x_A/M_A + x_B/M_B} \tag{32-2}$$

By definition, we also have

$$\rho_A + \rho_B = \rho \tag{32-3}$$

$$\tilde{\rho}_A + \tilde{\rho}_B = \tilde{\rho} \tag{32-4}$$

and

$$\rho_A = \tilde{\rho}_A M_A \tag{32-5}$$

The mass flux N of a mixture is now simply defined as

$$N = N_A + N_B \tag{32-6}$$

The flux when designated as N is the value of the flux relative to a set of axes fixed in space.

The velocity of a single object is intuitively apparent. The velocity of an aggregate of particles which move but retain the same positions relative

438

to each other is obviously the same as the velocity of any individual particle. The velocity of an aggregate is not apparent, however, when the individual particles move with different velocities. In this case we define the velocity of the aggregate, say of particles of molecular species A, as the mass flux of A divided by the concentration of A $(u_A = N_A/\rho_A)$.

For a mixture of A and B, the velocity of the mixture is defined by substituting for the fluxes in Eq. (32-6).

$$u\rho = u_A\rho_A + u_B\rho_B \qquad (32\text{-}7)$$

The quantity u is called the mass average velocity of the mixture. If we divide Eq. (32-7) by the density of the mixture, we obtain

$$u = x_A u_A + x_B u_B \qquad (32\text{-}8)$$

The molal flux is

$$\tilde{N} = \tilde{N}_A + \tilde{N}_B \qquad (32\text{-}9)$$

Because $u_A = N_A/\rho_A = \tilde{N}_A/\tilde{\rho}_A$ and $u_B = N_B/\rho_B = \tilde{N}_B/\tilde{\rho}_B$, we can substitute for $\tilde{N}_A$ and $\tilde{N}_B$ in Eq. (32-9) to obtain

$$\tilde{N} = u_A\tilde{\rho}_A + u_B\tilde{\rho}_B \qquad (32\text{-}10)$$

The flux $\tilde{N}$ can be expressed in terms of a molal average velocity $\tilde{u}$, which is defined as $\tilde{N}/\tilde{\rho}$, by writing

$$\tilde{u}\tilde{\rho} = u_A\tilde{\rho}_A + u_B\tilde{\rho}_B$$

This can also be written as

$$\tilde{u} = \tilde{x}_A u_A + \tilde{x}_B u_B \qquad (32\text{-}11)$$

In any of the equations derived in previous chapters for the integral or differential balances which apply to mixtures, the velocity used has been u, the mass average velocity.

An inspection of Eqs. (32-6) to (32-11) shows that the mass flux N is *not* equal to the molal flux $\tilde{N}$ times the average molecular weight, because u and $\tilde{u}$ are different. In the flow of a uniform mixture through a pipe, there is no interdiffusion effect, u_A and u_B are identical, and the mass flux *is* then equal to the molal flux multiplied by the average molecular weight. However, in cases for which there is a concentration gradient in the direction of flow, u_A and u_B differ, with the effect noted above. In many mass-transfer situations, the total flux is of the same order of magnitude as the fluxes caused by diffusion, so the above distinction is not merely academic.

We now proceed to develop the relations among the various diffusional fluxes. The symbols J_A and $\tilde{J}_A$ represent, respectively, the mass flux and molal flux [lb or lb moles/(hr)(sq ft)] of component A with respect to a set of axes moving at the mass average velocity u of the fluid. The symbols I_A and $\tilde{I}_A$ represent the fluxes with respect to a set of axes which moves at the molal average velocity $\tilde{u}$ of the fluid. The following equations hold:

$$J_A = \tilde{J}_A M_A \tag{32-12}$$

$$I_A = \tilde{I}_A M_A \tag{32-13}$$

The relations between J_A and $\tilde{I}_A$ and between $\tilde{J}_A$ and I_A are not so obvious and will be derived presently.

In·chemical engineering it is usually desired to relate the flux to a fixed surface such as a fluid interface rather than to an average velocity. Thus we need to use the mass and the molal flux referred to a set of axes fixed in space. These fluxes have been defined in Eqs. (32-6) to (32-11) as N_A and $\tilde{N}_A$, respectively.

In most work in ordinary diffusion it has become customary to use the flux $\tilde{I}_A$ defined by Eq. (31-1). However, the relations for thermal diffusion have been expressed in terms of a flux such as J_A. These two fluxes must sometimes be added algebraically, so we need to be able to convert the flux $\tilde{I}_A$ into J_A. We shall presently develop the relation between $\tilde{I}_A$ and J_A, based on the definitions already given. We begin the study of the relations among the various fluxes by considering J_A and J_B.

$$J_A = -D_{AB}\frac{d\rho_A}{dy} \tag{7-19}$$

Equation (7-19) is valid for a system of constant density. Equation (32-3) shows that for such a system we can write

$$J_B = -D_{BA}\frac{d\rho_B}{dy} = +D_{BA}\frac{d\rho_A}{dy} \tag{32-14}$$

Since D_{AB} and D_{BA} are identical, it follows that

$$J_A + J_B = 0 \tag{32-15}$$

For ideal systems of variable density, an argument similar to that leading to Eq. (31-8) shows that Eq. (7-19) should be replaced by

$$J_A = -D'_{AB}\rho\frac{dx_A}{dy} \tag{32-16}$$

Since the sum of the mass fractions must equal unity, Eq. (32-15) still holds. Note that in a diffusing system of constant density, the molal density changes with position as the average molecular weight varies with concentration. An argument analogous to that leading to Eq. (32-15) gives the result

$$\tilde{I}_A + \tilde{I}_B = 0 \tag{32-17}$$

The equation connecting the fluxes $\tilde{N}_A$ and $\tilde{I}_A$ is obtained next. The molal flux of A with respect to fixed axes is $\tilde{I}_A$, the flux with respect to the molal average velocity, plus the flux caused by the bulk flow related to $\tilde{u}$, that is, the flux $\tilde{N}$. The equation expressing these relations is

$$\tilde{N}_A = \tilde{I}_A + \tilde{N}\tilde{x}_A \tag{32-18}$$

This may be written in terms of velocity as

$$u_A \tilde{\rho}_A = \tilde{I}_A + \tilde{u}\tilde{\rho}\frac{\tilde{\rho}_A}{\tilde{\rho}}$$

from which we obtain

$$\tilde{I}_A = \tilde{\rho}_A(u_A - \tilde{u}) \tag{32-19}$$

This equation reveals the basis of the statement that $\tilde{I}_A$ is the molal flux with respect to axes moving at the molal average velocity. We follow a similar procedure and write

$$N_A = J_A + Nx_A \tag{32-20}$$

which is expressed in terms of velocity as

$$u_A \rho_A = J_A + u\rho\frac{\rho_A}{\rho}$$

This is rearranged to give

$$J_A = \rho_A(u_A - u) \tag{32-21}$$

which indicates the basis of the statement that J_A is the flux of A relative to axes moving at the mass average velocity.

Next, $\tilde{J}_A$ and $\tilde{I}_A$ are related by the following reasoning. The molal flux $\tilde{J}_A$ with respect to the mass average velocity is equal to the molal flux with respect to the molal average velocity plus the flux of A caused by the bulk flux of moles with respect to the mass average velocity. This analysis is parallel to that leading to Eq. (32-18) and gives

$$\tilde{J}_A = \tilde{I}_A + (\tilde{J}_A + \tilde{J}_B)\tilde{x}_A \tag{32-22}$$

Equation (32-22) can be further simplified, for from Eqs. (32-12) and (32-15), we obtain

$$M_A \tilde{J}_A + M_B \tilde{J}_B = 0 \tag{32-23}$$

$$\tilde{J}_B = -\frac{M_A}{M_B}\tilde{J}_A \tag{32-24}$$

Equation (32-22) then becomes, with some rearrangement,

$$\tilde{I}_A = \tilde{J}_A\left(1 - \tilde{x}_A + \tilde{x}_A\frac{M_A}{M_B}\right) \tag{32-25}$$

or

$$\tilde{I}_A = \frac{\tilde{J}_A}{M_B}(M_B\tilde{x}_B + M_A\tilde{x}_A) \tag{32-26}$$

Since the quantity in parentheses is the average molecular weight, or $\rho/\tilde{\rho}$, the final general relation between $\tilde{I}_A$ and $\tilde{J}_A$ is

$$\tilde{I}_A = \frac{\tilde{J}_A \rho}{M_B \tilde{\rho}} \tag{32-27}$$

The derivations of the other relations among the fluxes follow those already given, and their development is left as an exercise for the reader.

The Differential Mass Balance

Mass Fluxes. The equations derived so far in this chapter apply only to steady one-dimensional flow with no generation. For more complicated situations the differential mass balances derived in Chap. 9 must be used. Let us now review these equations and relate them to the various kinds of fluxes we have defined.

In obtaining Eqs. (9-17) and (9-18), a diffusional flux J_A was considered superimposed upon the flux caused by the bulk flow, which we now know is represented by the mass average velocity. In Eq. (9-18),

$$\rho_A \left(\frac{\partial u_x}{\partial x} + \frac{\partial u_y}{\partial y} + \frac{\partial u_z}{\partial z} \right) + \frac{D\rho_A}{D\theta} + \frac{\partial J_{Ax}}{\partial x} + \frac{\partial J_{Ay}}{\partial y} + \frac{\partial J_{Az}}{\partial z} - r_A = 0$$

the quantities u_x, u_y, and u_z are the components of the mass average velocity. Equation (9-18) is convenient for use in systems of constant density, for which the term in parentheses is zero and for which we have

$$J_{Ax} = -D_{AB} \frac{\partial \rho_A}{\partial x} \tag{9-19}$$

Equations similar to Eq. (9-19) hold for the other two coordinate directions. For a fluid of constant density, Eq. (9-18) becomes

$$\frac{D\rho_A}{D\theta} = D_{AB} \left(\frac{\partial^2 \rho_A}{\partial x^2} + \frac{\partial^2 \rho_A}{\partial y^2} + \frac{\partial^2 \rho_A}{\partial z^2} \right) + r_A \tag{9-22}$$

if D_{AB} is constant. Many liquid solutions change relatively little in density as the concentration varies. For example,[1] the densities in aqueous ethyl alcohol solutions range from 62.4 to 49.9 lb/cu ft, whereas the molal densities range from 3.0 to 1.0 lb mole/cu ft.

For steady one-dimensional flow in the y direction, with no generation term, Eq. (9-22) becomes

$$u \frac{d\rho_A}{dy} = D_{AB} \frac{d}{dy} \frac{d\rho_A}{dy} \tag{32-28}$$

This equation can be integrated immediately to yield

[1] Note, however, that D_{AB} for ethanol is a strong function of concentration (Table 31-2). We shall not study systems of variable D_{AB} in this book.

$$u\rho_A = D_{AB}\frac{d\rho_A}{dy} + \text{const} \tag{32-29}$$

The quantity $u\rho_A$ is the flux of A caused by the bulk flow u, and it equals Nx_A, or $(N_A + N_B)x_A$. The diffusion term is $-J_A$, so we can write Eq. (32-29) as

$$\text{const} = J_A + (N_A + N_B)x_A \tag{32-30}$$

The right-hand side of Eq. (32-30) represents the sum of the flux caused by diffusion and that caused by bulk flow, so it is thus equal to the total flux of A with respect to fixed axes, that is, N_A. The constant of integration is therefore N_A, and Eq. (32-30) is identical with Eq. (32-20).

Molal Fluxes. For isothermal gaseous systems near atmospheric pressure the molal density of the mixture is constant. The derivation of the equation of continuity at the beginning of Chap. 9 can be repeated in terms of moles, and the result, similar to Eq. (9-12), is, in the absence of chemical reaction,

$$\frac{\partial \tilde{u}_x}{\partial x} + \frac{\partial \tilde{u}_y}{\partial y} + \frac{\partial \tilde{u}_z}{\partial z} + \frac{1}{\tilde{\rho}}\frac{D\tilde{\rho}}{D\theta} = 0 \tag{32-31}$$

The quantities $\tilde{u}_x$, $\tilde{u}_y$, $\tilde{u}_z$ are the components of the molal average velocity $\tilde{u}$. For a system of constant molal density, $D\tilde{\rho}/D\theta$ is zero, so we have

$$\frac{\partial \tilde{u}_x}{\partial x} + \frac{\partial \tilde{u}_y}{\partial y} + \frac{\partial \tilde{u}_z}{\partial z} = 0 \tag{32-32}$$

For a molal balance on component A, Eq. (9-16) becomes

$$d(\tilde{u}_x\tilde{\rho}_A + \tilde{I}_{Ax})\,dy\,dz = \left[\frac{\partial(\tilde{u}_x\tilde{\rho}_A)}{\partial x} + \frac{\partial \tilde{I}_{Ax}}{\partial x}\right]dx\,dy\,dz \tag{32-33}$$

The analysis leads to

$$\tilde{\rho}_A\left(\frac{\partial \tilde{u}_x}{\partial x} + \frac{\partial \tilde{u}_y}{\partial y} + \frac{\partial \tilde{u}_z}{\partial z}\right) + \frac{D\tilde{\rho}_A}{D\theta} + \frac{\partial \tilde{I}_{Ax}}{\partial x} + \frac{\partial \tilde{I}_{Ay}}{\partial y} + \frac{\partial \tilde{I}_{Az}}{\partial z} = 0 \tag{32-34}$$

This equation is analogous to Eq. (9-18), but the generation term $\tilde{r}_A$ has been omitted. Equation (32-31) applies only to nonreacting systems, for $\Sigma\tilde{r}_i$ is not in general zero; Σr_i is always zero. If $\tilde{\rho}$ is constant, Eq. (32-32) holds, and we also have

$$\tilde{I}_{Ax} = -D_{AB}\frac{\partial \tilde{\rho}_A}{\partial x} \tag{32-35}$$

This equation is the equivalent of Eq. (31-1); similar relations hold for the other two coordinate directions. For a system of constant molal density, with no reaction occurring, Eq. (32-34) can be written as

$$\frac{D\tilde{\rho}_A}{D\theta} = D_{AB}\left(\frac{\partial^2 \tilde{\rho}_A}{\partial x^2} + \frac{\partial^2 \tilde{\rho}_A}{\partial y^2} + \frac{\partial^2 \tilde{\rho}_A}{\partial z^2}\right) \tag{32-36}$$

which is analogous to Eq. (9-22).

For one-dimensional steady flow in the y direction, Eq. (32-36) becomes

$$\tilde{u} \frac{d\bar{\rho}_A}{dy} = D_{AB} \frac{d}{dy} \frac{d\bar{\rho}_A}{dy} \qquad (32\text{-}37)$$

Integration yields

$$\tilde{u}\bar{\rho}_A = D_{AB} \frac{d\bar{\rho}_A}{dy} + \text{const} \qquad (32\text{-}38)$$

The constant is equal to the molal flux $\tilde{N}_A$, so that Eq. (32-38) is equivalent to Eq. (32-18).

Application of the Differential Balances.   The simultaneous solution of the differential mass, energy, and momentum equations for a multicomponent system can be exceedingly complicated.   For instance, in a gaseous system Eq. (32-36) might be useful, but the Navier-Stokes equations are expressed in terms of mass units, not molal units.   It would be necessary to use Eq. (9-18), for variable ρ, with equations similar to Eq. (11-50), rather than the Navier-Stokes equations for constant ρ [Eqs. (11-52) to (11-54)].   Fortunately, in most practical situations the solutions of the Navier-Stokes equations which hold when no mass transfer is taking place are not appreciably affected by the occurrence of mass transfer.   For instance, the parabolic velocity profile associated with laminar flow in a tube is little changed if the walls of the tube are made of some soluble material which diffuses toward the centerline.   For mass transfer, Eq. (9-22) can be used with solutions of gases for which the variation of concentrations never becomes large enough to have an appreciable effect on the density.   However, in an analysis of a flowing gaseous reaction system involving large changes in concentrations, appreciable errors may be made if the secondary effects omitted in simpler situations are not considered.

Similar remarks can be made about the use of Eqs. (10-11) and (10-14) for systems in which mass transfer is taking place.   Fluxes of energy caused by diffusion have been omitted from these equations, but these effects can be ignored in many common situations.   Such effects will, however, be studied in Chap. 38.   For a binary system, the velocities appearing refer to the mass average velocity.

Diffusion of A through Stagnant B

In the situation illustrated in Fig. 32-1, water vapor is diffusing at a constant rate from the liquid surface up through the layer of stagnant air in the tube.   The air is not moving with respect to fixed axes, so $N_B = \tilde{N}_B = 0$.   Since we are dealing with gases for which $\bar{\rho}$ is constant, we use Eq. (32-18) and write it with $\tilde{N}_B = 0$:

$$\tilde{N}_A = \tilde{I}_A + \tilde{N}_A \tilde{x}_A \qquad (32\text{-}39a)$$

$$\tilde{N}_A = \frac{\tilde{I}_A}{1 - \tilde{x}_A} \qquad (32\text{-}39b)$$

Equation (31-1) is next substituted into Eq. (32-39b) to give

$$\tilde{N}_A = -\frac{D_{AB}\tilde{\rho}}{1 - \tilde{x}_A} \frac{d\tilde{x}_A}{dy} \qquad (32\text{-}40)$$

This equation can be integrated between 0 and L and $\tilde{x}_{Ao}$ and $\tilde{x}_{AL}$ to give

$$\tilde{N}_A \int_0^L dy = -D_{AB}\tilde{\rho} \int_{\tilde{x}_{Ao}}^{\tilde{x}_{AL}} \frac{d\tilde{x}_A}{1 - \tilde{x}_A} \qquad (32\text{-}41)$$

and

$$\tilde{N}_A = \frac{D_{AB}\tilde{\rho}}{L} \ln \frac{1 - \tilde{x}_{AL}}{1 - \tilde{x}_{Ao}} \qquad (32\text{-}42)$$

or

$$\tilde{N}_A = \frac{D_{AB}\tilde{\rho}}{L} \ln \frac{\tilde{x}_{BL}}{\tilde{x}_{Bo}} \qquad (32\text{-}43)$$

An equivalent form of Eq. (32-43) is

$$\tilde{N}_A = \frac{D_{AB}\tilde{\rho} \ln (\tilde{x}_{BL}/\tilde{x}_{Bo})}{L(\tilde{x}_{BL} - \tilde{x}_{Bo})} (\tilde{x}_{Ao} - \tilde{x}_{AL}) \qquad (32\text{-}44)$$

A logarithmic mean mole fraction is defined by

$$\tilde{x}_{B,lm} = \frac{\tilde{x}_{BL} - \tilde{x}_{Bo}}{\ln (\tilde{x}_{BL}/\tilde{x}_{Bo})} \qquad (32\text{-}45)$$

so that Eq. (32-44) can be written as

$$\tilde{N}_A = \frac{D_{AB}\tilde{\rho}}{L\tilde{x}_{B,lm}} (\tilde{x}_{Ao} - \tilde{x}_{AL}) \qquad (32\text{-}46)$$

This equation has the familiar form in which a flux equals a coefficient multiplied by a concentration difference. A mass-transfer coefficient $k_{\tilde{x}}$ can be defined by

$$\tilde{N}_A = k_{\tilde{x}}(\tilde{x}_{Ao} - \tilde{x}_{AL}) \qquad (32\text{-}47)$$

and

$$k_{\tilde{x}} = \frac{D_{AB}\tilde{\rho}}{L\tilde{x}_{B,lm}} \qquad (32\text{-}48)$$

For dilute solutions of A, $\tilde{x}_{B,lm}$ is approximately unity. Since $D_{AB}\tilde{\rho}$ does not vary with pressure for ideal gases, $k_{\tilde{x}}$ is independent of pressure. The preceding derivation can also be done in terms of partial pressures, beginning with Eq. (31-1), in the form

$$\tilde{I}_A = -\frac{D_{AB}\tilde{\rho}}{p} \frac{d\overline{p}_A}{dy} = \frac{-D_{AB}}{RT} \frac{d\overline{p}_A}{dy} \qquad (32\text{-}49)$$

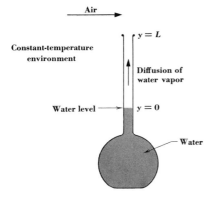

Air →

Constant-temperature
environment

y = L

Diffusion of
water vapor

Water level → y = 0

Water

Fig. 32-1. *Diffusion of water vapor through a stagnant film of air.*

It is left to the reader to obtain equations analogous to Eqs. (32-40) to (32-48) in terms of partial pressures.

Gas-phase diffusivities have been measured experimentally using an arrangement similar to the one shown in Fig. 32-1. We shall refer again to Eq. (32-47) in Chap. 33 in connection with the definition of mass-transfer coefficients.

Example 32-1

An apparatus of the type shown in Fig. 32-1 is used for the experimental determination of the diffusivity of a vapor through gas. For the air-water system, calculate the value of D_{AB} from the following information.

The entire apparatus is enclosed in a constant-temperature environment at 130°F and 1 atm, and the air is circulated over a desiccant so that the concentration of water vapor in the air is zero. It is assumed that there is no convective mixing in the tube above the level of the water. If 29 hr is required for the level to fall from 5 to 6 in. below the top of the tube, what is the diffusivity in the water-air system at 130°F?

The molal flux $\tilde{N}_A$ is related to the rate at which the water level falls by

$$\tilde{N}_A = \frac{\tilde{\rho}_{AL}\, dL}{d\theta} \tag{1}$$

where $\tilde{\rho}_{AL}$ = molal density of liquid water
L = length of diffusion path

The flux is also given by Eq. (32-46), which was derived for steady-state diffusion. The path for diffusion increases in length by only 20 per cent in 29 hr, so steady-state diffusion can be assumed. Thus we write

$$\tilde{\rho}_{AL}\, \frac{dL}{d\theta} = \frac{D_{AB}\tilde{\rho}(\tilde{x}_{Ao} - \tilde{x}_{AL})}{L\tilde{x}_{B.lm}} \tag{2}$$

In this equation $\tilde{x}_{Ao}$ is the mole fraction water vapor in the gas just above the water level, and $\tilde{x}_{AL}$ is measured at the outlet of the tube. Equation (2) is now integrated from $\theta = 0$ to $\theta = \theta$ and from $L = L_o$ to $L = L$:

$$\int_0^\theta d\theta = \frac{\tilde{\rho}_{AL}\tilde{x}_{B.lm}}{\tilde{\rho}D_{AB}(\tilde{x}_{Ao} - \tilde{x}_{AL})} \int_{L_o}^L L\, dL \tag{3}$$

This equation is solved for D_{AB} to give

$$D_{AB} = \frac{\tilde{\rho}_{AL}\tilde{x}_{B,lm}}{\theta\tilde{\rho}(\tilde{x}_{Ao} - \tilde{x}_{AL})} \frac{L - L_o{}^2}{2} \tag{4}$$

In the present problem we have

$$\tilde{\rho}_{AL} = 61.6/18 = 3.42 \text{ lb moles/cu ft}$$

$$\tilde{\rho} = \frac{p}{RT} = \frac{1}{(0.729)(590)} = 0.00233 \text{ lb mole/cu ft}$$

$$\tilde{x}_{AL} = 0$$
$$\tilde{x}_{Ao} = 2.22/14.70 = 0.1512$$

$$\tilde{x}_{B,lm} = \frac{1 - 0.849}{\ln(1/0.849)} = 0.925$$

$$L = \tfrac{5}{12} \text{ ft}$$
$$L_o = \tfrac{6}{12} \text{ ft}$$
$$\theta = 29 \text{ hr}$$

When these quantities are substituted into Eq. (4), it is found that D_{AB} equals 1.19 sq ft/hr.

Example 32-2

We consider the diffusion of salt (NaCl) through water in an apparatus similar to the one shown in Fig. 32-1. The equipment is maintained at 68°F, and the bulb contains a quantity of salt crystals. It is assumed that the liquid in the bulb is well mixed and that there is no eddy mixing in the diffusion tube. Thus the concentration at the lower end of the tube is constant; it is a saturated solution of salt in water at 68°F. The water surrounding the tube contains a negligible amount of salt.

The mechanism of the diffusion of an electrolyte in water is complicated and has been extensively studied. Although the different ions may tend to travel at different rates, the requirement of electrical neutrality makes it possible to regard the diffusion of a single salt as a diffusion of salt molecules. The diffusivity is a function of concentration; Reid and Sherwood [1] give a curve of the diffusivity of salt in water versus concentration. The variation is rather small; we choose a value of D_{AB} at 68°F as 1.35×10^{-5} sq cm/sec, or 5.22×10^{-5} sq ft/hr.

As the solid salt goes into solution to replace the salt which has diffused out of the tube, the volume of the solid phase decreases. There must be an inward flow of solution to fill this volume. The analysis is started from Eq. (32-20), which is convenient for a system of constant density,

$$N_A = J_A + (N_A + N_B)x_A \tag{1}$$

which can be written as

$$N_A = -D_{AB}\rho \frac{dx_A}{dy} + (N_A + N_B)x_A \tag{2}$$

The flux of solution inward must cause a volumetric flow just equal to the volume decrease caused by the dissolution of the salt:

$$\frac{N_A + N_B}{\rho} = \frac{-N_A}{\rho_{AS}} \tag{3}$$

[1] R. C. Reid and T. K. Sherwood, "The Properties of Gases and Liquids," p. 294, McGraw-Hill Book Company, Inc., New York, 1958.

in which ρ_{AS} is the density of solid salt.   Equation (3) is combined with Eq. (2) to give

$$N_A = \frac{-D_{AB}\rho}{1 + Kx_A}\frac{dx_A}{dy} \tag{4}$$

in which K equals ρ/ρ_{AS}.   We next integrate:

$$N_A \int_0^L dy = -D_{AB}\rho \int_{x_{Ao}}^{x_{AL}} \frac{dx_A}{1 + Kx_A} \tag{5}$$

and get

$$N_A = \frac{D_{AB}\rho_{AS}}{L} \ln \frac{1 + Kx_{Ao}}{1 + Kx_{AL}} \tag{6}$$

Equation (6) is analogous to Eq. (32-42).

If the length of the tube is 6 in., we can calculate N_A from Eq. (6):

$$N_A = \frac{(5.22 \times 10^{-5})(135.0)}{0.5} \ln \frac{1 + (68.7/135.0)(0.265)}{1}$$

$$= 0.00178 \text{ lb salt/(hr)(sq ft)}$$

Data on density and solubility are from Perry, pp. 125, 182, and 198.   As salt diffuses out at $N_A = 0.00178$ lb/(hr)(sq ft), water diffuses inward at $N_B = -0.00269$ lb/(hr)(sq ft), as can be calculated from Eq. (3).

Equimolal Counterdiffusion

If a mole of B diffuses to the left for every mole of A that diffuses to the right, $\tilde{N}_A = -\tilde{N}_B$ and Eq. (32-18) becomes simply

$$\tilde{N}_A = \tilde{I}_A = -D_{AB}\tilde{\rho}\frac{d\tilde{x}_A}{dy} \tag{32-50}$$

For steady state this equation can be integrated to yield

$$\tilde{N}_A = \frac{D_{AB}\tilde{\rho}}{L}(\tilde{x}_{Ao} - \tilde{x}_{AL}) \tag{32-51}$$

We shall see in a later chapter that this equation is useful in describing the rate of mass transfer in distillation problems.   An energy balance often requires that 1 mole of A diffuse to a liquid surface, condense, and liberate just enough heat to evaporate 1 mole of B, which diffuses away from the liquid surface.

Another case in which equimolal counterdiffusion occurs is in the interdiffusion of two gases.   Consider a cylinder with a transverse partition at the center dividing the vessel into two parts.   The space on either side of the partition is occupied by a different gas at the same pressure and temperature.   If the partition is now removed, the two gases will interdiffuse at equal molal rates, for the molal density $\tilde{\rho}$ remains constant.   Equation (32-50) applies at any instant.

If the two interdiffusing components were liquids of essentially equal densities, we should have $N_A = -N_B$ and also

$$N_A = J_A = -D_{AB}\rho \frac{dx_A}{dy} \tag{32-52}$$

Equation (32-50) or (32-52) cannot be integrated directly for this situation, since N_A and dx_A/dy are functions of both position and time. Rather, the differential balance must be used for this unsteady-state problem. Equation (32-36) reduces to

$$\frac{\partial \bar{\rho}_A}{\partial \theta} = D_{AB} \frac{\partial^2 \bar{\rho}_A}{\partial y^2} \tag{32-53}$$

for the gaseous system, and Eq. (9-22) reduces to

$$\frac{\partial \rho_A}{\partial \theta} = D_{AB} \frac{\partial^2 \rho_A}{\partial y^2} \tag{32-54}$$

for the liquid system.   The boundary values pertinent to this problem can be specified, and the solution obtained by the method of the separation of the variables illustrated in Example 21-2.   The interdiffusion of two fluids described above is analogous to the heat-transfer problem of calculating the temperature distribution as a function of position and time in two conducting plates, initially at different uniform temperatures and suddenly brought into contact.

In order to study a problem in unsteady-state diffusion without introducing any new mathematics, let us consider the following example, which is the analog of Example 21-2.

Example 32-3

A slab of porous solid ½ in. thick is soaked in pure ethanol.   The void space in the solid occupies 50 per cent of its volume.   The pores are fine, so that molecular diffusion can take place through the liquid in the passages; there is no convective mixing.   The effective diffusivity of the system ethanol-water in the pores is one-tenth that in the free liquid.

If the slab is placed in a large well-agitated reservoir of pure water at 77°F, how long will it take for the mass fraction of ethanol at the center of the slab to fall to 0.009? Assume that there is no resistance to mass transfer in the water phase and that the concentration of ethanol in the water, and thus at the surface of the slab, is constant at zero.

Since the densities of alcohol and water differ by only 20 per cent, we shall assume that ρ is constant; it is sufficiently accurate to use Eq. (32-54):

$$\frac{\partial \rho_A}{\partial \theta} = D_{AB} \frac{\partial^2 \rho_A}{\partial y^2} \tag{1}$$

or

$$\frac{\partial x_A}{\partial \theta} = D_{AB} \frac{\partial^2 x_A}{\partial y^2} \tag{2}$$

These equations imply that D_{AB} is constant, whereas Table 31-2 shows that it varies greatly with concentration.   In order to avoid mathematical complication we shall assume D_{AB} is constant at an average value of 1.0 sq cm/sec.   During most of the time spent in achieving a low ethanol concentration at the center of the slab, the ethanol concentration in the slab is quite low.   Therefore an average value of D_{AB} corresponding to a small x_A has been chosen.

We now make the following substitutions:

$$\tau = \frac{D_{AB}\theta}{y_o{}^2}$$

$$Y = x_A$$

$$n = \frac{y}{y_o}$$

The distance y is measured normal to the center of the slab; y_o is half the thickness of the slab.

By substitution, Eq. (2) becomes

$$\frac{\partial Y}{\partial \tau} = \frac{\partial^2 Y}{\partial n^2} \tag{3}$$

This is the same as Eq. (2) of Example 21-2.   The boundary conditions on $Y(n,\tau)$ are as follows:

$$\frac{\partial Y}{\partial n}(0,\tau) = 0$$

$$Y(1,\tau) = 0$$
$$Y(n,0) = 1.0$$

These are identical with the boundary conditions of Example 21-2, so we can write the solution immediately from the results of that example, as follows:

$$Y = \sum_{i=1}^{i=\infty} \frac{-2(-1)^i}{\frac{2i-1}{2}\pi} \exp\left[\frac{-(2i-1)^2\pi^2\tau}{4}\right] \cos\left(\frac{2i-1}{2}\right)\pi n \tag{4}$$

For $n = 0$ and $Y = 0.009$, it is found that $\tau = 2.01$.   Thus we have

$$\theta = \frac{\tau y_o{}^2}{D_{AB}}$$

$$= \frac{(2.01)(\frac{1}{48})^2}{(\frac{1}{10})(1.0)(3.87)}$$

$$= 0.0217 \text{ hr, or } 1.30 \text{ min}$$

The concentration profiles at various times can be calculated from Eq. (4).   Their appearance is the same as the curves shown in Fig. 21-2, if the ordinate is interpreted as the mass fraction water.

A great variety of problems in heat conduction have been solved in the literature.[1] The analogy to molecular diffusion is such that the solutions of most of these problems can be used to find immediately the solution of the corresponding diffusion problems. Solutions to many problems in molecular diffusion are given by Crank.[2]

---

[1] See, for example, H. S. Carslaw and J. C. Jaeger, "Conduction of Heat in Solids," 2d ed., Clarendon Press, Oxford, 1959.

[2] J. Crank, "Mathematics of Diffusion," Clarendon Press, Oxford, 1956.

Thermal Diffusion

It has been mentioned that in addition to ordinary molecular diffusion there exist thermal diffusion, pressure diffusion, and forced diffusion. If two regions in a mixture are maintained at different temperatures so that there is a flux of heat, it has been found that a concentration gradient is set up. In a binary mixture, one kind of molecule tends to travel toward the hot region and the other kind toward the cold region. This is called the Soret effect. Usually this effect has a negligible influence on mass transfer, but it is useful in the separation of certain mixtures. An analogous phenomenon, called the Dufour effect, is the tendency toward the generation of a temperature gradient in conjunction with mass transfer arising from a concentration gradient.

Pressure diffusion occurs when there is a gradient of pressure in a fluid mixture, as in a deep closed well or in a closed tube which is rotated around an axis perpendicular to the axis of the tube. The lighter component tends to travel toward the region of lower pressure, i.e., the top of the well or the end of the tube near the axis of rotation. The ultracentrifuge operates according to the principles of pressure diffusion.

Forced diffusion is caused by the action of an external force other than gravity on the molecules. This external force must be such that it acts to a different degree on different species. An example is the diffusion of the ions in an electrolyte in an electric field.

As a result of the concentration gradient generated by one of the above phenomena, ordinary diffusion occurs in a direction opposite that of the other kind of diffusion. In many situations a steady state is reached at which the flux by ordinary diffusion just balances that by one of the types described above, so that the properties of the system at a given point remain constant with time. As an example of such a case, we consider the following example of thermal diffusion.

The two bulbs shown in Fig. 32-2 are connected by a capillary tube made of nonconducting material. The gas in the tube is stagnant, i.e., there is no convective mixing, whereas the gas in the bulbs is well mixed by convection. The flux caused by thermal diffusion in a binary mixture is obtained from irreversible thermodynamics[1] as

$$J_{AT} = -D_{ABT} \frac{1}{T} \frac{dT}{dy} \tag{32-55}$$

Although there is a temperature gradient from one bulb to another, at

---

[1] A concise, readable introduction to this subject is the book by K. A. Denbigh, "Thermodynamics of the Steady State," Methuen & Co., Ltd., London, 1951.

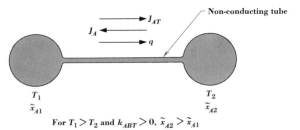

For $T_1 > T_2$ and $k_{ABT} > 0$, $\tilde{x}_{A2} > \tilde{x}_{A1}$

Fig. 32-2.   Thermal diffusion in a binary mixture at steady state.

steady state the temperature at any point is constant.   There is also no net flow of A or B from one bulb to the other, so

$$N_A = 0 \qquad\qquad (32\text{-}56)$$

or

$$J_{AT} + J_A = 0 \qquad\qquad (32\text{-}57)$$

Thus we have

$$D_{ABT} \frac{1}{T} \frac{dT}{dy} = -D_{AB}\rho \frac{dx_A}{dy} \qquad\qquad (32\text{-}58)$$

However, it is customary to express the composition in terms of mole fractions rather than mass fractions, so we use Eqs. (32-27), (32-12), and (31-1) to obtain

$$D_{ABT} \frac{1}{T} \frac{dT}{dy} = \frac{-D_{AB}\tilde{\rho}^2 M_A M_B}{\rho} \frac{d\tilde{x}_A}{dy} \qquad\qquad (32\text{-}59)$$

A thermal-diffusion ratio K_{ABT} is defined by

$$K_{ABT} = \frac{D_{ABT}\rho}{D_{AB}\tilde{\rho}^2 M_A M_B} \qquad\qquad (32\text{-}60)$$

so that Eq. (32-59) can be written as

$$\frac{d\tilde{x}_A}{dy} = -K_{ABT} \frac{1}{T} \frac{dT}{dy} \qquad\qquad (32\text{-}61)$$

Although K_{ABT} is actually a complicated function of temperature, an estimate of the relation between the temperature and concentration profiles can be obtained by the integration of Eq. (32-61) with K_{ABT} constant. The result is

$$\tilde{x}_{A2} - \tilde{x}_{A1} = K_{ABT} \ln \frac{T_1}{T_2} \qquad\qquad (32\text{-}62)$$

The thermal-diffusion ratio may be evaluated at a mean temperature in this approximate equation.   The quantity K_{ABT} can be either positive or negative, depending on the particular system under consideration.   A positive value of K_{ABT} means that component A tends to accumulate in the colder part of the system. The thermal-diffusion ratio is also a function of composition, but $\tilde{x}_{A2} - \tilde{x}_{A1}$ is usually so small that the variation can be ignored in the integration of Eq. (32-61). A few values of K_{ABT} are listed in Table 32-1.

Table 32-1. Some Values† of the Thermal-diffusion Ratio K_{ABT}

System A-B	Temperature, °C	Composition $\tilde{x}_A$	$100 K_{ABT}$
He-Ne..................	−68	0.538	7.65
	57	0.538	7.82
	92	0.538	7.83
He-Ar..................	57	0.10	2.50
	57	0.30	6.60
	57	0.50	9.31
H₂-He..................	57	0.50	−4.81
He-N₂..................	−13	0.345	8.31
H₂-Ar..................	−15	0.47	−6.35
H₂-N₂..................	−9	0.42	7.49
H₂-CO..................	−27	0.53	7.38
H₂-CO₂.................	27	0.53	6.89

† From J. O. Hirschfelder, C. F. Curtiss, and R. B. Bird, "Molecular Theory of Gases and Liquids," pp. 584–585, John Wiley & Sons, Inc., New York, 1954.

Mass Transfer with Chemical Reaction

Diffusion in solid catalyst pores to the surface of catalyst pellets and at other interphase boundaries has an important effect on the design of certain chemical reactors. The study of the interrelation between diffusion and chemical reaction is deferred to Chap. 43. In the intervening chapters we shall study more of the fundamentals of mass transfer and their effect on physical separation operations.

PROBLEMS

32-1. One gram of iodine is placed in a bulb like that illustrated in Fig. 32-1. If the tube through which diffusion takes place is 3 in. long and $\frac{1}{16}$ in. in diameter, how long will it take the solid to disappear at 85°C? The air in the bulb is assumed to be saturated with iodine, and the iodine concentration in the surrounding atmosphere is zero.

32-2. If the bulb of Prob. 32-1 is initially filled with methanol to the outlet of the tube, how long will it take for the methanol level to fall to the bottom of the tube, i.e., 3 in.? The surrounding fluid is air at 25°C.

32-3. A porous sphere of $\frac{1}{8}$ in. diameter is saturated with methanol. It is dropped into a large tank of pure water at 25°C. If it is assumed that the interdiffusion process is controlled by the rate of diffusion within the sphere, calculate the time required to remove 99 per cent of the methanol. The effective diffusivity is one-tenth of the ordinary molecular diffusivity.

The solution may be obtained by the use of the graphs in Perry, p. 462, which have been referred to in Chap. 21.

32-4. The vapor pressure of naphthalene at 60°F is 0.0363 mm Hg. Find the rate of evaporation of naphthalene from a sphere ½ in. in diameter at 60°F if the rate is so slow that the sphere diameter can be assumed to be constant. The sphere will be considered to be surrounded by an infinite stagnant mass of air at the same temperature. Express your answer in mass per cent evaporated per day with reference to the mass of the sphere when its diameter is ½ in. The density of naphthalene is 71.9 lb/cu ft.

CONVECTIVE MASS-TRANSFER
COEFFICIENTS
33

Mass Transfer between Phases

Mass transfer may occur across a single phase, as, for example, in a gaseous system in which a substance evaporates at one interface and condenses at another interface. Mass transfer may also occur by a coupled process of transfer of a substance from the interior of one phase to the phase boundary and then into the interior of a second phase. If interfacial resistances are neglected, the total resistance to mass transfer in the first example is the resistance of the single gaseous phase. In the second example the total resistance is the sum of the resistances of the two phases which are in series. These phases are usually either two immiscible liquids or a gas and a liquid.

To solve mass-transfer problems the boundary conditions must be known. The boundaries of the mass-transfer systems are either the phase interfaces or arbitrarily chosen average conditions within the phases. Regardless of how the mathematical boundaries for solving the problem are chosen, phase equilibrium exists at the interface.[1] Although a concentration difference of the diffusing component exists across every interface, the difference is not necessarily a driving force for mass transfer. The compositions at an interface where equilibrium exists are not independent variables, but are fixed in accordance with the principles of physical equilibrium. The analogous situation in heat transfer is much easier to visualize. Thermal

---

[1] At unusually high mass fluxes there is evidence that the adjacent phases are not in equilibrium. This effect is equivalent to an interfacial resistance to mass transfer. An interfacial resistance may also be caused by the presence of impurities which may be segregated at the interface.

equilibrium between adjoining phases is implicitly assumed when we say that adjacent phases have the same temperature at the interface. In momentum transfer we usually assume that two phases have the same velocity at the interface.

The rate equations are written with composition difference as the driving force, and no difficulties are encountered if the rate equation is written for a single phase. However, if an over-all rate equation is desired, the difference in the actual compositions of two phases will not be an adequate expression for the driving force. Such a difference usually occurs even when the phases are in equilibrium. To avoid this difficulty, the composition of one of the phases is expressed in terms of an equilibrium composition, i.e., the composition the other phase would have if it were in equilibrium with the first. Thus the over-all driving force is expressed in units of composition based on one phase only.

Phase Equilibrium

Equilibrium in a multiphase system is subject to the restrictions of the phase rule. These restrictions are expressed in the equation

$$P + V = C + 2 \qquad (33\text{-}1)$$

where P = number of phases at equilibrium

V = number of variants or degrees of freedom of system

If no chemical reactions are occurring in the system, the quantity C is simply the number of chemical compounds or free elements present. If chemical reactions do occur, then C is the number of chemical compounds and free elements minus the number of chemical equilibria or other restrictions placed on the chemical behavior of the system.

The phase rule can be regarded as analogous to an algebraic system of variables and independent equations. The number of variables minus the number of equations determines how many variables may be assigned arbitrary values. This is comparable with the number of variants in a physical system. In an algebraic system when the number of variables and the number of equations are equal, no variable can be arbitrarily specified. An example of this in phase equilibrium is the occurrence of a "triple point," i.e., a situation in which a single pure compound exists as three phases in physical equilibrium. According to the phase rule, V has a value of zero in this instance, which means that there can be only one set of conditions at which these three phases coexist. No variable (such as pressure or temperature) may be altered without causing the disappearance of one of the phases.

The phase rule does not tell us the numerical values of any of the variables, nor does it tell us the forms of any of the relations which exist among variables. Nevertheless, it is of great value to the engineer and scientist in planning experiments in which numerical values are to be measured and analytical relations deduced. It is of equal value in chemical-plant design in that it indicates the number of process variables that can be controlled independently in any system at equilibrium. For example, in gas-absorption operations a constituent is usually absorbed from a gas stream by a liquid. Such a system, if it consists of three chemical compounds and exists as two phases, may be seen from Eq. (33-1) to have three variables at equilibrium. In process terms this means that pressure, temperature, and the concentration in one phase of the diffusing component may be arbitrarily specified.

Distillation operations may involve only binary mixtures, or there may be many components. In a binary, two-phase system only two variables exist. This means that if the pressure and temperature are fixed, the compositions of the equilibrium phases may not be varied. It is common in binary-distillation calculations to specify pressure and one composition variable. In such circumstances, the temperature is fixed and may be found by performing appropriate calculations.

In humidification operations air may be considered as a single chemical constituent since it enters no chemical reactions and always retains the same proportions of its various constituents in such operations. Therefore, in humidification, there are, in effect, two chemical constituents to be considered—air and water. Because there are also two phases to be considered, the number of variables is two. Most such systems operate at atmospheric pressure so that only a single variable remains to be controlled. Thus a choice of temperature automatically fixes the concentration of water in the gas phase (the humidity) when equilibrium exists.

Equilibrium Relations

It is desirable, at this point, to review some of the quantitative equations for calculating equilibrium compositions. These and many other useful equilibrium equations can be found in books on physical chemistry. It is our intention in this chapter to discuss only certain simple equations relating to vapor-liquid equilibrium and gas absorption. Other relations will be reviewed in later chapters as needed.

The partial pressure of a component in a gas phase is given by definition as

$$\bar{p}_A = \tilde{y}_A p \tag{33-2}$$

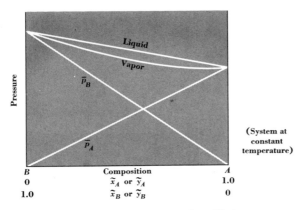

(System at
constant
temperature)

*Fig. 33-1.   Partial pressures and equilibrium
compositions for a system containing an ideal gas
and an ideal liquid solution.*

where $\bar{p}_A$ = partial pressure of component A

$\tilde{y}_A$ = mole fraction of component A in gas phase[1]

p = total pressure on system

This definition applies whether the gas is ideal or nonideal. Because the sum of the mole fractions must be unity, it follows that the sum of the partial pressures always equals the total pressure.

Raoult's law is a relation often used for determining the partial pressure of a constituent in a liquid solution. It is expressed as

$$\bar{p}_A = \tilde{x}_A p_A \tag{33-3}$$

where $\tilde{x}_A$ = mole fraction of component A in liquid

p_A = vapor pressure of substance A at temperature of system

This equation is valid when the gas and liquid phases behave as an ideal gas and an ideal solution, respectively. The concept of the ideal gas is familiar to most students, but the ideal solution is less so. It will suffice here to say that mixtures of nonpolar molecules of the same chemical type and approximately the same size approach ideal-solution behavior; an example is the adjacent members of a homologous series. The heat effect and volume change of mixing are zero for an ideal solution. If the partial pressures of both components are plotted as a function of mole fraction at constant temperature, as shown in Fig. 33-1, they are represented by straight lines with a slope equal to the vapor pressure. Raoult's law

[1] The symbols x_A and $\tilde{x}_A$ have until now been used to express composition in any phase. Henceforth, they will refer specifically to the liquid phase, and y_A and $\tilde{y}_A$ will refer to the vapor phase.

Fig. 33-2.   Partial pressure of sulfur dioxide in a solution of sulfur dioxide and water at 20°C.

usually matches experimental data best for components present in high concentrations.

Henry's law is a general form of which Raoult's law is a special case. It is expressed as

$$\bar{p}_A = \tilde{x}_A H_A \tag{33-4}$$

which simply expresses a linear relation between partial pressure and composition.   The quantity H_A is a constant which is usually found experimentally.   In the special case in which Raoult's law applies, the Henry's law constant H_A becomes the vapor pressure of component A.   Henry's law usually applies to the low-concentration range, as is illustrated by the experimental data in Fig. 33-2.   This law is of value in the design of gas-absorption systems because many of them operate with dilute solutions.

Example 33-1

A mixture of benzene and toluene exists as a gas-liquid system in equilibrium at 80°C. The gas phase contains 65 mole per cent benzene and 35 mole per cent toluene.   Find the total pressure on the system and the composition of the liquid phase, assuming the liquid to be an ideal solution and the gas to be ideal.   The vapor pressures of benzene and toluene at 80°C are 756 and 287 mm Hg, respectively.

We designate benzene as component A and toluene as component B.   The partial pressures, from Raoult's law, are

$$\bar{p}_A = 756\tilde{x}_A \tag{1}$$

$$\bar{p}_B = 287\tilde{x}_B \tag{2}$$

From the definition of partial pressure we write

$$\bar{p}_A = 0.65p \tag{3}$$

$$\bar{p}_B = 0.35p \tag{4}$$

Combining Eqs. (1) and (3) and (2) and (4), we obtain

$$756\tilde{x}_A = 0.65p \tag{5}$$

$$287\tilde{x}_B = 0.35p \tag{6}$$

In addition, we know the equation

$$\tilde{x}_A + \tilde{x}_B = 1 \tag{7}$$

Equations (5) to (7) are solved for the three variables:

$$\tilde{x}_A = 0.415$$
$$\tilde{x}_B = 0.585$$
$$p = 483 \text{ mm Hg}$$

Example 33-2

Derive equations for the equilibrium compositions of the gas and liquid in a system at constant temperature in which the two phases behave as an ideal gas and an ideal solution, respectively.

The two components are designated A and B. We write the partial pressures using Raoult's law.

$$\bar{p}_A = \tilde{x}_A p_A$$
$$\bar{p}_B = \tilde{x}_B p_B$$

The total pressure is the sum of the partial pressures.

$$p = \bar{p}_A + \bar{p}_B = \tilde{x}_A p_A + \tilde{x}_B p_B$$
$$= \tilde{x}_A p_A + (1 - \tilde{x}_A)p_B$$

Solving for $\tilde{x}_A$, we obtain

$$\tilde{x}_A = \frac{p - p_B}{p_A - p_B}$$

At a constant temperature the vapor pressures p_A and p_B are fixed. The liquid composition $\tilde{x}_A$ is therefore a linear function of the total pressure, as shown in Fig. 33-1; the total pressure ranges from $p = p_B$ at $\tilde{x}_A = 0$ to $p = p_A$ at $\tilde{x}_A = 1$. The vapor composition is found from the definition of partial pressure.

$$\bar{p}_A = \tilde{y}_A p = \tilde{x}_A p_A$$

from which we obtain

$$\tilde{y}_A = \frac{\tilde{x}_A p_A}{p}$$

$$= \frac{p_A}{p} \frac{p - p_B}{p_A - p_B}$$

Individual Mass-transfer Coefficients

The concept of the mass-transfer coefficient has already been discussed in Chap. 30 and coefficients defined in Eqs. (30-1) and (32-47). In this section we shall consider the mass-transfer coefficient in more detail.

Although the analogy between heat transfer and mass transfer has been useful for the solution of many mass-transfer problems, some basic differences often prevent us from making use of our knowledge of heat-transfer coefficients for predicting mass-transfer coefficients. One of these has to do with boundary conditions. In most heat-transfer systems where convective effects exist, heat is being transferred between a single-phase fluid and a solid. In most convective mass-transfer systems, however, two fluid phases are in contact and mass transfer occurs between the fluid phases. In the heat-transfer system the fluid has zero velocity at the interface and an adjacent laminar sublayer exists; in the mass-transfer system the velocity at the interface between the fluids is probably not zero and the existence of a laminar sublayer is often unlikely. The difference in flow behavior has the practical result that much of the experimental information available on heat transfer is of little value in mass transfer, and vice versa. An additional complication arises in the analysis of transfer rates between two fluids in direct contact, for the average interfacial area is a function of flow conditions and is difficult or impossible to measure. There are some applications, however, in which heat and mass transfer occur in similar systems, and some in which they occur simultaneously. An example of the latter is spray drying, an operation in which a liquid spray is injected into a hot-air stream; heat and mass are transferred between adjacent fluid phases. The operation of a catalytic reactor represents a system in which heat and mass are transferred simultaneously between a fluid phase and a solid surface. When possible, in succeeding discussions on mass transfer, the reader will be referred to a previous discussion of heat-transfer coefficients. Frequently, however, mass-transfer systems will be discussed which have no counterpart of interest in heat transfer.

If a mass-transfer system consists of a solute dissolving at a steady rate from a solid surface and diffusing into a liquid stream, we define the mass-transfer coefficient $k_{\tilde{x}}$ by the following equation, which is similar to Eq. (32-47):

$$\tilde{N}_A = k_{\tilde{x}}(\tilde{x}_{As} - \tilde{x}_A) \tag{33-5}$$

In this equation $\tilde{N}_A$ is the moles of solute A leaving the interface per unit time per unit area of interface. The mole fraction of solute in the liquid at the interface $\tilde{x}_{As}$ represents the composition the solution would have if it were in equilibrium with the solid solute at the temperature of the system. The quantity $\tilde{x}_A$ represents the composition expressed in terms of the mole fraction of solute at some point within the fluid phase. If the flow is of the type known as boundary-layer flow, $\tilde{x}_A$ would be chosen as the mole fraction of solute at the edge of the concentration boundary layer and would be written $\tilde{x}_{Ao}$. If, however, the flow were in a closed conduit, the value $\tilde{x}_A$ would be chosen as the mole fraction of solute at the mixing-cup concentration. (The mixing-cup concentration is the concentration if the stream were uniform. It is defined in a manner similar to the mixing-cup temperature.) The mass-transfer coefficient $k_{\tilde{x}}$ is usually expressed in the units lb moles/(hr)(sq ft). The subscript $\tilde{x}$ signifies that it applies to a liquid phase and must be used in conjunction with a driving force expressed in terms of mole fraction in the liquid phase.

Mass transfer at a steady rate from a solid interface to a gas stream is described by the equation

$$\tilde{N}_A = k_{\tilde{y}}(\tilde{y}_{As} - \tilde{y}_A) \tag{33-6}$$

The flux $\tilde{N}_A$ has the same units as in Eq. (33-5). The mole fraction of solute in the gas phase adjacent to the interface is $\tilde{y}_{As}$. This is assumed to be the composition that would occur at equilibrium at the same temperature and pressure. The quantity $\tilde{y}_A$ is usually either the mole fraction of solute at the edge of the concentration boundary layer or the mole fraction at the mixing-cup concentration. The mass-transfer coefficient $k_{\tilde{y}}$ has the same units as $k_{\tilde{x}}$, but as the subscript indicates, it must be used with a driving force expressed as mole fraction in the gas phase.

A system in which a solute is being transferred at a steady rate from a gas phase to a liquid phase can be described by two equations:

$$\tilde{N}_A = k_{\tilde{y}}(\tilde{y}_A - \tilde{y}_{As}) \tag{33-7}$$

$$\tilde{N}_A = k_{\tilde{x}}(\tilde{x}_{As} - \tilde{x}_A) \tag{33-8}$$

In a system of adjacent gas and liquid phases the values of $\tilde{y}_A$ and $\tilde{x}_A$ are most likely to be mole fractions at the mixing-cup concentrations of the respective phases.

Over-all Mass-transfer Coefficients

For interphase transfer it is often convenient to use an over-all mass-transfer coefficient, just as an over-all heat-transfer coefficient was employed in heat transfer. The over-all mass-transfer coefficient may be defined by either of the following equations:

$$\tilde{N}_A = K_{\tilde{y}}(\tilde{y}_A - \tilde{y}_A^*) \tag{33-9}$$

$$\tilde{N}_A = K_{\tilde{x}}(\tilde{x}_A^* - \tilde{x}_A) \tag{33-10}$$

The quantities $\tilde{y}_A^*$ and $\tilde{x}_A^*$ represent equilibrium concentrations. The quantity $\tilde{y}_A^*$ is the mole fraction of solute in a gas at equilibrium with a liquid of composition $\tilde{x}_A$. Likewise, $\tilde{x}_A^*$ is the mole fraction of solute in the liquid at equilibrium with a gas of composition $\tilde{y}_A$. Therefore $\tilde{y}_A - \tilde{y}_A^*$ and $\tilde{x}_A^* - \tilde{x}_A$ are expressions representing the over-all driving force for mass transfer between two fluid phases.

An equation relating the over-all mass-transfer coefficients to the coefficients for the individual phases can be found by rewriting Eqs. (33-7) and (33-8) as follows:

$$\tilde{y}_A - \tilde{y}_{As} = \frac{\tilde{N}_A}{k_{\tilde{y}}} \tag{33-11}$$

$$\tilde{x}_{As} - \tilde{x}_A = \frac{\tilde{N}_A}{k_{\tilde{x}}} \tag{33-12}$$

Equilibrium between the gas and liquid phases is assumed to follow Henry's law. If the partial pressure found from Eq. (33-4) is divided by the total pressure, we obtain

$$\tilde{y}_A = \frac{\tilde{x}_A H_A}{p} \tag{33-13}$$

The quantity H_A/p is designated as m, and Eq. (33-13) is written as

$$\tilde{y}_A = m\tilde{x}_A \tag{33-14}$$

At an interface $\tilde{y}_A$ and $\tilde{x}_A$ in Eq. (33-14) are written $\tilde{y}_{As}$ and $\tilde{x}_{As}$, and we assume that equilibrium exists at the interface. Therefore we write Eq. (33-12) as

$$\frac{\tilde{y}_{As}}{m} - \tilde{x}_A = \frac{\tilde{N}_A}{k_{\tilde{x}}} \tag{33-15}$$

and multiply by m to obtain

$$\tilde{y}_{As} - m\tilde{x}_A = \frac{\tilde{N}_A m}{k_{\tilde{x}}} \tag{33-16}$$

This expression is added to Eq. (33-11) to give

$$\tilde{y}_A - m\tilde{x}_A = \tilde{N}_A \left(\frac{1}{k_{\tilde{y}}} + \frac{m}{k_{\tilde{x}}} \right) \tag{33-17}$$

The term $m\tilde{x}_A$ represents the mole fraction of solute in a gas at equilibrium with a liquid of mole fraction $\tilde{x}_A$. Thus we recognize that $m\tilde{x}_A$ is identical with $\tilde{y}_A^*$. Making this substitution, we write Eq. (33-17) as

$$\tilde{y}_A - \tilde{y}_A^* = \tilde{N}_A \left(\frac{1}{k_{\tilde{y}}} + \frac{m}{k_{\tilde{x}}} \right) \tag{33-18}$$

The defining expression for $K_{\tilde{y}}$, Eq. (33-9), is written in similar fashion.

$$\tilde{y}_A - \tilde{y}_A^* = \frac{\tilde{N}_A}{K_{\tilde{y}}} \tag{33-19}$$

Fig. 33-3.   *Graph showing compositions at an interface between phases.*

By comparing Eqs. (33-18) and (33-19) we see that $K_{\tilde{y}}$ can be defined in terms of the coefficients for the individual phases as

$$K_{\tilde{y}} = \frac{1}{1/k_{\tilde{y}} + m/k_{\tilde{x}}} \tag{33-20}$$

By similar procedures we find an expression for $K_{\tilde{x}}$.

$$K_{\tilde{x}} = \frac{1}{1/k_{\tilde{x}} + 1/mk_{\tilde{y}}} \tag{33-21}$$

Even though the individual coefficients $k_{\tilde{y}}$ and $k_{\tilde{x}}$ may be constant throughout a system, the over-all coefficient may vary as a result of variation of m. The quantity m, as we have already seen, is a function of concentration, temperature, and total pressure; it is usually constant only for dilute solutions at a constant temperature in a column in which the fractional change in pressure is negligible.   As we shall show below, Eqs. (33-20) and (33-21) are not correct if the equilibrium line is curved, i.e., if m is not constant.

The discussion above is illustrated by Fig. 33-3.   From an over-all mass balance on a piece of contacting equipment, such as a gas-absorption tower, we shall find in Chap. 37 that there is an algebraic relation between the bulk-gas composition and the bulk-liquid composition at any horizontal section in a tower, i.e., at any value of $\tilde{x}_A$.   This relation is represented in Fig. 33-3 by the upper curve, called an operating line.   The position of this line depends on the compositions at the ends of the tower and on the flow rates of the two phases.

At the point P in Fig. 33-3, the gas and liquid compositions are $\tilde{y}_A$ and $\tilde{x}_A$, respectively.   The compositions at the interface, $\tilde{y}_{As}$ and $\tilde{x}_{As}$, are found by combining Eqs. (33-7) and (33-8) to give

$$-\frac{k_{\tilde{x}}}{k_{\tilde{y}}} = \frac{\tilde{y}_A - \tilde{y}_{As}}{\tilde{x}_A - \tilde{x}_{As}} \tag{33-22}$$

This equation is represented by a straight line of slope $-k_{\tilde{x}}/k_{\tilde{y}}$ passing through $\tilde{x}_A$, $\tilde{y}_A$ and $\tilde{x}_{As}$, $\tilde{y}_{As}$. Since the latter point is on the equilibrium line, the values of $\tilde{x}_{As}$ and $\tilde{y}_{As}$ are found by the construction shown in the figure. Also given in Fig. 33-3 are the composition $\tilde{y}_A^*$, which is in equilibrium with $\tilde{x}_A$, and the composition $\tilde{x}_A^*$, which is in equilibrium with $\tilde{y}_A$.

In the derivation of Eq. (33-20), $\tilde{x}_{As}$ was replaced by $\tilde{y}_{As}/m$ in Eq. (33-15). Thus the m appearing in Eqs. (33-16) *et seq.* is the value of m corresponding to $\tilde{x}_{As}$. In going from Eq. (33-17) to (33-18), $m\tilde{x}_A$ was replaced by $\tilde{y}_A^*$; this substitution is valid only if the m at $\tilde{x}_{As}$ is the same as the m at $\tilde{x}_A$. For a curved equilibrium line, these m's are not identical, and so Eqs. (33-20) and (33-21) are not correct.[1]

The above restrictions on the use of the over-all coefficient become irrelevant if it is approximately equal to one of the individual coefficients. For example, if $m/k_{\tilde{x}}$ is negligible in comparison with $1/k_{\tilde{y}}$, it is said that the gas-phase resistance is controlling and $K_{\tilde{y}}$ is the same as $k_{\tilde{y}}$. Note that it is not sufficient for m to be small or $k_{\tilde{x}}$ to be large; their *ratio* must be small compared with $1/k_{\tilde{y}}$.[†] Similar remarks apply to a situation for which the liquid-phase resistance is controlling and $K_{\tilde{x}}$ and $k_{\tilde{x}}$ are the same.

Although an over-all coefficient should not be used for systems with a curved equilibrium line, reference to the literature shows that such a coefficient is often the only one reported. It is almost impossible in two-fluid contactors to measure $\tilde{x}_{As}$ and $\tilde{y}_{As}$ experimentally and to calculate $k_{\tilde{y}}$, for example, directly from data on the rate of mass transfer between phases. Usually only $\tilde{x}_A$ and $\tilde{y}_A$ can be measured, and the individual resistances must be estimated indirectly. In heat transfer in a heat exchanger, the situation is more tractable, for it is possible to measure the analogous temperatures, which are those at the surfaces of the tube walls.

A justification for the use of over-all coefficients is the lack of precision of most data on mass transfer. Standard deviations of 20 to 30 per cent are not uncommon, so that minor errors introduced by the use of an over-all coefficient may not be significant. This lack of precision is not caused by carelessness, but by the difficulty of obtaining reproducible data on compositions and velocities in a device such as a packed absorption tower.

[1] This matter is discussed in some detail in T. K. Sherwood and R. L. Pigford' "Absorption and Extraction," 2d ed., p. 124, McGraw-Hill Book Company, Inc., New York, 1952.

[†] In many systems a chemical reaction occurs in the liquid phase. This does not, however, make m zero even when the equilibrium partial pressure of the solute is zero. The reason for this is that the solute may have to diffuse a significant distance into the liquid before reacting. Absorption with chemical reaction will be studied in Chap. 43.

Mass-transfer Coefficients and Bulk Flow

The characteristics of the mass-transfer coefficients which we have defined depend to some extent on whether they apply to a case for which $\tilde{N}_A = -\tilde{N}_B$ or to a case for which $\tilde{N}_B = 0$. The former case is encountered in adiabatic binary distillation, where an energy balance often results in the requirement that a mole of A be transferred in one direction for every mole of B transferred in the opposite direction. The latter case is encountered in gas absorption and liquid-liquid extraction, where the solute is transferred toward or away from the interface through the second component of the phase, which does not dissolve.

In order to discuss this situation clearly, we must define another mass-transfer coefficient $k_{\tilde{x}}^o$ (or $k_{\tilde{y}}^o$, k_{ρ}^o, etc.). This is the value which $k_{\tilde{x}}$ would have for the given fluids and the given hydrodynamic conditions if the net rate of mass transfer (the bulk flow, $\tilde{N}_A + \tilde{N}_B$) were zero. This coefficient is different from $k_{\tilde{x}}$ for appreciable rates of mass transfer when $\tilde{N}_B$ is zero; for small transfer rates or for $\tilde{N}_B = -\tilde{N}_A$, $k_{\tilde{x}}^o$ and $k_{\tilde{x}}$ are indistinguishable.

The relation between $k_{\tilde{x}}^o$ and $k_{\tilde{x}}$ can be obtained rigorously only for certain cases of laminar flow. For most systems, including turbulent flow, such a relation is not known; the following analysis is at best a good approximation. The flux for $\tilde{N}_A = -\tilde{N}_B$ across a layer of fluid may be expressed by the equation

$$\tilde{N}_A = \frac{\tilde{\rho} D_{AB}}{\delta_m} (\tilde{x}_{As} - \tilde{x}_A) \tag{33-23}$$

which has been obtained from Eq. (32-51). The path length for diffusion L has been replaced by a fictitious "film" thickness δ_m. This thickness is chosen so as to give the transfer rate for the actual system in terms of the resistance of a stagnant layer of thickness δ_m which would offer the same resistance. We compare Eqs. (33-8) and (33-23) and find that for equimolal counterdiffusion the coefficient $k_{\tilde{x}}$ can be expressed as

$$k_{\tilde{x}} = \frac{\tilde{\rho} D_{AB}}{\delta_m} \tag{33-24}$$

Because $k_{\tilde{x}}$ and $k_{\tilde{x}}^o$ are equal in this special case, Eq. (33-24) also serves as the definition of $k_{\tilde{x}}^o$.

If we have $\tilde{N}_B = 0$, the analysis is based on Eqs. (32-46) to (32-48), with the result

$$k_{\tilde{x}} = \frac{\tilde{\rho} D_{AB}}{\delta_m (1 - \tilde{x}_A)_{lm}} \tag{33-25}$$

which is found by combining Eqs. (33-8) and (32-46). We have already defined $k_{\bar{x}}^o$ as $\bar{\rho}D_{AB}/\delta_m$; hence, for the special case of $\bar{N}_B = 0$, we obtain

$$k_{\bar{x}}^o = k_{\bar{x}}(1 - \bar{x}_A)_{lm} \qquad (33\text{-}26)$$

We shall use Eq. (33-26) to estimate the effect of composition on $k_{\bar{x}}$. It is assumed that the coefficient $k_{\bar{x}}^o$ is not affected by composition, but is fixed by the fluid properties and velocities and the dimensions of the system. For example, correlations will be obtained involving a Nusselt-like group for mass transfer, which is called the Sherwood number. This group is defined in terms of $k_{\bar{x}}^o$ as

$$\mathsf{Sh} = \frac{k_{\bar{x}}^o D}{\bar{\rho}D_{AB}} = \frac{k_\rho^o D}{D_{AB}} \qquad (33\text{-}27)$$

If it is desired to use the value of $k_{\bar{x}}^o$ obtained from such a correlation for $\bar{N}_B = 0$ and concentrated solutions, $k_{\bar{x}}^o$ must be replaced by $k_{\bar{x}}(1 - \bar{x}_A)_{lm}$.

Height of a Transfer Unit

The convective mass-transfer coefficients have been arbitrarily defined just as heat-transfer coefficients were defined. To obtain the transfer rate, the flux must be multiplied by the area across which the transfer is occurring. This computation is possible in a heat exchanger or in mass transfer between a solid surface and a fluid. However, the interfacial area between a liquid flowing down over the packing in an absorption tower and the gas rising in the tower is difficult to measure or compute and so is often unknown. This is also true of spray towers and liquid-liquid extraction devices.

To assist in analyzing situations in which the magnitude of the interfacial area is not available, we define the quantity a, the interfacial area per unit volume of contacting device. The rate of mass transfer per unit volume of tower is then given as

$$\frac{\text{Rate of mass transfer}}{\text{Volume}} = k_{\bar{x}}a(\bar{x}_{As} - \bar{x}_A) \qquad (33\text{-}28)$$

Since the rate of transfer per unit volume and the driving force are readily measurable, coefficients obtained from experiments on packed towers and similar devices are usually given on a volumetric basis; one finds data for $k_{\bar{y}}a$, $k_{\bar{x}}a$, $K_{\bar{y}}a$, and $K_{\bar{x}}a$, in units such as lb moles/(hr)(cu ft).

In a packed gas-absorption tower the quantity a is not the same as the surface area of the solid packing. The interfacial contact area between gas and liquid per unit volume of tower is a function of the gas and liquid flow rates, and it does not necessarily vary in the same way as the convective coefficient.[1]

---

[1] H. L. Shulman, C. F. Aldrich, A. Z. Proulx, and J. O. Zimmerman, *AIChE Journal*, **1**:253 (1955).

The determination of the size of mass-transfer equipment may be done starting with Eq. (33-28) or similar equations containing mass-transfer coefficients. However, a more common procedure in equipment design is to use transfer units which are defined according to the equation

$$z = H_G n_G \qquad (33\text{-}29)$$

where z = height of device

H_G = height of a transfer unit (HTU)

n_G = number of transfer units (NTU)

We give now the definition of a transfer unit only. The basis of this definition and methods of calculating the number of transfer units in a contacting device are to be found in Chap. 37.

The symbol H_G in Eq. (33-29) is arbitrarily defined by

$$H_G = \frac{\tilde{G}}{k_{\bar{y}}^o a} \qquad (33\text{-}30)$$

and is called the height of a transfer unit for the gas phase. The quantity $\tilde{G}$ is the molal flux of the gas phase through the tower, based on the cross-sectional area of the empty tower. For the liquid phase we also have, by definition,

$$H_L = \frac{\tilde{L}}{k_{\bar{x}}^o a} \qquad (33\text{-}31)$$

The over-all transfer units are defined by similar equations.

$$H_{OG} = \frac{\tilde{G}}{K_{\bar{y}}^o a} \qquad (33\text{-}32)$$

$$H_{OL} = \frac{\tilde{L}}{K_{\bar{x}}^o a} \qquad (33\text{-}33)$$

One reason why the transfer-unit system is useful is that the height of a transfer unit always has the dimension simply of length. The forms in Eqs. (33-30) to (33-33) are used for calculations when mole fractions are used for the driving force. However, there is a permanence of form, so that if concentrations are used for the driving force, we have

$$H_G = \frac{u_G}{k_\rho^o a} = \frac{u_G}{k_{\bar{p}}^o a} \qquad (33\text{-}34)$$

in which u_G is the superficial velocity of the gas phase, equal to G/ρ or $\tilde{G}/\bar{\rho}$; k_ρ^o is identical to $k_{\bar{p}}^o$. Equations similar to (33-34) can be written for H_L, H_{OG}, and H_{OL}.

In much of the literature, the gas-phase mass-transfer coefficient is expressed in terms of a driving force of partial pressure.

$$\tilde{N}_A = k_G(\overline{p}_A - \overline{p}_{As}) \qquad (33\text{-}35)$$

This leads to the definition of H_G as $\tilde{G}/k_G^o a p$ because $k_G^o p$ is identical to k_y^o.

The equations given in this chapter can be applied to gas absorption, distillation, liquid-liquid extraction, and other separation operations. The symbols y and G have referred to the gas phase, and x and L to the liquid phase; if both phases are liquids, however, the equations apply equally well. We merely designate one of the phases as the y phase and the other as the x phase. For example, in liquid-liquid extraction we usually refer to the extract phase as the y phase and refer to the raffinate phase as the x phase.

In liquid-liquid extraction and in leaching, it is common to express compositions in mass fractions rather than mole fractions. All our previous equations are easily adapted to this basis. For example, the y-phase HTU is

$$H_G = \frac{G}{k_y^o a} \tag{33-36}$$

where

$$N_A = k_y(y_{As} - y_A) \tag{33-37}$$

and

$$k_y^o = k_y(1 - y_A)_{lm} \tag{33-38}$$

For situations in which mass-transfer resistances are given in terms of HTUs, it is convenient to use these quantities directly to find $\tilde{x}_{As}$ and $\tilde{y}_{As}$. Equation (33-22) becomes

$$-\frac{H_G \tilde{L}(1 - \tilde{y}_A)_{lm}}{H_L \tilde{G}(1 - \tilde{x}_A)_{lm}} = \frac{\tilde{y}_A - \tilde{y}_{As}}{\tilde{x}_A - \tilde{x}_{As}} \qquad N_B = 0 \tag{33-39}$$

In Chaps. 34 and 35 we shall consider applications of the differential and over-all balances to the laminar and then to the turbulent boundary layer. The flow interactions will be similar to those studied in the analogous chapters on momentum transfer and on energy transfer, and it will usually be convenient to express the results in terms of convective mass-transfer coefficients. However, in Chap. 36, where some coefficients useful in the design of packed towers and other devices will be given, it will prove more convenient to use HTUs. It will be found that HTUs for packed gas-absorption towers are of the order of 0.3 to 3 ft; for liquid-liquid extraction, as high as 60 to 100 ft; and for gas-solid adsorption, as low as 0.01 ft. In Chap. 37 we shall study the calculation of the number of transfer units, and in subsequent chapters a number of separation operations will be discussed.

PROBLEMS

33-1. A gas contains 70 mole per cent benzene and 30 mole per cent toluene at 80 °C. The pressure on the system is increased isothermally until condensation begins. Find this pressure and the composition of the first drop of liquid condensate.

33-2. A gaseous mixture at 1 atm pressure contains 10 mole per cent n-heptane, 70 mole per cent n-hexane, and 20 mole per cent water vapor. It is cooled at constant pressure until it is completely condensed.

(*a*) Find the temperature at which condensation begins and the composition of the first drop of condensate.

(*b*) Find the temperature at which condensation is completed and the composition of the last bubble of vapor before it condenses.

Assume that n-heptane and n-hexane form an ideal-liquid solution which is immiscible with water. The following table contains vapor-pressure data for the pure compounds in millimeters of mercury.

Compound	Temperature, °C				
	50	60	70	80	90
Water.................	90	150	230	355	525
n-Heptane..............	150	220	310	435	590
n-Hexane..............	410	584	815	1115	1420

33-3. A gas-absorption column operates at a temperature of 20°C and an average pressure of 1 atm. Water flows down through the column and absorbs sulfur dioxide from a gas stream flowing up. At the top of the column the water entering is essentially free from sulfur dioxide and the gas leaving contains 10 mole per cent sulfur dioxide in air. At the bottom of the column the water contains 0.7 mole per cent sulfur dioxide and the gas contains 30 mole per cent sulfur dioxide. The individual mass-transfer coefficients $k_{\bar{x}}$ and $k_{\bar{y}}$ are constant throughout the column at 4.0 and 0.3 lb mole/(hr)(sq ft), respectively. Find the over-all mass-transfer coefficients $K_{\bar{x}}$ and $K_{\bar{y}}$ at both the top and bottom of the column and, in addition, find the interfacial compositions at both points.

MASS TRANSFER WITH LAMINAR FLOW 34

Mass transfer occurs in only a few systems in which the fluid is in laminar flow. The principal reason for this is that most mass-transfer systems contain more than one fluid phase, so that stable laminar boundary layers cannot be built up in that part of the system in which mass transfer is important. There are a few systems, however, in which mass transfer occurs between a solid and a fluid, and in such systems we have not only a laminar boundary layer adjacent to the solid surface, but also the possibility of developed laminar flow throughout the fluid phase.

The problem of mass transfer between a fluid and a solid is similar to the problem of heat transfer between a fluid and a solid. Although the systems are usually not completely analogous, simplifications can often be made so that the heat-transfer analysis is applicable to the mass-transfer systems. The present chapter covers only mass transfer in a fluid in laminar flow and corresponds to Chap. 24, Heat Transfer with Laminar Flow.

Laminar Flow Parallel to a Flat Plate

A fluid flowing over a flat plate contains a momentum boundary layer in which the velocity of the fluid changes from zero at the plate to the free-stream velocity at the edge of the boundary layer. If mass is being transferred between the fluid and the plate, a concentration boundary layer also exists in which the concentration of the solute changes from the equilibrium value at the solid-fluid interface to the free-stream concentration in the fluid. Just as thermal and momentum boundary layers are often of different thickness in one system, so the concentration and momentum boundary

471

layers may be of different thickness. In fact, it is not uncommon to have heat and mass transfer occurring in the same flow system, so that the three kinds of boundary layer occur simultaneously, and all may be of different thickness.

If the flow is laminar, mass transfer occurs normal to the bulk motion of the fluid only by molecular diffusion and the associated convective flow discussed in Chap. 32. The differential mass balance for a multicomponent system in which molecular diffusion occurs was derived in Chap. 9. If Eq. (9-21) is written for steady, two-dimensional flow of a binary mixture of constant density, we obtain

$$u_x \frac{\partial \rho_A}{\partial x} + u_y \frac{\partial \rho_A}{\partial y} = D_{AB} \left(\frac{\partial^2 \rho_A}{\partial x^2} + \frac{\partial^2 \rho_A}{\partial y^2} \right) + r_A \tag{34-1}$$

If no generation of component A occurs and diffusion in the x direction is neglected, Eq. (34-1) becomes

$$u_x \frac{\partial \rho_A}{\partial x} + u_y \frac{\partial \rho_A}{\partial y} = D_{AB} \frac{\partial^2 \rho_A}{\partial y^2} \tag{34-2}$$

This equation is similar to the simplified form of the differential momentum balance for two-dimensional flow of a fluid of constant density and viscosity:

$$u_x \frac{\partial u_x}{\partial x} + u_y \frac{\partial u_x}{\partial y} = \nu \frac{\partial^2 u_x}{\partial y^2} \tag{34-3}$$

A solution for this latter equation is presented graphically in Fig. 12-8, in which the dimensionless velocity u_x/u_o is plotted against the function $y(u_x/\nu x)^{1/2}$ (usually designated as η).

If the diffusivity D_{AB} and the kinematic viscosity ν are equal, Eqs. (34-2) and (34-3) become identical, except for the dependent variables ρ_A and u_x. These may be replaced in the two differential equations by dimensionless quantities, so that the boundary values are similar, the new variables being u_x/u_o and $(\rho_{As} - \rho_A)/(\rho_{As} - \rho_{Ao})$. The concentrations ρ_{As} and ρ_{Ao} at the plate and in the free stream, respectively, are assumed constant. The boundary conditions for boundary-layer flow over the flat plate with diffusion from the plate into the stream are

At $y = 0$ $\dfrac{\rho_{As} - \rho_A}{\rho_{As} - \rho_{Ao}} = 0, \dfrac{u_x}{u_o} = 0$

At $y = \infty$ $\dfrac{\rho_{As} - \rho_A}{\rho_{As} - \rho_{Ao}} = 1, \dfrac{u_x}{u_o} = 1$

At $x = 0$ $\dfrac{\rho_{As} - \rho_A}{\rho_{As} - \rho_{Ao}} = 1, \dfrac{u_x}{u_o} = 1$

Consequently, in this specific case the solutions of the diffusion and momentum equations become identical. From this we conclude that the dimensionless concentration and velocity profiles in the boundary layer are the same; therefore the concentration and momentum boundary layers have an equal thickness.

It is significant that one requirement which leads to the identical solutions described above is that D_{AB} and ν be identical. The quotient ν/D_{AB} is a dimensionless group known as the Schmidt number and must be equal to unity in this special case. The Schmidt number indicates the same relation between mass and momentum transfer that the Prandtl number does between heat and momentum transfer. It will be recalled that in Chap. 24 the energy equation was compared with the momentum equation and the two found to be identical when the Prandtl number was unity. Equations (34-2) and (34-3) are analogous to Eq. (24-1); the boundary conditions above may be compared with those given on page 299.

As mentioned earlier, a solution for Eq. (34-3) has been presented graphically in Fig. 12-8. This graphical solution is valid for Eq. (34-2) for a Schmidt number of unity, but only in the limiting case in which the diffusion rate approaches zero. This is because the solution presented in Fig. 12-8 was derived on the assumption that the normal velocity at the plate u_{ys} was zero. If diffusion is occurring at a steady rate from the plate into the stream, the velocity component u_y cannot be zero at the plate, and only in the limiting case when u_{ys} approaches zero is the solution presented in Fig. 12-8 valid for mass transfer.

The solution to Eqs. (34-2) and (34-3) when u_y at the plate is not zero is found by transforming the partial differential equations into ordinary differential equations by means of the similarity transformations

$$\eta = y \sqrt{\frac{u_o}{\nu x}} \tag{12-68}$$

$$f(\eta) = \frac{\psi}{\sqrt{x\nu u_o}} \tag{12-69}$$

The transformation converts Eq. (34-2) into the form

$$\frac{d^2 \left(\dfrac{\rho_{As} - \rho_A}{\rho_{As} - \rho_{Ao}} \right)}{d\eta^2} + \frac{\mathsf{Sc}\, f(\eta)}{2} \frac{d \left(\dfrac{\rho_{As} - \rho_A}{\rho_{As} - \rho_{Ao}} \right)}{d\eta} = 0 \tag{34-4}$$

which is analogous to Eq. (24-3).

For the boundary condition for which $y = 0$ ($\eta = 0$), the requirement that $(\rho_{As} - \rho_A)/(\rho_{As} - \rho_{Ao})$ be zero has already been given. The requirement that u_x/u_o be zero leads to $df(\eta)/d\eta = 0$, as may be seen from Eq. (12-72). In Chaps. 12 and 24, u_{ys} has been zero, so Eq. (12-73) has led to a requirement that $f(\eta)$ also be zero. In the present case, Eq. (12-73) leads

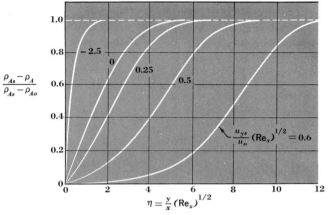

Fig. 34-1. *Concentration profiles for mass transfer in a laminar boundary layer on a flat plate; Sc = 1. [From J. P. Hartnett and E. R. G. Eckert, Trans. ASME, 19:247 (1957).]*

to $f(\eta) = -2u_{ys}x/\sqrt{x\nu u_o}$. Since $f'(\eta)$ is zero, $f(\eta)$ must be constant, so u_{ys} must vary as $1/\sqrt{x}$ in order for the transformation being used to be valid.

At $y = \infty$, we have seen that $(\rho_{As} - \rho_A)/(\rho_{As} - \rho_{Ao}) = 1.0$. Since $u_x/u_o = 1.0$, Eq. (12-72) shows that $df(\eta)/d\eta = 1.0$. The boundary conditions discussed above are summarized by

$$\text{At } y = 0 \qquad \frac{\rho_{As} - \rho_A}{\rho_{As} - \rho_{Ao}} = 0, \frac{df(\eta)}{d\eta} = 0, f(\eta) = \frac{u_{ys}x}{\sqrt{x\nu u_o}}$$

$$= \frac{u_{ys}}{u_o}(\mathbf{Re}_x)^{\frac{1}{2}} = \text{const}$$

$$\text{At } y = \infty \qquad \frac{\rho_{As} - \rho_A}{\rho_{As} - \rho_{Ao}} = 1, \frac{df(\eta)}{d\eta} = 1$$

In the first boundary condition, the constant contains the factor -2. The velocity at the surface must vary according to

$$\frac{u_{ys}}{u_o} = \frac{\text{const}}{(\mathbf{Re}_x)^{\frac{1}{2}}} \tag{34-5}$$

It has been shown by Eckert and Drake[1] that this condition is achieved with the condition of constant temperature and concentration at the wall.

A graph of the solution of Eq. (34-4) is shown in Fig. 34-1 for a binary fluid with a Schmidt number of unity. Both positive and negative values of the parameter $(u_{ys}/u_o)(\mathbf{Re}_x)^{\frac{1}{2}}$ are represented; the positive values apply when mass transfer occurs from the plate to the fluid, and the negative

[1] E. R. G. Eckert and R. M. Drake, Jr., "Heat and Mass Transfer," 2d ed., chap. 16, McGraw-Hill Book Company, Inc., New York, 1959.

values when mass transfer is from the fluid to the plate. The line for which the parameter is zero represents a system in which the mass-transfer rate is negligible compared with the velocity of the free stream. This line is identical with the dimensionless velocity profile in Fig. 12-8. It is also identical with the line for $\mathsf{Pr} = 1$ in Fig. 24-1. If heat and mass transfer are occurring simultaneously in boundary-layer flow, the identity of the differential energy and diffusion equations and their boundary conditions leads to identical temperature and composition profiles when Sc/Pr is unity. This ratio of dimensionless groups readily reduces to the ratio of thermal to molecular diffusivity, which is known as the Lewis number.

The results shown in Fig. 34-1 can be presented in terms of a mass-transfer coefficient k_ρ'. The transfer rate between the fluid and plate may be written by equating the values of N_A found by substituting the appropriate quantities in Eqs. (30-1) and (32-20).

$$N_A = k_\rho(\rho_{As} - \rho_{Ao}) = -D_{AB}\left(\frac{\partial \rho_A}{\partial y}\right)_{y=0} + \rho_{As}u_{ys}$$

$$= k_\rho'(\rho_{As} - \rho_{Ao}) + \rho_{As}u_{ys} \quad (34\text{-}6)$$

The coefficient k_ρ' thus defined can be written as

$$k_\rho' = \frac{-D_{AB}}{\rho_{As} - \rho_{Ao}}\left(\frac{\partial \rho_A}{\partial y}\right)_{y=0}$$

or as

$$k_\rho' = D_{AB}\left\{\frac{\partial[(\rho_{As} - \rho_A)/(\rho_{As} - \rho_{Ao})]}{\partial y}\right\}_{y=0} \quad (34\text{-}7)$$

The relation of k_ρ' to k_ρ in some special cases is discussed in Chap. 38.

The behavior of the mass-transfer coefficient can be inferred qualitatively by a comparison of Eq. (34-7) with the curves of Fig. 34-1. Systems for which the parameter is negative (indicating mass transfer from the fluid to the plate) have large slopes at the origin ($y = 0$, $\eta = 0$), indicating high mass-transfer coefficients. Systems in which the parameter is large and positive have low slopes at the origin, indicating much lower mass-transfer coefficients. The systems represented by a positive parameter are those in which mass is transferred away from the plate.

A numerical value of the local mass-transfer coefficient can be computed for a fluid with $\mathsf{Sc} = 1$ by measuring the slope at the origin of the appropriate curve in Fig. 34-1 and using Eq. (34-7) to compute k_ρ'. For the limiting case of $u_{ys} = 0$, $k_\rho = k_\rho' = k_\rho^o$ and the slope at the origin is 0.33. Consequently, we can write

$$\left\{\frac{\partial[(\rho_{As} - \rho_A)/(\rho_{As} - \rho_{Ao})]}{\partial y}\right\}_{y=0} = \frac{0.33}{x}(\mathsf{Re}_x)^{\frac{1}{2}}$$

Inserting this in Eq. (34-7), we obtain

$$\frac{k_p^o x}{D_{AB}} = 0.33 \ (\mathbf{Re}_x)^{1/2} \tag{34-8}$$

For a fluid with $\mathbf{Sc}$ other than unity, curves similar to those in Fig. 34-1 could be obtained from a solution of Eq. (34-4). For the case of $u_{ys} = 0$, the curves given in Fig. 24-1 apply to mass transfer if the ordinate is interpreted as $(\rho_{As} - \rho_A)/(\rho_{As} - \rho_{Ao})$ and the parameter $\mathbf{Pr}$ is interpreted as $\mathbf{Sc}$. An approximate expression for the mass-transfer coefficient corresponding to the concentration profiles of Fig. 24-1 is

$$\frac{k_p^o x}{D_{AB}} = 0.33 \ (\mathbf{Re}_x)^{1/2} \ \mathbf{Sc}^{1/3} \tag{34-9}$$

The dimensionless group $k_p^o x/D_{AB}$ is known as the Sherwood number and corresponds to the Nusselt number in heat transfer. The procedures followed and assumptions used in obtaining Eq. (34-9) are similar to those employed in the analysis of heat transfer in Chap. 24, which resulted in Eq. (24-8). As for Eq. (24-8), Eq. (34-9) is valid for $\mathbf{Sc} > 0.6$; in addition, both equations apply only if u_{ys} is negligible.

Mean mass-transfer coefficients for a plate of finite length can be found by writing Eq. (34-9) to obtain k_p^o for a differential element of surface and integrating over the length of the plate. This procedure was illustrated in Chap. 24 in the determination of mean heat-transfer coefficients for a flat plate from local coefficients. As in the heat-transfer analysis, the equation giving the mean coefficient differs from the equation for the local coefficient by a factor of 2. Thus the equation for the mean coefficient is

$$\mathbf{Sh}_m = 0.66 \ (\mathbf{Re}_L)^{1/2} \ \mathbf{Sc}^{1/3} \tag{34-10}$$

in which the mean Sherwood number contains the mean mass-transfer coefficient for a plate of length L.

Very few experimental investigations of mass transfer from a flat plate have been reported; this is in contrast to the many investigations of heat transfer. A recent paper by Christian and Kezios[1] describes measurements of local and mean mass-transfer coefficients for naphthalene subliming outward into an air stream flowing parallel to the axis of a hollow cylinder. Their results are shown in Fig. 34-2. The straight lines drawn through the data are represented by equations differing from Eqs. (34-9) and (34-10) only in the coefficients, which are 0.339 and 0.678, respectively. These results might be expected to differ somewhat from the flat-plate equations because of the curvature of the surface; however, for the cylin-

---

[1] W. J. Christian and S. P. Kezios, *AIChE Journal*, **5**(1):61 (1959).

Fig. 34-2. Local and mean Sherwood numbers for sublimation of naphthalene into air in a laminar boundary layer. [From W. J. Christian and S. P. Kezios, AIChE Journal, 5:61 (1959).]

ders chosen (0.75 and 1 in. diameter), the radius of curvature was so large compared with the boundary-layer thickness that flat-plate behavior was obtained. The Schmidt number for the air-naphthalene system was 2.40.

In boundary-layer systems in which combined heat and mass transfer occur and $Pr = Sc = 1.0$, the dimensionless temperature profiles are also represented by the curves of Fig. 34-1. The reasoning concerning mass-transfer coefficients can be extended to heat-transfer coefficients. The heat-transfer rate from a hot gas stream flowing over a flat plate is reduced by the transfer of mass into the boundary layer from the surface of the plate. One method of achieving this effect is to force a second gas through the porous flat plate into the boundary layer. In high-speed flow, sublimation of the plate itself may occur, with the effect not only of absorbing the latent heat of sublimation, but also of reducing the heat-transfer coefficient as a result of the mass-transfer effect just discussed. The effect is achieved more simply by evaporation of a liquid from the surface of the plate. The opposite effect of a high heat-transfer coefficient is illustrated by the high heat-transfer coefficients encountered in desuperheating of steam near a surface on which condensation occurs.

Mass Transfer with Developed Velocity Distribution in a Pipe

The development of a concentration boundary layer on a flat plate is similar to the development of a concentration profile near the entrance of a pipe. When the boundary layer fills the pipe, the flow is said to be developed. If the partial pressure of the diffusing component is constant at the wall, the concentration profile in the pipe will eventually become flat. This condition might be achieved in the pipe whose inner surface is coated with some material soluble in the fluid stream.   It might also be achieved in a very long wetted-wall column operated in such a way that the fluid flowing down the column (or pipe) is at a constant temperature throughout and has, therefore, a constant vapor pressure.   A different boundary condition is achieved if the walls of the pipe are porous and the solute is forced through the walls at a constant rate per unit area at all points along the pipe.

The two methods of operation described above are analogous to the boundary conditions of constant wall temperature and constant heat flux in heat-transfer systems.   We have seen earlier in this chapter that the differential equations for molecular diffusion of mass and for conduction of heat are similar.   We have also seen that in mass-transfer systems in which the normal velocity at the wall is small compared with the free-stream velocity, the mass-transfer results are analogous to heat-transfer results in which no mass transfer is taking place.   The fortunate consequence of this is that the results for heat transfer in a pipe presented in Chap. 24 can be used to predict mass-transfer coefficients by merely substituting the Sherwood number for the Nusselt number and the Schmidt number for the Prandtl number in the heat-transfer solutions.   Solutions for the local Sherwood number can be obtained from Fig. 24-3 for either uniform flux or uniform concentration at the wall for fluid streams with flat and parabolic profiles.   Solutions for arithmetic average and log-mean driving force can be obtained from Fig. 24-4.

Other Systems

Mass transfer in a fluid may cause density differences which will result in natural convective flow similar to natural convection by heat transfer. The convective mass-transfer coefficients can be predicted from the equations used in heat transfer by substituting the Sherwood and Schmidt numbers for the Nusselt and Prandtl numbers, respectively.   The Grashof number for mass transfer is $gL^3(\rho_o - \rho_s)/\nu^2\rho_s$.

Mass transfer also occurs by molecular diffusion inside drops.   Various conditions may prevail within the drops, ranging from complete stagnation to complete mixing.   An intermediate condition is one in which viscous circulation occurs within the drops.   An analysis of this special case of mass transfer with laminar flow will be deferred until Chap. 36, when all the fluid-flow patterns and their effects on mass transfer inside drops will be considered simultaneously.

PROBLEMS

34-1. A thin sheet of naphthalene 0.1 in. thick and 4 in. square is placed in an air stream parallel to the direction of flow. The air is at 32°F and 1 atm and is moving in laminar flow with a uniform velocity of 50 ft/sec. How long must the sheet be exposed to the air before half of its mass will have sublimed? Assume that the upper and lower surfaces remain flat at all times. The molecular diffusivity for the air-naphthalene system is 0.199 sq ft/hr, and the Schmidt number is 2.57 under the conditions given in the problem. The vapor pressure of naphthalene at 32°F is 0.0059 mm Hg. The temperature drop between the air and the naphthalene as a result of the vaporization of naphthalene can be assumed to be negligible. Neglect evaporation from the edges.

34-2. A wetted-wall column with air flowing countercurrent to water is to be constructed from a pipe 6 in. in diameter. If the water flowing in a thin film down the interior surface is recirculated until it reaches the adiabatic saturation temperature of the system (60°F), find the length of pipe necessary to give an exit-gas humidity 90 per cent of the saturation humidity. The physical properties of the gas in the system can be assumed to be the same as for air at the entering conditions of 1 atm pressure and 80°F. Entrance effects can be neglected, and the velocity profile of the air can be assumed to be flat. The velocity of the air relative to the water is 30 ft/sec.

MASS TRANSFER WITH TURBULENT FLOW

35

Much of our understanding of the mechanism of mass transfer with turbulent flow has been gained from analogous studies of heat transfer with turbulent flow. The analogy between heat and mass transfer is very useful; however, its limitations must frequently be considered, and this is particularly true in applications involving turbulent flow.

In this chapter we shall consider mass transfer with turbulent flow in somewhat the same order as we considered heat transfer with turbulent flow in Chap. 25. It is desirable to consider mass transfer in a turbulent boundary layer on a flat plate because of the small but increasing number of direct applications of this theory; a more important reason is that this study leads to an understanding of mass transfer with flow over surfaces of more complex geometry. We shall also consider the classical analogies among heat, mass, and momentum transfer between a fluid and the inner wall of a pipe. Finally, we shall examine the penetration theory, which is of importance as a mechanistic picture. One unique feature of the penetration theory is that it describes mass transfer (and heat transfer) between two fluid phases. This is in contrast to most transport theories, which are more or less restricted in applicability to transport between a fluid and a solid phase.

Turbulent Flow Parallel to a Flat Plate

The equations for mass transfer in a turbulent boundary layer cannot be solved analytically. However, like the problems of heat and momentum transfer in a turbulent boundary layer, the mass-transfer problem can be

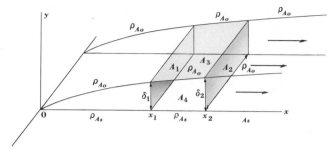

Fig. 35-1.   *Mass transfer from a flat plate to a turbulent boundary layer.*

attacked using the von Kármán integral method.   The treatment is similar to that in Chap. 25, but will be given in some detail so that the assumptions will be evident.

The velocity in the turbulent boundary layer will be represented by the well-known empirical equation

$$\frac{u_x}{u_o} = \left(\frac{y}{\delta}\right)^{\frac{1}{7}} \tag{13-95}$$

This expression has been established for turbulent-boundary-layer flow without mass transfer, so that its use in this derivation is probably limited to systems with low concentrations of the diffusing component.

The composition profile of the boundary layer is assumed to follow an analogous equation.

$$\frac{\rho_{As} - \rho_A}{\rho_{As} - \rho_{Ao}} = \left(\frac{y}{\delta_c}\right)^{\frac{1}{7}} \tag{35-1}$$

We assume that the Schmidt number is unity, so that the momentum-boundary-layer thickness δ and the concentration-boundary-layer thickness δ_c are the same at any distance x from the leading edge of the plate.   The concentration ρ_{As} of the diffusing component at the surface of the plate will be taken as constant at all points on the plate, and it will be assumed that there is no flow of component B from the plate into the boundary layer.

A material balance for component A is written for the control volume shown in Fig. 35-1.   Molecular diffusion in the x direction is assumed to be negligible compared with the transport due to fluid motion in this direction.   Velocity and concentration gradients do not exist in the z direction.

The net inflow of solute A through the lower surface A_4 equals the net outflow through the upper surface A_3 and through surfaces A_1 and A_2 at steady state.   The flows are written using Eq. (3-1).

$$\iint\limits_{A_1} \rho_A u \cos \alpha \, dA + \iint\limits_{A_2} \rho_A u \cos \alpha \, dA + \iint\limits_{A_3} \rho_{Ao} u \cos \alpha \, dA$$

$$= \iint\limits_{A_4} k_\rho(\rho_{As} - \rho_{Ao}) \, dA \qquad (35\text{-}2)$$

At surface A_1, $u \cos \alpha = -u_x$, and at A_2, $u \cos \alpha = u_x$, so that we write

$$\iint\limits_{A_2} \rho_A u_x \, dA - \iint\limits_{A_1} \rho_A u_x \, dA + \iint\limits_{A_3} \rho_{Ao} u \cos \alpha \, dA$$

$$= \iint\limits_{A_4} k_\rho(\rho_{As} - \rho_{Ao}) \, dA \qquad (35\text{-}3)$$

To eliminate the term for flow of solute through surface A_3, we write a total mass balance on the control volume.

$$\iint\limits_{A_2} \rho u_x \, dA - \iint\limits_{A_1} \rho u_x \, dA + \iint\limits_{A_3} \rho u \cos \alpha \, dA = \iint\limits_{A_4} k_\rho(\rho_{As} - \rho_{Ao}) \, dA$$

$$(35\text{-}4)$$

We restrict our analysis to dilute solutions for which the concentration of the diffusing component is low so that we can assume that the total density of the fluid is uniform throughout the boundary layer. Therefore we can divide each term in Eq. (35-4) by the total density ρ and multiply by ρ_{Ao}, which is also constant. The result of making this change is shown in Eq. (35-5), which has been solved for the flow through A_3.

$$\iint\limits_{A_3} \rho_{Ao} u \cos \alpha \, dA = \iint\limits_{A_1} \rho_{Ao} u_x \, dA - \iint\limits_{A_2} \rho_{Ao} u_x \, dA$$

$$+ \iint\limits_{A_4} k_\rho(\rho_{As} - \rho_{Ao}) \frac{\rho_{Ao}}{\rho} \, dA \qquad (35\text{-}5)$$

Equation (35-5) is then substituted in Eq. (35-3) to give

$$\iint\limits_{A_2} (\rho_A - \rho_{Ao}) u_x \, dA - \iint\limits_{A_1} (\rho_A - \rho_{Ao}) u_x \, dA$$

$$= \iint\limits_{A_4} [k_\rho(\rho_{As} - \rho_{Ao})] \left(1 - \frac{\rho_{Ao}}{\rho}\right) dA \qquad (35\text{-}6)$$

All surfaces have the same width in the z direction; none of the variables is a function of z, so that Eq. (35-6) can be written as a sum of single integrals.

$$\int_0^{\delta_2} (\rho_A - \rho_{Ao}) u_x \, dy - \int_0^{\delta_1} (\rho_A - \rho_{Ao}) u_x \, dy$$

$$= \int_{x_1}^{x_2} [k_\rho(\rho_{As} - \rho_{Ao})] \left(1 - \frac{\rho_{Ao}}{\rho}\right) dx \qquad (35\text{-}7)$$

As the length $x_2 - x_1$ approaches zero, the left-hand side of Eq. (35-7) approaches differential magnitude. The right-hand side applies to a segment of finite width in the z direction, but differential width dx in the x direction. Therefore we write

$$d\left[\int_0^\delta (\rho_A - \rho_{Ao})u_x\,dy\right] = [k_\rho(\rho_{As} - \rho_{Ao})]\left(1 - \frac{\rho_{Ao}}{\rho}\right)dx \qquad (35\text{-}8)$$

from which we obtain

$$k_\rho = \frac{d}{dx}\left(\int_0^\delta \frac{\rho_A - \rho_{Ao}}{\rho_{As} - \rho_{Ao}}u_x\,dy\right)\frac{\rho}{\rho - \rho_{Ao}} \qquad (35\text{-}9)$$

The concentration term under the integral sign can be rewritten as

$$\frac{\rho_A - \rho_{Ao}}{\rho_{As} - \rho_{Ao}} = 1 - \frac{\rho_{As} - \rho_A}{\rho_{As} - \rho_{Ao}}$$

$$= 1 - \left(\frac{y}{\delta}\right)^{1/7} \qquad (35\text{-}10)$$

The local velocity is

$$u_x = u_o\left(\frac{y}{\delta}\right)^{1/7} \qquad (35\text{-}11)$$

Equations (35-10) and (35-11) are substituted in Eq. (35-9) and integrated as in Chap. 25. The result is

$$k_\rho = \frac{7u_o}{72}\frac{d\delta}{dx}\frac{\rho}{\rho - \rho_{Ao}} \qquad (35\text{-}12)$$

The thickness of the boundary layer was found in Chap. 13 to be

$$\delta = 0.376x\,(\mathbf{Re}_x)^{-1/5} \qquad (13\text{-}102)$$

This equation is differentiated to give

$$\frac{d\delta}{dx} = 0.301\,(\mathbf{Re}_x)^{-1/5} \qquad (35\text{-}13)$$

which is substituted in Eq. (35-12) to give

$$k_\rho = 0.0292u_o\,(\mathbf{Re}_x)^{-1/5}\frac{\rho}{\rho - \rho_{Ao}} \qquad (35\text{-}14)$$

The quantity $\rho/(\rho - \rho_{Ao})$ in Eq. (35-14) will make only a slight contribution to k_ρ in dilute systems. If the diffusing component is not present in the free stream, the quantity has a value of unity.

If bulk transport from the plate is negligible, $\rho/(\rho - \rho_{Ao})$ does not appear in Eq. (35-14). The value obtained for k_ρ is designated k_ρ^o for this special case, as mentioned in Chap. 33. We obtain a solution similar to the heat-transfer solution of Chap. 25. Both sides of the equation are multiplied by $xu_o\rho/\mu$ and $\mu/\rho D_{AB}$ to give

$$\frac{k_\rho^o x}{D_{AB}} = 0.0292 \, (\mathbf{Re}_x)^{4/5} \, \mathbf{Sc} \tag{35-15}$$

It was assumed initially that the Schmidt number was unity, so that the concentration and momentum boundary layer could be assumed to be of equal thickness. Thus Eq. (35-15) is written as

$$\frac{k_\rho^o x}{D_{AB}} = 0.0292 \, (\mathbf{Re}_x)^{4/5} \tag{35-16}$$

which is analogous to Eq. (25-15) for the local coefficient of heat transfer in turbulent flow over a flat plate.

Eddy Mass Diffusivity and Mixing Length

The eddy kinematic viscosity ν_e and the eddy thermal diffusivity α_e have been defined in Eqs. (13-37) and (25-21). In the discussions leading to these definitions, it was indicated that a similar quantity known as the eddy mass diffusivity D_{ABe} could be defined in equations for mass transfer with turbulent flow.[1] The derivation for D_{ABe} is based on a flow system as represented in Fig. 35-2. Velocities and concentrations are shown at two points separated by a distance equal to the Prandtl mixing length ℓ. Fluid is transported between the two points with a velocity equal to $\overline{|u_y'|}$, whereas component A is transported with a mass rate per unit area equal to the product of velocity and concentration difference, $-\overline{|u_y'|}\ell(d\bar{\rho}_A/dy)$. This concept has already been employed in Chaps. 13 and 25. In Chap. 13 it was shown that the fluctuating velocity component $\overline{|u_y'|}$ could be expressed in terms of the Prandtl mixing length and the velocity gradient as

$$\overline{|u_y'|} = \ell \left| \frac{d\bar{u}_x}{dy} \right| \tag{13-40}$$

Therefore the mass-transfer rate due to turbulent transport is

$$N_A = -\ell^2 \left| \frac{d\bar{u}_x}{dy} \right| \frac{d\bar{\rho}_A}{dy} \tag{35-17}$$

The quantity $\ell^2 |d\bar{u}_x/dy|$ has previously been shown to be equal to the eddy kinematic viscosity and also to the eddy thermal diffusivity. The derivation given above shows that it is also a proportionality constant in the equation for turbulent mass transfer. Consequently, it will be referred to as the eddy mass diffusivity, and by analogy to the molecular mass diffusivity D_{AB}, it will be designated D_{ABe}. A phenomenological

---

[1] The eddy mass diffusivity is often referred to simply as the eddy diffusivity.

Fig. 35-2.   *Eddy transport of mass.*

equation for the mass flux due to the combined mechanisms of molecular and eddy diffusion is

$$N_A = -(D_{AB} + D_{ABe}) \frac{d\bar{\rho}_A}{dy} \tag{35-18}$$

The eddy mass diffusivity in a system bounded by a solid wall is a function of the distance from the wall because the wall affects the character of turbulence in the adjacent fluid.   In the laminar sublayer the Prandtl mixing length and D_{ABe} are ordinarily taken as zero.   Mass transfer in this region is a function of the molecular diffusivity D_{AB}.   Far from the wall, however, D_{ABe} is usually much greater than D_{AB}, so that in this region the molecular diffusivity can often be neglected.

The assumption that D_{ABe}, α_e, and ν_e are identical is often made in theoretical derivations, though the model which is the basis of these definitions is vastly oversimplified.   Experimental work indicates that the terms are of the same magnitude but are not equal.

Sherwood and Woertz[1] measured diffusion of water vapor from one plane wall to another across streams of air, helium, and carbon dioxide.   Values of D_{ABe} and ν_e were determined from measurements of the concentration and velocity profiles at the center of the rectangular duct.   As mentioned in earlier chapters, comparisons of heat and momentum transfer indicate a range of values for α_e/ν_e between 0.5 and 2.0; the value of this quotient is shown in Fig. 25-4 to vary with distance from the wall and also to be a function of **Re**.   Thus it would seem likely that D_{ABe}/ν_e would behave in similar fashion.   In the work of Sherwood and Woertz the ratio D_{ABe}/ν_e was approximately constant at 1.6 for $2000 < $ **Re** $ < 120{,}000$.   No values were reported for locations other than at the centerline, but it is likely that some variation with position should be expected.

An interesting application of turbulent-flow theory is found in the effect

---

[1] T. K. Sherwood and B. B. Woertz, *Ind. Eng. Chem.*, **31**:1034 (1939).

of wire grids on eddy diffusivity. As Hinze[1] points out, the presence of a grid decreases the scale of turbulence in the fluid downstream from the grid but causes an increase in the intensity of the turbulence. If the grid openings are sufficiently small, the net effect is to decrease the eddy diffusivity. The decrease in the scale of turbulence apparently has a greater effect in this case in diminishing D_{ABe} than the increase in intensity has in raising it. Thus a grid inserted in a fluid stream for the purpose of increasing the rate of mixing may, in fact, cause a decrease in the rate of mixing.

The Analogy between Momentum Transfer and Mass Transfer

Although Reynolds was concerned only with the analogy between heat and momentum transfer, the equations which are referred to as the Reynolds analogy can be readily extended to cover mass transfer. This is also true for the equations of Prandtl and Taylor, von Kármán, etc., which were derived or referred to in Chap. 25. In this section we shall consider primarily relations between mass and momentum transfer. The relations between heat and mass transfer, if desired, can be obtained by combining the mass-transfer equations from the present chapter with the heat-transfer equations from Chap. 25.

The proportionality of mass and momentum transfer which leads to the Reynolds analogy can be arrived at by considering a fluid flowing in a pipe. The fluid is transferring both momentum and mass from the stream to the wall of the pipe. The following flux and rate expressions are considered:

(a) The mass flux from the fluid to the pipe wall for negligible bulk radial flow, $k_{\bar{x}}^{o}(\bar{x}_A - \bar{x}_{As})$, lb moles/(hr)(sq ft)

(b) The momentum flux at the wall, $\tau_s g_c$, (lb)(ft/hr)/(hr)(sq ft)

(c) The rate at which mass available for radial transfer is transported parallel to the pipe wall, $(w/M_m)(\bar{x}_A - \bar{x}_{As})$, lb moles/hr

(d) The rate at which momentum is transported parallel to the pipe wall, wu_b, (lb)(ft/hr)/hr

It is postulated that these quantities are related by the proportionality

$$\frac{a}{c} = \frac{b}{d}$$

from which it follows that

$$k_{\bar{x}}^{o} M_m = \frac{\tau_s g_c}{u_b} \tag{35-19}$$

[1] J. O. Hinze, "Turbulence: An Introduction to Its Mechanism and Theory," p. 341, McGraw-Hill Book Company, Inc., New York, 1959.

It was shown in Chap. 13 that the shear stress at the wall of a pipe is related to the friction factor by the equation

$$\tau_s g_c = \frac{f u_b{}^2 \rho}{2} \tag{13-67}$$

If Eq. (13-67) is substituted in Eq. (35-19), we obtain

$$k_{\bar{x}}^{o} M_m = \frac{f u_b \rho}{2} \tag{35-20}$$

in which M_m is the mean (or mixing-cup) molecular weight of the fluid in the pipe. By combining Eqs. (25-19) and (35-20), we relate the heat- and mass-transfer coefficients.

$$\frac{h}{C_p k_{\bar{x}}^{o} M_m} = \frac{h}{\tilde{C}_p k} = \frac{h}{C_p k_x^{o}} = 1 \tag{35-21}$$

This expression is sometimes called the Lewis equation.

Equations (35-20) and (35-21) can also be derived analytically. The analytical procedure was presented in Chap. 25 as an alternative to the intuitive statement of proportionality relating heat and momentum transfer. A similar treatment with similar assumptions will yield the equations given above, relating the friction factor and the heat- and mass-transfer coefficients.

The value of the analytical approach is that it bares the assumptions which must be true for the answer to have validity. One of these assumptions is that the mass flux is described by the same radial function as shear stress:

$$\frac{\tau}{\tau_s} = \frac{\tilde{N}_A}{\tilde{N}_{As}} = 1 - \frac{y}{r_i} \tag{35-22}$$

It can be seen that if D_{ABe}/ν_e is a function of radial position, the first two parts of Eq. (35-22) are not likely to be equal.

Another assumption in the analytical procedure is that the molecular diffusivities D_{AB} and ν are negligible compared with the eddy diffusivities. This limits the use of the Reynolds analogy to the turbulent core except for the case where the Schmidt number of the fluid is unity. The Schmidt number is by definition ν/D_{AB}, and at a value of **Sc** $= 1$, ν equals D_{AB}. If in addition ν_e is equal to D_{ABe}, Eq. (35-20) can be obtained without neglecting the molecular-transport coefficients. For a fluid with **Sc** $= 1$, therefore, the Reynolds analogy applies not only in the turbulent core, but also in the laminar sublayer. Similarly, if $\alpha = D_{AB}$, Eq. (35-21) can be derived for a system containing both laminar- and turbulent-flow regions.

The more complex forms of the analogy between mass and momentum transfer also parallel the forms presented in Chap. 25. The derivations are similar, so few details will be given here. In the Prandtl-Taylor analysis molecular transport of mass and momentum are assumed to be the only mechanisms of importance in the laminar sublayer. In the turbulent core, Reynolds' analogy is applied. The two sets of equations are then combined to give an equation for the over-all mass flux, from which the following equation is obtained:

$$k_{\bar{x}}^{o} M_m = \frac{f u_b \rho / 2}{1 + 5\sqrt{f/2}\,(\mathbf{Sc} - 1)} \tag{35-23}$$

If both sides of this equation are multiplied by $D/\rho D_{AB}$, the equation may be rearranged to give

$$\frac{k_{\bar{x}}^{o} M_m D}{\rho D_{AB}} = \frac{(f/2)(D u_b \rho/\mu)(\mu/\rho D_{AB})}{1 + 5\sqrt{f/2}\,(\mathbf{Sc} - 1)} \tag{35-24}$$

which is expressed in terms of dimensionless groups as

$$\mathbf{Sh} = \frac{(f/2)\ \mathbf{Re\ Sc}}{1 + 5\sqrt{f/2}\,(\mathbf{Sc} - 1)} \tag{35-25}$$

The quantity D is the pipe diameter, so $\mathbf{Re}$ is the Reynolds number for the pipe; the density ρ is the mixing-cup density of the fluid in pounds per cubic foot. The quantity $k_{\bar{x}}^{o} M_m/\rho$ can be expressed as $k_{\bar{x}}^{o} RT/p$, if the fluid is an ideal gas; it has the dimensions of length/time, as does k_{ρ}^{o}.

The von Kármán analogy can also be expressed in terms of mass and momentum transfer. The equation comparable with Eq. (25-41) is

$$\mathbf{Sh} = \frac{(f/2)\ \mathbf{Re\ Sc}}{1 + 5\sqrt{f/2}\,\{\mathbf{Sc} - 1 + \ln\,[(1 + 5\,\mathbf{Sc})/6]\}} \tag{35-26}$$

The dimensionless groups in Eq. (35-26) contain exactly the same variables as are found in Eq. (35-25).

One final form of the analogy is the empirical j-factor relation proposed by Colburn, which was also discussed in Chap. 25. This analogy may be written for mass transfer as

$$\frac{k_{\bar{x}}^{o} M_m}{u_b \rho}\,\mathbf{Sc}^{2/3} = j_M = \frac{f}{2} \tag{35-27}$$

or, in terms of dimensionless groups, as

$$\frac{\mathbf{Sh}}{\mathbf{Re\ Sc}^{1/3}} = j_M = \frac{f}{2} \tag{35-28}$$

The term j_M is known as the j factor for mass transfer. As pointed out in Chap. 25, for systems in which form drag is absent, it is generally found that $j_M = j_H = f/2$; if form drag is present, the equality is between only j_M and j_H. The essence of the j-factor relation is that the term $\mathbf{Sc}^{2/3}$ is suggested as a simple empirical replacement for the complex denominators on the right-hand side of the Prandtl-Taylor equation (35-25) and the von Kármán equation (35-26). As in the case of the heat-transfer equations, all forms of the analogy shown here reduce to the simple Reynolds analogy for $Sc = 1$.

The Penetration Theory

The penetration theory of mass transfer was first suggested by Higbie[1] as a mechanistic picture of mass transfer from a gas-liquid interface into a liquid. The methods of analysis which we have presented to this point are adequate for describing transfer across a stationary interface. The penetration theory applies, in addition, to transfer across a fluid-fluid interface which may not be stationary.

Previous notions of the mechanism of interphase mass transfer were derived from the concept of a stagnant film in each fluid adjacent to the interface. Although it was known that a stable film was not actually present in most mass-transfer systems, the concept of a somewhat flexible film of indefinite thickness comparable with the viscous sublayer in boundary-layer flow was the basis of most mass-transfer models. Mass was visualized as being transferred through this film by molecular diffusion in accordance with the equations for steady-state mass transfer. This theory led to the definition of transfer coefficients in terms of the diffusivity and the thickness of the film. In this book we have almost always presented the individual phase-transfer coefficients for turbulent flow as empirical quantities without reference to the film theory. In most systems, such as flow over a flat plate, we have seen that there is no stagnant film; the quantity transferred from the plate into the boundary layer flows normal to the plate by diffusion and parallel to the plate by the motion of the fluid. The film theory has been used briefly, however, in Chap. 33 to obtain a relation between $k_{\bar{x}}$ and $k_{\bar{x}}^o$ for turbulent flow [refer to Eqs. (33-23) to (33-26)].

Higbie proposed that the principal mechanism of mass transfer involved the motion of turbulent eddies from the core of the fluid to the interface, followed by a short interval of unsteady-state molecular diffusion from the interface into the fluid before it was displaced from the surface by subsequent eddies. The average rate of mass transfer with this model depends on the time of exposure of an eddy at the interface and the total amount of the diffusing component that is transferred from the interface into the eddy during this time.

Higbie assumed that all eddies which reach the interface have the same

[1] R. Higbie, *Trans. AIChE*, **31**:365 (1935).

Fig. 35-3. *The Gauss-error-integral function representing unsteady-state diffusion [Eq.(35-30)].*

exposure time. During this time, diffusion into the eddy is expressed by an equation which we recognize as a simplified form of Eq. (9-22).

$$\frac{\partial \rho_A}{\partial \theta} = D_{AB} \frac{\partial^2 \rho_A}{\partial y^2} \tag{35-29}$$

The boundary conditions are

(1) $\rho_A = \rho_{Ao}$ $\theta = 0$
(2) $\rho_A = \rho_{As}$ $\theta > 0, y = 0$
(3) $\rho_A = \rho_{Ao}$ $y = \infty$

The surface concentration ρ_{As} and the concentration at a great distance from the surface ρ_{Ao} are constant. Equation (35-29) is a familiar form which has already been solved in Example 21-2 for unsteady-state heat conduction and in Example 32-3 for unsteady-state mass diffusion. These problems, however, involved slabs of finite thickness, whereas boundary condition 3 of the present problem is for diffusion into a medium of infinite thickness. The problem is solved to give

$$\frac{\rho_{As} - \rho_A}{\rho_{As} - \rho_{Ao}} = \operatorname{erf} \frac{y}{2\sqrt{\theta D_{AB}}} \tag{35-30}$$

where

$$\operatorname{erf} z = \frac{2}{\sqrt{\pi}} \int_0^z e^{-z^2} \, dz$$

The right-hand side is a tabulated function known as the Gauss error integral, for which values may be found in most sets of mathematical tables. A graphical representation of the function is shown in Fig. 35-3.

Fig. 35-4. *Schematic representation of concentration gradients for a single eddy.*

A schematic representation of the concentration gradients obtained by this method is shown in Fig. 35-4 for a single eddy.

The rate of diffusion from the interface is

$$N_A = -D_{AB} \left(\frac{\partial \rho_A}{\partial y} \right)_{y=0} \tag{35-31}$$

if we neglect the convective-transport term. The function in Eq. (35-30), when differentiated and inserted in Eq. (35-31), gives

$$N_A = (\rho_{As} - \rho_{Ao}) \sqrt{\frac{D_{AB}}{\pi \theta}} \tag{35-32}$$

The total amount of solute transferred per unit of interfacial area in a contact time θ_c is found by integrating, as in the expression

$$\int_0^{\theta_c} N_A \, d\theta = (\rho_{As} - \rho_{Ao}) \left(\frac{D_{AB}}{\pi} \right)^{\frac{1}{2}} \int_0^{\theta_c} \frac{d\theta}{\theta^{\frac{1}{2}}}$$

$$= 2(\rho_{As} - \rho_{Ao}) \left(\frac{\theta_c D_{AB}}{\pi} \right)^{\frac{1}{2}} \tag{35-33}$$

The average rate over the time θ_c is found by dividing the total amount of solute transferred by θ_c to give

$$N_{A,av} = 2(\rho_{As} - \rho_{Ao}) \left(\frac{D_{AB}}{\pi \theta_c} \right)^{\frac{1}{2}} \tag{35-34}$$

If Eq. (35-34) is compared with Eq. (34-6), defining the mass-transfer coefficient in a steady-state system, we obtain

$$k_\rho(\rho_{As} - \rho_{Ao}) = 2(\rho_{As} - \rho_{Ao}) \left(\frac{D_{AB}}{\pi \theta_c} \right)^{\frac{1}{2}}$$

from which

$$k_\rho = 2 \left(\frac{D_{AB}}{\pi \theta_c} \right)^{1/2} \tag{35-35}$$

This equation is of little value as a method of calculating k because the average contact time of an eddy at the interface θ_c is not usually known. The most valuable conclusion that can be drawn from Eq. (35-35) is that if the penetration theory is correct, the mass-transfer coefficient must be proportional to the square root of the molecular diffusivity. Most mass-transfer correlations are of the type

$$\mathsf{Sh} = a \, \mathsf{Re}^b \, \mathsf{Sc}^c \tag{35-36}$$

The molecular diffusivity D_{AB} appears to the first power in the denominator of the Sherwood number. Because D_{AB} also appears in the denominator of the Schmidt number to the first power, the exponent c must have a value of 0.5 if k_ρ is to be proportional to $D_{AB}^{1/2}$.

If the concept of the stagnant film as the controlling resistance to mass transfer were realized, the mass-transfer coefficient would be related to D_{AB} by the equation[1]

$$k_\rho = \frac{D_{AB}}{\delta_m} \tag{35-37}$$

in which δ_m is the equivalent thickness of the film. This equation is equivalent to Eq. (33-24). The first power dependence of k_ρ on D_{AB} gives a value of zero for the exponent c in Eq. (35-36). Most experimental work indicates a value of c closer to 0.5 than to zero, thus supporting the belief that the penetration theory is a more accurate mechanism for representing interphase mass transfer than the stagnant-film theory.

The penetration theory has been modified by Danckwerts,[2] who proposed that the times of exposure of the surface elements are not the same and that the average rate of mass transfer depends on the distribution of the elements of surface among the various "age groups." The average absorption rate is found by multiplying the fraction of surface which has age θ by the instantaneous absorption rate for a surface of that age and then summing this expression for all elements of surface. Danckwerts proposed a distribution function $\phi(\theta)$ such that the fraction of surface having terminal ages between θ and $\theta + d\theta$ is $\phi(\theta) \, d\theta$. The instantaneous rate of absorption per element is given in Eq. (35-32), so that the instantaneous rate for all elements of age between θ and $\theta + d\theta$ is

---

[1] In this discussion of the penetration theory the mass transferred by bulk flow is not included, so that k_ρ and k_ρ° are identical.

[2] P. V. Danckwerts, *Ind. Eng. Chem.*, **43**:1460 (1951).

$$\phi(\theta)(\rho_{As} - \rho_{Ao}) \left(\frac{D_{AB}}{\pi\theta}\right)^{\frac{1}{2}} d\theta$$

Summing over all ages between $\theta = 0$ and $\theta = \infty$, we obtain, for the instantaneous rate per unit of interfacial area,

$$N_A = \int_0^\infty \phi(\theta)(\rho_{As} - \rho_{Ao}) \left(\frac{D_{AB}}{\pi\theta}\right)^{\frac{1}{2}} d\theta \qquad (35\text{-}38)$$

Danckwerts considered it likely that there is no relation between the age of an element and the probability that the element may be replaced. This distribution of ages can be represented by a function $\phi(\theta)$ of the form

$$\phi(\theta) = se^{-s\theta} \qquad (35\text{-}39)$$

in which s is the fractional rate of renewal of surface (the dimension is reciprocal time). This expression is inserted in Eq. (35-38) to give

$$N_A = (\rho_{As} - \rho_{Ao}) \left(\frac{D_{AB}}{\pi}\right)^{\frac{1}{2}} \int_0^\infty \frac{se^{-s\theta}}{\theta^{\frac{1}{2}}} d\theta = (\rho_{As} - \rho_{Ao})(sD_{AB})^{\frac{1}{2}} \qquad (35\text{-}40)$$

This equation may be combined with the definition of the mass-transfer coefficient k_ρ to give

$$k_\rho(\rho_{As} - \rho_{Ao}) = (\rho_{As} - \rho_{Ao})(sD_{AB})^{\frac{1}{2}}$$

from which we get

$$k_\rho = (sD_{AB})^{\frac{1}{2}} \qquad (35\text{-}41)$$

The constant s must be found experimentally, so that Eq. (35-41) does not provide a direct means of predicting k_ρ. However, it does confirm the square-root relationship between k_ρ and D_{AB} obtained by Higbie.

Although the initial applications suggested for the penetration theory were limited to mass transfer at a gas-liquid interface, it is likely that it is an equally valid picture as a mechanism for transporting heat.[1] It has also been suggested that the mechanism represents transfer in a fluid adjacent to a solid-liquid interface. Johnson and Huang[2] measured rates of solution of organic solids in an agitated vessel and found that the mass-transfer coefficient was related to the diffusivity by an equation similar to Eq. (35-36), in which values of the exponent c ranged from 0.422 to 0.526. Hanratty[3] has also shown that the penetration model represents mass transfer in the vicinity of a solid surface. Figure 35-5 shows a comparison of the dimensionless concentration profiles plotted by Hanratty for mass transfer from a fluid to a solid. The dashed line represents the equation

[1] H. L. Toor and J. M. Marchello, *AIChE Journal*, **4**:97 (1958).
[2] A. I. Johnson and Chen Huang, *AIChE Journal*, **2**:412 (1956).
[3] T. J. Hanratty, *AIChE Journal*, **2**:359 (1956).

Fig. 35-5.   Concentration profile compared with predictions from penetration theory. [From T. J. Hanratty, Journal, AIChE 2:359 (1956).]

of Higbie, which is based on equal ages for all elements.   Danckwerts' results, assuming an age distribution, are shown by the solid line.

Interfacial Turbulence

Although mass transfer of a solute between stagnant, immiscible liquids might be expected to proceed entirely by molecular diffusion, spontaneous interfacial turbulence has been found to occur in a number of systems. The effect of this turbulence is to give much higher mass-transfer rates than would be obtained solely by molecular diffusion.   A recent paper by Sternling and Scriven[1] summarizes a large number of reported instances of this effect.   For example, a solution of 10 per cent methanol in toluene placed quietly in water causes a turbid emulsion of water droplets to appear in the organic phase.   The water phase, however, remains clear. Numerous other examples are cited, and the various forms of observed interfacial turbulence are described.   It is noted that no effect is observed at a liquid-liquid interface when no solute is present.   Sternling and Scriven attribute the turbulence to hydrodynamic instability caused by fluctuations in interfacial tension associated with mass transfer across the interface.

PROBLEMS

35-1. Derive an equation for the mean Sherwood number for a flat plate on which the turbulent boundary layer extends from the leading edge.

35-2. Repeat Prob. 34-1 for a plate 4 in. wide and 2 ft long.   Assume that the transition from a laminar to a turbulent boundary layer occurs at $Re_x = 3 \times 10^5$.

[1] C. V. Sternling and L. E. Scriven, *AIChE Journal*, **5**:514 (1959).

35-3. A pan containing water is placed in a position where it is exposed to a 10-mile-per-hour wind. The pan contains a uniform depth of $\frac{1}{2}$ in. of water, is quite wide, and has a length of 8 ft in the wind direction. The water in the pan is at a constant temperature of 60°F; the moisture content of the air far from the pan is 0.005 lb water/lb air. Find the length of time required for all the water in the pan to evaporate. List any assumptions you must make to work this problem. The kinematic viscosity of the air is 1.70×10^{-4} sq ft/sec; $D_{AB} = 2.79 \times 10^{-4}$ sq ft/sec. The transition to turbulent flow occurs at $\mathbf{Re}_x = 3 \times 10^5$.

SOME DESIGN EQUATIONS FOR
CONVECTIVE MASS TRANSFER
36

The Application of Dimensional Analysis to Mass Transfer

In the two preceding chapters we have derived a number of equations for predicting convective-mass-transfer coefficients in laminar- and turbulent-flow systems. As in the study of heat transfer, we have seen that these equations could be obtained by three methods: (1) the analytical solutions of the basic differential equations, (2) the von Kármán integral method, and (3) the classical Reynolds analogy and subsequent improvements based on a knowledge of the flow regimes adjacent to a solid surface. In addition, we examined the penetration theory, which is based on the principle of surface renewal and seems especially appropriate for describing mass transfer between two fluid phases.

One more method of obtaining equations for predicting mass-transfer coefficients is the use of dimensional analysis. Because this method can be used for both laminar and turbulent systems, it is considered in the present chapter rather than in either of the previous two chapters.

The principles and methods of dimensional analysis have been discussed extensively in Chap. 14 and illustrated by examples in Chaps. 14 and 26. The following example is presented as an illustration of the methods of dimensional analysis applied to mass transfer.

Example 36-1

The principles of dimensional analysis are to be used to find the dimensionless groups which might appear in an equation for predicting the mass-transfer coefficient k_p for a fluid in a vertical pipe. Mass will be assumed to be transferred between the fluid and the pipe wall as the result of a concentration difference $\Delta\rho_A$. The fluid in the pipe may be moving as the result of natural convection associated with density gradients, or as the result of forced convection.

The variables chosen are listed below. They contain only three fundamental dimensions: length $[L]$, mass $[M]$, and time $[\theta]$. Because the variables do not contain any dimensions which can be derived from these three, e.g., force or energy, it is not necessary to include in the list of variables any dimensional constants such as the mechanical equivalent of heat J or the proportionality constant g_c from Newton's second law.

Variable	Symbol	Dimension
Diameter of pipe...................	D	$[L]$
Bulk-fluid density..................	ρ	$[M/L^3]$
Bulk-fluid viscosity................	μ	$[M/L\theta]$
Mass-transfer coefficient...........	k_ρ^o	$[L/\theta]$
Concentration difference............	$\Delta\rho_A$	$[M/L^3]$
Gravitational acceleration...........	g	$[L/\theta^2]$
Bulk velocity......................	u_b	$[L/\theta]$
Molecular diffusivity...............	D_{AB}	$[L^2/\theta]$
Length of pipe.....................	L	$[L]$

The list contains nine variables expressed in terms of three dimensions. It can be determined by manipulating the variables that the maximum number of variables which will not form a dimensional group in this situation equals the number of fundamental dimensions, which is three. If an additional variable is added, however, it becomes possible to form dimensionless groups so that these various groups will be constructed from three common variables combined successively with each of the remaining six variables. The result will be six dimensionless groups.

The first three variables in the list are chosen as common to all groups. The first group is

$$\pi_1 = D^a\rho^b\mu^c(k_\rho^o)^d$$

The dimensions are substituted to give

$$1 = [L]^a \left[\frac{M}{L^3}\right]^b \left[\frac{M}{L\theta}\right]^c \left[\frac{L}{\theta}\right]^d$$

The exponents on the dimensions are summed to give the following equations:

$[L] \qquad 0 = a - 3b - c + d$
$[M] \qquad 0 = b + c$
$[\theta] \qquad 0 = -c - d$

These equations can be solved to give $c = -a = -b = -d$, so that the group π_1 is found to be $(\mu/D\rho k_\rho^o)^c$.

The second group π_2 is formed by writing

$$\pi_2 = D^a\rho^b\mu^c(\Delta\rho_A)^d$$

which gives the following relation among dimensions:

$$1 = [L]^a \left[\frac{M}{L^3}\right]^b \left[\frac{M}{L\theta}\right]^c \left[\frac{M}{L^3}\right]^d$$

The sums of the exponents give the equations

$$[L] \quad 0 = a - 3b - c - 3d$$
$$[M] \quad 0 = b + c + d$$
$$[\theta] \quad 0 = c$$

From the solution of these equations we find $a = c = 0$ and $b = -d$. Thus $\pi_2 = (\Delta\rho_A/\rho)^d$.

Four additional groups are formed by combining D, ρ, and μ with each of the four remaining variables. These groups are found to be

$$\pi_3 = \frac{D^3\rho^2 g}{\mu^2}$$

$$\pi_4 = \frac{D u_b \rho}{\mu}$$

$$\pi_5 = \frac{\mu}{\rho D_{AB}}$$

$$\pi_6 = \frac{L}{D}$$

The six groups found in the preceding example contain at least two groups which have already been found by analytical procedures to affect mass transfer. These are π_4, the Reynolds number, and π_5, the Schmidt number. Additional groups can be recognized by forming suitable combinations. For example, π_5/π_1 reduces to $k_\rho^\circ D/D_{AB}$, which we call the Sherwood number. The product $\pi_2\pi_3\pi_6{}^3$ is the Grashof number for mass transfer, $gL^3\rho\,\Delta\rho/\mu^2$, which was mentioned in Chap. 34.

The combinations of dimensionless groups which describe a series of experimental results (and can be used for predicting future performance) are found by writing equations of the form

$$\pi_1 = \alpha\pi_2{}^\beta\pi_3{}^\gamma\pi_4{}^\delta\pi_5{}^\epsilon\pi_6{}^\zeta \cdots \tag{36-1}$$

and determining the constants by statistical analysis. If the system of Example 36-1 were limited to natural convection, it is likely that the exponent on Reynolds number in Eq. (36-1) would be very close to zero. The other groups would probably have exponents which could be combined to give an equation of the form

$$\frac{\pi_5}{\pi_1} = \alpha(\pi_2\pi_3\pi_6{}^3)^\beta\pi_5{}^\gamma \tag{36-2}$$

which we recognize in more familiar notation as

$$\mathsf{Sh} = \alpha\,\mathsf{Gr}^\beta\,\mathsf{Sc}^\gamma \tag{36-3}$$

If the fluid in the pipe were moving as the result of forced convection, the groups which might influence natural convection (π_2 and π_3) would be found to have small exponents. Hence they would not appear in the final correlation, which would be of the form

$$\frac{\pi_5}{\pi_1} = \alpha \pi_4{}^\beta \pi_5{}^\gamma \pi_6{}^\delta \tag{36-4}$$

The group π_6, L/D, is a measure of the importance of the entrance region for turbulent systems and would likely disappear from most correlations for long pipes, so that the final correlation would be of the form

$$\frac{\pi_5}{\pi_1} = \alpha \pi_4{}^\beta \pi_5{}^\gamma \tag{36-5}$$

which is more familiar when written as

$$\mathsf{Sh} = \alpha \, \mathsf{Re}^\beta \, \mathsf{Sc}^\gamma \tag{36-6}$$

Mass-transfer Coefficients for Flow in Pipes

Most data on mass transfer between a fluid and a pipe wall have been obtained using wetted-wall columns. This device consists basically of a vertical section of circular pipe in which a gas is usually flowing upward. A volatile liquid flows down the inside surface of the pipe and evaporates into the gas stream. The principal reason for the use of wetted-wall columns for studying mass transfer is that the interfacial area is known. This makes it possible to determine the actual mass-transfer coefficient, for example, k_ρ, rather than the product, $k_\rho a$. The gas is usually only slightly soluble in the liquid, so that the liquid at the interface is almost pure. The liquid may be supplied at the adiabatic-saturation temperature.[1] If the column operates adiabatically, the liquid remains at this temperature as it falls through the section, so that the concentration ρ_{As} of the diffusing component in the gas phase at the interface is constant. The wetted-wall column can be used with the gas phase in either laminar or turbulent flow, but care must be taken to avoid the formation of ripples at the vapor-liquid interface since these make it difficult to determine the interfacial area.

It would seem that the correct velocity to be used in the Reynolds number describing the gas flow would be the velocity of the gas relative to that of the liquid, i.e., the sum of the bulk gas velocity and the gas-liquid interfacial velocity (when flow is countercurrent). However, since the interfacial velocity is usually not known, it is customary to use simply the bulk velocity of the gas relative to the wall of column.

Another method of obtaining data on mass-transfer coefficients in pipes is to use pipes cast from some soluble material and to pass a suitable solvent through the pipe. Alternatively, one might cast the pipe from a volatile

[1] This term is defined in Chap. 38.

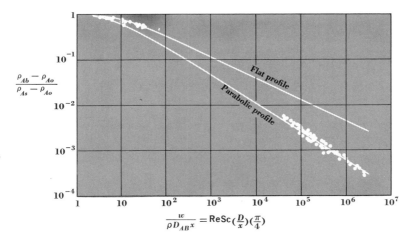

$$\frac{\rho_{Ab} - \rho_{Ao}}{\rho_{As} - \rho_{Ao}}$$

$$\frac{w}{\rho D_{AB} x} = \text{Re} \text{Sc} \left(\frac{D}{x}\right)\left(\frac{\pi}{4}\right)$$

*Fig. 36-1.   Exit concentration of solute for laminar flow in a pipe.
[From W. H. Linton, Jr., and T. K. Sherwood, Chem. Eng. Progr.,
46:258 (1950).]*

substance and pass a gas through the pipe. In both cases solid materials which dissipate very slowly must be used to prevent significant increases in the pipe diameter during an experimental run. Liquid-phase systems usually yield results at higher Schmidt numbers ($\text{Sc} \backsim 2000$) than gases ($\text{Sc} \backsim 1$) because the molecular diffusivity of liquids is of the order of 10^{-5} times the molecular diffusivity of gases.

Laminar Flow. In Chap. 34 it was indicated that predictions of mass transfer for laminar flow in a pipe could be made using the results presented in Chap. 24 on heat transfer with laminar flow in a pipe. Heat-transfer solutions were presented for systems with flat and parabolic velocity profiles for both constant wall temperature and constant heat flux. The solutions for constant wall concentration, which are analogous to the solutions for constant wall temperature, will be considered here; the solutions for a constant mass flux from the wall will not be considered.

The integrated Graetz solutions for the mixing-cup concentration ρ_{Ab} with constant wall concentration and parabolic and flat velocity profiles are shown in Fig. 36-1. The solutions are obtained as follows. The line representing the parabolic profile is found by inserting the mass-transfer solution, which is equivalent to the Graetz solution for heat transfer, Eq. (24-18), into an integral expression for mixing-cup concentration, similar to Eq. (24-19), and integrating over the pipe cross section. The equivalent mass-transfer solution used is simply Eq. (24-18), with the dependent variable taken as $(\rho_{As} - \rho_A)/(\rho_{As} - \rho_{Ao})$ instead of $(t_s - t)/(t_s - t_o)$. The independent variable in Eq. (24-18) is $\text{Re} \, \text{Pr} \, (r_i/x)$. The quantity represented on the abscissa in Fig. 36-1 differs from this by the factor $\pi/2$; it is written $w/\rho D_{AB}x$, which we recognize as $\mathbf{Re}\ \mathbf{Sc}\ \dfrac{D}{x}\dfrac{\pi}{4}$.

The line for the parabolic profile is represented at values of $w/\rho D_{AB}x$ above 400 by means of the approximate equation proposed by Lévêque. This portion can be seen to be linear and is described by the equation

$$\frac{\rho_{Ab} - \rho_{Ao}}{\rho_{As} - \rho_{Ao}} = 5.5 \left(\frac{w}{\rho D_{AB}x}\right)^{-\frac{2}{3}} \tag{36-7}$$

The Lévêque solution was discussed in Prob. 24-2, and as in the case of heat transfer, it applies only for pipe lengths sufficiently short so that the concentration boundary layers do not meet at the center of the pipe.

The solution for a flat velocity profile is also shown in Fig. 36-1. This curve can be calculated from Eq. (24-22) by making the same changes of variables as indicated for the parabolic system. For short tubes (high values of $w/\rho D_{AB}x$) this function can be represented approximately by the equation

$$\frac{\rho_{Ab} - \rho_{Ao}}{\rho_{As} - \rho_{Ao}} = 4.0 \left(\frac{w}{\rho D_{AB}x}\right)^{-\frac{1}{2}} \tag{36-8}$$

The data in Fig. 36-1 at high values of $w/\rho D_{AB}x$ were obtained by the use of soluble pipe walls, as described earlier. This technique was used with Schmidt numbers as high as 3000. It can be seen that the data fit the theoretical line for the parabolic profile quite well. At low values of $w/\rho D_{AB}x$ the results appear to be closer to the line based on the assumption of a flat velocity profile. These data were obtained by the operation of a wetted-wall column in which liquids were vaporized into a gas stream. For these systems the Schmidt number was approximately unity. The fact that the values lie above the line representing the parabolic profile has been attributed to natural-convection effects.

Turbulent Flow. Extensive data on mass transfer with turbulent flow in wetted-wall columns have been obtained by Gilliland and Sherwood.[1] Results for nine liquids evaporating into air are shown in Fig. 36-2. The best-fitting straight line is represented by the equation

$$\frac{k_c^o D}{D_{AB}} = 0.023 \left(\frac{D u_b \rho}{\mu}\right)^{0.83} \left(\frac{\mu}{\rho D_{AB}}\right)^{0.44} \tag{36-9}$$

The Sherwood number in this equation is often written as $\dfrac{k_p D}{D_{AB}}\dfrac{p_{B,lm}}{p}$ when applied to gases. In these groups $k_p p_{B,lm}/p$ is identical with $k_p(1 - \bar{x}_A)_{lm}$ if the gas phase is ideal. The group $k_p(1 - \bar{x}_A)_{lm}$ represents a form of the

[1] E. R. Gilliland and T. K. Sherwood, *Ind. Eng. Chem.*, **26**:516 (1934).

Fig. 36-2.   Mass-transfer coefficients for vaporization of liquids with turbulent gas flow in a wetted-wall column. [From E. R. Gilliland and T. K. Sherwood, Ind. Eng. Chem., 26:516 (1934).]

mass-transfer coefficient which is independent of concentration effects and is defined in Chap. 33 as k_ρ^o.

Additional equations for turbulent mass transfer in a pipe can be obtained from the analogies between mass and momentum transfer in Chap. 35. Equation (35-28) relates the Sherwood number to the friction factor as follows:

$$\frac{\mathsf{Sh}}{\mathsf{Re}\,\mathsf{Sc}^{\frac{1}{3}}} = \frac{f}{2} \tag{35-28}$$

This equation is based on Colburn's *j*-factor relation. If an empirical equation for the friction factor is combined with Eq. (35-28), we obtain an equation which can be solved directly for the Sherwood number. Equation (13-72) is a convenient form, applicable to a smooth pipe.

$$f = 0.046\,\mathsf{Re}^{-0.20} \tag{13-72}$$

If this expression is combined with Eq. (35-2), we obtain

$$\mathsf{Sh} = 0.023\,\mathsf{Re}^{0.80}\,\mathsf{Sc}^{0.33} \tag{36-10}$$

This expression gives results quite close to those predicted by Eq. (36-9), differing chiefly in the exponent on the Schmidt number. The experimental results which led to Eq. (36-9) were obtained for systems in which the Schmidt number varied only from 0.6 to 2.5, so the exponent 0.44 is questionable. In the work of Linton and Sherwood, referred to in the section on laminar flow, some runs were made in the turbulent-flow regime with Schmidt numbers between 1000 and 2200. These results, when combined with the wetted-wall data of Gilliland, indicate that the correct exponent on the Schmidt number is 0.33. Consequently, Eq. (36-10) is recommended as being applicable over a wider range than Eq. (36-9).

The Prandtl-Taylor and von Kármán analogies can also be combined with Eq. (13-72) to give equations for predicting mass-transfer coefficients. However, the Colburn analogy has been found to give generally satisfactory results and has the advantage of simplicity.

The mass-transfer coefficients for turbulent flow in Eqs. (36-9) and (36-10) can be applied either to point conditions in the region of developed flow or to the entire pipe surface if the pipe length is greater than 50 diameters. The mass-transfer coefficient at the pipe entrance is infinite, just as is the heat-transfer coefficient. However, with turbulent flow the region of developed flow is usually attained in 10 pipe diameters or less, after which the coefficient is substantially constant at the value predicted from the correlation. When the pipe length exceeds 50 diameters, the high values of the coefficient near the entrance contribute so little to the total mass transfer that the mean coefficient for the entire pipe is approximately the same as the local coefficient in the developed flow region.

Example 36-2

Air passes through a naphthalene tube which has an inside diameter of 1 in. and a length of 6 ft at bulk velocities of (a) 2 ft/sec and (b) 50 ft/sec. The air is at 50°F and has an average pressure of 1 atm. Assuming that the change in pressure along the tube is negligible and that the naphthalene surface is at 50°F, find the per cent saturation of the discharge air and the sublimation rate of naphthalene in the tube in pounds per hour.

Properties of air at 50°F, 1 atm $\rho = 0.078$ lb/cu ft
$\mu = 1.20 \times 10^{-5}$ lb/(ft)(sec)

Properties of naphthalene at 50°F   Vapor pressure $= 0.0209$ mm Hg
Molecular diffusivity in air $= 0.200$ sq ft/hr
Molecular weight $= 128.2$

(a) $u_b = 2$ ft/sec

$$\text{Re} = \frac{(\frac{1}{12})(2)(0.078)}{1.20 \times 10^{-5}}$$

$$= 1080 \qquad \text{(hence laminar flow)}$$

$$\text{Sc} = \frac{(1.20 \times 10^{-5})(3600)}{(0.078)(0.200)}$$

$$= 2.77$$

$$\text{Re Sc} \frac{D}{x} \frac{\pi}{4} = (1080)(2.77)(\tfrac{1}{72}) \left(\frac{\pi}{4} \right)$$

$$= 32.6$$

From Fig. 36-1, using the curve for the parabolic profile, we find

$$\frac{\rho_{Ab} - \rho_{Ao}}{\rho_{As} - \rho_{Ao}} = 0.42$$

The air entering the tube is assumed to be free from naphthalene, so that $\rho_{Ao} = 0$. The concentration ρ_{As} of naphthalene at the interface is found from the vapor pressure by the following approximation (valid for dilute mixtures):

$$\rho_{As} = \frac{(0.0209)(128)(0.078)}{(760)(29)}$$

$$= 9.5 \times 10^{-6} \text{ lb/cu ft}$$

Therefore the exit concentration of naphthalene is

$$\rho_{Ab} = (0.42)(9.5 \times 10^{-6})$$
$$= 4.0 \times 10^{-6} \text{ lb/cu ft}$$

$$\text{Total evaporation rate} = \left(\frac{\pi}{4}\right)\left(\frac{1}{12}\right)^2 (2)(4.0 \times 10^{-6})(3600)$$

$$= 1.6 \times 10^{-4} \text{ lb/hr}$$

The exit air is 42 per cent saturated, as was shown by the reading from Fig. 36-1.

(b) $u_b = 50$ ft/sec

$$\textsf{Re} = \frac{(\frac{1}{12})(50)(0.078)}{1.20 \times 10^{-5}}$$

$$= 27,000$$

For turbulent flow we use Eq. (36-10) to find the mass-transfer coefficient.

$$\textsf{Sh} = 0.023(27,000)^{0.8}(2.77)^{0.33}$$
$$= (0.023)(3500)(1.40)$$
$$= 113$$

The mole fraction of naphthalene is so low that $(1 - \tilde{x}_A)_{lm} \sim 1$. Hence $k_\rho^o = k_\rho$.

$$k_\rho = \frac{(113)(0.200)}{(\frac{1}{12})}$$

$$= 271 \text{ ft/hr}$$

A naphthalene balance is written for a differential length of tube. Because of the low vaporization rate, the total volumetric rate of flow can be assumed to be independent of the distance from the tube inlet.

$$\frac{\pi}{4}\left(\frac{1}{12}\right)^2 (50) \, d\rho_{Ab} = k_\rho \frac{\pi}{12} \, dx \, (\rho_{As} - \rho_{Ab})$$

This is rearranged to give

$$\int_0^{\rho_{Ab}} \frac{d\rho_{Ab}}{\rho_{As} - \rho_{Ab}} = \frac{48}{50} k_\rho \int_0^6 dx$$

This equation is integrated and gives the expression

$$-\ln \frac{\rho_{As} - \rho_{Ab}}{\rho_{As}} = \frac{(48)(271)(6)}{(50)(3600)}$$

$$= 0.43$$

from which we obtain

$$\frac{\rho_{As}}{\rho_{As} - \rho_{Ab}} = 1.54$$

This is solved to give the exit mixing-cup concentration.

$$\rho_{Ab} = 0.35\rho_{As}$$
$$= (0.35)(9.5 \times 10^{-6})$$
$$= 3.33 \times 10^{-6} \text{ lb/cu ft}$$

$$\text{Total evaporation rate} = \frac{\pi}{4}\left(\frac{1}{12}\right)^2 (50)(3.33 \times 10^{-6})(3600)$$

$$= 3.3 \times 10^{-3} \text{ lb/hr}$$

The exit air is 35 per cent saturated.

Mass-transfer Coefficients for Two-phase Flow in Packed Beds

The measurement of mass-transfer coefficients for packed beds has been the subject of much research for the past thirty years. In spite of this effort, the complexity of the problem is so great that the reliability of predicted mass-transfer rates is still far from satisfactory. In the correlations for packed beds to be presented in this chapter, experimental results frequently deviate by as much as 25 per cent from the recommended correlations, and in a number of systems the deviation is even greater.

Some of the reasons for these deviations have been indicated in preceding chapters. The principal difficulty seems to be in the determination of the interfacial area. Another difficulty arises from the fact that most measurements are for over-all coefficients representing a pair of resistances in series. To determine single-phase coefficients, the experimental system must be arranged so that one resistance is either negligible or can be calculated. A third difficulty is that very little is known regarding entrance effects in packed beds. Most experimental systems involve much shorter beds than are found in industry. As a consequence, end effects may exert a greater influence in the experimental systems than in the industrial systems.

As a result of the inadequacy of theoretical methods for predicting mass-transfer coefficients, the designers of mass-transfer equipment lean heavily on performance data whenever possible. Perry's Handbook gives several pages (pp. 687–698) of data on HTUs (these were defined in Chap. 33) for both single- and two-phase systems for a variety of fluid systems and packings. A summary of articles containing data on HTUs is given by Cornell, Knapp, and Fair.[1] In addition, correlations to be given below can be used for the calculation of individual coefficients or HTUs.

Gases. The experimental results for gas-phase resistance have been measured in a variety of ways. One way has been to absorb a gas in a liquid in which it has a very low vapor pressure or in which a rapid reac-

[1] D. Cornell, W. G. Knapp, and J. R. Fair, *Chem. Eng. Progr.*, **56**:68 (1960).

tion occurs between the absorbed solute and some nonvolatile component in the liquid. The resistance to mass transfer in the liquid phase is assumed to be negligible, so that the over-all coefficient is identical with the gas-phase coefficient. This technique must be used with discretion; in the past it has sometimes been used in systems in which the resistance in the liquid phase has not been negligible. A second method has been to vaporize a pure liquid flowing down the tower into an insoluble gas passing the liquid. As a third method, the resistance of the liquid phase may be predicted from appropriate correlations and subtracted from the total resistance to give the gas-phase resistance. This latter method has been used by Fellinger for the determination of gas-phase coefficients in systems in which ammonia is absorbed from air into water flowing over various kinds of packing. A substantial amount of Fellinger's data is reproduced in the section of Perry referred to above. Curves for both H_G and H_{OG} are shown to depend on both gas and liquid rates. The data for H_G, expressed in feet, have been correlated by an empirical equation of the form

$$H_G = \alpha G^\beta L^\gamma Sc^{0.5} \qquad (36\text{-}11)$$

in which gas and liquid mass velocities are expressed in lb/(hr)(sq ft). The use of the Schmidt number is to permit generalization of the results to systems other than air and ammonia. The exponent on the Schmidt number of 0.5 is justifiable on the basis of the penetration theory, in which the mass-transfer coefficient k_ρ was shown to be a function of $D_{AB}^{0.5}$. The exponents in Eq. (36-11) are not really constants, but depend on both the packing and the gas and liquid rates. A table of these values is given by Treybal; sample results are shown in Table 36-1.

Table 36-1. Constants† for Determining H_G in Eq. (36-11)

Type of packing	α	β	γ	Range of values, lb/(hr)(sq ft)	
				G	L
Raschig rings:					
⅜-in..............	2.32	0.45	−0.47	200–500	500–1500
1-in...............	7.00	0.39	−0.58	200–800	400–500
	6.41	0.32	−0.51	200–600	500–4500
2-in...............	3.82	0.41	−0.45	200–800	500–4500
Berl saddles:					
½-in..............	32.4	0.30	−0.74	200–700	500–1500
	0.811	0.30	−0.24	200–700	1500–4500
1-in...............	1.97	0.36	−0.40	200–800	400–4500
1½-in............	5.05	0.32	−0.45	200–1000	400–4500

† From R. E. Treybal, "Mass-transfer Operations," p. 239, McGraw-Hill Book Company, Inc., New York, 1955.

A similar correlation for gas-phase coefficients has been suggested by Sherwood [1] as representative of the data of a number of investigators. This correlation, when expressed in the form of Eq. (36-11), proposes values of 1.01, 0.31, and −0.33 for the constants α, β, and γ, respectively. Within the limits of accuracy of the data, there is no distinction associated with packing size.

Liquids. Most experimental results for liquid-phase mass-transfer coefficients have been obtained by the absorption or desorption in water of gases of slight solubility. Typical gases used have been oxygen, hydrogen, and carbon dioxide. For these systems the slope of the line representing Henry's law is quite large, so that the average over-all mass-transfer coefficient (which is measured from terminal conditions) and the liquid-phase mass-transfer coefficient are approximately equal, as can be deduced from Eq. (33-21).

An extensive investigation of liquid-phase mass transfer has been described by Sherwood and Holloway. Their results are correlated by the following empirical equation:

$$H_L = \phi \left(\frac{L}{\mu} \right)^{\eta} \mathbf{Sc}^{0.5} \tag{36-12}$$

The height of a transfer unit H_L is expressed in feet, the liquid rate L in lb/(hr)(sq ft), and the viscosity μ of the liquid phase in lb/(ft)(hr). The Schmidt number applies to the liquid phase. The constants ϕ and η depend on the type of packing. Typical values recommended by Sherwood and Holloway are given in Table 36-2.

Table 36-2. *Constants† for Determining H_L in Eq. (36-12)*

Type of packing	ϕ	η	Range of L
Raschig rings:			
⅜-in....................	0.0018	0.46	400–15,000
1-in.....................	0.010	0.22	400–15,000
2-in.....................	0.012	0.22	400–15,000
Berl saddles:			
½-in....................	0.0067	0.28	400–15,000
1-in.....................	0.0059	0.28	400–15,000
1½-in...................	0.0062	0.28	400–15,000

† From T. K. Sherwood and F. A. L. Holloway, *Trans. AIChE,* **36**:39 (1940).

Most experimental results show that H_L is independent of the gas rate except at very high gas velocities, so that Eq. (36-12) does not contain the term G. The definition of H_L is given as

[1] T. K. Sherwood and R. L. Pigford, "Absorption and Extraction," 2d ed., p. 285, McGraw-Hill Book Company, Inc., New York, 1952.

Gas rate G, lb/(hr)(sq ft)

Fig. 36-3. Effective interfacial area for 0.5-in. Raschig rings. [From H. L. Shulman, C. F. Ulrich, A. Z. Proulz, and J. O. Zimmerman, AIChE Journal, 1:253 (1955).]

$$H_L = \frac{\tilde{L}}{k_{\tilde{x}}^o a} \qquad (33\text{-}31)$$

Thus it can be seen that H_L varies directly with the liquid rate and also as a result of whatever effect the liquid rate has on $k_{\tilde{x}}^o$ and a. The net effect of these three factors is expressed in the empirical constant η in Eq. (36-12). As for the dependence of H_L on the gas rate, it can be seen from Eq. (33-31) that if the gas rate affects either $k_{\tilde{x}}^o$ or a, then H_L should be dependent on G. Investigations by Shulman et al.[1] indicate that $k_{\tilde{x}}^o$ is independent of the gas rate and that the interfacial area a is almost independent of gas velocity for Raschig rings and Berl saddles with a size of 1 in. and greater. For smaller sizes, however, a significant increase occurs and should be reflected in any correlation such as Eq. (36-12).

The same investigation by Shulman and coauthors indicates the reason for the strong dependence of H_G on both gas and liquid rates. H_G is defined as

$$H_G = \frac{\tilde{G}}{k_{\tilde{y}}^o a} \qquad (33\text{-}30)$$

In this equation the mass-transfer coefficient $k_{\tilde{y}}^o$ and the gas rate $\tilde{G}$ establish a dependence of H_G on the gas velocity while the strong effect of liquid rate on the interfacial area a makes H_G also dependent on L. Hence

[1] H. L. Shulman, C. F. Ulrich, A. Z. Proulx, and J. O. Zimmerman, *AIChE Journal*, 1:253 (1955).

both G and L enter Eq. (36-11) for calculating H_G. Figure 36-3 shows typical data for the interfacial area as a function of G and L to illustrate the basis for these assertions.

Mass Transfer from Spheres and Cylinders

Extensive data have been taken on both heat and mass transfer from single spheres. Much of the mass-transfer work has been done using liquid spheres evaporating into a passing air stream. Other investigations have employed spheres of solid material which have either sublimed into passing air streams or dissolved into a passing stream of liquid. As might be expected, the results of both heat- and mass-transfer research are represented by similar equations. Equation (26-11) for heat transfer from single spheres describes mass transfer if the Nusselt and Prandtl numbers are replaced by the Sherwood and Schmidt numbers. For mass transfer it is written as

$$\frac{k_\rho^o D}{D_{AB}} = 2 + 0.6 \left(\frac{\mu}{\rho D_{AB}}\right)^{1/3} \left(\frac{D u_o \rho}{\mu}\right)^{1/2} \tag{36-13}$$

The constant 2 in this equation can be derived in the manner suggested for the analogous situation in heat transfer in Chap. 26. The analysis is based on a system in which molecular diffusion of a single component occurs at steady state outward from a spherical surface into an infinite, stagnant medium. The second term on the right-hand side of Eq. (36-13) represents the contribution of the fluid motion to mass transfer from the sphere.

Mass transfer from beds of spheres and other solids is important in the analysis of the performance of beds of catalyst particles. Most of the investigations in this field have been with beds of porous solids in which water is evaporated into an air stream. Hobson and Thodos[1] have extended the correlations of previous workers by measuring mass-transfer rates from packed beds to liquid streams. Figure 36-4 shows their results, with the line recommended as fitting the data. The correlation applies to cylinders as well as spheres; the equivalent diameter of a cylinder is taken as $(D_c x_e + D_c^2/2)^{1/2}$, in which D_c is the actual diameter of the cylinder and x_e is the length. The velocity term in **Re** is the superficial velocity.

An alternative method of estimating mass-transfer coefficients for a packed bed is to use the procedure suggested by Ranz, which is described in detail for heat transfer in Chap. 26. The technique is to multiply the superficial fluid velocity in the bed by 10.73 and to use this figure for the velocity in **Re** in Eq. (36-13). The value obtained for the mass-transfer coefficient as a result of this procedure is about 10 per cent higher than the

[1] M. Hobson and G. Thodos, *Chem. Eng. Progr.*, **45**:517 (1949).

Fig. 36-4.   Average mass-transfer coefficients for single-phase flow in packed beds.   [From M. Hobson and G. Thodos, Chem. Eng. Progr., 45:517 (1949).]

average mass-transfer coefficient for a bed of randomly packed, nearly spherical particles.   The data used by Ranz to test this hypothesis are those of Gamson, Thodos, and Hougen, which are shown in Fig. 36-4. Since these data are represented by the correlations of both Ranz and Hobson and Thodos, it is obvious that the two methods are equivalent over the range tested.   Additional experimental results of Hobson and Thodos in Fig. 36-4, however, cover a much wider range of $\mathbf{Re}$ than has been tested by Ranz.

Mass transfer in both fixed and fluidized beds has been studied by Bradshaw.[1]   Experimental measurements were made of the rates of evaporation of moisture from beds of porous spheres and pellets.   The results for fixed beds check closely those of Hobson and Thodos and other investigators, shown in Fig. 36-4.   The results for fixed beds extend as low as $\mathbf{Re}_p = 400$ and for fluidized beds as high as $\mathbf{Re}_p = 12,000$.   The mass-transfer coefficients for both fixed and fluidized beds were correlated for the entire range of Reynolds number by the equation

$$j_M = 1.90 \, (\mathbf{Re}_p)^{-0.50} \tag{36-14}$$

The standard deviation of this correlation was 18 per cent for the five

[1] Robert D. Bradshaw, Ph.D. thesis in chemical engineering, Purdue University, Lafayette, Ind., August, 1961.

different kinds of particles used. A similar equation was found to correlate heat-transfer coefficients in fixed and fluidized beds.

Mass Transfer in Spheres, Drops, and Bubbles

A number of operations involve mass transfer between a continuous fluid and a discontinuous phase. The discontinuous phase may be solid spheres or other particles which are being dried; it may consist of liquid drops from which a solute is being extracted, or it may consist of bubbles in which transfer of a less volatile substance is occurring to the vapor-liquid interface, with simultaneous transfer of a more volatile component back into the gaseous phase. In the preceding section of this chapter we have considered mass transfer in a continuous phase. We shall now examine mass transfer in the discontinuous phase.

If the discontinuous phase consists of solid material or of stagnant gas or liquid, the only mechanism of transport within this phase is molecular diffusion. The partial differential equations for unsteady-state diffusion may be written in spherical coordinates and solved if the discontinuous phase has spherical symmetry. The solution for the concentration of diffusing component at any radial position as a function of time may then be integrated from the center to the surface to obtain the bulk, or mixing-cup, concentration as a function of time. A solution to this problem is shown in Fig. 36-5 for a sphere of uniform initial concentration ρ_{Ao} immersed in a continuous phase of bulk concentration ρ_{As}. The bulk concentration ρ_{Ab} in the sphere is shown as a function of molecular diffusivity D_{AB}, sphere diameter D, and time of contact θ.

The solution for the rigid sphere referred to above is found in a number of advanced textbooks on heat transfer and diffusion.[1] The family of curves in Fig. 36-5 is applicable both to systems in which the interfacial concentration is constant and to systems in which the interfacial concentration varies because of a resistance to mass transfer in the continuous phase. The resistance to mass transfer in the continuous phase determines the value of the parameter $k_p^o D/D_{AB}$. The mass-transfer coefficient k_p^o for the continuous phase can be estimated from Eq. (36-13). D_{AB} is the molecular diffusivity of the solute with respect to the second constituent in the sphere, and D is the sphere diameter.

If the discontinuous phase is a fairly nonviscous liquid and if the sphere is a liquid drop greater than 1 or 2 mm in diameter, it is likely that the drop will not be stagnant. It has been shown by a number of investigators that viscous circulation often occurs within spherical drops in the manner

[1] J. Crank, "The Mathematics of Diffusion," p. 91, Clarendon Press, Oxford, 1956.

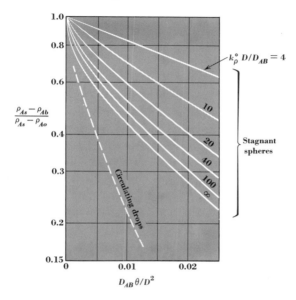

Fig. 36-5.   Bulk concentration change in stagnant and circulating drops.

shown in Fig. 36-6.   The liquid is stagnant only along a circular ring which cuts the horizontal plane of the drop shown here at points A.   On the outer surface of the drop there is circulation from B to C to D.

An analysis of mass transfer in circulating drops has been made by Kronig and Brink,[1] who assumed that the streamlines shown in Fig. 36-6 are lines of constant concentration and that unsteady-state molecular diffusion occurs normal to the streamlines.   Their solution is shown graphically as the dashed line in Fig. 36-5.   Unlike the solution for the stagnant drops shown on the same figure, the solution for the circulating drops applies only for negligible resistance to mass transfer in the continuous phase.   In this way it corresponds to the bottom line of the family of curves for stagnant drops.

Other possible mechanisms of mass transfer within drops include natural convection due to concentration gradients.   This mechanism might be superimposed on the circulation mechanism described above.   Circulation is also affected if dirt or other foreign material collects at the interface between the drop and the bulk phase.   A final possibility is that a state of turbulent mixing may exist within the drop so that its concentration may be nearly uniform at any instant.   This would be equivalent to assuming negligible resistance to mass transfer within the drop.   Such a

[1] R. Kronig and J. C. Brink, *Appl. Sci. Research*, **A2**:142 (1950).

Fig. 36-6. *Circulating pattern for a rising drop or bubble.*

condition probably exists for most large gas bubbles. In these circumstances nearly the entire resistance is in the continuous phase.

A condition of complete mixing may be approached for liquid drops which rise only a short distance. During formation and immediately afterward, the drops may undergo considerable oscillation, which causes mixing. For a short time of rise, this oscillation may persist for the entire period of immersion, with the result that the dispersed phase will offer a negligible resistance to mass transfer. Under these circumstances the outside resistance will also be decreased from the value predicted for a perfect sphere from Eq. (36-13).

The contacting of two fluid phases in the manner described above is done in vessels known as spray towers, which are little more than empty shells. An extensive discussion of the operation of this type of equipment is given by Treybal.[1] Performance data are also presented by Treybal for predicting flow capacities and extraction rates. The extraction-rate data are of limited value because of uncertainty regarding the size of drops produced. The effect of drop size on mass-transfer rate is very great, as can be seen in Fig. 36-5.

PROBLEMS

36-1. A cylindrical tube with an ID of 1 in. is cast from benzoic acid. Water at 57°F flows through the tube at a bulk velocity of 0.1 ft/sec. How long must the tube be if the solution leaving the tube is to be 1 per cent saturated with benzoic acid? What is the mean mass-transfer coefficient for this system based on an arithmetic

[1] R. E. Treybal, "Liquid Extraction," chap. 10, McGraw-Hill Book Company, Inc., New York, 1951.

average driving force?   The saturation concentration of benzoic acid in water at 57°F is 2.36 g/1, and the Schmidt number is 1870.

36-2. Repeat Prob. 36-1 for a bulk velocity of 10 ft/sec.

36-3. A stream of air at 25°C containing 5 mole per cent ethanol is passed upward at the rate of 400 lb/(hr)(sq ft) through a tower packed with 1-in. Raschig rings.   The ethanol is to be absorbed by a countercurrent stream of water at 25°C flowing at a rate of 1000 lb/(hr)(sq ft).   Find H_L, H_G, H_{OL}, and H_{OG}.   How would you account for the relative magnitude of the gas- and the liquid-phase resistances?

36-4. A naphthalene sphere with a diameter of ½ in. is placed in a closed room at 50°F.   Find the length of time required for the sphere to disappear completely, assuming the air in the room to be an infinite, stagnant medium.   The unsteady-state process of evaporation is so slow that sublimation from the surface of the sphere at any instant can be treated as though it were occurring from a sphere of constant diameter.   The physical properties of air and naphthalene can be found in Example 36-2.

36-5. The naphthalene sphere of Prob. 36-4 is suspended in an air stream at 50°F moving with a velocity of 30 ft/sec.   Find the length of time required for the sphere to sublime completely, assuming it to remain spherical.   Comment on the shape the particle will actually acquire.

36-6. Acetic acid is to be removed from an aqueous solution by allowing droplets of acetic acid–water solution to fall through a column of benzene.   The initial concentration of acetic acid is 0.01 weight per cent, and this is to be reduced to 0.005 weight per cent.   Find the distance the drops must fall if the drops have a diameter of 1 mm and are assumed to be (a) stagnant, (b) circulating, (c) completely mixed.   Both fluid phases are at 20°C.   At this temperature the diffusivity of acetic acid in water is 0.88×10^{-5} sq cm/sec, and the diffusivity of acetic acid in benzene is 1.92×10^{-5} sq cm/sec.   The drops may be assumed to achieve their terminal velocity very quickly.   This velocity can be estimated using a drag coefficient taken from Fig. 15-6.   For part (b) it is necessary to neglect the resistance to mass transfer in the continuous phase.

CONTINUOUS CONTACTING OF
IMMISCIBLE PHASES
37

Mass-transfer coefficients and transfer units have been defined and ap-plied to a number of flow situations in Chaps. 33 to 36. The material in these chapters is analogous to that in Chaps. 23 to 26 on convective heat-transfer coefficients. Chapters 27 and 28 have no counterpart in mass transfer, but Chap. 29, which discusses the integration of the heat-transfer-rate equation over the area of a heat exchanger, has many points of sim-ilarity to this chapter. We shall discuss here the integration of the mass-transfer-rate equation over the area of interphase contact in equip-ment such as a gas-absorption tower or a liquid-liquid-extraction tower.

In the study of convective heat transfer we considered the flow of heat from one fluid to another through a conducting wall. The wall prevented direct contact between the fluids. In mass transfer there is no wall and the fluids are in direct contact. However, if the fluids are immiscible, the mass-transfer area is found by methods similar to the methods used for finding the heat-transfer area as shown in Chap. 29. In the present chapter we study mass transfer between immiscible fluids for simple cases for which heat-transfer effects are not important. In Chap. 38 we shall study the simultaneous transfer of heat and mass between immiscible phases.

The study of the application of the principles of mass transfer to the separation operations is complicated in comparison with heat transfer by two additional factors. First, the interphase contacting is often performed by stages, rather than continuously, as in heat exchangers. Second, the phases in direct contact may be partially miscible, and this situation causes complications in the solutions of the mass balances for the ternary or multicomponent systems which must be considered. Operations involving these additional factors are studied in Chaps. 39 *et seq.*

Integrated Equations for a Tower

We begin the study of separation operations by a consideration of the gas-absorption tower shown in Fig. 37-1. A mixture of air and a solute A, which is soluble in water, is blown into the bottom of the tower and rises at a rate $\tilde{G}$, measured in lb moles/(hr)(sq ft of cross section of empty tower). The tower is filled with a packing made of ceramic rings. Water, which absorbs component A, flows down over the packing at $\tilde{L}$ lb moles/(hr)(sq ft of cross section of empty tower).

Although the concentration in each phase diminishes with distance z up the tower, mass transfer in the z direction is usually assumed to be negligible. The solute is transferred in the direction of decreasing concentration from the bulk of the gas phase to the liquid interface and then to the bulk of the liquid phase. Transfer occurs by both eddy and molecular diffusion and is described by the various convective mass-transfer coefficients. If the tower is very high, almost all the solute is removed from the gas leaving at the top.

Any one of the rate equations (33-7) to (33-10) applies at a point in the tower. The total amount of A transferred per unit time in the tower can be expressed by an equation like

$$(\tilde{N}_A)_{\text{av}} A_i = k_{\tilde{y},\text{av}}(\tilde{y}_A - \tilde{y}_{As})_{\text{av}} A_i \tag{37-1}$$

in which A_i is the total interfacial area. The right-hand side of Eq. (37-1) contains the average concentration difference. In general, this quantity must be found by integration, but in some simplified cases we shall see that the logarithmic mean of the terminal concentration differences applies, just as the logarithmic mean temperature difference applied to certain heat exchangers. The left-hand side of Eq. (37-1) is equal to the change from the top to the bottom of the tower of the product of the flow rate of one of the phases and its concentration; this quantity is analogous to the total heat-transfer rate in an exchanger.

We now proceed to the derivation of an equation giving the tower height in terms of the flow rates, coefficients, and terminal concentrations. At any height z above the bottom of the tower, we assume that the concentrations are uniform over the cross section of the tower. Since conditions change with z, Eq. (33-7), for example, applies only for a differential element of interfacial area dA_i of height dz. It is customary to express A_i

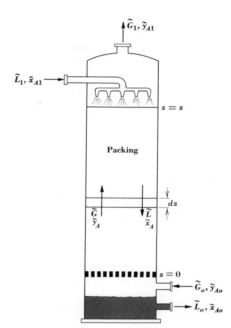

Fig. 37-1.   Packed gas-absorption tower.

in terms of the quantity a (the interfacial area per unit volume of tower), the height z, and the cross-sectional area of the empty tower A:

$$A_i = aAz \tag{37-2}$$

or if a is assumed constant,

$$dA_i = aA \, dz \tag{37-3}$$

We then write Eq. (33-7) as

$$\tilde{N}_A \, dA_i = k_{\tilde{y}} a(\tilde{y}_A - \tilde{y}_{As}) A \, dz \tag{37-4}$$

The left-hand side of Eq. (37-4) is the mass transferred in the height dz; this is also given by

$$-\tilde{N}_A \, dA_i = A d(\tilde{G}\tilde{y}_A) = A d(\tilde{L}\tilde{x}_A) \tag{37-5}$$

This equation can be integrated over the tower between the concentration limits shown in Fig. 37-1 to yield

$$(\tilde{N}_A)_{av} A_i = A(\tilde{G}_o\tilde{y}_{Ao} - \tilde{G}_1\tilde{y}_{A1}) = A(\tilde{L}_o\tilde{x}_{Ao} - \tilde{L}_1\tilde{x}_{A1}) \tag{37-6}$$

Alternatively, the mass balances can be integrated from the bottom of the tower to any intermediate point where the concentrations are $\tilde{x}_A$ and $\tilde{y}_A$.

$$\tilde{G}_o\tilde{y}_{Ao} - \tilde{G}\tilde{y}_A = \tilde{L}_o\tilde{x}_{Ao} - \tilde{L}\tilde{x}_A \tag{37-7}$$

or

$$\tilde{y}_A = \frac{\tilde{L}}{\tilde{G}}\,\tilde{x}_A + \frac{1}{\tilde{G}}\,(\tilde{G}_o\tilde{y}_{Ao} - \tilde{L}_o\tilde{x}_{Ao}) \qquad (37\text{-}8)$$

The concentrations of contiguous phases in a tower are given by Eqs. (37-7) and (37-8). The line representing Eq. (37-8) on a graph of $\tilde{y}_A$ versus $\tilde{x}_A$ is called an operating line. With the units used here, the operating line is in general curved; $\tilde{G}$ and $\tilde{L}$ are functions of $\tilde{x}_A$. However, for dilute solutions, the operating line becomes straight.

Equations (37-4) and (37-5) are now combined to give

$$-dz = \frac{d(\tilde{G}\tilde{y}_A)}{k_{\tilde{y}}a(\tilde{y}_A - \tilde{y}_{As})} \qquad (37\text{-}9)$$

Since the phases are immiscible, the molal mass velocity of inert fluid in the z direction (air in this case), $\tilde{G}_B$, is a constant. Thus an equation for $\tilde{G}$ is

$$\tilde{G} = \frac{\tilde{G}_B}{1 - \tilde{y}_A} \qquad (37\text{-}10)$$

This expression for $\tilde{G}$ is substituted in Eq. (37-9), and the indicated differential is taken. We obtain

$$-dz = \frac{\tilde{G}\,d\tilde{y}_A}{k_{\tilde{y}}a(1 - \tilde{y}_A)(\tilde{y}_A - \tilde{y}_{As})} \qquad (37\text{-}11)$$

The right-hand side of Eq. (37-11) appears difficult to integrate, for $\tilde{G}$ varies, and $k_{\tilde{y}}a$ is a function of $\tilde{G}$ and $(1 - \tilde{y}_A)_{lm}$. However, the coefficient $k_{\tilde{y}}^o a$ is by definition independent of $(1 - \tilde{y}_A)_{lm}$ [Eq. (33-26)]. We therefore write Eq. (37-11) as

$$-dz = \frac{\tilde{G}}{k_{\tilde{y}}^o a}\,\frac{(1 - \tilde{y}_A)_{lm}\,d\tilde{y}_A}{(1 - \tilde{y}_A)(\tilde{y}_A - \tilde{y}_{As})} \qquad (37\text{-}12)$$

We recognize the group $\tilde{G}/k_{\tilde{y}}^o a$ as the height of the transfer unit H_G [Eq. (33-34)]. Since H_G is roughly proportional to $\tilde{G}^{0.3}$ (Table 36-1), a 20 per cent change in $\tilde{G}$ produces a change of only about 6 per cent in H_G. Since $\tilde{G}$ rarely changes by more than 20 per cent, it is permissible to neglect the variation of H_G over a tower. The limits of integration can be deduced from Figs. 37-1 and 37-2, so that Eq. (37-12) becomes

$$z = H_G \int_{\tilde{y}_{A1}}^{\tilde{y}_{Ao}} \frac{(1 - \tilde{y}_A)_{lm}\,d\tilde{y}_A}{(1 - \tilde{y}_A)(\tilde{y}_A - \tilde{y}_{As})} \qquad (37\text{-}13)$$

The number of y-phase transfer units is then

$$n_G = \int_{\tilde{y}_{A1}}^{\tilde{y}_{Ao}} \frac{(1 - \tilde{y}_A)_{lm}\,d\tilde{y}_A}{(1 - \tilde{y}_A)(\tilde{y}_A - \tilde{y}_{As})} \qquad (37\text{-}14)$$

which is found from Eq. (37-13) and the definition of n_G:

$$z = H_G n_G \qquad (33\text{-}29)$$

Fig. 37-2.   Graph of compositions in tower of Fig. 37-1.

a.   **Operating line.**

b.   **Equilibrium line.**

c.   Slope $= -\dfrac{H_G \bar{L}(1 - \tilde{y}_A)_{lm}}{H_L \bar{G}(1 - \tilde{x}_A)_{lm}}$.

Given the precision of most mass-transfer data, it is permissible to replace the logarithmic mean mole fraction of inert fluid by the arithmetic mean:

$$(1 - \tilde{y}_A)_{lm} = \frac{(1 - \tilde{y}_A) + (1 - \tilde{y}_{As})}{2} \tag{37-15}$$

When this equation is substituted in Eq. (37-14), there results

$$n_G = \frac{1}{2} \int_{\tilde{y}_{A1}}^{\tilde{y}_{Ao}} \frac{d\tilde{y}_A}{\tilde{y}_A - \tilde{y}_{As}} + \frac{1}{2} \int_{\tilde{y}_{A1}}^{\tilde{y}_{Ao}} \frac{(1 - \tilde{y}_{As})\, d\tilde{y}_A}{(1 - \tilde{y}_A)(\tilde{y}_A - \tilde{y}_{As})} \tag{37-16}$$

The second integral can be evaluated using the method of partial fractions, and Eq. (37-16) reduces to

$$n_G = \int_{\tilde{y}_{A1}}^{\tilde{y}_{Ao}} \frac{d\tilde{y}_A}{\tilde{y}_A - \tilde{y}_{As}} + \frac{1}{2} \ln \frac{1 - \tilde{y}_{A1}}{1 - \tilde{y}_{Ao}} \tag{37-17}$$

The integral in Eq. (37-17) must be evaluated graphically for concentrated solutions. Values of $1/(\tilde{y}_A - \tilde{y}_{As})$ are obtained as a function of $\tilde{y}_A$ from a graph such as Fig. 37-2. At a number of values of $\tilde{y}_A$ between $\tilde{y}_{Ao}$ and $\tilde{y}_{A1}$, $\tilde{y}_{As}$ is determined from Eq. (33-39) by drawing a line through $\tilde{x}_A$, $\tilde{y}_A$ (i.e., a point on the operating line), with a slope $-H_G \bar{L}(1 - \tilde{y}_A)_{lm}/H_L \bar{G}(1 - \tilde{x}_A)_{lm}$. This slope may vary considerably through the tower. It is thus evident that n_G can be determined only if *both* H_G and H_L are known.

The above analysis can also be done on the basis of the liquid, or x-phase, resistance. The resulting equations are

$$z = H_L n_L \tag{37-18}$$

and

$$n_L = \int_{\tilde{x}_{A1}}^{\tilde{x}_{Ao}} \frac{d\tilde{x}_A}{\tilde{x}_{As} - \tilde{x}_A} + \frac{1}{2} \ln \frac{1 - \tilde{x}_{A1}}{1 - \tilde{x}_{Ao}} \qquad (37\text{-}19)$$

Over-all coefficients or transfer units should not be used for concentrated solutions unless no data on the individual resistances are available, or one of the resistances controls so that the over-all and individual coefficients are identical anyway.

The equations given above apply to all transfer operations for which $\tilde{N}_B$ is zero. The proper forms to use with compositions expressed in mass fractions, concentrations, or partial pressures can be derived by the reader.

If we have $\tilde{N}_A = -\tilde{N}_B$, as is usually assumed in binary distillation, the second terms in Eqs. (37-17) and (37-19) are omitted. In addition, Eq. (33-26) does not hold, but rather $k_{\tilde{x}} = k_{\tilde{x}}^o$.

Simplifications for Dilute Solutions

General Remarks. We have seen that the only rigorously correct way to treat the countercurrent contacting of concentrated solutions is by the use of the individual coefficients or HTUs. The interfacial compositions must be computed and the number of transfer units found from a graphical integration. The operating and equilibrium lines are generally curved, but if the solutions are dilute, both lines are approximately straight. The distinction between dilute and concentrated solutions is arbitrary, for the curvature of the equilibrium line depends on the particular system involved. In any event, the curvature of the operating line becomes appreciable as mole fractions rise above 0.05. Thus, by dilute solutions, we mean situations for which $\tilde{L}$, $\tilde{G}$, and m can be considered constant.

Since m is constant, the over-all coefficients can be employed. These quantities are easier to use than the individual coefficients, for the interfacial compositions need not be computed. For the over-all gas-phase resistance, the driving force $\tilde{y}_A - \tilde{y}_A^*$ is simply $\tilde{y}_A - m\tilde{x}_A$, the vertical distance between the operating and equilibrium lines. Similarly, for the liquid side, the driving force is $\tilde{x}_A^* - \tilde{x}_A$ or $(\tilde{y}_A/m) - \tilde{x}_A$, the horizontal distance between the lines.

If the over-all coefficients are not given directly, they are easily calculated from the individual coefficients by Eq. (33-20) or (33-21). The definitions of the transfer units [Eqs. (33-30) to (33-33)] can be used with Eqs. (33-20) and (33-21) to yield the relations (for dilute solutions)

$$H_{OG} = H_G + \frac{m\tilde{G}}{L} H_L = \frac{m\tilde{G}}{L} H_{OL} \qquad (37\text{-}20)$$

The quantity $\tilde{L}/m\tilde{G}$ is called the absorption factor α. For many separations it has a value near unity; for simple gas absorption an economic optimum value is said[1] to be approximately 1.4.

The factors $(1 - \tilde{y}_A)_{lm}$ and $(1 - \tilde{x}_A)_{lm}$ have not been included in the equations for the over-all coefficients and HTUs. For dilute solutions, to which these coefficients are applicable, the factors in question are negligibly different from unity. Thus $k_{\tilde{z}}$ and $k_{\tilde{z}}^{o}$, for example, are indistinguishable.

Since the quantities $1 - \tilde{y}_A$ and $(1 - \tilde{y}_A)_{lm}$ are both approximately unity, Eq. (37-14) can be adapted to give the number of over-all gas-transfer units as

$$n_{OG} = \int_{\tilde{y}_{A1}}^{\tilde{y}_{Ao}} \frac{d\tilde{y}_A}{\tilde{y}_A - \tilde{y}_A^*} \tag{37-21}$$

In a similar way, we obtain from Eq. (37-19)

$$n_{OL} = \int_{\tilde{x}_{A1}}^{\tilde{x}_{Ao}} \frac{d\tilde{x}_A}{\tilde{x}_A^* - \tilde{x}_A} \tag{37-22}$$

Logarithmic Mean Driving Force. It is not necessary to evaluate the integrals of Eq. (37-21) or (37-22) graphically. The integrals can be found analytically by a procedure similar to that leading to Eq. (29-7).

Since the operating and equilibrium lines are straight, the driving force is also a linear function of composition. In terms of the gas-phase composition, this fact leads to

$$\frac{d\Delta}{d\tilde{y}_A} = \text{const} = \frac{\Delta_o - \Delta_1}{\tilde{y}_{Ao} - \tilde{y}_{A1}} \tag{37-23}$$

where Δ is $\tilde{y}_A - \tilde{y}_A^*$. The differential $d\tilde{y}_A$ in Eq. (37-21) is replaced using Eq. (37-23), and we get

$$n_{OG} = \frac{\tilde{y}_{Ao} - \tilde{y}_{A1}}{\Delta_o - \Delta_1} \int_{\Delta_1}^{\Delta_o} \frac{d\Delta}{\Delta} \tag{37-24}$$

Integration yields

$$n_{OG} = \frac{\tilde{y}_{Ao} - \tilde{y}_{A1}}{(\tilde{y}_A - \tilde{y}_A^*)_{lm}} \tag{37-25}$$

where

$$(\tilde{y}_A - \tilde{y}_A^*)_{lm} = \frac{(\tilde{y}_A - \tilde{y}_A^*)_o - (\tilde{y}_A - \tilde{y}_A^*)_1}{\ln\left[(\tilde{y}_A - \tilde{y}_A^*)_o / (\tilde{y}_A - \tilde{y}_A^*)_1\right]} \tag{37-26}$$

A similar analysis gives

$$n_{OL} = \frac{\tilde{x}_{Ao} - \tilde{x}_{A1}}{(\tilde{x}_A^* - \tilde{x}_A)_{lm}} \tag{37-27}$$

[1] Perry, pp. 707–711.

Operating lines   Equilibrium lines

Fig. 37-3.   *Errors arising from the assumption of dilute solutions.*

Colburn's Equation for the Number of Transfer Units.   An alternative method of integrating Eq. (37-21) has been given by Colburn.[1]   For a straight equilibrium line which passes through the origin, $\tilde{y}_A^*$ is equal to $m\tilde{x}_A$.   In turn, $\tilde{x}_A$ can be expressed in terms of $\tilde{y}_A$ by Eq. (37-8), which is linear for a straight operating line; that is, $\tilde{L}/\tilde{G} = \text{const}$.   By these two substitutions Eq. (37-21) is rearranged so that the only variable under the integral sign is $\tilde{y}_A$.   The details of the integration are not given here; the resulting equation for the number of over-all gas-transfer units is

$$n_{OG} = \frac{\ln \left\{ (1 - \mathcal{S})[(\tilde{y}_{Ao} - m\tilde{x}_{A1})/(\tilde{y}_{A1} - m\tilde{x}_{A1})] + \mathcal{S} \right\}}{1 - \mathcal{S}} \tag{37-28}$$

in which

$$\mathcal{S} = \frac{m\tilde{G}}{\tilde{L}} = \frac{1}{\alpha} \tag{37-29}$$

A similar equation can be derived for n_{OL}; this expression is given in Perry, pp. 554 and 555, along with a graphical solution of Eq. (37-28) and a table facilitating the application of this equation to a number of separation operations.

Applicability of the Simplified Equations.   It may sometimes be expedient to use Eq. (37-25) or (37-28) when the operating and equilibrium lines are actually slightly curved, and it is useful to have an idea of the effect of the simplifying assumptions on the accuracy of the result.   Figure 37-3 shows the operating and equilibrium lines which might apply to a calculation of n_{OG} from given values of $\tilde{y}_{A1}$, $\tilde{y}_{Ao}$, $\tilde{x}_{A1}$, and $m\tilde{G}/\tilde{L}$.   The ratio of the slopes of the equilibrium and operating lines is taken as the value at the dilute (1) end of the tower.   These values of $\tilde{L}$ and $\tilde{G}$ are, to a good ap-

[1] A. P. Colburn, *Trans. AIChE*, **35**:211 (1939).

proximation, the mass velocities of the solute-free streams, and m is based on the Henry's law constant at extreme dilution.

The data given can be used to calculate $\tilde{x}_{Ao}$ by Eq. (37-6), so that the ends of the operating line are fixed. Since the slope of the line is known at its dilute end, the actual operating line A can be sketched with little error with no further computation. If actual solubility data are known, the equilibrium line A in Fig. 37-3 can also be drawn as shown. The number of over-all liquid-transfer units, for example, could then be obtained with little error from these lines and an integration of Eq. (37-22).

The use of Eq. (37-27), which contains the log mean driving force, corresponds to the assumption that the ends of the actual curved operating and equilibrium lines A are connected by the straight lines B. For the lines shown in Fig. 37-3, Eq. (37-27) would give slightly more than the correct number of over-all x-phase transfer units, since the average driving force $\tilde{x}_A^* - \tilde{x}_A$ obtained from the lines B is less than the correct value obtained from the lines A.

The use of the equation for n_{OL} analogous to Eq. (37-28) corresponds to the assumption that a straight operating line passes through $\tilde{x}_{A1}$, $\tilde{y}_{A1}$ with a slope $\tilde{L}_1/\tilde{G}_1$. The straight equilibrium line passes through the origin with a slope m. These lines are labeled C in Fig. 37-3, and it can be seen that the average driving force $\tilde{x}_A^* - \tilde{x}_A$ obtained from them is greater than the actual average driving force. Thus the value of n_{OL} calculated in this way is less than the correct value. Note also that the value of $\tilde{x}_{Ao}$ found from the lines C is in error.

The curvature of the equilibrium line can have the opposite sign from the curvature shown in Fig. 37-3. The evaluation of the error made by the use of Eq. (37-25), (37-27), or (37-28) must be based on the behavior of the specific system involved.

Modes of Operation

Generality of Equations. It has been mentioned several times that the equations of this chapter and of Chap. 33 can be applied to a number of separation operations. The specific example of gas absorption has been used, so that our explanation would not be too abstract. However, the symbols G and L and y_A and x_A can apply to two liquid phases or to a fluid and a solid phase as well as to the gas and liquid phases in gas absorption or distillation. The subscript o always refers to the rich end of the counter-current contacting device, and the subscript 1 to the dilute end. This convention means that $z = 0$ is sometimes at the top of the actual tower. Either mass or molal units can be used.

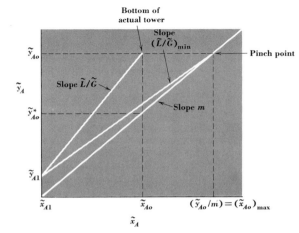

Bottom of actual tower

Fig. 37-4.   Graph for gas absorption showing $(\tilde{L}/\tilde{G})_{min}$.

Gas Absorption. For gas absorption the operating line on a $\tilde{y}_A$ versus $\tilde{x}_A$ diagram is placed above the equilibrium line; molal units are generally used. The solute A is transferred from a mixture with a gas B into a liquid C; B and C are immiscible. The appropriate driving force is $\tilde{y}_A - \tilde{y}_{As}$, $\tilde{y}_A - \tilde{y}_A^*$, $\tilde{x}_{As} - \tilde{x}_A$, or $\tilde{x}_A^* - \tilde{x}_A$. Figure 37-4 shows a typical $\tilde{y}_A$ versus $\tilde{x}_A$ diagram for dilute solutions. Equation (37-25) shows that the number of transfer units increases as the average distance between the operating and equilibrium lines is decreased. In the most common situation, we desire to reduce the concentration of A in a known quantity of gas to a certain value, using liquid of a known composition. Thus $\tilde{y}_{A1}$, $\tilde{y}_{Ao}$, $\tilde{x}_{A1}$, and $\tilde{G}$ are fixed. The lower end of the operating line is fixed, so that as the amount of absorbing liquid L is varied, the slope of the line is changed, and its upper end moves along the horizontal line $\tilde{y}_A = \tilde{y}_{Ao}$. The minimum value of $\tilde{L}$ is one which causes the driving force to be zero at any point in the tower. For the straight lines shown in Fig. 37-4, the point of touching, or pinch point, occurs at the rich end where $\tilde{x}_{Ao}$ equals $\tilde{y}_{Ao}/m$. At a pinch point the driving force is zero, and from Eq. (37-21) it is evident that the number of transfer units is infinite.

The value of the slope $\tilde{L}/\tilde{G}$ which causes a pinch point is the minimum possible, and the actual operating conditions are often defined with reference to $(\tilde{L}/\tilde{G})_{min}$. For example, it is common to operate gas-absorption equipment at $\tilde{L}/\tilde{G}$ equal to about $1.5(\tilde{L}/\tilde{G})_{min}$. There is an economic optimum value of $\tilde{L}/\tilde{G}$. Too low a value results in a very high tower, and too large a value requires a large amount of absorbing liquid; this increases the cost of recovering the solute from this liquid, and the diameter of the

$m\tilde{x}_{Ao}$

$(\tilde{y}_{Ao})_{max}$

Pinch point

Operating line for minimum gas flow. Slope $= (\tilde{L}/\tilde{G})_{max}$

$\tilde{y}_{Ao}$

$\tilde{y}_A$

Top of actual tower

Fig. 37-5.   Graph for gas desorption or stripping showing $(\tilde{L}/\tilde{G})_{max}$.

Actual operating line

$\tilde{y}_{A1}$

$\tilde{x}_{A1}$ $\tilde{x}_{Ao}$

$\tilde{x}_A$

absorption tower must be increased to accommodate the large liquid flow.

Desorption, or Stripping.   The operation of transferring a volatile solute A from a liquid C to a gas B is called desorption, or stripping.   The gas phase can be regarded as a solvent which removes the solute from the liquid.   The rich liquid feed is introduced to the top of a contacting tower, and a gas is blown into the bottom.   The rich gas leaves the top of the tower, and the stripped liquid leaves the bottom.   Mass is transferred in the opposite direction from that for gas absorption, and the appropriate driving force is $\tilde{y}_{As} - \tilde{y}_A$, $\tilde{y}_A^* - \tilde{y}_A$, $\tilde{x}_A - \tilde{x}_{As}$, or $\tilde{x}_A - \tilde{x}_A^*$.

The operating line is below the equilibrium line, as shown in Fig. 37-5. In the usual case the lower end of the operating line is fixed, and various amounts of gas may be used to treat the liquid feed of concentration $\tilde{x}_{Ao}$. The minimum gas rate corresponds to a maximum slope $\tilde{L}/\tilde{G}$.

For gas absorption the rich (o) end of the tower is at the bottom of the actual tower, whereas for desorption, it is at the top.   The equations for the number of transfer units can be used with no change except the sign of the appropriate driving force.   Figure 37-5 shows that the pinch point does not necessarily occur at one end of a tower if the operating or equilibrium line is not straight.

Liquid-Liquid Extraction.   In this operation a liquid solvent B is used to extract a solute A from a second liquid C in which it is dissolved.   We consider in this chapter only systems for which liquids B and C are immiscible.   Liquid extraction is useful for separating A from C when A and C have similar volatilities, so that separation by distillation is difficult. The solute A is extracted by solvent B, which is chosen so that A and B are easily separable by distillation or some other means.   The rich solvent stream is called the extract, and the stripped C stream is called the raffinate.

It is seen that extraction is very similar to desorption, or stripping, so we adopt the convention that the solvent is the y or G phase and the raffinate

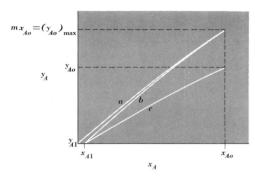

*Fig. 37-6. Graph for liquid-liquid
extraction showing conditions for
minimum solvent (concentrated
solutions).*

a. **Equilibrium line.**
b. **Operating line for
     minimum solvent.**
c. **Actual operating line.**

is the x or L phase. It is common to use mass units rather than molal
units. As shown in Fig. 37-6, the operating line is below the equilibrium
line. The minimum amount of solvent corresponds to the maximum possible slope L/G for the extraction of a given feed with a solvent of given
composition.

The equations of Chaps. 33 and 37 given in terms of mole fractions are
valid in terms of mass fractions if the superscripts are removed.

$$n_G = \int_{y_{A1}}^{y_{Ao}} \frac{(1 - y_A)_{lm}\, dy_A}{(1 - y_A)(y_{As} - y_A)} \tag{37-30}$$

This equation is to be used with H_G or k_y defined by Eqs. (33-36) and
(33-37). An alternative, more cumbersome procedure is to use H_G defined
by Eq. (33-30) and find n_G by replacing the mole fractions in Eq. (37-14) or
(37-17) by mass fractions according to Eq. (32-2). Although this procedure is slightly more rigorous, the low precision of available mass-transfer
data would probably not justify the use of this approach.

For dilute solutions, Eq. (37-27) becomes

$$n_{OL} = \frac{x_{Ao} - x_{A1}}{(x_A - x_A^*)_{lm}} \tag{37-31}$$

The equilibrium line in Fig. 37-6 is sometimes referred to as a distribution
line. The constant slope m is called a distribution coefficient, because it
indicates the equilibrium distribution of A between the liquids B and C.

For liquid-liquid extraction, the rich end of a countercurrent contactor
can be either the top or the bottom of the actual tower, depending on
whether the extract is lighter or heavier than the raffinate.

Figure 37-7 shows two ways in which a liquid-extraction tower may be
operated. The phase which forms the drops is called the dispersed, or
discontinuous, phase; the other phase is the continuous phase. There are
no internals in the spray tower shown; for a more efficient contact between
the phases, the tower might be filled with packing or fitted with baffles
or agitators.

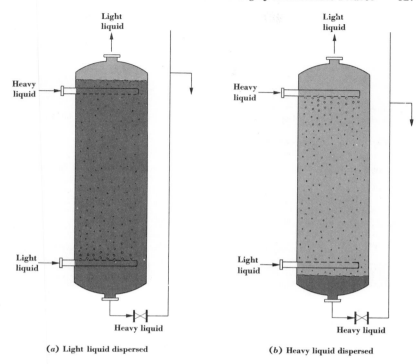

(a) Light liquid dispersed   (b) Heavy liquid dispersed

Fig. 37-7.   Alternate ways of operating a spray tower.

Operation with Concurrent Flow.   Although countercurrent flow has many advantages over concurrent flow, the latter may be used in some situations.   For instance, the flow in an individual stage of some stagewise contactors may be concurrent.   Also, some towers are operated with concurrent flow in order to achieve high velocities and the resultant high mass-transfer coefficients.   The position of the operating line for concurrent gas absorption is shown in Fig. 37-8.   The method of calculating the

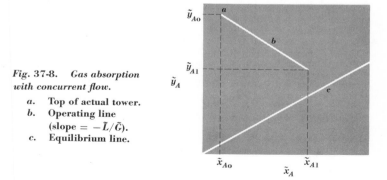

Fig. 37-8.   Gas absorption with concurrent flow.

- *a.*   Top of actual tower.
- *b.*   Operating line (slope $= -\bar{L}/\bar{G}$).
- *c.*   Equilibrium line.

Rashig ring   Lessing ring   Berl saddle   Intalox saddle

Fig. 37-9.   A few examples of tower packings.

tower height is not changed from the methods applied to countercurrent
flow.

Notes on Equipment Design

Gas-Liquid Operations.   The most common kind of continuous contacting device is the packed tower.   A few types of packing are shown in Fig.
37-9; the properties of these packings are given in Table 37-1.   Packing

Table 37-1.   Tower Packing Characteristics†

Nom-inal size, in.	Stoneware Raschig rings			Carbon Raschig rings			Berl saddles			Intalox saddles	
		a_p/ϵ^3			a_p/ϵ^3			a_p/ϵ^3			
	ϵ	Dry-packed	Wet-packed	ϵ	Dry-packed	Wet-packed	ϵ	Dry-packed	Wet-packed	ϵ	a_p/ϵ^3
¼	.....	768	719	.....	2770	1869	.....	4225			
½	0.568	570	547	0.707	373	357	.....	574	481		
¾	0.742	199	218	.....	336	329	0.71	190			
1	0.685	159	164	0.745	170	169	0.764	229	208	0.74	100
1½	0.711	108	116	0.67	92	99	0.76	79	...	0.80	52

† From R. E. Treybal, "Mass-transfer Operations," p. 141, McGraw-Hill Book Company, Inc., New York, 1955.

is designed to promote a large area of contact between phases with a
minimum resistance to the flow of the two phases.

We have seen that the height of a packed tower is determined by the rate
of mass transfer; the diameter of the tower is set by the flow rate of material
to be treated.   If the gas and liquid rates to a tower are doubled, the tower
cross-sectional area must be doubled in order to keep the design mass
velocities the same.   The height of the tower and the number of transfer
units are unchanged.

In Chap. 15 we studied the flow of a single fluid through a packed bed;

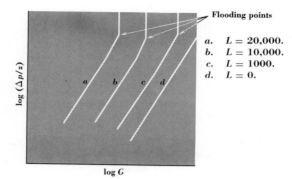

Flooding points

a.	$L = 20{,}000.$
b.	$L = 10{,}000.$
c.	$L = 1000.$
d.	$L = 0.$

Fig. 37-10. Example of the effect of fluid velocities on pressure drop in a packed column (countercurrent flow).

we now wish to consider the countercurrent flow of a gas and a liquid. If liquid flows down over the packing, a certain amount is held in the various interstices and cavities of the rings or saddles; there is a minimum liquid holdup, no matter how low the liquid-flow rate is. As L is increased, the holdup is increased. Even if there is no upward gas flow, the rate of liquid flow downward can be increased until the tower is flooded, i.e., completely filled with liquid.

When liquid flows down over the packing at an intermediate rate, so that there is not an excessive holdup, gas can be blown up through the tower. The pressure drop is larger than with unirrigated packing, for the cross section available to flow is reduced by the liquid holdup. As G is increased with a fixed L, the interphase friction increases and the holdup increases. Finally, at a certain value of G, the holdup is so high that the tower starts to fill with liquid. The tower cannot be operated above this flooding velocity, which is a function of the liquid velocity, the fluid properties, and the characteristics of the packing.

A typical plot showing schematically the relation between the pressure drop over a tower and the liquid and gas flow rates is given in Fig. 37-10. In Fig. 37-11 a correlation is given for the flooding velocity in packed columns. The data from Table 37-1 can be used to estimate a_p/ϵ^3, which appears in the ordinate of Fig. 37-11, but actual data should be used if possible; the void fraction is very sensitive to the manner in which the packing is dumped in a particular tower. It is customary to fix the diameter of a gas-absorption tower so that the gas rate is 50 to 70 per cent of the flooding rate. Extensive data on pressure drop and flooding are given in Perry's Handbook.[1]

Liquid-Liquid Operations. The situation in a packed liquid-extraction tower is basically the same as in a packed tower for gas-liquid contacting.

[1] Pages 680–686. See also T. K. Sherwood and R. L. Pigford, "Absorption and Extraction," 2d ed., chap. 7, McGraw-Hill Book Company, Inc., New York, 1952.

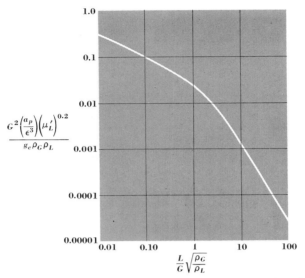

$$\frac{G^2\left(\dfrac{a_p}{\epsilon^3}\right)\left(\mu_L'\right)^{0.2}}{g_c\rho_G\rho_L}$$

$$\frac{L}{G}\sqrt{\frac{\rho_G}{\rho_L}}$$

Fig. 37-11. Flooding velocities for random packings, gas absorption. Units: lb, hr, ft, except μ_L' which is expressed in centipoises. [From T. K. Sherwood, G. H. Shipley, and F. A. L. Holloway, Ind. Eng. Chem., 30:765-769 (1938).]

Since the densities of the two phases are not widely different, the limiting velocities in countercurrent liquid-liquid operations are less than those in gas-liquid operations. A correlation for flooding velocities in packed towers is given in Fig. 37-12.

Unpacked spray towers, as shown in Fig. 37-7, are sometimes used for liquid-liquid operations. The flooding velocities can be estimated from the

$$\frac{\mu_c'}{\Delta\rho}(\sigma')^{0.2}\left(\frac{a_p}{\epsilon}\right)^{1.5}$$

$$\frac{(u_c^{0.5}+u_D^{0.5})^2\rho_c}{a_p\mu_c'}$$

Fig. 37-12.   Flooding velocities in packed extraction towers. [From J. W. Crawford and C. R. Wilke, Chem. Eng. Progr., 47:423 (1951).]

u_c=superficial velocity of continuous phase, ft/hr
u_D=superficial velocity of dispersed phase, ft/hr
ρ_c=density of continuous phase, lb/cu ft
a_p=packing area, sq ft/cu ft
μ_c'=viscosity of continuous phase, centipoises
σ'=interfacial tension, dynes/cm
ϵ=void fraction in packing
$\Delta\rho=\rho_c-\rho_D$

minimum fluidization velocity of the solid particle of the same diameter as the dispersed-phase droplets.[1] The diameter of the droplets is governed by the size of the holes in the distribution nozzles. Correlations giving the pertinent relations are found in Treybal.[2]

Example 37-1

It is desired to absorb 95 per cent of the acetone in a 2.00 mole per cent mixture of acetone in air in a continuous, countercurrent absorption tower using 20 per cent more than the minimum water rate. Pure water is introduced at the top of the tower, and the gas mixture is blown into the bottom of the tower at 1000 lb/hr. Find the height and diameter of a tower packed with 1-in., wet-packed, stoneware Raschig rings and operated at 50 per cent of flooding velocity.

It will be assumed that the tower operates isothermally at atmospheric pressure and 80°F; the equilibrium relation is $\tilde{y}_A = 2.53 \tilde{x}_A$. The diffusivities are acetone-air, $D_{AB} = 0.368$ sq ft/hr; acetone-water (liquid), $D_{AC} = 4.81 \times 10^{-5}$ sq ft/hr.

The streams are labeled as in Fig. 37-1, and the conditions of the problem give $\tilde{y}_{Ao} = 0.02$ and $\tilde{x}_{A1} = 0$. The rate of air flow at both ends of the tower is the same, so that it is convenient to find the exit-air composition by using molal ratios, as follows: $\tilde{Y}_{Ao} = 0.02/0.98 = 0.0204$ mole acetone/mole air. At the dilute end of the tower, for 95 per cent absorption, $\tilde{Y}_{A1} = (0.05)(0.0204) = 0.00102 \cong y_{A1}$.

Since both the operating and equilibrium lines are almost straight, the minimum water rate corresponds to equilibrium at the rich end of the tower, so that $(\tilde{x}_{Ao})_{\max} = 0.02/2.53 = 0.00790$. We then compute $(\tilde{L}/\tilde{G})_{\min}$.

$$\left(\frac{\tilde{L}}{\tilde{G}}\right)_{\min} = \frac{0.0200 - 0.00102}{0.00790 - 0} = 2.41$$

Figure 37-13 illustrates this procedure. The actual slope of the operating line is then $1.2(2.41) = 2.89$, and $\tilde{x}_{Ao} = 0.00658$.

The number of transfer units can be calculated from Eqs. (37-25) and (37-26).

$$(\tilde{y}_A - \tilde{y}_A^*)_o = 0.02 - 0.00658(2.53) = 0.00336$$
$$(\tilde{y}_A - \tilde{y}_A^*)_1 = 0.00102 - 0 = 0.00102$$
$$(\tilde{y}_A - \tilde{y}_A^*)_{lm} = 0.001967$$

$$n_{OG} = \frac{0.0200 - 0.00102}{0.001967} = 9.65$$

Alternatively, Eq. (37-28) can be used with S equal to 0.875.

The value of H_{OG} is needed to calculate the tower height, but the liquid and vapor mass velocities must be found before the height of the transfer unit can be determined. The flooding velocity is found from Fig. 37-11 as follows:

$$\frac{L}{G} \sqrt{\frac{\rho_G}{\rho_L}} = \frac{2.89(18)}{29} \sqrt{\frac{0.0737}{62.3}} = 0.0617$$

$$0.14 = \frac{G^2(a_p/\epsilon^3)(\mu_L')^{0.2}}{g_c \rho_G \rho_L}$$

$$G^2 = \frac{(0.14)(4.17 \times 10^8)(0\ 0737)(62.3)}{(164)(0.860)^{0.2}}$$

$$G = 1300 \text{ lb/(hr)(sq ft) at flooding}$$

[1] R. E. C. Weaver, L. Lapidus, and J. C. Elgin, *AIChE Journal*, **5**:533 (1959).
[2] R. E. Treybal, "Liquid Extraction," chap. 10, McGraw-Hill Book Company, Inc., New York, 1951.

$\tilde{y}_{Ao} = 0.020$

$\tilde{y}_A$, mole fraction acetone in vapor

0.010

$\tilde{y}_{A1}$

0

0.005 0.010

$\tilde{x}_{Ao} = 0.00658$ $(\tilde{x}_{Ao})_{max} = 0.00790$

$\tilde{x}_A$, mole fraction acetone in liquid

Fig. 37-13.   Operating diagram for Example 37-1.

a. **Actual operating line.**

b. **Equilibrium line.**

The tower is to operate at half this mass velocity, or 650 lb/(hr)(sq ft).   The required tower diameter for a gas flow of 1000 lb/hr is

$$D = \sqrt{\frac{(4)(1000)}{(3.14)(650)}} = 1.40 \text{ ft}$$

The liquid rate is $(650)(2.89)(^{18}\!/_{29}) = 1167$ lb/(hr)(sq ft).

The height of the gas-phase transfer unit is found from Eq. (36-11) and Table 36-1.

$$\mathsf{Sc} = \frac{\mu}{\rho D_{AB}} = \frac{(0.018)(2.42)}{(0.0737)(0.368)} = 1.607$$

$$\begin{aligned} H_G &= 6.41 G^{0.32} L^{-0.51} \mathsf{Sc}^{0.5} \\ &= (6.41)(650)^{0.32}(1167)^{-0.51}(1.607)^{0.5} \\ &= 1.78 \text{ ft} \end{aligned}$$

For the liquid phase we have

$$\mathsf{Sc} = \frac{(0.860)(2.42)}{(62.3)(4.81 \times 10^{-5})} = 694$$

Equation (36-12) and Table 36-2 yield

$$H_L = 0.01 \left[\frac{1167}{(0.860)(2.42)}\right]^{0.22} (694)^{0.5}$$

$$= 1.06 \text{ ft}$$

The over-all gas-phase HTU is obtained from Eq. (37-20):

$$H_{OG} = 1.78 + (0.875)(1.06) = 2.71 \text{ ft}$$

The tower height required is

$$z = (9.65)(2.71) = 26.2 \text{ ft}$$

The pressure drop obtained from a plot like Fig. 37-10 is 0.568 psi, which corresponds to a power consumption of approximately

$$\frac{(0.568)(144)(1000)}{(0.0737)(3600)(550)(0.70)} = 0.802 \text{ hp}$$

The compression efficiency is assumed to be 70 per cent.

Fig. 37-14. *Operating diagram for Example 37-2.*
  a. **Equilibrium line.**
  b. **Operating line.**

Example 37-2

A solution of acetic acid in water containing 0.15 mass fraction acetic acid is to be extracted using pure methyl isobutyl ketone as a solvent. The extract is to contain 0.075 mass fraction acetic acid, and the raffinate 0.010 mass fraction acid. Estimate the height of a tower to perform this separation.

The equilibrium data are plotted in Fig. 37-14; the line is slightly curved. The solutions are too concentrated to assume that the operating line is straight, so L/G must be considered a variable.

We shall solve this problem by assuming that the phases are immiscible; the following relations then hold:

$$G = \frac{(1 - y_{Ao})G_o}{1 - y_A}$$

$$L = \frac{(1 - x_{Ao})L_o}{1 - x_A}$$

The computations are simplified by expressing the material balance in terms of the flows of water and ketone and using concentrations based on mass ratios:

$$Y_A = \frac{y_A}{1 - y_A}$$

$$X_A = \frac{x_A}{1 - x_A}$$

$$y_A = \frac{Y_A}{1 + Y_A}$$

$$x_A = \frac{X_A}{1 + X_A}$$

The equation analogous to Eq. (37-6) is

$$\frac{L_C}{G_B} = \frac{Y_{Ao} - Y_{A1}}{X_{Ao} - X_{A1}} \tag{1}$$

where C refers to water and B to ketone. For the present problem we have

$$
\begin{aligned}
y_{Ao} &= 0.075 & Y_{Ao} &= 0.0811 \\
x_{Ao} &= 0.150 & X_{Ao} &= 0.1768 \\
y_{A1} &= 0 & Y_{A1} &= 0 \\
x_{A1} &= 0.0100 & X_{A1} &= 0.0101
\end{aligned}
$$

Thus we have

$$\frac{L_C}{G_B} = \frac{0.0811}{0.1768 - 0.0101} = 0.487$$

We write Eq. (1) for a general point as

$$Y_A = 0.487 X_A - 0.0050 \tag{2}$$

and refer to the following table:

X_A	Y_A	x_A	y_A
0.0101	0	0.0100	0
0.0527	0.0206	0.0500	0.0202
0.1111	0.0491	0.1000	0.0468
0.1768	0.0811	0.1500	0.0750

The operating line is plotted in Fig. 37-14; it is also slightly curved.

It is normal to calculate n_{OL} or n_L for extraction (stripping) operations. Since the equilibrium and operating lines are similarly curved, Eq. (37-31) can be used to a good approximation. Strictly, the individual transfer units should be used, but the only data available for the system are in terms of over-all transfer units.

We proceed to apply Eq. (37-31):

$$x_{A1} - x_{A1}^* = 0.0100 - 0 = 0.0100$$
$$x_{Ao} - x_{Ao}^* = 0.1500 - 0.1030 = 0.0470$$

$$(x_A - x_A^*)_{lm} = \frac{0.0370}{\ln 4.70} = 0.0207$$

$$n_{OL} = \frac{0.1500 - 0.0100}{0.0207} = 6.77$$

The same result is obtained by graphical integration.

Values of the HTU for a spray tower have been reported in the literature and are given in Treybal.[1] If water is the dispersed phase, as shown in Fig. 37-7b, it is found that the HTU for the continuous phase, that is, H_{OG}, is 6 ft. From Eq. (37-20) we have

$$H_{OL} = \frac{L}{Gm} H_{OG}$$

$$m \cong 0.700$$

$$\frac{L}{G} = 0.487$$

$$H_{OL} = (0.696)(6) = 4.17 \text{ ft}$$
$$z = (6.27)(4.17) = 28.3 \text{ ft}$$

Alternatively, n_{OG} can be calculated directly from Fig. 37-14, using, however, mass fractions rather than mole fractions. A much longer portion of the equilibrium curve must be used in this case so that the effects of the curvatures of the two lines do not appear to cancel out. A graphical integration is done, starting from the following table:

[1] *Ibid.*, p. 325.

y_A	$y_A^* - y_A$	$\dfrac{1}{y_A^* - y_A}$
0	0.0065	154.0
0.0125	0.0110	90.9
0.0250	0.0160	62.5
0.0375	0.0215	48.8
0.0500	0.0285	35.1
0.0625	0.0350	28.6
0.0750	0.0415	24.1

$$n_{OG} = 4.44$$
$$z = (4.44)(6) = 26.7$$

This height is a good check with that previously obtained. Note that a term similar to the second term on the right-hand side of Eq. (37-19) has not been included because of the approximate nature of the calculations.

The effect of using a packed tower can be found from data given in Treybal.[1] If the ketone is dispersed as in Fig. 37-7a and ½-in. C rings are used as packing, H_{OG} is 1.43 ft. Thus z is (1.43)(4.44), or only 6.37 ft. The increase in extraction rate is caused by the increased turbulence and interfacial area given by the packing. The HTU values are strongly influenced by the type and size of distributing nozzle, by the direction of mass transfer, and by the choice of which phase is dispersed. These matters are best considered empirically at present; a detailed discussion is given by Treybal.

PROBLEMS

37-1. Ammonia is to be absorbed from an air stream in a tower packed with 1-in. Raschig rings. The inlet gas is 2 mole per cent ammonia, and 90 per cent of the ammonia is to be recovered in the exit liquid using pure water as the absorbent. Calculate the height of packing required if a liquid rate 25 per cent more than the minimum is used with a gas mass velocity of 400 lb/(hr)(sq ft). Assume that the temperature is constant at 30°C and the total pressure is 1 atm throughout. Data are given in Perry.

37-2. The benzoic acid in a toluene solution is to be extracted using pure water as the solvent in a continuous, countercurrent packed tower. The feed solution contains 0.010 lb mole benzoic acid/cu ft, and 12.5 volumes of water per volume of toluene is used. Ninety-five per cent of the acid is to be recovered in the water phase.

The equilibrium data are:

Concentration of benzoic acid in water phase, lb moles/cu ft	Concentration of benzoic acid in toluene phase, lb moles/cu ft
1.0×10^{-4}	0.7×10^{-3}
2.0×10^{-4}	1.2×10^{-3}
4.0×10^{-4}	3.0×10^{-3}
6.0×10^{-4}	5.6×10^{-3}
8.0×10^{-4}	9.8×10^{-3}
9.0×10^{-4}	12.7×10^{-3}

[1] *Ibid.*, p. 334.

The two phases can be considered immiscible.

Find the height of packing needed if the individual transfer unit based on the toluene phase (H_L) is 3 ft and the mass-transfer coefficient in the water phase is three times that in the toluene phase.

Although the equations necessary for the solution of this problem have been derived using mole or mass fractions, it is a simple matter to express them in terms of concentrations, so that the data given here need not be converted to mass fractions.

37-3. It is desired to absorb the ammonia from an air stream at 1 atm in a tower packed with 2-in. Raschig rings operating at 30°C. The inlet gas is 10 mole per cent ammonia, and 99.9 per cent of the ammonia is to be recovered in the solution leaving the tower. Pure water is fed to the top of the tower at a rate 20 per cent greater than the minimum rate. Find the height and diameter of a tower designed to operate at one-half the flooding velocity needed to treat 3000 lb/hr of gas.

37-4. One hundred pounds per hour of a 20 mass per cent solution of dioxane in water is to be treated with pure benzene at 25°C in a tower packed with 1-in. Raschig rings to reduce the dioxane content in the raffinate to 3.0 mass per cent. The two phases may be considered immiscible; the equilibrium relation is $y_A = 1.30x_A$. Estimate the height and diameter of a tower operating at a solvent rate 40 per cent above the minimum. The height of the over-all transfer unit based on the water phase (H_{OL}) is 4 ft.

37-5. Individual mass-transfer coefficients are sometimes found by the Wilson method, which has been described for heat transfer in Chap. 29. Describe the experiments which would be necessary and how the data would be interpreted in order to find individual mass-transfer coefficients by this method.

37-6. R. P. Whitney and J. E. Vivian [*Chem. Eng. Progr.*, **45**:323 (1949)] have measured rates of absorption of SO_2 in water and found the following expressions for 1-in. Raschig rings at 70°F:

$$k_L a = 0.044 L^{0.82}$$
$$k_G a = 0.028 G^{0.7} L^{0.25}$$

Wilson's method of analysis was used.

Use these equations to specify the height and diameter of a tower to treat 40,000 cu ft/hr at 1 atm and 70°F of air containing 20 mole per cent SO_2. It is planned to recover 99.5 per cent of the SO_2 by using a liquid rate 25 per cent greater than the minimum. A gas rate of 50 per cent of flooding may be used. Note that the driving forces for $k_L a$ and $k_G a$ are, respectively, in lb moles/cu ft and atmospheres. Check the values of the HTUs obtained by equations of Whitney and Vivian against those found from the general correlations given in this chapter. Can you explain any discrepancies?

SIMULTANEOUS MOMENTUM, HEAT, AND MASS TRANSFER

38

In studying mass-transfer coefficients for binary mixtures in some of the previous chapters, we learned that the mass flux has an effect on the mass-transfer coefficient. For the laminar boundary layer on a flat plate, the effect was evaluated quantitatively in Chap. 34. For a packed tower or for turbulent flow, the effect of the net mass flux was taken into account approximately by the use of the factor $(1 - \bar{x}_A)_{lm}$ for the common case of $\tilde{N}_B$ equal to zero.

Because of the analogy between mass and energy transfer, it is logical that the net mass flux affect the value of the heat-transfer coefficient as well as the mass-transfer coefficient; this phenomenon has been discussed in Chap. 34. Notice that we are speaking here of the effect of the mass flux on the energy flux for a given Δt and given flow parameters such as u_o, μ, etc. The effect arises as a result of the influence of the normal velocity at the surface on the velocity distribution near the interface, i.e., on the boundary layer. This velocity distribution in turn controls the magnitude of the mass- and heat-transfer coefficients. Momentum transfer (as reflected in the value of f or C_D) may also be affected. In many common situations, however, the mass flux is not sufficiently large to have an appreciable effect on these coefficients.

This chapter will also deal with the effect of the mass flux on the energy flux as distinguished from its effect on the heat-transfer coefficient. For instance, the energy required to evaporate a liquid drop suspended in a gas, if there is no radiation from solids, must be transferred from the bulk of the gas phase. This heat transfer occurs only if there is a temperature-difference driving force, so the result is that the mass flux of evaporated vapor is coupled to the energy flux necessary to furnish the latent heat of vaporization at the liquid surface. Mass transfer from the region of high concentration at the liquid surface to the bulk of the gas is accompanied by simultaneous heat transfer in the opposite direction to furnish the necessary heat of vaporization. In order to transfer this heat, the drop must be cooler than the gas. The heat-transfer coefficient is the same as it would be without mass transfer unless the mass flux is high enough to bring into play the factors mentioned in the previous paragraph.

In liquid extraction or gas absorption in some dilute solutions, the temperature effects which arise from the mass transfer are negligible. We shall, however, consider a case of gas absorption for which the temperature changes are appreciable. The unit operations of humidification, dehumidification, and drying are concerned with the evaporation of a pure liquid, and the temperature difference between phases is often considerable. Some examples of these operations will be presented in the last part of this chapter to show some of the practical consequences of the simultaneous transfer of heat and mass.

Laminar Boundary Layer on a Flat Plate

In Chap. 34 mass transfer for a binary mixture in the laminar boundary layer on a flat plate was studied. The effect on the mass-transfer coefficient of a net mass flux in the direction perpendicular to the plate was evaluated quantitatively. The results are represented in Fig. 34-1. It was mentioned that this mass flux had an effect on the heat-transfer coefficient. We shall see that it also affects the drag coefficient, or friction factor.

In the present discussion, we extend the results of Chap. 34 to heat and momentum transfer. This extension is obtained by analogy; the detailed derivations are not given. We begin by writing the following equations, derived in previous chapters, for momentum, heat, and mass transfer in the laminar boundary layer on a flat plate. From Eqs. (12-70) and (12-72) we have

$$\frac{d^2(u_x/u_o)}{d\eta^2} + \frac{f(\eta)}{2}\frac{d(u_x/u_o)}{d\eta} = 0 \tag{38-1}$$

from Eq. (24-3):

$$\frac{d^2[(t_s - t)/(t_s - t_o)]}{d\eta^2} + \frac{f(\eta)}{2}\,\mathsf{Pr}\,\frac{d[(t_s - t)/(t_s - t_o)]}{d\eta} = 0 \tag{38-2}$$

and from Eq. (34-4):

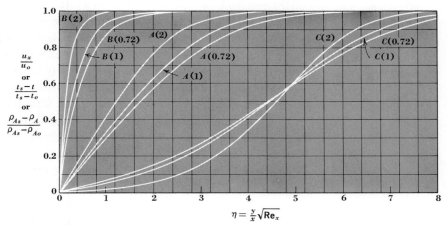

Fig. 38-1. *Profiles in the laminar boundary layer on a flat plate. (From H. S. Mickley, R. C. Ross, A. L. Squyers, and W. E. Stewart, NACA Tech. Note 3208, 1954.)*

$$\frac{d^2[(\rho_{As} - \rho_A)/(\rho_{As} - \rho_{Ao})]}{d\eta^2} + \frac{f(\eta)}{2}\, \mathsf{Sc}\, \frac{d[(\rho_{As} - \rho_A)/(\rho_{As} - \rho_{Ao})]}{d\eta} = 0$$

$$(38\text{-}3)$$

The definitions of η and $f(\eta)$ are given in Chap. 12 as

$$\eta = y\sqrt{\frac{u_o}{\nu x}} = \frac{y}{x}\sqrt{\mathsf{Re}_x} \qquad (12\text{-}68)$$

$$f(\eta) = \frac{\psi}{\sqrt{xu_o\nu}} \qquad (12\text{-}69)$$

In Eq. (12-69) ψ is the stream function. The analogy among momentum, energy, and mass transfer is well illustrated by Eqs. (38-1) to (38-3). For the case in which $\mathsf{Pr} = \mathsf{Sc} = 1.0$, the solutions for these three equations give u_x/u_o, $(t_s - t)/(t_s - t_o)$, and $(\rho_{As} - \rho_A)/(\rho_{As} - \rho_{Ao})$ as the same function of the position variable η. Thus, in Fig. 38-1, the curve $A(1)$ gives the variation of the velocity, temperature, and concentration as a function of Re_x and position in the boundary layer. It is natural for the curve representing these three quantities to be identical for Prandtl and Schmidt numbers of unity because the Prandtl number is the ratio of the diffusivity of momentum (kinematic viscosity) to the thermal diffusivity, and the Schmidt number is the ratio of the diffusivity of momentum to the diffusivity of mass (molecular diffusivity).

For the velocity distribution given by curve $A(1)$ there are other possible temperature and concentration distributions, depending on the values of Pr and Sc. Equations (38-2) and (38-3) can be solved for values of Pr and Sc

other than 1.0; two of the resulting functions are plotted as curve $A(0.72)$ (meaning **Pr** or **Sc** = 0.72) and curve $A(2)$ (meaning **Pr** or **Sc** = 2.0) in Fig. 38-1. For instance, for pentane vapor diffusing from a heated flat plate through a laminar boundary layer of air, we have **Pr** $\cong 0.72$ and **Sc** $\cong 2.0$; u_x/u_o is given by $A(1)$, $(t_s - t)/(t_s - t_o)$ is given by $A(0.72)$, and $(\rho_{As} - \rho_A)/(\rho_{As} - \rho_{Ao})$ is given by $A(2)$. For water vapor diffusing from a heated plate through air, **Pr** is still 0.72 and **Sc** is a little less than 0.72. Thus curve $A(0.72)$ represents approximately both the temperature and concentration profiles. The Lewis number **Sc/Pr** for this system is about unity.

In Chap. 34, we learned that the mass flux at the surface of the plate, represented by the dimensionless group $u_{ys}\sqrt{\mathbf{Re}_x}/u_o$, has an important effect on the curves in Fig. 34-1; this effect must now appear in Fig. 38-1. The group $u_{ys}\sqrt{\mathbf{Re}_x}/u_o$ becomes appreciably different from zero either because of a large concentration difference or because of the addition or withdrawal of fluid through pores provided in the flat plate. The curves B in Fig. 38-1 apply when mass is being transferred from the fluid stream to the plate at a rate such that $u_{ys}\sqrt{\mathbf{Re}_x}/u_o = -2.5$. The curves C are for mass transfer from plate to stream, and $u_{ys}\sqrt{\mathbf{Re}_x}/u_o = 1.0$.

It is of interest to give now the effect of the distributions shown in Fig. 38-1 on the transfer coefficients C_D, k_ρ, and h. These coefficients are proportional to the slopes of the lines in Fig. 38-1 at $y = 0$. The coefficient found from these slopes is a point coefficient. Since $u_{ys}\sqrt{\mathbf{Re}_x}/u_o$ is constant for the length of the plate [Eq. (34-5)], the correction to the average coefficient for a length of plate L is the same as it is for the point coefficient.

For momentum transfer, the drag coefficient is given by

$$C_D = \frac{2g_c F_d}{u_o^2 \rho A} = \frac{2g_c \tau_s}{u_o^2 \rho} \tag{12-81}$$

in which F_d/A should be interpreted as the point value of the shear stress at the surface τ_s. This quantity is given by

$$\tau_s = \frac{\mu}{g_c}\left(\frac{\partial u_x}{\partial y}\right)_{y=0} \tag{12-76}$$

Equations (12-81) and (12-76) are combined to yield

$$C_D = \frac{2\mu}{u_o \rho}\left[\frac{\partial(u_x/u_o)}{\partial y}\right]_{y=0} \tag{38-4}$$

By using the definition of η [Eq. (12-68)], Eq. (38-4) is readily converted to

$$\frac{C_D}{2} = \frac{\mu}{u_o \rho}\left[\frac{d(u_x/u_o)}{d\eta}\right]_{\eta=0}\sqrt{\frac{\rho u_o}{\mu x}} \tag{38-5}$$

Fig. 38-2. *The effect of mass transfer on transfer coefficients. The parameters on the curves refer to* Pr *or* Sc.*[From J. P. Hartnett and E. R. G.Eckert, Trans. ASME,79:247–254(1957).]*

or

$$\frac{C_D}{2} = \frac{1}{\sqrt{Re_x}}\left[\frac{d(u_x/u_o)}{d\eta}\right]_{\eta=0} \tag{38-6}$$

The derivative in Eq. (38-6) is obtained from the slopes at $\eta = 0$ of curves $A(1)$, $B(1)$, and $C(1)$ in Fig. 38-1, and it is evident that the drag coefficient is a strong function of the mass-transfer group $u_{ys}\sqrt{Re_x}/u_o$. The effect of this group on C_D is shown as curve 1 in Fig. 38-2; C_D^o is the value C_D would have if u_{ys} were zero.

The mass-transfer coefficient k_ρ', which is plotted as k_ρ'/k_ρ^o in Fig. 38-2, is defined by an equation equivalent to Eq. (34-6).

$$N_A = k_\rho'(\rho_{As} - \rho_{Ao}) + Nx_{As} \tag{38-7}$$

The fluxes N_A and N are those at s ($y = 0$). From Eq. (34-7) we obtain the definition of k_ρ'.

$$k'_\rho = D_{AB} \left\{ \frac{\partial[(\rho_{As} - \rho_A)/(\rho_{As} - \rho_{Ao})]}{\partial y} \right\}_{y=0} \tag{38-8}$$

This equation is analogous to Eq. (38-4). However, it will be recalled that in Chaps. 33 to 37, we have used a coefficient defined by

$$N_A = k_\rho(\rho_{As} - \rho_{Ao}) \tag{38-9}$$

We can obtain a relation between k'_ρ and k_ρ by combining Eqs. (38-7) and (38-9).

$$k_\rho = \frac{k'_\rho(\rho_{As} - \rho_{Ao}) + Nx_{As}}{\rho_{As} - \rho_{Ao}}$$

In the limit of $N = 0$ this equation shows that k_ρ and k'_ρ are identical. In this situation they are designated as k^o_ρ. In the common case for which $N_B = 0$ and $N = N_A$, we have, from Eqs. (38-7) and (38-9),

$$k'_\rho = (1 - x_{As})k_\rho \tag{38-10}$$

Equation (38-8) is next changed so that the independent variable in the derivative is η, and we get

$$k'_\rho = D_{AB} \left\{ \frac{d[(\rho_{As} - \rho_A)/(\rho_{As} - \rho_{Ao})]}{d\eta} \right\}_{\eta=0} \sqrt{\frac{\rho u_o}{\mu x}} \tag{38-11}$$

In terms of dimensionless groups, this equation becomes

$$\frac{k'_\rho}{u_o} = \frac{1}{\mathbf{Sc} \sqrt{\mathbf{Re}_x}} \left\{ \frac{d[(\rho_{As} - \rho_A)/(\rho_{As} - \rho_{Ao})]}{d\eta} \right\}_{\eta=0} \tag{38-12}$$

This equation, with the derivative evaluated from the slopes of the curves in Fig. 38-1, shows the effect of mass transfer on the coefficient k'_ρ; the results are also given in Fig. 38-2. The parameters (0.72) and (1) refer to values of the Schmidt number. The equation given above for mass transfer can also be given in terms of coefficients such as k_x, $k_{\bar{x}}$, etc. The coefficient k^o_ρ is the value k'_ρ would have if u_{ys} were zero; k_ρ is obtained from k'_ρ by Eq. (38-10) for $N_B = 0$.

The heat-transfer coefficient h, which is plotted as h/h^o in Fig. 38-2, is defined by

$$h = k \left\{ \frac{\partial[(t_s - t)/(t_s - t_o)]}{\partial y} \right\}_{y=0} \tag{24-5}$$

We proceed as in the previous paragraph and write

$$h = k \left\{ \frac{d[(t_s - t)/(t_s - t_o)]}{d\eta} \right\}_{\eta=0} \sqrt{\frac{\rho u_o}{\mu x}} \tag{38-13}$$

This equation can be converted to a relation among dimensionless groups by dividing both sides by $C_p u_o \rho$; the result is

$$\frac{h}{C_p u_o \rho} = \frac{k}{C_p \mu} \left\{ \frac{d[(t_s - t)/(t_s - t_o)]}{d\eta} \right\}_{\eta=0} \sqrt{\frac{\mu}{\rho u_o x}} \tag{38-14}$$

or

$$\mathsf{St} = \frac{1}{\mathsf{Pr}\sqrt{\mathsf{Re}_x}} \left\{ \frac{d[(t_s - t)/(t_s - t_o)]}{d\eta} \right\}_{\eta=0} \tag{38-15}$$

The derivative in Eq. (38-15) is found from the curves of Fig. 38-1; it is a function of both Pr and $u_{ys}\sqrt{\mathsf{Re}_x}/u_o$. The curves in Fig. 38-2 are applied to heat transfer by interpreting the parameters 0.72 and 1 on the curves as values of the Prandtl number. The coefficient h^o is the value h would have if u_{ys} were zero.

Simultaneous Heat and Mass Transfer with Turbulent Flow

An exact solution of the boundary-layer equation for heat transfer with simultaneous mass transfer is not available for turbulent flow. An approximate solution will be given which follows the methods used in Chap. 33 to obtain Eq. (33-26) for mass transfer. The present derivation is oriented toward an evaluation of the effect of mass transfer on heat transfer.

A stationary film is postulated adjacent to the surface which is exchanging heat and mass with the fluid. The effective thickness of the layer δ_m is such that the transfer rates through it equal those obtained for the actual flow situation. As before, $\tilde{N}_B$ is zero.

We study the more common case, for which the fluid is hotter than the surface. There is mass transfer of component A from the surface to the fluid and no net flow of B. The variables involved are shown in Fig. 38-3. The flux $\tilde{N}_A$ through the interface arises either from the evaporation of a volatile liquid or solid or from a forced flow of A through a porous plate. There is an enthalpy change $\tilde{H}_{As} - \tilde{H}_{A1}$ in bringing the transferred mass from its condensed state, or its state on the side of the porous plate away from the fluid, to its state in the vapor phase adjacent to the plate. For evaporation or sublimation $\tilde{H}_{As} - \tilde{H}_{A1}$ is simply the heat of vaporization. We assume that all the energy required for the evaporation is supplied by conduction from the fluid through the hypothetical layer of thickness δ_m. In addition, heat must be conducted in to make up for the energy which is carried by the molecules of A as they diffuse away from the surface. The over-all energy balance is thus written over the length δ_m as

$$\tilde{N}_A(\tilde{H}_{As} - \tilde{H}_{A1}) + \tilde{N}_A(\tilde{H}_{Ao} - \tilde{H}_{As}) = h'(t_o - t_s) \tag{38-16}$$

It is customary, however, to include in the heat-transfer coefficient the energy carried by the diffusing molecules of A, so that we have, by definition,

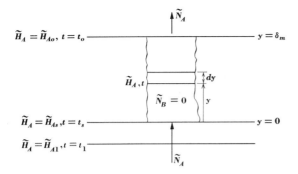

Fig. 38-3.   Film mechanism for simultaneous heat and mass transfer.

$$h(t_o - t_s) = \tilde{N}_A(\tilde{H}_{As} - \tilde{H}_{A1}) = h'(t_o - t_s) - \tilde{N}_A(\tilde{H}_{Ao} - \tilde{H}_{As}) \quad (38\text{-}17)$$

The use of the film theory and the application of an integral energy balance over the thickness δ_m have resulted in the definition of the coefficient h'. From the relation

$$\tilde{H}_{Ao} - \tilde{H}_{As} = \tilde{C}_{pA}(t_o - t_s) \quad (38\text{-}18)$$

and Eq. (38-17), we find

$$h' = h\left[1 + \frac{\tilde{C}_{pA}(t_o - t_s)}{\tilde{H}_{As} - \tilde{H}_{A1}}\right] \quad (38\text{-}19)$$

The coefficient h' is sometimes used in the analysis of simultaneous heat and mass transfer.

Since we usually apply the present analysis to a gas phase, we use molal units so that $\tilde{N}_A$ is constant for ideal gases for all values of y from zero to δ_m; that is, $\tilde{N}_B$ is everywhere zero. At some point in the film between $y = 0$ and $y = \delta_m$, we write

$$\tilde{N}_A(\tilde{H}_{As} - \tilde{H}_{A1}) + \tilde{N}_A(\tilde{H}_A - \tilde{H}_{As}) = k\frac{dt}{dy} \quad (38\text{-}20)$$

We next integrate this equation from $y = 0$ to $y = \delta_m$ and from $t = t_s$ to $t = t_o$. Before the integration, $\tilde{H}_{As} - \tilde{H}_{A1}$ is replaced by $\Delta\tilde{H}_A$ and $\tilde{H}_A - \tilde{H}_{As}$ by $\tilde{C}_{pA}(t - t_s)$. Equation (38-20) is then written as

$$\tilde{N}_A\int_0^{\delta_m} dy = k\int_0^{t_o - t_s} \frac{d(t - t_s)}{\Delta\tilde{H}_A + \tilde{C}_{pA}(t - t_s)} \quad (38\text{-}21)$$

Integration of Eq. (38-21) yields

$$\tilde{N}_A = \frac{k}{\delta_m\tilde{C}_{pA}} \ln\left[1 + \frac{\tilde{C}_{pA}}{\Delta\tilde{H}_A}(t_o - t_s)\right] \quad (38\text{-}22)$$

The total energy flux at the interface is $\tilde{N}_A \Delta\tilde{H}_A$, so that we get, by the definition of h [Eq. (38-17)],

$$h = \frac{k \, \Delta \tilde{H}_A \ln \left[1 + (\tilde{C}_{pA}/\Delta \tilde{H}_A)(t_o - t_s) \right]}{\delta_m \tilde{C}_{pA}(t_o - t_s)} \tag{38-23}$$

If there is no mass transfer, we have simply

$$h^o = \frac{k}{\delta_m} \tag{38-24}$$

From Eqs. (38-23) and (38-24) there results

$$h^o = h \left[1 + \frac{\tilde{C}_{pA}}{\Delta \tilde{H}_A} (t_o - t) \right]_{lm} \tag{38-25}$$

in which

$$\left[1 + \frac{\tilde{C}_{pA}}{\Delta \tilde{H}_A} (t_o - t) \right]_{lm} = \frac{(\tilde{C}_{pA}/\Delta \tilde{H}_A)(t_o - t_s)}{\ln \left[1 + (\tilde{C}_{pA}/\Delta \tilde{H}_A)(t_o - t_s) \right]} \tag{38-26}$$

Note that Eq. (38-20) reduces to the equivalent of Eq. (24-5) at $y = 0$ ($\tilde{H}_A = \tilde{H}_{As}$).

Equation (38-25) is analogous to Eq. (33-26). It has been derived for heat transfer toward the surface and mass transfer away from the surface, the most common situation. With a suitable adjustment in signs, Eq. (38-25) can be applied to other combinations of heat and mass transfer for which $\tilde{N}_B = 0$.

Although the analysis for diffusion and conduction through a hypothetical stagnant film is a model which is known to be only approximate, Eqs. (33-26) and (38-25) are all that are presently available for turbulent flow. The values of h^o and k_ρ^o are obtained from suitable correlations in Chaps. 25 and 35.

Example 38-1

The temperatures reached in rockets are so high that special precautions must be taken to prevent the walls of the combustion chamber from being destroyed. In a liquid-fueled rocket the walls may be cooled by making them porous and forcing liquid oxygen through the walls into the combustion chamber; this is called transpiration cooling. Let us study a situation for which the temperature of the gas stream is 3000°R and it is desired to keep the inside surface of the walls at 1160°R by adding liquid oxygen at 162°R. Calculate the necessary rate of oxygen addition if the heat-transfer coefficient for the turbulent flow with no addition is 250 Btu/(hr)(sq ft)(°F).

This situation corresponds to the transfer of A through stagnant B, and an approximate result can be obtained from Eq. (38-22); for turbulent flow, only the film theory is available. We replace k/δ_m by h^o, or 250, and get

$$\tilde{N}_A = \frac{h^o}{\tilde{C}_{pA}} \ln \left[1 + \frac{\tilde{C}_{pA}(t_o - t_s)}{\Delta \tilde{H}_A} \right]$$

For oxygen, an average value of $\tilde{C}_{pA}$ is taken as 7.20 Btu/(°F)(lb mole) between 162 and 1160°R, and the latent heat of vaporization is 2930 Btu/lb mole. Thus we get

$$\Delta \tilde{H}_A = 2930 + 7.20(1160 - 162) = 10{,}120$$

Between 1160 and 3000°R, $\tilde{C}_{pA}$ is taken as 8.50; thus we have

$$\tilde{N}_A = \frac{250}{8.50} \ln \left[1 + \frac{8.50(1840)}{10,120} \right]$$

$$= 27.5 \text{ lb moles/(hr)(sq ft)}$$

It is of interest to calculate the value of h from Eqs. (38-25) and (38-26):

$$\left[1 + \frac{\tilde{C}_{pA}}{\Delta \tilde{H}_A} (t_o - t) \right]_{lm} = \frac{1.545}{\ln (2.545)} = 1.658$$

$$h = \frac{h^o}{1.658} = \frac{250}{1.658} = 151 \text{ Btu/(hr)(sq ft)(°F)}$$

From Eq. (38-19) we calculate

$$h' = h(2.545) = 384 \text{ Btu/(hr)(sq ft)(°F)}$$

The significance of the three coefficients can be summarized as follows. If there were no mass transfer, the value $h^o = 250$ would prevail; because of the mass transfer, this value is changed to $h = 151$. However, this latter value of h includes the energy carried by the mass transfer of A; the rate of heat transfer by conduction across the fictitious film is given by $h' = 384$. If the flow were laminar, Fig. 38-2 could be used with a trial-and-error procedure; it would be found that h/h^o is of the same order as $1/1.658$.

Mass Transfer in a Nonisothermal Contactor

Let us now discuss a contacting tower in which an exothermic heat effect accompanies the dissolution of component A which is being transferred from one phase to another. The two phases are immiscible, so that N_B is again zero. In order to speak of a concrete example, we apply our reasoning to gas absorption, but the solutions obtained can be adapted to desorption, liquid-liquid extraction, or other separation operations.

If the absorbing liquid introduced at the top of a gas-absorption tower is at the same temperature as the rich gas introduced at the bottom, the liquid temperature increases as it flows down the column. The exothermic heat of absorption is converted to sensible heat in the liquid; the tower operation is taken as adiabatic. In rough calculations the heat transfer between phases is sometimes assumed to be zero. The gas-phase temperature is then constant throughout the tower, and the liquid temperature increases to a maximum at the bottom of the tower. Since the mass-transfer coefficient or HTU is only slightly affected by temperature, the only effect of the variation of liquid temperature is to increase the value of m as $\tilde{x}_A$ and $\tilde{y}_A$ increase. The operating line is unchanged, and the equilibrium line is concave upward; the situation is illustrated in Fig. 38-4.

The analysis we have just described may lead to incorrect results. From the analogy between heat and mass transfer it is evident that if mass is transferred between the phases at an appreciable rate, heat must be similarly transferred. This statement would be inaccurate only if the

Fig. 38-4.   *Operating diagram for the absorption of ammonia in water. The effect of the heat of absorption on the liquid temperature is shown. Heat transfer between phases is neglected. (From T. K. Sherwood and R. L. Pigford, "Absorption and Extraction," 2d ed., p. 162, McGraw-Hill Book Company, Inc., New York, 1952.)*

Lewis number were much greater than 1. For most gas-liquid systems, **Le** is of the order of unity, i.e., between 0.5 and 3.0.

A typical system in which the temperatures vary is shown in Fig. 38-5. The liquid entering the tower is in contact with gas which has been heated by the hot liquid lower in the tower; heat flows from gas to liquid, so that the liquid temperature increases more rapidly than it would have increased without interphase heat transfer. Near the bottom of the tower the liquid loses heat to the cold incoming gas. Its temperature thus increases less rapidly or decreases (as in Fig. 38-5) as the liquid flows downward.

Since the gas temperature is governed only by sensible heat effects, it is heated by the hot liquid near the bottom of the tower and cooled by the cold liquid near the top of the tower. The temperature curves of the two phases thus cross at a point within the tower. The gas temperature reaches a maximum at an interior point in the tower; the liquid temperature either increases to maximum at the bottom of the tower or reaches a maximum within the tower, depending on the particular situation.

We are simplifying our discussion by studying a case for which B and C are immiscible. Actual fluids may be partially miscible; for instance, water used as an absorbing liquid vaporizes if the gas phase is not saturated with water vapor.

In order to calculate the height of a nonisothermal contacting tower, we must in general resort to a numerical integration of the differential

Fig. 38-5.   *Estimated temperature profiles for the adiabatic absorption of acetone. (From T. K. Sherwood and R. L. Pigford, "Absorption and Extraction," 2d ed., p. 165, McGraw-Hill Book Company, Inc., New York, 1952.)*

equations which apply at a point within the tower.   We proceed to write these equations for a gas-absorption tower.   The rate of mass transfer between phases is, from Eqs. (37-12) and (33-30),

$$-\frac{d\tilde{y}_A}{dz} = \frac{\tilde{y}_A - \tilde{y}_{As}}{H_G} \frac{1 - \tilde{y}_A}{(1 - \tilde{y}_A)_{lm}} \tag{38-27}$$

or, for dilute solutions,

$$-\frac{d\tilde{y}_A}{dz} = \frac{\tilde{y}_A - \tilde{y}_{As}}{H_G} \tag{38-28}$$

The over-all mass balance applied to the differential height dz gives

$$\frac{d(\tilde{G}\tilde{y}_A)}{d(\tilde{L}\tilde{x}_A)} = 1.0 \tag{38-29}$$

and for dilute solutions

$$\frac{d\tilde{y}_A}{d\tilde{x}_A} = \frac{\tilde{L}}{\tilde{G}} \tag{38-30}$$

Equation (38-29) or (38-30) can be integrated independently from the other equations to give the operating line, Eq. (37-8).   In other words, for given terminal mole fractions and for a given $\tilde{L}/\tilde{G}$, the operating line is not affected by temperature.   However, the temperature of the liquid determines $\tilde{y}_{As}$ and thus has an important effect on Eq. (38-27) or (38-28).

The rate of heat transfer between phases is written in a form analogous to Eq. (37-9) as

$$-dz = \frac{d(\tilde{C}_{py}\tilde{G}t_y)}{h_y^o a(t_y - t_s)} \tag{38-31}$$

If $\tilde{C}_{py}$ and $\tilde{G}$ are assumed constant, Eq. (38-31) can be written as

$$-\frac{dt_y}{dz} = \frac{t_y - t_s}{H_{ty}} \tag{38-32}$$

in which H_{ty}, the height of a transfer unit for heat transfer for the y phase, is defined by

$$H_{ty} = \frac{\tilde{G}\tilde{C}_{py}}{h_y^o a} \tag{38-33}$$

It is interesting to observe that Eqs. (25-42) and (35-27) can be combined with the definitions of the HTUs to give

$$\frac{H_G}{H_{ty}} = \frac{h_y^o}{k_y^o \tilde{C}_{py}} = \mathbf{Le}^{\frac{2}{3}} \tag{38-34}$$

Since $\mathbf{Le}$ is close to unity for most systems, the two HTUs are of the same order of magnitude.

An over-all energy balance applied to a height of tower dz, assuming steady adiabatic operation, yields

$$d(\tilde{L}\tilde{H}_x) = d(\tilde{G}\tilde{H}_y) \tag{38-35}$$

The enthalpies are defined by

$$\tilde{H}_x = \tilde{C}_{px}(t_x - t_r) \tag{38-36}$$

and

$$\tilde{H}_y = \tilde{C}_{py}(t_y - t_r) + Q_r \tilde{y}_A \tag{38-37}$$

The quantity Q_r is the exothermic molal heat of solution of component A in the absorbing liquid at the reference temperature t_r. If it is assumed that $\tilde{L}$, $\tilde{C}_{px}$, $\tilde{G}$, and $\tilde{C}_{py}$ are constant, Eq. (38-35) can be put into the form

$$\tilde{L}\tilde{C}_{px}\frac{dt_x}{dz} = \tilde{G}\tilde{C}_{py}\frac{dt_y}{dz} + Q_r\tilde{G}\frac{d\tilde{y}_A}{dz} \tag{38-38}$$

The values of the interfacial mole fraction and temperature, $\tilde{y}_{As}$ and t_s, are found as described in Chap. 33 from

$$-\frac{k_{\tilde{x}}}{k_{\tilde{y}}} = \frac{\tilde{y}_A - \tilde{y}_{As}}{\tilde{x}_A - \tilde{x}_{As}} \tag{33-22}$$

and from the analogous equation for heat transfer,

$$-\frac{h_x}{h_y} = \frac{t_y - t_s}{t_x - t_s} \tag{38-39}$$

If it is possible to use over-all transfer coefficients, Eqs. (33-22) and (38-29) are not necessary and Eqs. (38-28) and (38-32) become

$$-\frac{d\tilde{y}_A}{dz} = \frac{\tilde{y}_A - \tilde{y}_A^*}{H_{OG}} \tag{38-40}$$

and

$$-\frac{dt_y}{dz} = \frac{t_y - t_x}{H_{toy}} \tag{38-41}$$

The equations given above cannot be integrated analytically; the calculation of the height of a nonisothermal tower must be done by a stepwise numerical method. The procedure is as follows. Assuming that the temperatures and compositions of both phases are known at the bottom of the tower ($z = 0$), the derivatives $d\tilde{y}_A/dz$ and dt_y/dz can be calculated from Eqs. (38-28) and (38-32) or (38-40) and (38-41). These derivatives also permit the calculation of dt_x/dz from Eq. (38-38). A short increment of tower height Δz is chosen over which it is assumed that the derivatives are constant. In this way the values of t_x, t_y, and $\tilde{y}_A$ can be calculated at the end of the first interval Δz_a. From the operating line and Eqs. (33-22) and (38-39), $\tilde{y}_{As}$ and t_s can be calculated at the end of the interval Δz_a. These values permit the calculation of new values of $d\tilde{y}_A/dz$, dt_y/dz, and dt_x/dz at the point $z = \Delta z_a$. A simple procedure is then to assume that these new values of the derivatives are constant over a second interval Δz_b; the calculations are continued until the mole fraction is reached corresponding to the top of the tower.

The integration procedure described above becomes more accurate as the magnitude of Δz is decreased; it is often not accurate for conveniently large values of the increment. With a reasonably large increment, improved accuracy can be obtained if the values of the derivatives at the two ends of an interval are averaged. Systematic procedures, such as the methods of Euler and of Runge and Kutta, are described in the literature.[1] These repetitive calculations are well suited for performance by automatic computing machines. The estimated temperatures in a tower absorbing acetone in water are shown in Fig. 38-5.

The equations and procedures given in this section can also be used if a volatile liquid is being vaporized or condensed in a tower. In general, the only simplifications for this case are that $k_{\tilde{x}}$ is infinite (there is no mass-transfer resistance in the pure liquid) and that $\tilde{y}_{As}$ is a function of t_s only, since $\tilde{x}_{As}$ and $\tilde{x}_A$ are always unity. A stepwise calculation is still necessary. However, added simplifications are possible if the liquid is water; also, a special nomenclature exists for air-water mixtures. These matters are discussed in the next section.

---

[1] For a discussion from an engineering point of view, see H. S. Mickley, T. K. Sherwood, and C. E. Reed, "Applied Mathematics in Chemical Engineering," 2d ed., chap. 5, McGraw-Hill Book Company, Inc., New York, 1957. A good treatment of the basic mathematics is given in F. B. Hildebrand, "Introduction to Numerical Analysis," McGraw-Hill Book Company, Inc., New York, 1956.

Air-Water Operations

Definitions. The *humidity* Y_A is defined as the pounds of water (component A) carried by one pound of dry air. A *molal humidity* $\tilde{Y}_A$ can be defined, but most of the accumulated literature on humidification and drying is in terms of Y_A. The two quantities are related by

$$Y_A = {}^{18}\!/_{29} \tilde{Y}_A \tag{38-42}$$

The humidity is then related to the mole fraction by

$$Y_A = \frac{18}{29} \frac{\tilde{y}_A}{1 - \tilde{y}_A} \tag{38-43}$$

Air is said to be saturated with water vapor at a given pressure and temperature when it holds the maximum possible amount of water vapor. This condition is achieved when the air is in equilibrium with liquid water. The *saturation humidity* Y_{As} is the value of Y_A corresponding to a partial pressure $\overline{p}_A$ equal to the vapor pressure of water p_A at the given temperature. The *relative humidity* is defined by

$$\text{Relative humidity} = 100 \frac{\overline{p}_A}{p_A} \tag{38-44}$$

The *per cent humidity*, or *saturation*, is given by

$$\text{Per cent saturation} = 100 \frac{Y_A}{Y_{As}} = \frac{\overline{p}_A}{p_A} \frac{1 - p_A}{1 - \overline{p}_A} (100) \tag{38-45}$$

where p_A and $\overline{p}_A$ are expressed in atmospheres.

The *humid heat* C_{pH} is defined by

$$C_{pH} = C_{pB} + Y_A C_{pA} \tag{38-46}$$

or

$$C_{pH} = 0.24 + 0.46 Y_A \tag{38-47}$$

or

$$C_{pH} = C_{py}(1 + Y_A) \tag{38-48}$$

and measured in Btu/(°F)(lb of dry air).

The *humid volume* is defined by

$$V_H = V_B + Y_A V_A \tag{38-49}$$

and measured in cu ft/lb of dry air.

The enthalpy of moist air is defined by Eq. (38-37) in units consistent with the present discussion:

$$H_y = C_{pH}(t_y - t_r) + \lambda_r Y_A \tag{38-50}$$

The units are Btu/lb of dry air; λ_r is the heat of vaporization at the refer-

Air

flow

Wick

Liquid
Reservoir

Fig. 38-6.   Sketch of a wet-bulb thermometer.

ence temperature t_r, which, for convenience, is taken as $0°F$ in many tables.[1]

The *adiabatic saturation temperature* of moist air is the temperature which air reaches when it is saturated adiabatically, i.e., at constant enthalpy. Consider a very tall air-water contacting tower; the air leaving the top of the tower is saturated at the temperature of the entering water. The water from the bottom of the tower is led to the top and recirculated through the tower; the entire apparatus is insulated from the surroundings. As air at a given state is blown through the tower, it is found that the recirculated water achieves an equilibrium temperature. Equation (38-38) can be integrated to give, with suitable adjustment of the units,

$$LC_{px}(t_{xo} - t_{x1}) = 0 = G_B C_{pH}(t_{yo} - t_{y1}) + \lambda_r G_B(Y_{Ao} - Y_{A1}) \quad (38\text{-}51)$$

It is recalled that this equation represents an application of the over-all energy balance. The adiabatic saturation temperature t_{as}, which equals t_{xo}, t_{x1}, or t_{y1} for the tall tower, is thus

$$t_{as} = t_{yo} - \frac{\lambda_r}{C_{pH}} (Y_{as} - Y_{Ao}) \quad (38\text{-}52)$$

In this equation Y_{A1} has been replaced by Y_{as}, the saturation humidity corresponding to t_{as}.

The *wet-bulb temperature* t_{wb} is the temperature attained by a small reservoir of water in contact with a large amount of air flowing past it. A device for measuring this temperature is shown in Fig. 38-6. All the energy required for the vaporization of the water flows to the water by sensible heat transfer from the air. This situation is the same as that leading to the derivation of Eq. (38-17). In our present nomenclature, we write

[1] See Perry, sec. 12.

$$N_A\lambda = k_Y(Y_{wb} - Y_A)\lambda = h_y(t_y - t_{wb}) \tag{38-53}$$

or

$$t_{wb} = t_y - \frac{k_Y\lambda}{h_y}(Y_{wb} - Y_A) \tag{38-54}$$

In terms of the units of the present discussion, Eq. (38-34) becomes, for dilute solutions ($k_Y = k_Y^o$, $h_y = h_y^o$),

$$\frac{h_y}{k_Y C_{py}} = \mathsf{Le}^{\frac{2}{3}} \tag{38-55}$$

so that Eq. (38-54) can be written as

$$t_{wb} = t_y - \frac{\lambda}{C_{py}\,\mathsf{Le}^{\frac{2}{3}}}(Y_{wb} - Y_A) \tag{38-56}$$

This equation applies to the vaporization of any liquid; for water in air, $\mathsf{Le} = 1.0$, and for sufficiently dilute gaseous solutions, $C_{pH} \cong C_{py}$, so that

$$t_{wb} = t_y - \frac{\lambda}{C_{pH}}(Y_{wb} - Y_A) \tag{38-57}$$

If, in addition, any difference between λ and λ_r is neglected, it is seen that t_{wb} and t_{as} are the same for the water-air system at temperatures low enough to form a dilute gas-phase solution (say $t = 120°F$). For other liquids, the adiabatic saturation and wet-bulb temperatures are not equal.

The *dew-point temperature* is the temperature at which a given sample of moist air becomes saturated as it is cooled at constant pressure and humidity. The dew-point pressure is the total pressure to which moist air must be compressed at constant temperature and humidity to bring it to saturation.

Humidity Chart. The relations among some of the foregoing variables are conveniently given by the humidity chart of Fig. 38-7. Its use is illustrated by the following example.

Example 38-2

The air used in a certain process at 760 mm Hg is found by measurement to have a dry-bulb temperature of 110°F and a wet-bulb temperature of 85°F.

From Fig. 38-7 the humidity is $Y_A = 0.0205$. If the air under these conditions is cooled to saturation, dew appears at 77.5°F. Air at 110°F could hold 0.0595 lb water/lb dry air; saturation is thus 34.5 per cent, as can also be read from the curved lines on the chart. The mole fraction water vapor in the moist air is found from Eq. (38-43), rearranged as

$$\bar{y}_A = \frac{Y_A}{{}^{18}\!/_{29} + Y_A}$$

$$\bar{y}_A = 0.0320$$

Fig. 38-7. *Humidity chart for the air-water system at 1 atm. (From G. G. Brown et al., "Unit Operations," fig. 499, p. 545, John Wiley & Sons, Inc., New York, 1950.)*

The partial pressure of water vapor is

$$\bar{p}_A = (0.0320)(760) = 24.3 \text{ mm Hg}$$

From Perry, p. 772, we have

$$p_A = 2.597 \text{ in. Hg} = 65.9 \text{ mm Hg}$$

The relative humidity is then 24.3/65.9, or 36.9 per cent.
The enthalpy of the moist air at 110°F is found from Eq. (38-50) as

$$H_y = (0.249)(110) + (1025)(0.0205)$$
$$= 49.5 \text{ Btu/lb dry air}$$

The value of the latent heat of vaporization used above is for the vaporization of liquid water at 32°F. Because the wet-bulb and adiabatic saturation temperatures for the air-water system have been assumed identical, the enthalpy of the moist air at 110°F should be the same as that of saturated air at 85°F. From the table in Perry, p. 763, it is found that $H_{as} = 49.4$ Btu/lb at 85°F (h_s in Perry's notation).

Cooling Towers. As warm water flows down a tower countercurrent to rising unsaturated air, the water is cooled by furnishing part of the latent heat required to vaporize some of the water into the air stream. The air is thus humidified as it rises. The calculation of the tower height for the vaporization of liquids other than water must be done by the stepwise procedure using Eqs. (38-27) to (38-41). For water, the fact that **Le** is unity leads to an important simplification. We first rewrite Eq. (38-38) in the units used with air-water operations:

$$LC_{px} \frac{dt_x}{dz} = G_B C_{pH} \frac{dt_y}{dz} + G_B \lambda_r \frac{dY_A}{dz} \tag{38-58}$$

The derivative dt_y/dz is replaced by using Eq. (38-32), and dY_A/dz is replaced by using

$$- \frac{dY_A}{dz} = \frac{Y_A - Y_{As}}{H_G} \tag{38-59}$$

which is analogous to Eq. (38-28). The result is

$$- LC_{px} \frac{dt_x}{dz} = G_B C_{pH} \frac{t_y - t_s}{H_{ty}} + G_B \lambda_r \frac{Y_A - Y_{As}}{H_G} \tag{38-60}$$

For the air-water system, H_{ty} approximately equals H_G, so we write

$$- LC_{px} \frac{dt_x}{dz} = \frac{G_B}{H_G} [C_{pH}(t_y - t_s) + \lambda_r(Y_A - Y_{As})] \tag{38-61}$$

If this equation is compared with Eq. (38-50), the definition of the enthalpy of the gas phase, it can be changed to

$$- LC_{px} \frac{dt_x}{dz} = \frac{G_B}{H_G} (H_y - H_{ys}) \tag{38-62}$$

The left-hand side of the equation is also equal to $-G_B(dH_y/dz)$ [Eq. (38-35)]. Therefore we have

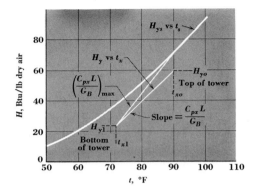

Fig. 38-8.   *Operating diagram for a cooling tower.*

$$- \frac{dH_y}{dz} = \frac{H_y - H_{ys}}{H_G} \tag{38-63}$$

In addition, we combine Eqs. (38-62) and (38-63) to give

$$LC_{px} \frac{dt_x}{dz} = G_B \frac{dH_y}{dz} \tag{38-64}$$

and thus

$$\frac{dH_y}{dt_x} = C_{px} \frac{L}{G_B} \tag{38-65}$$

Since the right-hand side of Eq. (38-65) is constant (it is assumed that the amount of water evaporated in the tower does not greatly change L), this equation represents a straight operating line on a graph of H_y versus t (Fig. 38-8). Equation (38-65) can be integrated to give the relation between H_y and t_x at any point in the tower.

$$H_y = \frac{C_{px}L}{G_B} t_x + H_{yo} - \frac{C_{px}L}{G_B} t_{xo} \tag{38-66}$$

From data on the vapor pressure of water and the enthalpies of air and water, the curve shown in Fig. 38-8 for H_{ys} versus t_s is obtained. If there is negligible resistance to heat transfer in the liquid phase ($h_y/h_x = 0$), t_s and t_x are identical. Once the operating and equilibrium lines are plotted on a graph like Fig. 38-8, it is possible to find $H_{ys} - H_y$ as a function of H_y and evaluate the integral for the tower height,

$$z = H_G \int_{H_{y1}}^{H_{yo}} \frac{dH_y}{H_{ys} - H_y} \tag{38-67}$$

The above procedure does not give the gas temperature t_y or the humidity Y_A as a function of H_y or t_x. This relation must be found by a stepwise numerical calculation[1] using the following equation, which is a combination of Eqs. (38-32) and (38-63):

$$\frac{dH_y}{dt_y} = \frac{H_y - H_{ys}}{t_y - t_s} \tag{38-68}$$

For the successful operation of a tower, the air must not become saturated, for this leads to fog formation. If the curve of H_y versus t_y crosses the equilibrium curve, fog forms in the air.

For the cooling or humidification tower which we have just discussed, the operating line lies below the equilibrium line. There is a minimum air rate which can be used to accomplish a specified water-cooling duty, as shown in Fig. 38-8 $[(C_{px}L/G_B)_{max}]$.

In a dehumidification tower cool water is used to reduce the humidity (and temperature) of air blown in at the foot of the tower. For this case the operating line is above the equilibrium line and there exists a minimum amount of water which can be used to dehumidify a given quantity of air.

Example 38-3

Water is to be cooled from 110 to 80°F in a forced draft tower under conditions such that H_G is 1.75 ft. Air enters the bottom of the tower at 75°F and a wet-bulb temperature of 70°F. Find the tower height if 1.33 times the minimum air rate is used. Neglect the heat-transfer resistance of the liquid phase.

The equilibrium curve shown in Fig. 38-9 is plotted from data in Perry on pp. 763 to 764. The enthalpy of the air entering the bottom of the tower is the same as the enthalpy of saturated air at 70°F, the adiabatic saturation temperature of the unsaturated inlet air. The point on Fig. 38-9 representing the inlet air having an adiabatic saturation temperature of 70°F is on a horizontal line to the right of the equilibrium curve, at an enthalpy of 34.1 Btu/lb. The end of the operating line is then fixed by the outlet water temperature, $t_{x1} = 80°F$.

The maximum slope of the operating line is shown in the diagram; the actual operating line, having a slope of 1/1.33 of the limiting line, results in a value of H_{yo} of 75.6 Btu/lb.

The number of transfer units is found from Eq. (38-67); the following table is made from Fig. 38-9.

t_x, °F	H_y	$1/(H_{ys} - H_y)$
80	34.1	0.1074
90	47.9	0.1395
100	61.8	0.1170
110	75.6	0.0689

[1] This procedure has been described by H. S. Mickley, *Chem. Eng. Progr.*, **45**:739 (1949).

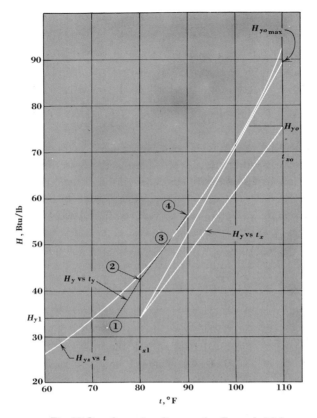

Fig. 38-9.   Operating diagram for Example 38-3.

A graphical or numerical integration can be performed; the result is

$$n_G = \int_{34.1}^{75.6} \frac{dH_y}{H_{ys} - H_y} = 5.0$$

and so we obtain

$$z = H_G n_G = (1.75)(5.0) = 8.75 \text{ ft}$$

Before accepting this result it is well to check the air temperature in the tower.   At the bottom of the tower, Eq. (38-68) is

$$\frac{dH_y}{dt_y} = \frac{H_{ys} - H_y}{t_{ys} - t_y} = \frac{43.7 - 34.1}{80 - 75} = 1.92 \text{ Btu/(°F)(lb)}$$

If an interval $\Delta t_y = 5°$ is chosen, H_y at $t_y = 80°F$ is $34.1 + 5(1.92) = 43.7$ Btu/lb. The slope at this point is

$$\frac{dH_y}{dt_y} = \frac{51.8 - 43.7}{87 - 80} = 1.16$$

The average slope over the 5° interval is $(\frac{1}{2})(1.92 + 1.16)$, or 1.54, so the revised value of H_y at $t_y = 80°$ is $34.1 + (5)(1.54) = 41.8$.   This point is labeled 2 on the line of H_y

versus t_y in Fig. 38-9. A horizontal line from 2 to the operating line locates the water temperature, $t_x = t_{ys} = 86°F$. In a similar way the curve of H_y versus t_y is extended to points 3 and 4, as shown in Fig. 38-9. Since this curve crosses the equilibrium line, there would be fog formation in the tower. It would be necessary to operate with a higher air rate in order to accomplish the desired cooling of the water without fog formation.

Drying

In the unit operation of drying, water or another liquid is removed from a solid material. The removal of moisture from gases and liquids is also called drying, but the present discussion concerns only the drying of solids.

In the most common type of drying equipment water is evaporated and carried off by a stream of air. However, another unsaturated phase such as superheated steam can also be used as a carrier gas. Alternatively, rather than blow an unsaturated gas past the solid, the pressure can be reduced by a vacuum pump so that the liquid boils at the prevailing temperature.

The heat required for the vaporization of the liquid in the solid is in most cases largely furnished from the inert carrier gas, which enters the drier hot. In some driers the solid is in contact with heated metal surfaces, so part of the heat of vaporization flows to the solid by conduction. In vacuum drying, for which there is no carrier gas, the heat of vaporization must be furnished by conduction or radiation; the capacity of the drier is largely influenced by the heat-transfer surface available.

There are a large number of types of drying equipment;[1] only a few of the most important types will be discussed here. The simplest drier is a tray drier, in which the material to be dried is placed on trays contained in an ovenlike enclosure. Heated air may be forced past the solid, or the enclosure may be evacuated. The material is dried in batches, and the trays are loaded and unloaded intermittently.

Continuous operation is usually desirable; a continuous belt drier is shown in Fig. 38-10. Wet material is fed to a moving belt and exposed to hot air as it moves through the tunnel-like drier. The dry material is discharged continuously from the far end of the drier. The rotary steam-tube drier shown in Fig. 38-11 is used for drying granular solids. As the body of the drier turns, the solids are lifted and fall through the central air space. Hot air is blown into one end of the drier or in through louvers in the shell. The heated surfaces in the drier increase the heat-transfer rate to the solid and thus promote rapid drying.

The moisture content of a solid being dried in a typical batch situation

---

[1] See Perry, pp. 815–877.

(a) Path of travel of permeable bed through a 3 unit through-circulation dryer.

(b) Air flow in wet end

(c) Air flow in dry end

Fig. **38-10.** *Continuous belt drier.* (*Proctor and Schwartz, Inc.*)

is plotted in Fig. 38-12 against time. From the slope of the line in Fig. 38-12 the drying-rate curve of Fig. 38-13 is obtained. In this discussion we assume that a large excess of air of constant wet- and dry-bulb temperatures is being used so that the humidity of the air does not change with time or change appreciably as it passes through the drier. The drying rate is then a function only of the moisture content of the solid.

Fig. **38-11.** *Continuous rotary drier.*

Fig. 38-12. *A typical curve of moisture content as a function of drying time for fixed air con ditions.*

a. **Critical moisture content.**
b. **Equilibrium moisture content.**

The shape of the curve shown in Fig. 38-13 is typical for many solids. At first the surface of the solid is flooded with liquid, so that water is carried away from the surface just as it would be from a liquid surface. For constant air conditions, the drying rate is constant; the solid temperature is the wet-bulb temperature of the air unless the solid is heated by conduction or radiation from other solid surfaces. The principles previously developed for air-water contacting permit the necessary design calculation for the constant-rate drying period.

During the constant-rate period water is supplied from the solid near the surface fast enough to keep the surface entirely wet. If the solid shrinks on drying, water is squeezed out from the solid, and there may be a long constant-rate period. At a certain *critical moisture content* dry patches begin to exist on the surface and the drying rate begins to fall. The liquid surface retreats into the interior of the solid, so that the evaporated moisture must diffuse through the pores of the solid. Because of the effect of capillarity, the liquid surface rises higher in small pores than in larger ones. Eventually the entire irregular liquid front moves to the interior of the solid and leaves the surface entirely dry. The time during which the surface is drying up is sometimes called the first falling-rate period. Often these periods are indistinguishable, but sometimes the rate falls more rapidly in the second period than in the first.

The diffusion of water vapor in the pores of a solid can be described by the differential mass balance, Eq. (9-22). The diffusivity based on the solid volume is less than that through air, for the cross section is partially filled with solid and the path for diffusion is lengthened by the tortuous nature of the pores. These effects reduce the effective diffusivity to something on the order of one-tenth that for air-water alone. Although the effective diffusivity within the solid is less than in the boundary layer, the effective thermal conductivity is usually higher than it is in the boundary layer. Heat flows through the dried solid by conduction. The result is that the temperature at the vapor-liquid interface rises above the wet-bulb temperature of the drying air.

The solution of Eq. (9-22) for the boundary values corresponding to the drying situation described above is difficult, but it is analogous to the

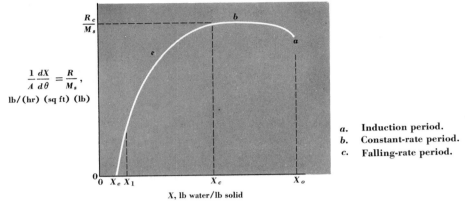

$$\frac{1}{A}\frac{dX}{d\theta} = \frac{R}{M_s},$$

lb/(hr) (sq ft) (lb)

R_c/M_s

a.   **Induction period.**
b.   **Constant-rate period.**
c.   **Falling-rate period.**

X, lb water/lb solid

Fig. 38-13.   Drying-rate curve for fixed air conditions.

freezing of a liquid by heat removal through the frozen layer. The un-frozen liquid is assumed to be well stirred. This heat-transfer problem has been discussed extensively.[1]

As the liquid surface retreats from the edge of the solid, islands of liquid may be left in the solid. In addition, the liquid may travel toward the surface by capillary movement through the pores or by diffusion in the fine structure of the solid itself. For these reasons the simple mechanism just described may not apply, and the rate of drying in many cases must be determined entirely empirically.

The rate of drying, as shown in Figs. 38-12 and 38-13, may reach zero before the solid is completely dry. The resulting *equilibrium moisture content* for a given solid is a function of temperature and of the condition of the drying air, as shown in Fig. 38-14.

The drying rate R for a mass M_s of solid being dried is defined as

$$R = \frac{M_s}{A}\frac{dX}{d\theta} \tag{38-69}$$

The units of R are lb water/(hr)(sq ft). For a batch-drying operation Eq. (38-69) is integrated to

$$\theta = -M_s \int_{X_o}^{X_1} \frac{dX}{AR} \tag{38-70}$$

In the simplest situation, A and R are constant, and Eq. (38-70) is integrated to

$$\theta = \frac{M_s}{AR}(X_o - X_1) \tag{38-71}$$

[1] H. S. Carslaw and J. C. Jaeger, "Conduction of Heat in Solids," 2d ed., chap. 11, Clarendon Press, Oxford, 1959.

Fig. 38-14.   *Equilibrium moisture content for various materials. (From "International Critical Tables," vol. 2, pp. 322–325, McGraw-Hill Book Company, Inc., New York, 1928.)*

If the variation of A and R is available in the form of a graph such as Fig. 38-13, Eq. (38-70) can be integrated graphically. Sometimes the curve of R versus X is simply a horizontal line followed by a straight line connecting the critical moisture content X_c, where $R = R_c$, to the equilibrium moisture content X_e, where $R = 0$. The integrated expression is then

$$\theta = \frac{M_s}{A R_c} \left[(X_o - X_c) + (X_c - X_e) \ln \frac{X_c - X_e}{X_1 - X_e} \right] \tag{38-72}$$

For a continuous drier, with air flow, for example, countercurrent to the movement of solid, the drying rate is a function both of moisture content of the solid and of the humidity and temperature of the air. The equations developed for a cooling tower apply to the constant-rate period. For the

Fig. 38-15.   Experimental drying data for Example 38-4.

falling-rate period, the calculations must be based on experimental data obtained under conditions which simulate those obtained in the actual countercurrent apparatus.[1]

Example 38-4

A granular solid containing 93 per cent water is to be dried in a fluidized drier to produce 100 lb/hr of dry material. Atmospheric air is passed through a steam-heated exchanger in which it is heated to 170°F and then passed through the bed of solid, from which it emerges 90 per cent saturated. The hot-air temperature is limited to 170°F because of the heat-sensitive nature of the solid. Base the design on the worst probable atmospheric conditions: $t = 100°F$, $t_{wb} = 100°F$. Estimate the quantity of air needed and the duty of the heat exchanger.

This problem is solved with the aid of Fig. 38-7. The humidity of the inlet air is 0.043 lb water/lb air. The humidity is unchanged as the air passes through the heat exchanger. At the entrance to the drier, where $Y_A = 0.043$ and $t = 170°F$, t_{wb} is 110°F. As the air flows through the fluidized bed of drying solid, the operation is adiabatic; it is assumed that no heat is exchanged with the surroundings. The average temperature of the solid particles and their associated water is constant. Thus the air follows an adiabatic cooling line; its wet-bulb temperature is constant at 110°F. At 90 per cent saturation the dry-bulb temperature is 113°F and $Y_A = 0.057$. Each pound of air thus carries away $0.057 - 0.043 = 0.014$ lb of water. The total water to be evaporated is $100/0.07 - 100 = 1330$ lb, so the air needed to produce 100 lb/hr of dry material is $1330/0.014 = 95,000$ lb/hr.

The heat required is computed from the enthalpies in Perry, pp. 763 to 764. At $t_{wb} = 110°F$, $H = 92.3$ Btu/lb, and at $t_{wb} = 100°F$, $H = 71.7$ Btu/lb, so the exchanger duty must be $(95,000)(92.3 - 71.7) = 1.96 \times 10^6$ Btu/hr. This figure neglects the heat capacity of the solid and the heat needed to heat the charge to about 110°F.

It is possible to reduce the amount of air required by reheating the air that has passed through the bed of solid and using it to dry a second bed. The air at $t = 113$, $t_{wb} = 110$ is heated to 170° at $Y_A = 0.057$; at this condition $t_{wb} = 116°F$. After passing through the wet solid the temperature at 90 per cent saturation is 119° and the humidity is 0.068. The total water carried is now $0.068 - 0.043$, or 0.025 lb/lb air, so the air required is reduced to 53,200 lb/hr.

The rate of drying is best determined by a small-scale experiment; the results of such a run are shown in Fig. 38-15 for single-stage drying. The drier could be designed for

[1] D. B. Broughton and H. S. Mickley, *Chem. Eng. Progr.*, **49**:319 (1953).

a batch of 400 lb with 3 hr for drying and 1 hr between runs. During the falling-rate period the temperature of the solid would rise above the wet-bulb temperature, so that some safety factor should be allowed in the design.

PROBLEMS

38-1. Calculate the ratio h/h^o for the gas phase in a cooling tower at a point where $t_x = t_s = 120°F$, $t_y = 140°F$, and $t_{ywb} = 105°F$.

38-2. Nitrogen at 1000°R and 1 atm is flowing past a flat plate. At a point 1 ft from the leading edge of the plate the temperature of the plate is 800°R and $\mathbf{Re}_x$ is 100,000. What is the heat flux at this point? Calculate the rate at which liquid nitrogen at about 1 atm must be added for transpiration cooling of the wall at the same heat flux from the hot gas if the new wall temperature is 500°R. The material of the wall is assumed to be a perfect insulator in the second case.

38-3. An air-water mixture has a dry-bulb temperature of 150°F and a wet-bulb temperature of 130° at 1 atm.

(*a*) What is the per cent saturation of this mixture?

(*b*) What is the absolute humidity?

(*c*) What is the volume in pounds per cubic foot dry air?

(*d*) What is the volume in pounds per cubic foot mixture?

(*e*) What is the dew point?

(*f*) The mixture is cooled to 105°F. What per cent of the moisture condenses out?

(*g*) The gaseous mixture from (*f*) left after condensation is then heated to 155°F. What is the relative saturation of this mixture?

(*h*) What is the humid heat, and how many Btu's are required to heat the air from 105 to 155°F?

38-4. Calculate the wet-bulb temperature of an ethanol-air mixture at 120°F and a relative saturation of 20 per cent.

38-5. Find the height and diameter of a cooling tower to cool 5000 gal/hr of water from 130 to 90°F using 2.5 times the minimum air rate. The air has a dry-bulb temperature of 80°F and a wet-bulb temperature of 65°F. The height of a transfer unit is 2 ft, and the tower will be operated at $G = 700$ lb/(hr)(sq ft). Neglect any resistance to heat transfer in the liquid phase.

38-6. A tray drier is to be used to dry sheets of material from 70 to 5 per cent moisture content. The sheets are 4 ft by 5 ft by 2 in. From experiments on this material with air at the same condition as that to be used in the full-scale drier, it is found that the rate during the constant-rate period is 1.5 lb water/(hr)(sq ft). The critical moisture content is 30 per cent, and the equilibrium moisture content is negligible. If the material is dried from both sides and has a bone-dry density of 25 lb/cu ft, calculate the time required for drying, assuming the falling-rate period to be linear.

38-7. Three thousand pounds (bone dry) of a granular solid is to be dried under constant drying conditions from a moisture content of 0.20 lb/lb to final moisture content of 0.02 lb/lb. The material has an effective area of 0.30 sq ft/lb. Under the same conditions, the following rates were previously known. Calculate the time required for the drying.

Moisture content	Rate, $lb/(hr)(sq\ ft)$
0.300	0.35
0.200	0.35
0.140	0.35
0.114	0.30
0.096	0.265
0.056	0.180
0.042	0.150
0.026	0.110
0.016	0.075

38-8. Nine hundred pounds per hour of sand (bone dry) is to be dried from a moisture content of 1 lb/lb to a moisture content of 0.2 by means of a continuous countercurrent tunnel drier.   The air enters the drier with a humidity of 0.013 and a temperature of 195°F at a rate of 40,000 lb dry air/hr.   The drier will operate adiabatically, and the sand can be considered to enter and leave at the wet-bulb temperature of the air. From laboratory experiments under constant drying conditions with the air at the initial condition, it was found that the sand had a critical moisture content of 0.5 lb/lb.   It was found that the rate was constant at 1.0 lb/(hr)(sq ft) above the critical point and fell off linearly to zero for bone-dry sand during the falling-rate period.

Calculate the length of drier required if the sand has an equivalent area of 7 sq ft/ft of drier, assuming that the rate is a linear function of humidity difference.

38-9. Solve Prob. 37-1 for an adiabatic tower, taking into account the heat effects. Data on the ammonia-water system can be found in Perry.

38-10. It is proposed to recover 99.0 per cent of the CO_2 in a gas mixture by scrubbing with a 1 N solution of diethanolamine in a tower packed with ¾-in. Raschig rings. The inlet gas is 25 mole per cent CO_2 and 75 mole per cent H_2 and is to be treated at 5000 cu ft/hr at 25°C and 1 atm.   Consider the effect of the temperature rise of the absorbing solution, but the sensible heat of the gas phase may be neglected.   The absorbing solution entering the top of the column contains 0.30 mole CO_2/mole amine and is to be supplied at a rate 2½ times the true minimum rate (not the isothermal minimum rate).   The necessary data can be found in an article by Cryder and Maloney, *Trans. AIChE*, **37**:827 (1941).   Estimate the height and diameter of the tower required.

SEPARATION BY EQUILIBRIUM STAGES; IMMISCIBLE PHASES

39

The Concept of the Ideal Stage

In Chap. 37 we studied separation operations in which two fluid phases flow past one another countercurrently or concurrently in such a way that they are in continuous contact. The solute tends to migrate from one phase to the other throughout the length of the contacting device. It was seen that an infinite interphase area is required to achieve equilibrium between the phases at one end of the tower, and it was assumed that there is negligible mixing in the direction of flow (longitudinal mixing).

A large proportion of industrial separations are performed in equipment in which the interphase contacting is done countercurrently in *stages*. The two phases are intimately mixed and then separated and led independently to the adjacent stages. The contact between the phases as they move through the device is intermittent rather than continuous. Typical stages used in liquid-liquid extraction are shown in Fig. 39-1.

In an ideal, or equilibrium, stage, the phases are mixed long enough so that the streams leaving the stage are in equilibrium, and the phases are mixed so thoroughly that there are no gradients of concentration in them. By contrast, in a real stage, there may not be sufficient contact between the phases to bring the streams into equilibrium. Such a stage accomplishes less interphase transfer than an ideal stage; it is said to be less efficient than an ideal stage. At the end of this chapter we shall study the factors

567

(a) Mixer-settler ideal stage

(b) Stage in a Scheibel column

Fig. 39-1.   Contactors for liquid-liquid extraction.

which affect stage efficiency, but first we shall consider the relation between the number of ideal stages and the separation achieved in a cascade of these stages.

Separation by a Single Equilibrium Contact

In gas absorption a single equilibrium contact can be obtained by introducing a gas containing solute A through a bubbler at the bottom of a vessel containing the absorbing solvent.   The gas is added at a constant rate V, and the liquid enters the contactor at a constant rate O.[1]   If the bubbles are small and the liquid is well mixed and deep enough to give sufficient time of contact, the gas leaving is in equilibrium with the liquid. The device is equivalent to one ideal stage.

---

[1] The quantities O and V are measured in pounds per hour for steady operation or simply in pounds for batch operation.   The ratios O/V and L/G are equal, but in stagewise operations it is not so natural to refer both items to the same cross-sectional area.   Especially when dealing with one stream alone, we use the symbols O and V rather than the mass velocities.

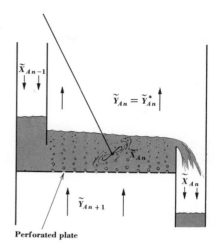

Fig. 39-2.   Sketch of a hypothetical ideal contacting stage.

In calculations for separations by stages the only need to consider mass-transfer resistance is in the case of real stages, for which the efficiency can be related to the mass-transfer rate between the phases in contact. It is simply assumed that in an ideal stage there is enough contact so that the phases leave the stage at equilibrium.

The material balance for the stage is conveniently expressed in terms of mole ratios and the flow rates of the immiscible inert streams. The units of composition used in Chaps. 37 and 38 were mole or mass fractions, which are the customary measure of the driving force for mass transfer. In mass-balance or operating-line equations, however, it is often convenient to use mole or mass ratio units ($\tilde{Y}_A$ or Y_A), as was illustrated in Examples 37-1 and 37-2, particularly if the phases are immiscible.

A single stage for gas absorption is shown schematically in Fig. 39-2. A mass balance on component A can be made to obtain the equation

$$\frac{\tilde{Y}_{An} - \tilde{Y}_{An+1}}{\tilde{X}_{An} - \tilde{X}_{An-1}} = -\frac{\tilde{O}_C}{\tilde{V}_B} \tag{39-1}$$

The symbol $\tilde{O}_C$ is the molal flow rate of inert constituent C in the liquid phase, while $\tilde{V}_B$ is the molal flow rate of the insoluble constituent B in the gas. For immiscible fluids, $\tilde{O}_C/\tilde{V}_B$ is a constant; that is, $\tilde{O}_{Cn} = \tilde{O}_{Cn-1}$, and $\tilde{V}_{Bn} = \tilde{V}_{Bn+1}$. If mole fractions were used, the analogous equation would of course be valid, but $\tilde{O}/\tilde{V}$ would be a function of the composition of a phase. The balance could also be expressed in terms of mass ratios or fractions.

The operating diagram for a single-stage contactor is shown in Fig.

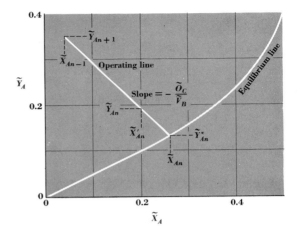

Fig. 39-3.   Operating diagram for a single stage.

39-3.   Since the streams leaving are in equilibrium, we have $\tilde{Y}_{An} = \tilde{Y}^*_{An}$; $\tilde{Y}^*_{An}$ and $\tilde{X}_{An}$ are on the equilibrium line.   The four compositions pertinent to the contactor are shown in Fig. 39-3.   The position of the operating line is similar to that given in Fig. 37-8.   However, for the well-mixed phases involved in the equilibrium contact, intermediate points on the operating line do not represent adjacent phases as in true concurrent flow. As applied to the equilibrium stage, only the extremities of the operating line shown in Fig. 39-3 have meaning.

If the time of contact or interfacial area in the stage is not sufficient to bring the phases leaving the contactor into equilibrium, the compositions of the streams are given by $\tilde{X}'_{An}$ and $\tilde{Y}_{An}$, shown in Fig. 39-3.   The efficiency of the stage can be defined by the equation

$$E_G = \frac{\tilde{Y}_{An+1} - \tilde{Y}_{An}}{\tilde{Y}_{An+1} - \tilde{Y}^*_{An}} \tag{39-2}$$

in which E_G is the Murphree V-phase efficiency of the stage.

In the device shown in Fig. 39-2 the liquid is well mixed and each phase may be presumed to leave the contactor with a uniform composition. However, interphase contacting is often done by a bubble-cap tray such as the one shown in Fig. 39-4.   The liquid flow is normal to the vapor flow, so that there must be a gradient of composition in the liquid phase within the stage.   As applied to this contacting device, the symbol $\tilde{Y}^*_{An}$ in Eq. (39-2) refers to the vapor composition, which would be in equilibrium with the actual liquid leaving the tray, that is, $\tilde{X}_{An}$.   As the liquid travels from inlet to outlet, its composition varies from $\tilde{X}_{An-1}$ to $\tilde{X}_{An}$.   The vapor entering the tray is assumed to have a uniform composition $\tilde{Y}_{An+1}$, and $\tilde{Y}_{An}$ is the bulk, or mixing-cup, composition of the vapor leaving the tray.

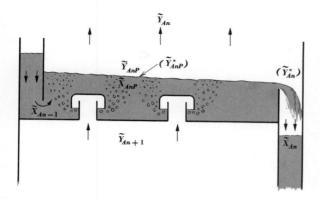

Fig. 39-4. *A bubble-cap tray.*

For a contactor with incompletely mixed phases we define a Murphree point efficiency,

$$E_{GP} = \frac{\tilde{Y}_{An+1} - \tilde{Y}_{AnP}}{\tilde{Y}_{An+1} - \tilde{Y}^*_{AnP}} \tag{39-3}$$

In this equation $\tilde{Y}_{AnP}$ and $\tilde{Y}^*_{AnP}$ represent the actual and equilibrium compositions at a point on the tray at the upper liquid surface, as shown in Fig. 39-4. The quantity E_{GP} is a measure of the efficiency of contacting in a small column of liquid located at the point P, in which the rising Y phase contacts an X phase of composition $\tilde{X}_{AnP}$. The Murphree point efficiency can be related to the mass-transfer rate in this hypothetical small column, as characterized, for example, by the quantities n_{OG} and H_{OG}. The maximum value of E_{GP} is unity.

If the contacting on the plate of Fig. 39-4 is good enough so that E_{GP} is everywhere equal to 1.0, it is evident that, for gas absorption, $\tilde{Y}_{An}$ would be less than $\tilde{Y}^*_{An}$, for the latter would be in equilibrium with the richest liquid. According to Eq. (39-2), E_G, the Murphree stage efficiency, would be greater than 1. Since an ideal stage is defined as one for which $E_G = 1.0$, a stage with cross flow such as shown in Fig. 39-4 would not be ideal if E_{GP} were everywhere unity. Note that for the well-mixed stage shown in Fig. 39-2, E_{GP} is everywhere equal to E_G.

The value of E_G can be obtained by the integration of E_{GP} over the plate. The quantity E_G/E_{GP} is a function of the flow pattern in the stage and the concentration distribution in the $\tilde{Y}_{An+1}$ stream, as well as the values of m and $\tilde{O}_C/\tilde{V}_B$. The possible variations of the flow pattern within a single stage can be compared with the various flow patterns which are possible in a heat exchanger. The integration procedure used to obtain the ratio E_G/E_{GP} is somewhat analogous to the integration used to obtain the correction factor Y for cross-flow or multipass heat exchangers.

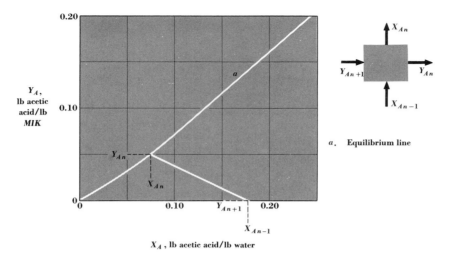

Fig. 39-5. Operating diagram for Example 39-1; single-stage extraction.

The units of composition used in Eqs. (39-2) and (39-3) can be changed as may be convenient. In liquid-liquid extraction, mass ratios or fractions may be used, and we shall find in Chap. 41 that mole fractions are used in the analysis of distillation, so that we can define another form as

$$E_G = \frac{\tilde{y}_{An+1} - \tilde{y}_{An}}{\tilde{y}_{An+1} - \tilde{y}^*_{An}} \qquad (39-4)$$

Before further discussion of stage efficiencies, it is necessary to discuss the operation of multistage separation equipment. We shall return to the subject of stage efficiency at the end of this chapter.

Example 39-1

The acetic acid in a solution in water containing 0.15 mass fraction acid is to be extracted in a single equilibrium stage using pure methyl isobutyl ketone as the solvent. Solvent is used in the amount of 1.745 lb for every pound of rich solution treated. Find the compositions of the streams leaving the stage.

The compositions of the entering streams are the same as those of Example 37-2. It is convenient to use mass-ratio units, so the equilibrium data are converted from mass fractions as shown in Fig. 37-14 to mass ratios as shown in Fig. 39-5. The equations given in Example 37-2 have been used for this calculation.

The equation for the operating line can be deduced from Eq. (39-1) to be

$$\frac{Y_{An} - Y_{An+1}}{X_{An} - X_{An-1}} = -\frac{O_C}{V_B} \qquad (1)$$

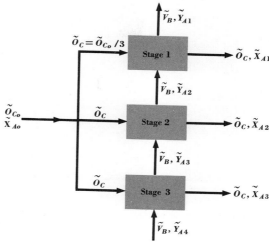

Fig. 39-6. *Schematic diagram of a three-stage contactor with fresh absorbent or solvent at each stage.*

For this problem, we have

$$X_{An-1} = 0.15/0.85 = 0.1768$$
$$Y_{An+1} = 0$$

$$\frac{O_C}{V_B} = 0.85/1.745 = 0.487$$

In Fig. 39-5, one end of the operating line is at X_{An-1}, Y_{An+1}, and its slope is $-O_C/V_B$, or -0.487. The intersection of the operating line with the equilibrium line is at X_{An}, Y_{An}, so that we obtain

$$X_{An} = 0.074$$
$$Y_{An} = 0.050$$

or, expressed in mass fractions,

$$x_{An} = 0.0688$$
$$y_{An} = 0.0476$$

These values show that much less extraction has been obtained in one equilibrium stage than was obtained in the continuous countercurrent tower of Example 37-2. Note that the ratio of solvent to feed is the same for both examples.

Multiple Contact with Fresh Absorbent (Solvent) at Each Stage

Let us reconsider the gas absorption discussed in the previous section. Instead of contacting the phases in a single stage, it is possible to use a number of stages. In Fig. 39-6 the absorbent is split into three equal parts and added to three stages as shown. The total amounts and the

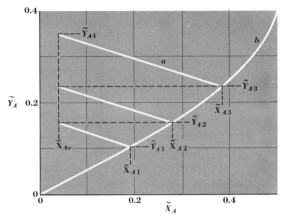

Fig. 39-7.   *Operating diagram for multiple-stage contact with fresh absorbent at each stage.*
a.   Slope $= -\tilde{O}_C/\tilde{V}_B$.
b.   Equilibrium line.

compositions of the two phases entering the system are the same as in Figs. 39-2 and 39-3.

The operation of the cascade of stages is analyzed in Fig. 39-7.   We start with stage 3, in which the phases of composition $\tilde{Y}_{A4}$ and $\tilde{X}_{Ao}$ are brought into contact.   Equation (39-1) applies, with $\tilde{O}_C = \tilde{O}_{Co}/3$.   All rates $\tilde{V}_{Bn}$ are equal because component B is insoluble in the O phases, so that these streams are referred to as $\tilde{V}_B$.   The same construction is used as in Fig. 39-3, and the points $\tilde{Y}_{A3}$ and $\tilde{X}_{A3}$ are found on Fig. 39-7.   In stage 2, $\tilde{Y}_{A3}$ is contacted with $\tilde{X}_{Ao}$, and the resulting phase compositions are $\tilde{Y}_{A2}$ and $\tilde{X}_{A2}$.   The first stage reduces the concentration in the V phase to $\tilde{Y}_{A1}$, which equals 0.102, as against 0.135 when all the contacting was done in one stage as shown in Fig. 39-3.

The method of analysis which has been outlined can be applied to liquid-liquid extraction, as shown in Fig. 39-8.   If the concentration of A in both phases is small, it is convenient to use mass fractions, and rates O and V can be considered constant through the system.   For extraction or stripping, the operating lines on a figure like Fig. 39-7 would be on the opposite side of the equilibrium line.

Let us analyze a simple extraction problem with dilute solutions for which the equilibrium line is given by $y_A = mx_A$ and for which an equal amount of pure solvent ($y_A = 0$) is added to each stage.   For this situation, with m, O, and V approximately constant, it is convenient to do the analysis algebraically.   For the first stage, we write the mass balance for A as

$$O(x_{Ao} - x_{A1}) = \frac{V}{N} y_{A1} \tag{39-5}$$

in which N is the total number of stages.

We next replace y_{A1} by mx_{A1} and solve for x_{A1} to get

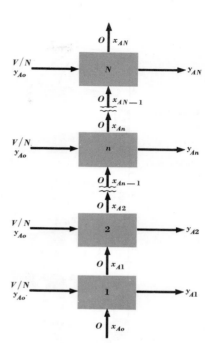

Fig. 39-8.   Multistage extraction with solvent at each stage.

$$x_{A1} = \left(\frac{O}{mV/N + O}\right) x_{Ao} \tag{39-6}$$

A balance around the second stage yields

$$x_{A2} = \left(\frac{O}{mV/N + O}\right) x_{A1} \tag{39-7}$$

These two equations can be combined to give

$$x_{A2} = \left(\frac{O}{mV/N + O}\right)^2 x_{Ao} \tag{39-8}$$

For the N stages we have, by induction,

$$\frac{x_{AN}}{x_{Ao}} = \left(\frac{1}{mV/NO + 1}\right)^N \tag{39-9}$$

This equation shows the extraction which is achieved in the N-stage system of Fig. 39-8.   This type of extraction is often used in organic-chemistry laboratory techniques.

We have seen that increasing the number of stages increases the fraction extracted; it is interesting to find the most extraction which would be possible with a fixed amount of solvent.   This quantity is found by taking

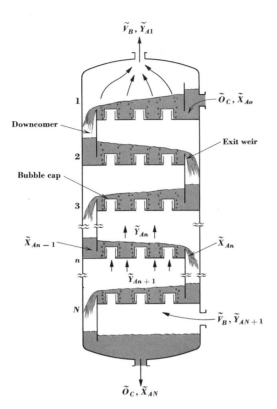

Fig. 39-9.   *Countercurrent gas-absorption tower.*

the limit of the ratio x_{AN}/x_{Ao} as N increases indefinitely.   We proceed by writing Eq. (39-9) as

$$\ln \frac{x_{AN}}{x_{Ao}} = \frac{\ln \left[1/(mV/NO + 1) \right]}{1/N} \tag{39-10}$$

This expression becomes indeterminate as N increases, so L'Hôpital's rule is used to find

$$\lim_{N \to \infty} \ln \frac{x_{AN}}{x_{Ao}} = -\frac{mV}{O} \tag{39-11}$$

or

$$\lim_{N \to \infty} \frac{x_{AN}}{x_{Ao}} = e^{-mV/O} \tag{39-12}$$

Multiple-stage Countercurrent Contact

We have seen in the previous sections of this chapter that the fraction of absorption or extraction obtained by a given amount of absorbent or

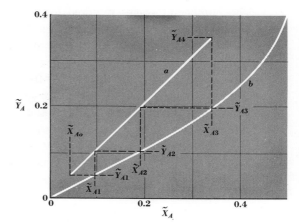

Fig. 39-10.   *Operating diagram for gas absorption by multiple-stage countercurrent contact.*

a.   Operating line slope $\tilde{O}_c/\tilde{V}_B$.
b.   Equilibrium line.

solvent can be increased by dividing it among a number of stages.   Referring to Fig. 39-8, it is evident that the extract emerging from the Nth stage contains little of component A and could be used as solvent in the richer stages of the system.   It is therefore logical to arrange the stages so that the flow is countercurrent, as is illustrated for gas absorption in Fig. 39-9.

A mass balance around the stage n of Fig. 39-9 can be written as

$$\frac{\tilde{Y}_{An+1} - \tilde{Y}_{An}}{\tilde{X}_{An} - \tilde{X}_{An-1}} = \frac{\tilde{O}_C}{\tilde{V}_B} \tag{39-13}$$

Alternatively, the balance can be written over the first n stages as

$$\frac{\tilde{Y}_{An+1} - \tilde{Y}_{A1}}{\tilde{X}_{An} - \tilde{X}_{Ao}} = \frac{\tilde{O}_C}{\tilde{V}_B} \tag{39-14}$$

or over all N stages as

$$\frac{\tilde{Y}_{AN+1} - \tilde{Y}_{A1}}{\tilde{X}_{AN} - \tilde{X}_{Ao}} = \frac{\tilde{O}_C}{\tilde{V}_B} \tag{39-15}$$

Although Eq. (39-13) is mathematically identical to Eq. (39-1), it is used in a different way.   In Eq. (39-1) $\tilde{Y}_{An}$ and $\tilde{X}_{An}$ were considered as the coordinates of a point on the operating line, as in concurrent flow.   In using Eqs. (39-13) and (39-14) we consider rather $\tilde{Y}_{An+1}$ and $\tilde{X}_{An}$ to be the coordinates of a point on the operating line.   These quantities are often spoken of as the compositions of adjacent or passing streams in a contactor.   Figure 39-10 shows the operating and equilibrium lines for the gas-absorption tower of Fig. 39-9.   A point on the operating line, Eq. (39-14), represents a value of $\tilde{Y}_{An+1}$ which corresponds to a value of $\tilde{X}_{An}$, that is, the composition of the V phase entering a stage which corresponds to the composition of the O phase leaving the stage.

The number of stages required for a given separation is found by a procedure which is illustrated by Figs. 39-9 and 39-10. The conditions at the bottom of the absorption tower shown are given by the coordinates at the upper end of the operating line—$\tilde{Y}_{A4}$ and $\tilde{X}_{A3}$ for the three-stage countercurrent contactor of Fig. 39-10. The liquid leaving the third equilibrium stage is in equilibrium with the vapor leaving the stage, so $\tilde{Y}_{A3}$ is found from the intersection of $\tilde{X}_{A3}$ and the equilibrium line. With $\tilde{Y}_{A3}$ known, the composition of the liquid leaving the second stage $\tilde{X}_{A2}$ is found from the intersection of $\tilde{Y}_{A3}$ with the operating line. The result of the analysis which we are describing is a set of steps drawn between the operating and equilibrium lines, as shown in Fig. 39-10. The number of stages is given by the number of times the steps must touch the equilibrium line in order to reach the compositions $\tilde{Y}_{A1}$ and $\tilde{X}_{Ao}$ at the other extremity of the operating line.

The procedure of counting stages could obviously have been started alternatively at the dilute end of the tower. In Fig. 39-10 an integral number of stages is obtained, but such is not usually the case. A fraction of a stage has no physical meaning; however, if the over-all stage efficiency is 50 per cent and $3\frac{1}{2}$ equilibrium stages are obtained by the stepwise construction, there would be seven actual stages. Thus it is customary to speak of a fraction of a stage rather than merely say that, for example, four stages are obtained by the graphical construction.

The ratio $\tilde{O}_C/\tilde{V}_B$ and the compositions $\tilde{X}_{Ao}$ and $\tilde{Y}_{AN+1} = \tilde{Y}_{A4}$ have been chosen in Fig. 39-10 to be the same as in Figs. 39-7 and 39-3. The operating line in Fig. 39-10 has been placed so that three equilibrium stages are needed, just as in Fig. 39-7. A comparison of the three methods of operation shows that for a rich gas composition ($\tilde{Y}_{AN+1} = 0.35$) the exit-gas composition is 0.135 by a single-stage-equilibrium contact, 0.102 by a three-stage system with fresh absorbent to each stage, and 0.05 by a three-stage system with countercurrent flow.

For given flow rates and terminal compositions, the operating and equilibrium lines are the same on an $\tilde{x}_A$-$\tilde{y}_A$ or on an $\tilde{X}_A$-$\tilde{Y}_A$ diagram for countercurrent stagewise contact as for countercurrent continuous contact in a packed tower. As the operating and equilibrium lines become closer together, the number of stages goes up just as the number of HTUs goes up. All the remarks in Chap. 37 concerning the minimum absorbent or solvent rates apply equally well for stagewise contact. If there is a pinch point, the number of stages becomes infinite. We have used mole ratios in Fig. 39-10 in order to obtain a straight operating line, but mole fractions could have been used equally well, as in Chap. 37.

Fig. 39-11. *Height of a packed section equivalent to a theoretical stage for gas absorption.*
    a.   Operating line.
    b.   Equilibrium line.

Algebraic Relations for the Number of Ideal Stages

From the methods of finding the number of theoretical stages for counter-current flow illustrated in this chapter, it may be suspected that there is a relation between the number of transfer units, say n_{OG}, and the number of theoretical stages, N.   If the operating and equilibrium lines are straight, the analysis is simple and is explained by reference to Fig. 39-11.   Consider a section of a packed tower which is just sufficient to accomplish the separation which would be obtained by one theoretical stage.   The height of this packed section is given for gas absorption by

$$z_{TS} = H_{OG} n_{OG}$$

$$= H_{OG} \frac{(\tilde{y}_{An+1} - \tilde{y}_{An}) \ln \left[(\tilde{y}_{An+1} - \tilde{y}_{An})/(\tilde{y}_{An} - \tilde{y}_{An-1}) \right]}{(\tilde{y}_{An+1} - \tilde{y}_{An}) - (\tilde{y}_{An} - \tilde{y}_{An-1})} \tag{39-16}$$

The logarithmic mean V-phase driving force has been used to find n_{OG} for the separation occurring at plate $n + 1$.

We can also write the identity

$$\frac{\tilde{y}_{An+1} - \tilde{y}_{An}}{\tilde{y}_{An} - \tilde{y}_{An-1}} = \frac{\tilde{y}_{An+1} - \tilde{y}_{An}}{\tilde{x}_{An} - \tilde{x}_{An-1}} \frac{\tilde{x}_{An} - \tilde{x}_{An-1}}{\tilde{y}_{An} - \tilde{y}_{An-1}} \tag{39-17}$$

The right-hand side of this equation is recognized as $\tilde{L}/m\tilde{G}$ or $1/\mathcal{S}$ [Eq. (37-29)], where $\mathcal{S}$ is called the stripping factor.   The height z_{TS}, which is sometimes called the height equivalent to a theoretical stage, or HETS, is found by combining Eqs. (39-16) and (39-17) with the definition of $\mathcal{S}$ to give

$$z_{TS} = \text{HETS} = \frac{H_{OG} \ln \mathcal{S}}{\mathcal{S} - 1} \tag{39-18}$$

For an entire tower we can write

$$z = \text{HETS} \, (N) = H_{OG} n_{OG} \tag{39-19}$$

so that we have

$$N = \left(\frac{\mathrm{S} - 1}{\ln \mathrm{S}}\right) n_{OG} \tag{39-20}$$

The combination of Eqs. (39-20) and (37-28) then gives the following formula for the number of theoretical stages:

$$N = \frac{\ln \{(1 - \mathrm{S})[(\tilde{y}_{AN+1} - m\tilde{x}_{Ao})/(\tilde{y}_{A1} - m\tilde{x}_{Ao})] + \mathrm{S}\}}{\ln (1/\mathrm{S})} \tag{39-21}$$

The subscripts on the compositions, given here as mole fractions, correspond for gas absorption to those given in Fig. 39-9. If the operating and equilibrium lines are parallel, Eq. (39-20) shows that the number of transfer units and the number of theoretical stages are identical.

Although the height of a packed tower can be found from the HETS and N, it is preferable to use HTUs and the methods of Chap. 37. However, Eq. (39-21) is convenient for stagewise contactors if the operating and equilibrium lines are straight.

If the number of theoretical stages is given, it is desirable to obtain an expression for the degree of separation as an explicit function of N. The first step is to rearrange Eq. (39-21) to yield

$$\frac{\tilde{y}_{A1} - m\tilde{x}_{Ao}}{\tilde{y}_{AN+1} - m\tilde{x}_{Ao}} = \frac{\mathrm{Q} - 1}{\mathrm{Q}^{N+1} - 1} \tag{39-22}$$

where $1/\mathrm{S}$ has been replaced by the absorption factor Q (that is, $\tilde{L}/m\tilde{G}$). We write next the identity

$$\frac{\tilde{y}_{A1} - \tilde{y}_{Ao}}{\tilde{y}_{AN+1} - \tilde{y}_{Ao}} = 1 - \frac{\tilde{y}_{AN+1} - \tilde{y}_{A1}}{\tilde{y}_{AN+1} - \tilde{y}_{Ao}} \tag{39-23}$$

in which $\tilde{y}_{Ao}$ has replaced $m\tilde{x}_{Ao}$. Equation (39-22) then becomes

$$\frac{\tilde{y}_{AN+1} - \tilde{y}_{A1}}{\tilde{y}_{AN+1} - \tilde{y}_{Ao}} = \frac{\mathrm{Q}^{N+1} - \mathrm{Q}}{\mathrm{Q}^{N+1} - 1} \tag{39-24}$$

This equation is convenient because its left-hand side is the ratio of the actual absorption accomplished by N stages to the maximum possible absorption which could be obtained. This maximum occurs when $N = \infty$ and $\tilde{y}_{A1} = \tilde{y}_{Ao}$ for the more common case of $\mathrm{Q} > 1.0$. It was mentioned in Chap. 37 that Q (or $1/\mathrm{S}$) often has an economic value of about 1.4 for absorption in packed towers; the same is true for stagewise contactors such as the bubble-cap tower shown in Fig. 39-9. Equation (39-24) was first derived by Kremser[1] and by Souders and Brown[2] by a method different from the one we have used.

The algebraic relations for N given in this section assume Q (or S) is

[1] A. Kremser, *Natl. Petrol. News*, **22**(21):42 (1930).

[2] M. Souders and G. G. Brown, *Ind. Eng. Chem.*, **24**:519 (1932).

Fig. 39-12.   *Operating diagram for Example 39-2; countercurrent absorption.*

constant through the tower.   If there is a slight variation, the value of $\mathfrak{a}$ to use is that in the region where the operating lines and equilibrium line are close together.   For the usual situation this region is at the dilute end of the contactor ($\mathfrak{a} > 1.0$ for absorption, $\mathfrak{s} > 1.0$ for stripping or extraction).

Example 39-2

It is desired to absorb 95 per cent of the acetone in a 2.00 mole per cent mixture of acetone in air in a countercurrent bubble-cap tower using 20 per cent more than the minimum water rate.   Pure water is introduced at the top of the tower, and the gas mixture is blown into the bottom at 1000 lb/hr.   Find the number of equilibrium stages required for this separation.   It is assumed that the tower operates isothermally at 80°F and 1 atm; the equilibrium relation is $\tilde{y}_A = 2.53\tilde{x}_A$.

The separation to be performed is the same as that of Example 37-1, and the equilibrium and operating lines of Fig. 39-12 are the same as those of Fig. 37-13.   The terminal compositions are

$$\tilde{x}_{Ao} = 0$$
$$\tilde{x}_{AN} = 0.00658$$
$$\tilde{y}_{AN+1} = 0.0200$$
$$\tilde{y}_{A1} = 0.00102$$

The slope of the operating line is $\tilde{L}/\tilde{G} = 2.89$.

The stages are counted as shown on Fig. 39-12, starting at the first stage, i.e., the top of the tower.   The points on the equilibrium line represent the compositions of streams leaving a given stage.   Points on the operating line represent the compositions of the

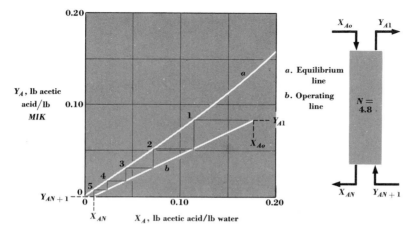

Fig. 39-13.   *Countercurrent extraction by stages; Example* 39-3.

streams passing between stages, such as $\bar{y}_{A5}$ and $\bar{x}_{A4}$.   The number of stages required is 9.0.

If Eq. (39-21) is used with $\mathcal{S} = 0.875$ and $\bar{y}_{AN+1}/\bar{y}_{A1} = 20$ ($\bar{x}_{Ao} = 0$), it is found that $N = 9.0$.   Since the operating and equilibrium lines are almost parallel, the number of stages differs little from the number of transfer units found in Example 37-1 as 9.65.

Example 39-3

The acetic acid in a solution in water containing 0.15 mass fraction acid is to be extracted using pure methyl isobutyl ketone as a solvent.   The extract is to contain 0.075 mass fraction acetic acid and the raffinate 0.010 mass fraction acid.   Estimate the number of equilibrium stages required for this separation if countercurrent multiple contact is used.

The terminal compositions are the same as those of Example 37-2 and give the following mass ratios:

$$Y_{A1} = 0.0811$$
$$X_{Ao} = 0.1768$$
$$Y_{AN+1} = 0$$
$$X_{AN} = 0.0101$$

The operating line is straight and connects these terminal points as shown on Fig. 39-13.

The stages are counted starting from the rich end of the tower.   We need about 4.8 stages for the desired separation.

In the discussion and in the examples which have been presented, it has been assumed that the temperature is constant throughout the tower. However, the same heat effects occur in a stagewise contactor as have been described for the continuous contactors of Chap. 38.   Thus an energy balance as well as a mass balance must be made around a stage when heat effects are important.   These temperature effects will displace the equilibrium line, as shown in Chap. 38.   Sometimes cooling coils or intercoolers are placed between certain stages in order to keep the net temperature change over a contactor to a minimum.

Determination of the Number of Real Stages

Earlier in this chapter we defined the Murphree stage efficiency and the Murphree point efficiency. These quantities have been based on y-phase compositions; although similar equations exist in terms of x-phase compositions, we use only those in terms of y-phase compositions in this discussion. Let us now see how the values of E_G and E_{GP} may be found and used to determine the number of real stages in a separation device.

The point efficiency E_{GP} has been defined with respect to the performance of a small column of fluid at a point on a bubble-cap tray or similar contacting device. We again base our explanation on the example of gas absorption, but the generality of the equations should be recalled; they apply to liquid-liquid extraction, to distillation, and to other operations, provided suitable units are used. By analogy with Eq. (39-3), we have

$$E_{GP} = \frac{\tilde{y}_{An+1} - \tilde{y}_{AnP}}{\tilde{y}_{An+1} - \tilde{y}^*_{AnP}} \tag{39-25}$$

Mole fractions are the appropriate units for gas absorption involving dilute solutions, and they will also be used for distillation.

The operation of the hypothetical column at a point on the tray shown in Fig. 39-4 can also be expressed in terms of the equations of Chap. 37. For example, we have, from Eq. (37-21),

$$n_{OG} = \int_{\tilde{y}_{AnP}}^{\tilde{y}_{An+1}} \frac{d\tilde{y}_A}{\tilde{y}_A - \tilde{y}^*_A} \tag{39-26}$$

The liquid composition at a point on the tray is taken as constant over the height of the little column; $\tilde{y}^*_A$ is thus constant and equal to $\tilde{y}^*_{AnP}$. Equation (39-26) is integrated to give

$$n_{OG} = \ln \frac{\tilde{y}_{An+1} - \tilde{y}^*_{AnP}}{\tilde{y}_{AnP} - \tilde{y}^*_{AnP}} \tag{39-27}$$

This equation is rearranged to give

$$\frac{\tilde{y}_{AnP} - \tilde{y}^*_{AnP}}{\tilde{y}_{An+1} - \tilde{y}^*_{AnP}} = e^{-n_{OG}} \tag{39-28}$$

The left-hand side of this equation can be changed to give

$$\frac{\tilde{y}_{An+1} - \tilde{y}^*_{AnP}}{\tilde{y}_{An+1} - \tilde{y}^*_{AnP}} - \frac{\tilde{y}_{An+1} - \tilde{y}_{AnP}}{\tilde{y}_{An+1} - \tilde{y}^*_{AnP}} = e^{-n_{OG}} \tag{39-29}$$

or, from Eq. (39-25),

$$1 - E_{GP} = e^{-n_{OG}} \tag{39-30}$$

The number of transfer units is equal to z/H_{OG}, where z is the height of the little column in which the rising bubbles are in contact with the liquid on the tray. Equation (37-20) can be written in terms of the number of transfer units as

$$\frac{1}{n_{OG}} = \frac{1}{n_G} + \frac{m\tilde{G}}{\tilde{L}}\frac{1}{n_L} \tag{39-31}$$

The number of individual transfer units is in turn equal to z/H_G or z/H_L, and we know from Chap. 36 that H_G and H_L are functions of the Reynolds number and the Schmidt number for the appropriate phase. A number of empirical correlations exist for finding n_G and n_L from the Schmidt number, the tray geometry, and the flow rates.[1] These correlations are based on a considerable amount of data for gas-liquid contactors; little work has been done for other systems.

Strictly speaking, the equations given require a constant value of m, but it is permissible, within the precision of the method, to use the average slope of the equilibrium line (not $\tilde{y}/\tilde{x}$) for the concentration range on the tray.

The next step in finding the number of real trays is to obtain E_G by integrating E_{GP} over the surface area of the tray. The process has been described qualitatively earlier in this chapter. The result depends on a number of factors, such as the extent of mixing in the phase; if both phases are well mixed, $E_G = E_{GP}$. Another possible assumption is that the gas phase is well mixed but that the liquid flows across the tray with no mixing in the direction of flow. A third assumption might be that the gas phase retains a concentration gradient in the horizontal direction as it rises from one plate to the next. A number of these situations have been evaluated.[2] Values of E_G/E_{GP} considerably more than unity are common in practice, and the ratio can increase to the order of 10s or 100s in special situations.

As the rate at which gas is bubbled through the liquid on the tray is increased, a point is reached where a considerable quantity of liquid droplets is carried up to the tray above. This entrainment partially nullifies the countercurrent flow and decreases the efficiency of the tray. An equation can be derived [3] which gives the effect on the efficiency of the entrainment of a known fraction of the liquid flowing across a plate. Entrainment is kept at a minimum in a properly designed tower.

The way in which the number of real stages for $E_G = 0.5$ is found is

[1] For an excellent reference on this subject see Bubble-tray Design Manual, American Institute of Chemical Engineers, New York, 1958.

[2] For example, see W. K. Lewis, *Ind. Eng. Chem.*, **28**:399 (1936).

[3] A. P. Colburn, *Ind. Eng. Chem.*, **28**:526 (1936).

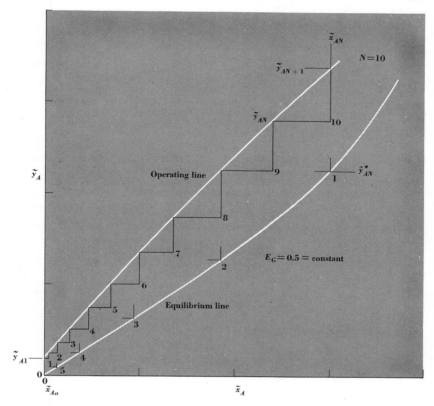

Fig. 39-14. *Calculation of the number of real trays for gas absorption.*

shown in Fig. 39-14. Starting from the rich end of the tower, the liquid leaving the bottom plate has the composition $\tilde{x}_{AN}$. The gas passing this liquid is $\tilde{y}_{AN+1}$, and the gas which would be in equilibrium with the liquid is $\tilde{y}_{AN}^*$. Since the value of E_G is 0.5, we proceed only one-half the way from $\tilde{y}_{AN+1}$ to $\tilde{y}_{AN}^*$ in order to locate $\tilde{y}_{AN}$, as shown in Fig. 39-14. The succeeding steps are counted as shown; 10 trays are needed for the separation shown.

The over-all efficiency E_o is defined as the ratio of the number of ideal stages to the number of real stages. If this ratio is known, it is a simple matter to obtain the number of real stages after calculating the number of ideal stages. However, the value of E_G may vary with position in a contactor, and even if it is constant, as shown in Fig. 39-14, E_o does not equal E_G unless the operating and equilibrium lines are straight and parallel. The inequality of E_G and E_o may be verified by counting off the theoretical stages on Fig. 39-14; only about 4.5 are required, so E_o is 0.45.

There is an analytical relation[1] between E_G and E_o if the operating and equilibrium lines are straight and E_G is constant.

The method of approach just outlined, which is that of the AIChE Manual, is the most reliable procedure now available. However, a rough estimate of E_o can be obtained from empirical correlations,[2] one of which is given in Perry, p. 614.

Notes on Tower Design

It has already been mentioned that entrainment is undesirable in a gas-liquid contactor. The allowable gas velocity in a tower is limited to a value which does not cause appreciable entrainment. A liquid drop will be entrained when the upward vapor velocity exceeds the terminal velocity of the drop. The drops are usually large enough so that the flow is turbulent, and Eq. (16-40) applies. This equation is written as

$$u_t \left(\frac{\rho_G}{\rho_L - \rho_G} \right)^{\frac{1}{2}} = (3Dg)^{\frac{1}{2}} \tag{39-32}$$

The diameters of the drops which may be entrained are influenced by the depth of liquid over the slots in the bubble caps, and the allowable approach to the terminal velocity is governed by the distance between plates. The correlation shown in Fig. 39-15 is based on these facts.

Equation (39-32) may also be written as

$$G_a = K_V \sqrt{\rho_G(\rho_L - \rho_G)} \tag{39-33}$$

in which G_a is the allowable mass velocity. Values of K_V are given in Perry, p. 598. All velocities are based on the empty cross section of the tower.

The pressure drop from one tray to the next and the liquid head needed to cause the liquid to flow across the tray are discussed in Perry, sec. 9. The methods of calculation are applications of the principles of fluid dynamics presented in the first part of this book. The resistance to liquid flow determines the height to which the liquid backs up into the downspouts and thus the necessary plate spacing. If the liquid forms a foam in the tower, the height of liquid plus foam in the downcomer necessary to overcome a given resistance of flow increases, and flooding may result.

The liquid flowing across a tray is deeper on the upstream side near the exit of the downcomer from the tray above. Thus the gas tends to flow

---

[1] *Ibid.*

[2] H. G. Drickamer and J. R. Bradford, *Trans. AIChE*, **39**:319 (1943); H. E. O'Connell, *ibid.*, **42**:741 (1946).

Fig. 39-15.   *Allowable gas velocity u_a in gas-liquid tray towers. (From C. S. Robinson and E. R. Gilliland, "Elements of Fractional Distillation," 4th ed., p. 430, McGraw-Hill Book Company, Inc., New York, 1950.)*

preferentially through the bubble caps or other gas openings near the exit weir on the tray.   The pressure drop through the various rows of caps may be adjusted to equalize the gas flow, but the tray cannot operate at maximum efficiency with large variations in liquid or gas rates.   Some of the recently developed valve-type plates almost eliminate the effects of the hydraulic gradient over a tray and have a somewhat wider operating range.

PROBLEMS

39-1. Find the number of ideal stages required for the separation of Prob. 37-1. Determine the allowable gas mass velocity if bubble-cap trays are used with a slot submergence or liquid seal of 2 in. and a tray spacing of 24 in.

39-2. Estimate the number of real bubble-cap trays needed in Prob. 39-1 by using correlations found in Perry.

39-3. Calculate the number of ideal stages needed for the separation of Prob. 37-2.

39-4. Estimate the height and diameter of a plate-type column with a 2-ft plate spacing and $E_o = 0.60$ to perform the separation of Prob. 37-3.   The liquid seal is 2 in.

39-5. Find the number of theoretical stages required for the separation of Prob. 37-4.

39-6. Derive the equation

$$E_o = \frac{\ln [1 + E_G(\mathcal{S} - 1)]}{\ln \mathcal{S}} \tag{39-34}$$

in which $\mathcal{S}$ and E_G are constant over the tower.   One approach is to find the height of a packed tower equivalent to a real stage and then obtain an equation which can be compared with Eq. (39-21) to find the desired relation.

39-7. The solubility of a substance A in water is given by the equation

$$\bar{y}_A = 1.4\bar{x}_A - 20\bar{x}_A^2$$

(a) What is the minimum ratio of water rate to air rate which can be used in a tower with infinite plates to absorb all the entering solute using pure water as the solvent? The inlet gas contains 0.02 mole fraction A.

(b) What is the concentration of the strong liquor in part (a)?

(c) If the tower is used to desorb A from water, what is the minimum ratio of air rate to water rate which could be used if all the solute is to be desorbed using pure air as the desorber? The inlet liquid contains 0.02 mole fraction A.

This problem is best solved analytically.

CONTACTING OF PARTIALLY MISCIBLE PHASES

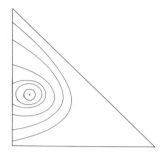

Phase-equilibrium Relations

In the study of separation processes up to this point we have been concerned with cases for which the two phases in contact are immiscible. The distributed component A (the solute) is present in both phases, but there has been no C in the B phase (which we refer to as the extract) and no B in the C phase, which we call the raffinate. This condition is approximately fulfilled for most gas-absorption problems and for certain problems in liquid-liquid extraction for low concentrations of solute. However, in many extraction problems the phases are partly miscible; i.e., there is considerable B in the raffinate phase and considerable C in the extract phase. In this chapter our explanation will be given in terms of liquid-liquid extraction, but the principles and equations can also be applied to other separation operations such as gas absorption or leaching.

Phase relations for ternary systems are shown graphically by triangular diagrams such as Fig. 40-1. The mass fraction of A is plotted in the horizontal direction, and lines of constant x_A or y_A are parallel to the BC side of the triangle. The mass fraction of B is plotted vertically, and lines of constant x_B and y_B are parallel to the AC side of the triangle. The mass fraction of C is easily found from the equation $x_C = 1 - (x_A + x_B)$; lines of constant x_C or y_C are parallel to the AB side of the triangle. These principles are illustrated in Fig. 40-1 by the point F, which has the composition $x_{AF} = 0.3$, $x_{BF} = 0.4$, $x_{CF} = 0.3$.

The line DEG in Fig. 40-1 is the solubility envelope of a liquid system. At equilibrium, two liquid phases are present within the solubility curve;

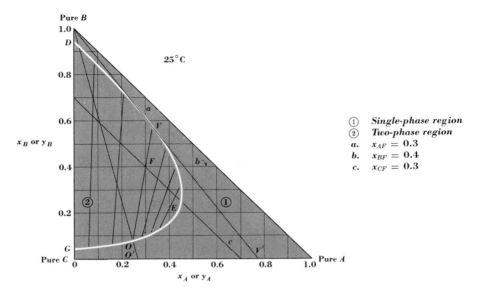

Fig. 40-1.   *Equilibrium in a liquid-liquid system.*

one phase is present in the rest of the triangle.   A mixture which has an over-all composition lying within the two-phase region separates into two layers.   The compositions of these layers, which are in equilibrium, are given by the slanting lines connecting points on the DE branch of the solubility curve to points on the EG branch.   These lines are called tie lines. For example, if the composition of the raffinate phase is at O, the composition of the extract phase in equilibrium with it is at V, the other end of the tie line starting at O.   The composition x_A is associated with the point O, and y_A with the point V.   From the set of tie lines on Fig. 40-1 it is possible to construct the y-x, or distribution, diagram of Fig. 40-2.   The point E in Figs. 40-1 and 40-2 is called the plait point; here the compositions of the two phases become identical.

Fig. 40-2.   *Distribution diagram which corresponds to Fig. 40-1.*

    a. $y_A = mx_A$.

    b.   *E,* plait point.

Fig. 40-3. *Two types of liquid equilibrium systems.*

At low concentrations of A the so-called distribution law, $y_A = mx_A$, is followed as shown on Fig. 40-2. In this range of concentration there is only a small amount of C in the extract phase and B in the raffinate phase. The operating line can be found here to a good approximation by the methods of Chaps. 37 and 39. At higher concentrations of A the effect of the miscibility of the phases may be considerable in locating the operating line. However, once the operating and equilibrium lines are plotted on a diagram such as Fig. 40-2, the number of stages can be stepped off graphically as was done in Chap. 39. This chapter is concerned principally with graphical methods of applying the over-all mass balance to find the curved operating line which we see plotted in Fig. 40-12, for example.

Although Fig. 40-1 shows a common type of solubility curve, other configurations are often encountered; some of these are shown in Fig. 40-3. All the phase diagrams shown so far are for systems at one temperature. As the temperature is increased, miscibility almost always increases, as shown in Fig. 40-4.

We use right triangles to represent data on ternary systems, but equilateral triangles are often used in the literature. The principles set forth in this chapter apply to triangular diagrams of any shape or proportions. A right triangle is preferred because it is easy to construct on ordinary graph paper, and its proportions can be adjusted to expedite quantitative graphical procedures.

Mass-balance calculations are readily done graphically on a triangular diagram, and a number of similar diagrams[1] by use of the so-called lever-

---

[1] Extraction calculations are also often done on a Janecke diagram; see R. E. Treybal, "Liquid Extraction," McGraw-Hill Book Company, Inc., New York, 1951.

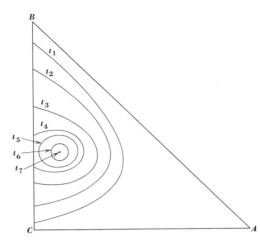

Fig. 40-4. *The effect of temperature on solubility in a typical liquid system; $t_{k+1} > t_k$.*

arm principle. When two streams of different composition are mixed, this principle requires that the point representing the composition of the resulting mixture lie on a straight line between the points. Conversely, if a mixture is separated into two streams, the over-all mass balance requires that the points representing the compositions of the three streams involved lie on a straight line through the points. We now proceed to prove these assertions and show that certain quantitative relations exist among the various line segments.

Figure 40-5 can represent any physical separation process, such as distillation, in which a ternary feed stream is separated into two product streams. For the present example the feed stream is taken as a well-mixed, two-phase fluid which is introduced into a settling tank. In this tank the mixture separates into two layers which can be drawn off independently. The following mass balances can be written:[1]

$$F = O + V \tag{40-1}$$

$$Fx_{AF} = Ox_A + Vy_A \tag{40-2}$$

$$Fx_{BF} = Ox_B + Vy_B \tag{40-3}$$

The mass balance on C is not an independent equation. Referring now to Fig. 40-5b, we wish to prove that the slope of the line $\overline{OF}$ is the same as the slope of the line $\overline{FV}$; if this is so, then $\overline{OFV}$ is a straight line. From the triangle in the figure we have

---

[1] The symbols G and L represent mass velocities. V and O are flow rates in a steady process in pounds per hour; L/G and O/V are identical.

Fig. 40-5. *Demonstration of the lever-arm principle.*

$$\text{Slope of } \overline{OF} = \frac{x_{BF} - x_B}{x_{AF} - x_A} \tag{40-4}$$

Equations (40-1) and (40-3) can be solved for x_A and x_B to yield

$$x_A = \frac{(O + V)x_{AF} - Vy_A}{O} \tag{40-5}$$

$$x_B = \frac{(O + V)x_{BF} - Vy_B}{O} \tag{40-6}$$

When these equations are substituted in Eq. (40-4), we obtain

$$\text{Slope of } \overline{OF} = \frac{y_B - x_{BF}}{y_A - x_{AF}} \tag{40-7}$$

This equation is also the slope of the line $\overline{FV}$, so the assertion that $\overline{OFV}$ is a straight line is proved.

From Eqs. (40-1) and (40-2) we can also obtain

$$\frac{O}{V} = \frac{y_A - x_{AF}}{x_{AF} - x_A} \tag{40-8}$$

$$\frac{O}{F} = \frac{y_A - x_{AF}}{y_A - x_A} \tag{40-9}$$

$$\frac{V}{F} = \frac{x_{AF} - x_A}{y_A - x_A} \tag{40-10}$$

These equations show that the ratios of the quantities of each stream can easily be found graphically. By the principle of similar triangles it can be seen that the ratios can be found from the vertical distances or from the ratios of the line segments $\overline{OF}$, $\overline{FV}$, and $\overline{OV}$, themselves. For quantitative work using a right-triangular diagram, the horizontal or vertical distances are easily read from the graph.

The graphical principles we have just described can be applied to the system shown in Fig. 40-1. If a two-phase mixture having a composition given by point F is fed to a separator, represented schematically by Fig. 40-5a, the two phases into which the feed separates must lie both on

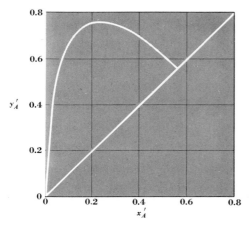

y'_A 0.4

x'_A

Fig. 40-6. Selectivity diagram which corresponds to Fig. 40-1.

a tie line and on a line through F, that is, on a tie line through F. The compositions of the two streams are given by the points O and V in Fig. 40-1. For a unit mass of F, we have, using B compositions,

$$O = \frac{0.57 - 0.40}{0.57 - 0.08} = \frac{0.17}{0.49} = 0.347$$

The amount of V is $1 - 0.347$, or 0.653.

The lever-arm principle can also be used for subtraction. For instance, if the stream V is put through a distillation column which removes all the B as one pure product, the remaining mixture of A and C must be on the AC side of the triangle and on a line through B and V, as shown by the point V' on Fig. 40-1. Here y_A equals 0.763. We refer to the composition given by point V' as the solvent-free composition of the mixture at V; we symbolize it by y'_A. The solvent-free composition of point O is found by drawing a line through B and O to $x'_A = 0.26$.

The solvent-free compositions of points O and V are of particular interest, for they represent the separation achieved between A and C after the extraneous solvent B has been removed. The values of x'_A and y'_A found in this fashion from Fig. 40-1 can be plotted as in Fig. 40-6. Such a graph is called a selectivity diagram.

The lever-arm rule, which has been illustrated in connection with this description of phase-equilibrium relations in liquid-liquid systems, will be used extensively in the application of mass and energy balances to calculate operating lines for problems in extraction and distillation.

Separation by a Single Equilibrium Contact

Let us now study the separation of A from a mixture of A and C by extraction with a solvent B. If one equilibrium stage is used, the process

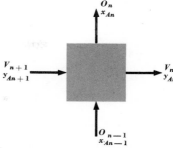

Fig. 40-7. *Schematic diagram of a single-stage extraction.*

can be schematically represented by the diagram in Fig. 40-7. The operation is the same as that illustrated by Fig. 39-5. The stream O_{n-1}, for which x_{An-1} is 0.25, is treated with pure solvent stream V_{n+1}; the liquid layers leaving the contactor are O_n and V_n; the mass fractions of solute A are shown on the diagram also.

The problem is solved on the triangular diagram of Fig. 40-8. When streams V_{n+1} and O_{n-1} are mixed, a stream of composition given by the point M is obtained. The position of M on the line between V_{n+1} and O_{n-1} is found from the relative quantities of the two streams and the application of the lever-arm principle. If 0.408 lb of solvent is used per pound of feed O_{n-1}, the ratio of lines $\overline{O_{n-1}M}/\overline{V_{n+1}M}$ must equal 0.408. The ratio $\overline{O_{n-1}M}/\overline{O_{n-1}V_{n+1}}$ is then 0.408/1.408, or 0.290. Rather than measure 0.29

Fig. 40-8. *Extraction by a single equilibrium stage.*

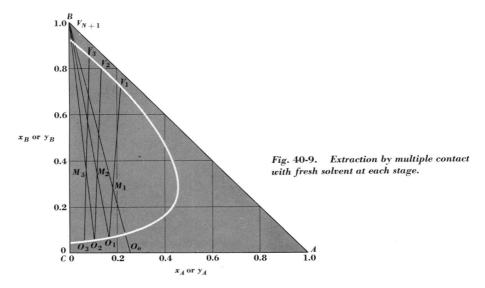

Fig. 40-9.   *Extraction by multiple contact with fresh solvent at each stage.*

of the distance from O_{n-1} to V_{n+1} along the line $\overline{O_{n-1}V_{n+1}}$, it is much simpler to use the ratios of the vertical coordinates of the points. The point M is thus simply located on an ordinate of 0.290, as shown. The point M represents the net composition of the fluid entering the contactor, and it must also be the net (over-all) composition of the fluid leaving the contactor. This stream divides into two layers which are in equilibrium; thus points O_n and V_n are on the ends of a tie line through M. The mass fraction of A in the raffinate stream has been reduced to $x_A = 0.16$, or, on a solvent-free basis, $x_A' = 0.17$.

Note that in the problems treated in this chapter, O, V, and similar symbols can represent either flow rates in pounds per hour for a steady operation or quantities in pounds for a batch extraction. Although these symbols will be referred to as flow rates, the second interpretation is sometimes useful.

Multiple Contact with Fresh Solvent at Each Stage

This operation has been described in Chap. 39, and we refer to the sketch of the flows shown in Fig. 39-8.

The operation of a three-stage system is explained by reference to Fig. 40-9. To the first stage is added 0.408 lb of solvent for every pound of feed O_o. The point M_1 is the same as the point M on Fig. 40-8, and O_1 and V_1 correspond to O_n and V_n. The stream O_1 is now introduced to the second stage, to which is added another 0.408 lb solvent/lb feed O_o. To find M_2, we must first know the quantity O_1. The lever-arm rule gives $O_1/M_1 = \overline{V_1M_1}/\overline{V_1O_1}$; from the ordinates of the three points on $O_1M_1V_1$ we find $O_1/M_1 = 0.435/0.658 = 0.661$. Since we know that $M_1 = 0.408 + 1.00$, we have $O_1 = (0.661)(1.408) = 0.931$.

When 0.408 lb of solvent is mixed in stage 2 with 0.931 lb of raffinate from stage 1, the result is the mixture M_2; this point is located on the line $\overline{O_1M_2V_{N+1}}$ by the lever-arm rule. The mixture M_2 separates into two layers having compositions given by the ends of the tie line through M_2. This line is easily found by trial and error with the aid of Fig. 40-2 plus Fig. 40-9 and a straightedge. The compositions of O_2 and V_2 are shown. For the example given, we obtain $M_2 = 1.339$ lb, $O_2 = 0.815$ lb, and $V_2 = 0.524$ lb. The computations are continued to a third stage, for which $M_3 = 1.223$ lb, $O_3 = 0.740$ lb, and $V_3 = 0.483$ lb. The mass fraction of A in the raffinate from the third stage has been reduced to $x_{A3} = 0.060$ or $x'_{A3} = 0.061$ on a solvent-free basis. This result compares with $x'_{An} = 0.17$ for the same feed with a single stage, but three times as much solvent has been used in this example. Note that the quantity O_n varies from stage to stage, and O_{Cn} also varies by about 10 per cent; this computation could thus not be done conveniently on a diagram such as Fig. 39-7 since O_{Cn}/V_{Bn+1} (or L_C/G_B) is not constant.

Multiple-stage Countercurrent Contact

The method of countercurrent contacting with multiple stages is shown in Fig. 40-10. The rectangle which symbolizes each stage can represent a compartment or tray in a vertical tower or one of a train of stages each composed of a mixer and a settler. The symbols V and O refer to the extract and raffinate streams; for a vertical tower, the flows shown in Fig. 40-10 are obtained when the extract phase is lighter than the raffinate phase. If the reverse is true, the raffinate phase flows upward and the extract phase flows downward. In any case the stages are usually counted from the A-rich end of the system.

Let us suppose that the composition of the four terminal streams of Fig. 40-10 are those shown in Fig. 40-11; that is, $x_{Ao} = 0.25$, $x_{AN} = 0.06$, $y_{A1} = 0.325$, and $y_{AN+1} = 0$. From the equation

$$V_{N+1} + O_o = V_1 + O_N = M \tag{40-11}$$

and the lever-arm rule, it is seen from Fig. 40-11 that V_{N+1}/O_o is 0.408, as in the discussions in the previous sections. Equation (40-11) and the cor-

Fig. 40-10. *Schematic diagram of a countercurrent extraction operation using multiple stages.*

responding mass balances on components A and B are symbolized by the lines $\overline{O_N M V_1}$ and $\overline{V_{N+1} M O_o}$ and represent the over-all mass balance for the multiple-stage system.

The number of stages required to achieve the separation described above can be stepped off directly on Fig. 40-11, or the stages can be stepped off on the $x - y$ diagram of Fig. 40-2 once the operating line has been plotted. A mass balance around the first stage is written as

$$V_1 - O_o = V_2 - O_1 = \Delta \tag{40-12}$$

with similar equations for components A and B. The quantity Δ is the net flow toward the rich end of the cascade. For the first two stages, we have

$$V_1 - O_o = V_3 - O_2 = \Delta \tag{40-13}$$

for the first n stages,

$$V_1 - O_o = V_{n+1} - O_n = \Delta \tag{40-14}$$

and for all N stages,

$$V_1 - O_o = V_{N+1} - O_N = \Delta \tag{40-15}$$

These equations show that the net flow Δ is constant throughout the

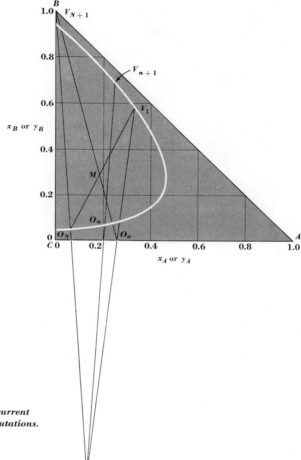

Fig. 40-11.   *Graph for countercurrent multiple-contact extraction computations.*

cascade.   From the four known terminal compositions and the requirement according to Eqs. (40-12) and (40-15) that $\overline{V_1 O_o \Delta}$ and $\overline{V_{N+1} O_N \Delta}$ be straight lines, the position of Δ is found as shown on Fig. 40-11.

From Fig. 40-11, O_o is the sum of Δ and V_1.   Thus O_o is larger than V_1 and Δ is negative; this means that the net flow is toward the lean (N) end of the cascade.   The lever-arm rule can be used to find the quantities of the streams.   For instance, $O_o/V_1 = \overline{V_1 \Delta}/\overline{O_o \Delta}$; from the ordinates of the three points we obtain $O_o/V_1 = 1.60/1.02 = 1.57$.   If O_o is 1.0, V_1 is 0.637 and $\Delta = -0.363$.

If the separation is changed so that V_1 travels along the V-phase solubility line toward smaller values of y_A, and V_{N+1}, O_N, and V_1 remain un-

Fig. 40-12. *Stages for counter-current multiple-contact extraction counted on a distribution diagram.*
a. Equilibrium line.
b. Operating line.

changed, the ratio O_o/V_1 decreases. When the lines $\overline{V_1 O_o \Delta}$ and $\overline{V_{N+1} O_N \Delta}$ become parallel, O_o/V_1 is unity and Δ is zero. Further displacement of V_1 to the left means that Δ is now located above the triangle; Δ is positive, and V_1 is greater than O_o. There is a net flow toward the rich (1) end of the cascade.

An arbitrary line can be drawn through Δ cutting the solubility envelope between the terminal compositions. We know that for ideal stages the compositions of all streams in the cascade are found on the solubility envelope. Thus, if the composition of a stream O_n is as shown on Fig. 40-11, the composition of the stream V_{n+1} is found by the intersection of a line through O_n and Δ and the upper boundary of the solubility envelope, which is the locus of V-phase compositions. An operating line can be drawn on an x-y diagram by choosing arbitrary values of x_{An} on the O-phase solubility curve and using the Δ point to find the corresponding values of y_{An+1} for the passing streams. By this technique the operating line shown in Fig. 40-12 has been drawn.

Once the operating and equilibrium lines are plotted in Fig. 40-12, the stages are stepped off just as they were in similar diagrams in Chap. 39. From the known value of y_{A1} found from Fig. 40-11, x_{A1} is found from the equilibrium curve. The value of y_{A2} is found from the intersection of x_{A1} with the operating line. From y_{A2} and the equilibrium curve, x_{A2} is found. This construction is continued until x_{AN} is reached. The number of stages is counted as shown in the figure.

The stages can be counted directly on Fig. 40-11, although it is usually preferable to use a diagram such as Fig. 40-12 for this purpose so that the triangular diagram is not confounded with many lines. The composition of O_1 is at the intersection of a tie line through V_1 and the O-phase solubility curve. The composition of the passing phase V_2 is found from the intersection of a line through O_1 and Δ and the V-phase solubility curve. In this way stages are counted until x_{AN} is reached.

Just as for the contacting of immiscible phases, there is a minimum ratio V_{N+1}/O_o which gives an operable system. As V_{N+1}/O_o is decreased, M travels toward O_o and V_1 travels along the solubility curve to the right (higher y_{A1}). The upper end of the operating line in Fig. 40-12 approaches the equilibrium line; the minimum solvent/feed ratio occurs when these lines touch and create a pinch point. Although the pinch point often occurs at one of the ends of the cascade, if the operating and equilibrium lines are curved, the lines may become tangent at an intermediate point.

For an operable system the slope of any possible line $\overline{V_{n+1}O_n\Delta}$ must be greater than the slope of the tie line through the corresponding point O_n. Minimum solvent corresponds to a condition for which these lines coincide at any stage within the cascade.

Countercurrent Contact with Reflux

The countercurrent system described in the previous section can strip most of component A from component C. If pure solvent is used, x_{AN} can be reduced to an arbitrarily small quantity by the use of a suitable ratio O_o/V_{N+1} and a sufficiently large number of stages. However, the concentration of A in the rich extract y_{A1} is limited; if an infinite number of stages are used, y_{A1} can be increased only to a value in equilibrium with x_{Ao}. It is to enrich the solvent stream to a concentration greater than y_{Ao}^* that a recycle, or reflux, stream is used at the extract end of the system.

A cascade of stages with reflux "above" the feed is shown in Fig. 40-13. An enriching section has been added; the solvent stream is enriched by contact with a raffinate stream obtained by returning to the enriching section a portion of the extract product D from the system. The returned stream is called reflux, and the ratio O_o/D is the reflux ratio. The extract product and the reflux are obtained from the extract V_1 by removing the solvent in a distillation tower, as shown in Fig. 40-13.

In the enriching section of the cascade we have the mass balances

$$V_1 - O_o = V_2 - O_1 = \Delta' \tag{40-16}$$

$$V_{n+1} - O_n = \Delta' \tag{40-17}$$

$$V_f - O_{f-1} = \Delta' \tag{40-18}$$

The point Δ' is on a straight line through O_o and V_1 and will serve to locate

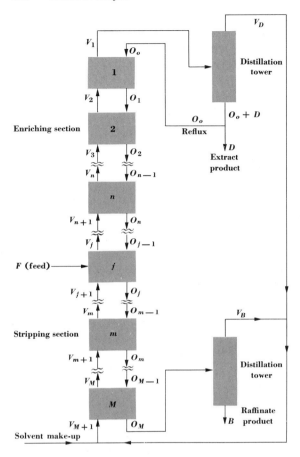

Fig. 40-13.   Countercurrent multiple contact with extract reflux.

the operating line for the enriching section.   For the rest of the column, called stripping section, the mass balances are

$$V_{f+1} - O_f = \Delta \tag{40-19}$$

$$V_{m+1} - O_m = \Delta \tag{40-20}$$

$$V_{M+1} - O_M = \Delta \tag{40-21}$$

The operating point Δ for the stripping section is on a line through V_{M+1} and O_M.

The over-all mass balance for the cascade is written

$$F + V_{M+1} - O_M = V_1 - O_o \tag{40-22}$$

From this equation and Eqs. (40-16) and (40-21) we obtain

$$F + \Delta = \Delta' \tag{40-23}$$

and $\overline{F\Delta'\Delta}$ is a straight line.

If F and O_o are combined mathematically to give J, as follows,

$$F + O_o = J \tag{40-24}$$

then the over-all mass balance can also be written as

$$J + V_{M+1} = O_M + V_1 = M \tag{40-25}$$

The reflux ratio can vary between a certain minimum operable value and total reflux, where no product D is removed. In the latter case F and B are also zero. With total reflux, the minimum possible number of stages is required. Note that under these conditions, Δ coincides with Δ' and O_m/V_{m+1} is a minimum.

As the reflux ratio is progressively decreased, the operating lines on a graph such as Fig. 40-12 approach the equilibrium line and more and more stages are required for the separation. At the minimum reflux ratio, the lines touch at a pinch point and an infinite number of stages would be required for the separation. The pinch point can occur anywhere in the cascade, but it usually occurs at the intersection of the two operating lines. On a triangular diagram, minimum reflux is reached as soon as any line through one of the Δ points coincides with a tie line.

There is an economic optimum value of the reflux ratio. Operation near minimum reflux reduces solvent losses and the size of the individual stages but results in a large number of stages. Operation at high reflux ratios reduces the number of stages but increases the size of the individual stages because of the high circulation rates.

There is a maximum solvent-free mass fraction of A that can be obtained in the extract product with a system such as that of Fig. 40-1. This y'_{A1} is given by a line through pure B, tangent to the upper solubility envelope. For the system of Fig. 40-1, this maximum is given by the line $\overline{BVV'}$ in Fig. 40-1; $y'_{A1,max}$ is 0.77.

For a ternary system such as that of Fig. 40-3a, a cascade with reflux such as shown in Fig. 40-13 can produce *both* almost pure C and almost pure A. For instance, a mixture of hexane and methylcyclopentane can be separated into almost pure fractions by a system like that of Fig. 40-13, which uses aniline as a solvent.

PROBLEMS

40-1. A countercurrent liquid-liquid extraction battery operates as shown in Fig. 40-14. Find the number of stages necessary to give the desired separation.

40-2. It is proposed to separate a mixture F containing 50 mass per cent n-heptane and 50 mass per cent methylcyclohexane (MCH) into a raffinate stream O_M containing 8 mass per cent MCH and a product stream D containing 87 mass per cent MCH and 8 mass per cent aniline. A stream of pure solvent (aniline) is supplied to the extraction battery, and a lesser amount of the same solvent (also pure) is produced from the reflux unit. The system operates at a reflux ratio O_o/D of 3. Assuming the feed to be added

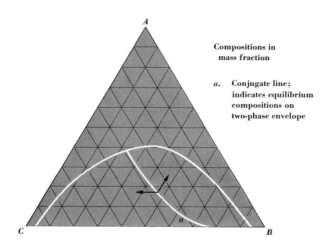

Compositions in
mass fraction

a. Conjugate line;
indicates equilibrium
compositions on
two-phase envelope

Fig. 40-14.   *Countercurrent extraction battery and triangular diagram for Prob.* 40-1.

at the optimum location in the system, find the number of stages required to produce
the desired separation when the system is operated as shown in Fig. 40-13.   Equilibrium data for the ternary system have been reported at 25°C by K. A. Vartaressian
and M. R. Fenske, *Ind. Eng. Chem.*, **29**:270 (1937), and are as follows:

Hydrocarbon layer		Solvent layer	
MCH	Heptane	MCH	Heptane
Mass per cent			
0	92.6	0	6.2
9.2	83.1	0.8	6.0
18.6	73.4	2.7	5.3
33.8	57.6	4.6	4.5
46.0	45.0	7.4	3.6
59.7	30.7	9.2	2.8
71.6	18.2	12.7	1.6
83.3	5.4	15.6	0.6
88.1	0	16.9	0

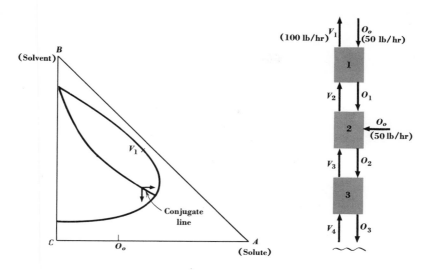

Fig. 40-15. Data for Prob. 40-3.

40-3. An extraction battery operates as shown in Fig. 40-15. Find the points on the triangular diagram which represent the composition of streams V_4 and O_3. Stream V_4 is not pure solvent but is saturated ternary mixture from a stage not shown.

40-4. Fish oil is to be extracted from pulverized fish heads containing 70 mass per cent insoluble solid and 30 mass per cent oil. The extraction is to be accomplished in a multiple-contact extraction battery consisting of two equilibrium stages with fresh solvent added to each stage. The feed rate is 1000 lb/hr of fish heads, and the solvent rate is 500 lb/hr to each stage. The underflow from each stage contains 0.30 lb solution/lb solids. Find the fraction of oil initially present in the fish heads that is recovered in the extract stream.

40-5. Sixty tons per day of oil sand (25 mass per cent oil and 75 mass per cent sand) is to be extracted with 40 tons/day of naphtha in a continuous, countercurrent extraction battery. The final extract from the battery is to contain 40 mass per cent oil and 60 mass per cent naphtha, and the underflow from each unit is expected to consist of 35 mass per cent solution and 65 mass per cent sand. If the over-all efficiency of the battery is 50 per cent, how many stages will be required?

DISTILLATION OF BINARY MIXTURES

In this chapter we shall consider the separation of binary mixtures by the technique of distillation. The importance of understanding the principles of binary distillation lies only partly in their industrial application; these principles are equally important because of the assistance they provide in understanding the principles of multicomponent distillation, in which most of the same concepts exist but are encumbered by a large amount of algebra necessary to describe the behavior of all the components.

The batch distillation of what are essentially binary mixtures of ethanol and water has been practiced by brewers and distillers for centuries. It is only in the present century, however, that distillation has been developed on a large scale as a steady-state operation. The major contributions in this field have come from engineers in the petroleum industry, where large numbers of multistage distillation towers operate on a continuous basis.

Although the term distillation is occasionally used to describe the removal of volatile materials from solids, we shall be concerned primarily with the separation of volatile components found in liquid solutions. If a homogeneous liquid mixture is boiled, the vapor bubbles leaving are richer in the more volatile components than is the liquid, whereas the liquid remaining is richer in the less volatile components. If a batch of liquid is treated in this way until, say, half of it has been vaporized, the liquid remaining will have a different composition from the original mixture. The overhead vapor, if removed from the system continuously and condensed, would have a composition also different from that of the original mixture. Thus a separation would be achieved.

It should not be thought that either the overhead product or the residual liquid would necessarily be very pure. At any instant the vapor leaving would not be richer than the equilibrium composition. Thus the collected overhead product could be regarded as the sum of a number of increments of vapor, each of which was in equilibrium with the liquid at the time it was produced. For example, a liquid with an initial composition of 50 per cent A and 50 per cent B might give a cumulative overhead product containing 70 per cent A and 30 per cent B, with a residual liquid containing 20 per cent A and 80 per cent B.

Unless an azeotrope is formed in the system, a greater separation may be achieved than in the example chosen. In batch distillation, however, as the liquid becomes richer in the less volatile component, the amount of liquid remaining becomes smaller. In the example chosen, if the vapor were continually removed and boiling continued until the liquid was nearly all gone, the liquid composition would approach 100 per cent B. The collected overhead product would, of course, have almost the same composition as the original charge of liquid, so no useful result would have been achieved.

In continuous, multistage distillation the separation of components into nearly pure streams requires large numbers of stages compared with the number of stages required, say, for the production of streams of 90 per cent purity. The difficulty of preparing very pure products by distillation is reflected by thermodynamic calculations[1] for the minimum work of separation, which show that the minimum work required increases sharply as the purity of the products approaches 100 per cent.

The simplest distillation operation, which we call batch distillation, can be carried out using a vessel called a still, equipped with a steam jacket or heating coil. The vapor bubbles produced at the heating surface rise through the liquid and pass out the top of the vessel to a condenser, where they are condensed back into liquid form and collected in a receiver. As was seen in Chap. 36, mass transfer to and from vapor bubbles rising through a liquid proceeds very rapidly, so the vapor composition is seldom

---

[1] B. F. Dodge, in "Chemical Engineering Thermodynamics," p. 597, McGraw-Hill Book Company, Inc., New York, 1944, shows the following results for the calculation of the minimum work for separating a mixture of 50 mole per cent benzene in toluene into the following products at 25°C:

1. Both products 95 mole per cent pure, −526 Btu/lb mole feed
2. Both products 99 mole per cent pure, −555 Btu/lb mole feed
3. Both products 100 per cent pure, −738 Btu/lb mole feed

far from the equilibrium value when the bubbles break the upper surface of the liquid in the still.

A more complex piece of distillation apparatus is the fractionating column. This is a cylindrical vessel containing various types of internal construction devised for the purpose of bringing the vapor and liquid into successive contact as the two phases move generally countercurrent in the column. In this device liquid reflux must be added at the top of the tower; this liquid is usually supplied by condensing part of the overhead vapor. The internal construction may consist of nothing more than a fixed bed of Berl saddles, Raschig rings, or some other kind of packing commonly used in gas absorption. More often, however, the internal construction consists of a series of plates or stages. The plates may be perforated with holes or rectangular slots, or they may be of the more elaborate bubble-cap or valve-plate construction. A bubble-cap tray has been shown in Fig. 39-4. Most of our analysis of multistage distillation will be made with the bubble-cap plate column as an implicit model. As usual, it will be assumed that for an ideal stage the gas and liquid phases *leaving* each plate are in equilibrium. The discussion of stage efficiency given in Chap. 39 of course applies also to distillation.

The batch still as we have described it consists of a vessel which provides one equilibrium stage. The fractionating column, on the other hand, usually operates under steady conditions and contains a number of plates, each of which is approximately an equilibrium stage. The two pieces of apparatus can be combined by having the vapors from the batch still pass up into the fractionating column so that the batch distillation is performed with a number of stages operating simultaneously. The composition at any point in the fractionating column is then a function of time; the system is operated only for a sufficient period to produce cumulative overhead and residual products of the desired composition.

Phase Equilibrium

Extensive use is made of the principles of phase equilibrium in distillation calculations. In Chap. 33 we discussed the use of the phase rule in determining the number of independent variables that could be specified in a system at equilibrium. In a two-phase binary system we saw from Eq. (33-1) that two variables could be arbitrarily specified. Because pressure is usually fixed by design considerations, the specification of only one additional variable for any particular binary system is sufficient to fix all other variables in the system. For example, if a liquid is boiling in a batch still at 1 atm pressure and the liquid composition is 65 mole per cent ethanol and 35 mole per cent water, then both the temperature of the liq-uid-vapor system and the composition of the vapor are fixed. As another example, if the pressure in a fractionating column is 1 atm and the tem-perature of the liquid leaving the top plate is known, then for a particular binary system the compositions of both the vapor and liquid streams leaving the plate are fixed if they are in equilibrium.

The equilibrium compositions are found from experimental measure-ments and by the use of various equations. In Chap. 33 we saw how Raoult's law could be used to predict equilibrium compositions in a vapor-liquid system if the liquid phase were an ideal solution and the gas phase an ideal gas.

One useful concept is relative volatility. The volatility, which has the units of pressure, is written for component A as

$$v_A = \frac{\overline{p}_A}{\tilde{x}_A} \tag{41-1}$$

For a pure substance the volatility is identical with the vapor pressure. The relative volatility is written as

$$\alpha_{AB} = \frac{v_A}{v_B} = \frac{\overline{p}_A \tilde{x}_B}{\tilde{x}_A \overline{p}_B} \tag{41-2}$$

The choice of components for A and B is usually made so that α_{AB} is greater than 1. In this sense component A is the more volatile of the two. From the definition of partial pressure, Eq. (33-2), we can write

$$\alpha_{AB} = \frac{\tilde{x}_B \, \tilde{y}_A}{\tilde{x}_A \, \tilde{y}_B} \tag{41-3}$$

or if Raoult's law applies to the system, we can substitute Eq. (33-3) in Eq. (41-2) to give

$$\alpha_{AB} = \frac{p_A}{p_B} \tag{41-4}$$

The discussion in this chapter is restricted to binary systems, so we shall usually simplify the nomenclature from this point on by dropping the sub-scripts which designate components A and B. Henceforth, the mole fractions of the more volatile component A in the vapor and liquid will be written as $\tilde{y}$ and $\tilde{x}$, respectively, and the mole fractions of the less volatile component B as $1 - \tilde{y}$ and $1 - \tilde{x}$. Using this convention, we write Eq. (41-3) as

$$\alpha = \frac{1 - \tilde{x}}{\tilde{x}} \frac{\tilde{y}}{1 - \tilde{y}} \tag{41-5}$$

which may be solved for $\tilde{y}$ to give

$$\tilde{y} = \frac{\alpha \tilde{x}}{1 + (\alpha - 1)\tilde{x}} \tag{41-6}$$

This relationship is particularly useful in binary distillation when the temperature range between the boiling points of the pure components is small. Under these conditions the relative volatility is often approximately constant. This makes it possible to construct a plot of $\tilde{y}$ versus $\tilde{x}$ over the composition range of 0 to 1 by using a single mean value of α. If the binary system obeys Raoult's law, α can be calculated from the ratio of vapor pressures as shown in Eq. (41-4). Although the vapor pressures may change considerably over the range of temperatures involved, the ratio of vapor pressures will change much less.

If the liquid and gas phases do not behave as an ideal solution and an ideal gas, respectively, the relative volatility can often be calculated with the aid of thermodynamics. However, the relative volatility is used for little more than calculating the phase compositions, so the thermodynamic calculations are usually made instead for a quantity which we shall write as K. For this quantity, known as the vapor-liquid equilibrium ratio,[1] we have the simple definition

$$K = \frac{\tilde{y}}{\tilde{x}} \tag{41-7}$$

which enables us to calculate phase compositions.

It is not our purpose here to discuss the thermodynamic calculations from which K values are determined. This topic is found in most textbooks on chemical-engineering thermodynamics. It will be sufficient here to remind the student that K is a function of temperature, pressure, and generally also of composition. Although K values are available from a variety of sources, we shall use only the values given by Perry. These values depend only on pressure and temperature; hence they apply only to liquids and gases which behave as ideal solutions. If more accurate values are required, the student is referred to a series of 276 charts known as the Kellogg charts,[2] which are applicable to nonideal solutions.

[1] This quantity is known by a variety of names. S. B. Adler and D. F. Palazzo, in *Chem. Eng.*, June 29, 1959, p. 95, point out that it is also known as the vaporization constant, the vaporization ratio, the volatility equilibrium distribution ratio, and simply as the equilibrium constant. They give a concise summary of equations for calculating values of K.

[2] The M. W. Kellogg Company, "Liquid-Vapor Equilibria in Mixtures of Light Hydrocarbons," New York, 1950. The data in these charts are summarized in articles by C. L. DePriester, *Chem. Eng. Progr. Symp. Ser.*, no. 7, p. 1 (1953), and W. C. Edminster and C. L. Ruby, *Chem. Eng. Progr.*, **51**:95 (1955).

Example 41-1

Construct a diagram of $\tilde{y}$ versus $\tilde{x}$ for mixtures of n-butane and n-hexane under the following conditions:

(a) Total pressure is 20 psia. Assume that Raoult's law applies.
(b) Total pressure is 115 psia. Use K values from Perry.

(a) At 20 psia the boiling points of n-butane and n-hexane are 50 and 175°F, respectively (from Perry, p. 564, fig. 2). Hence mixtures of these two components can exist as a vapor-liquid system at equilibrium at 20 psia only between these two temperatures. The relative volatility at 50°F is found using Eq. (41-4).

$$\alpha = 20/1.50 = 13.3$$

At 175°F the relative volatility is

$$\alpha = 150/20 = 7.5$$

The variation of relative volatility in this example is such that it would be unwise to attempt to use an average value of α in the relation between $\tilde{y}$ and $\tilde{x}$ [Eq. (41-6)]. As an alternative, we select a number of temperatures betweén 50 and 175°F and calculate $\tilde{x}$ and $\tilde{y}$ as shown below. The partial pressures are written using Raoult's law and added:

$$\tilde{x}p_A + (1 - \tilde{x})p_B = 20 \tag{1}$$

Solving for $\tilde{x}$, we obtain

$$\tilde{x} = \frac{20 - p_B}{p_A - p_B} \tag{2}$$

At 100°F the vapor pressure of n-butane is 52 psia, and the vapor pressure of n-hexane is 5 psia. Substituting these numbers in Eq. (2), we obtain

$$\tilde{x} = \frac{20 - 5}{52 - 5}$$

$$= 0.32 \tag{3}$$

The vapor composition is found by dividing the partial pressure of n-butane by the total pressure:

$$\tilde{y} = \frac{(0.32)(52)}{20}$$

$$= 0.83 \tag{4}$$

We proceed in this fashion to find values of $\tilde{y}$ versus $\tilde{x}$, which are plotted on Fig. 41-1.

(b) At 115 psia we see from the K chart (Perry, p. 569) that the K values for n-butane and n-hexane are unity at 155 and 310°F, respectively. These represent, therefore, the boiling points of the pure components at this pressure. We designate n-butane as component A and n-hexane as component B and write

$$\tilde{x}_A + \tilde{x}_B = 1 \tag{1}$$

$$\tilde{y}_A + \tilde{y}_B = 1 \tag{2}$$

Using the definition of K, we substitute, in Eq. (2),

$$K_A\tilde{x}_A + K_B\tilde{x}_B = 1 \tag{3}$$

Fig. 41-1. Mole fraction n-butane in the vapor vs. mole fraction n-butane in the liquid for systems containing n-butane and n-hexane at total pressures of 20 and 115 psia (calculated as shown in Example 41-1).

a.   20 psia.
b.   115 psia.

We then substitute Eq. (1) in Eq. (3),

$$K_A \tilde{x}_A + K_B(1 - \tilde{x}_A) = 1 \tag{4}$$

and solve for $\tilde{x}_A$ from Eq. (4),

$$\tilde{x}_A = \frac{1 - K_B}{K_A - K_B} \tag{5}$$

At 200°F $K_A = 1.60$ and $K_B = 0.30$. We substitute these values in Eq. (5) and find $\tilde{x}_A = 0.54$. The vapor composition is

$$\tilde{y}_A = (1.60)(0.54)$$
$$= 0.86$$

Values of $\tilde{y}_A$ versus $\tilde{x}_A$ are calculated in this manner at a number of temperatures between 155 and 310°F and plotted on Fig. 41-1.

It will be noticed on Fig. 41-1 that the curve of $\tilde{y}$ versus $\tilde{x}$ for a pressure of 115 psia is closer to a line drawn at 45° through the origin than is the curve for 20 psia. The 45° line represents the relation $\tilde{y} = \tilde{x}$; a vapor-liquid equilibrium curve coinciding with this line would represent a condition at which no separation could be achieved by distillation. On the other hand, a vapor-liquid equilibrium curve at a great distance from the 45° line represents a system in which a substantial separation is achieved by distillation. Thus the separation of mixtures of *n*-butane and *n*-hexane could be more easily achieved at 20 psia than at 115 psia. By this we mean that fewer stages would be required to achieve a specified separation in a fractionating column, or a greater difference in vapor and liquid composition would occur with a single-stage batch distillation.

When an azeotrope occurs in a binary system, the curve of $\tilde{y}$ versus $\tilde{x}$ crosses the 45° line. Thus, if the system is ethanol and water at 1 atm and the mole fraction of ethanol in the vapor is plotted against the mole fraction of ethanol in the liquid, the curve of $\tilde{y}$ versus $\tilde{x}$ is above the 45° line from $\tilde{x} = 0$ up to the azeotrope composition of 0.894 mole fraction

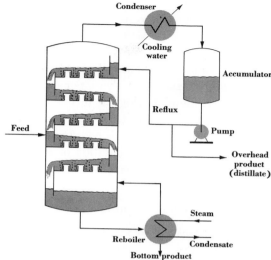

Fig. 41-2. *Schematic diagram of operation of a fractionating column containing bubble-cap plates.*

ethanol. At this point the curve crosses the 45° line and continues beneath the line up to $\bar{x} = 1$.

The Operation of a Fractionating Column

A fractionating column operating at steady state is shown schematically in Fig. 41-2. A feed enters the column somewhere near the middle; overhead and bottom products are withdrawn as shown. The column contains a number of bubble-cap plates. Vapor from the top plate passes to a condenser, where it is condensed to a saturated liquid which is collected in a vessel known as an accumulator. As we shall see later, the condenser may also be operated to produce either a subcooled liquid or a mixture of liquid and vapor; for the present purpose, however, we shall consider the product to be a liquid at its saturation temperature. Some of the liquid in the accumulator is returned as reflux continuously to the top plate of the column because it is necessary to have liquid on this plate and on succeeding plates to achieve any mass transfer. The remainder of the liquid is withdrawn continuously and is referred to as the overhead-product stream, or distillate.

At the bottom of the column the liquid collects in the reboiler, where it is heated, usually by steam coils. The reboiler may be an integral part of the cylindrical vessel which constitutes the column, or it may be a vessel of different shape attached to the column, or it may be a vessel external to the column (as shown in Fig. 41-2). In all cases the function of the reboiler is to receive the liquid overflow from the lowest bubble-cap plate and to return a portion of this as a vapor stream while the remainder is withdrawn continuously as a liquid bottom product. The conditions for mass transfer in the reboiler such as degree of mixing and time of contact are usually such that the vapor returned to the column is in equilibrium with the liquid leaving the reboiler as a bottom product.

The feed entering the column may be a saturated liquid, a saturated vapor, a mixture of both liquid and vapor, a subcooled liquid, or a superheated vapor. The condition of the feed affects the performance of the column, as we shall see later in this chapter.

The Sorel Method of Analysis

The bases of most methods of analysis of fractionating columns lie in the equations of Sorel.[1] These equations are fundamental to the solution of multicomponent distillation problems, which are usually solved by an electronic computer. The equations are generally not used for binary systems because, although the general approach is rather simple, the solution requires numerous trial-and-error calculations. Simpler methods are available: the McCabe-Thiele graphical method, in which certain simplifying assumptions are made, and the Ponchon-Savarit method, which is the graphical equivalent of the Sorel method but does not require a trial-and-error solution. We shall examine first the Sorel method.

A portion of a fractionating column is shown in Fig. 41-3. The vapor and liquid streams are shown schematically for the top few plates. The designations not only identify the streams, but also represent the amounts in pound moles per hour. A material balance around the top plate gives

$$\tilde{O}_R + \tilde{V}_2 = \tilde{O}_1 + \tilde{V}_1 \tag{41-8}$$

and an enthalpy balance around the top plate yields[2]

$$\tilde{O}_R \tilde{h}_R + \tilde{V}_2 \tilde{H}_2 = \tilde{O}_1 \tilde{h}_1 + \tilde{V}_1 \tilde{H}_1 \tag{41-9}$$

These two equations contain eight variables, so it is apparent that six variables must be known if the equations are to be solved. In the initial stages of design the column pressure is usually specified, as we shall see near the end of this chapter. Because all streams are binary mixtures and are assumed to be at saturation conditions, we need to specify only one variable for each stream, in addition to pressure, to fix the properties

---

[1] E. Sorel, "La Rectification de l'alcool," Paris, 1893.

[2] The symbols h and $\tilde{H}$ refer to the enthalpies in Btu/lb mole of liquid and vapor phases, respectively.

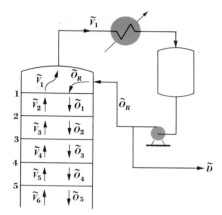

Fig. 41-3.   *Upper section of a fractionating column with bubble-cap plates.*

of the stream.   For example, the composition of the distillate stream $\tilde{x}_D$ is usually specified arbitrarily.   All the vapor entering the condenser leaves as condensate of the same composition, so $\tilde{x}_D = \tilde{x}_R = \tilde{y}_1$.   Furthermore, stream O_1 is in equilibrium with V_1, so we can find $\tilde{x}_1$ from a value of $\tilde{y}_1$ and a plot of $\tilde{y}$ versus $\tilde{x}$.   Therefore we can determine the compositions of all streams arriving at or leaving plate 1 except V_2.   Knowing the three stream compositions and the total pressure, we find the stream temperatures and enthalpies $\tilde{H}_1$, $\tilde{h}_R$, and $\tilde{h}_1$ from tabulated information in handbooks or in the literature.

Two other variables in Eqs. (41-8) and (41-9) can be found directly. The amount of overhead product $\tilde{D}$ is usually specified at the beginning of the problem or determined from an over-all material balance.   In addition, the reflux ratio, which we define as $\tilde{O}_R/\tilde{D}$, is more or less arbitrarily chosen.   These two pieces of information make it possible to calculate the reflux rate $\tilde{O}_R$, and hence the amount of vapor leaving the top plate $\tilde{V}_1$.

The three variables in Eqs. (41-8) and (41-9) which we do not know are the rates $\tilde{O}_1$ and $\tilde{V}_2$ and the enthalpy $\tilde{H}_2$.   To obtain a solution we assume a value for one of the variables.   For example, as a first trial we might say that $\tilde{H}_2$ is the same as $\tilde{H}_1$ (which is known).   This permits us to solve the two equations for the remaining variables $\tilde{O}_1$ and $\tilde{V}_2$.   To check the assumed value of $\tilde{H}_2$, we write a material balance around plate 1 for the more volatile component.   This equation is

$$\tilde{O}_R\tilde{x}_R + \tilde{V}_2\tilde{y}_2 = \tilde{O}_1\tilde{x}_1 + \tilde{V}_1\tilde{y}_1 \tag{41-10}$$

which may be rearranged to give

$$\tilde{y}_2 = \frac{\tilde{O}_1}{\tilde{V}_2}\tilde{x}_1 + \frac{\tilde{V}_1\tilde{y}_1 - \tilde{O}_R\tilde{x}_R}{\tilde{V}_2} \tag{41-11}$$

The numerator of the last term in Eq. (41-11) is simply $\tilde{D}\tilde{x}_D$, so we write the expression as

$$\tilde{y}_2 = \frac{\tilde{O}_1}{\tilde{V}_2}\tilde{x}_1 + \frac{\tilde{D}\tilde{x}_D}{\tilde{V}_2} \tag{41-12}$$

All the variables on the right-hand side of this equation are known or have been found in the calculations described above, so we solve Eq. (41-12) directly for $\tilde{y}_2$. Knowing the composition of this stream and the temperature, we can find its enthalpy $\tilde{H}_2$ from tables of enthalpy data, and in this way we check the value assumed for $\tilde{H}_2$ earlier in the calculations.

After the calculations for conditions around plate 1 have been repeated until they give consistent results, the entire procedure is repeated with balances around plate 2. As before, the material and enthalpy balances contain eight variables, of which five are known and three are unknown ($\tilde{O}_2$, $\tilde{V}_3$, $\tilde{H}_3$). $\tilde{H}_3$ is assumed (as a first guess we should assume $\tilde{H}_3 = \tilde{H}_2$), and the balances solved for $\tilde{O}_2$ and $\tilde{V}_3$. A balance is then written around the plate for the volatile component. This yields

$$\tilde{y}_3 = \frac{\tilde{O}_2}{\tilde{V}_3}\tilde{x}_2 + \frac{\tilde{D}\tilde{x}_D}{\tilde{V}_3} \tag{41-13}$$

which is solved for $\tilde{y}_3$ and permits the independent determination of $\tilde{H}_3$ as a check on the assumed value of $\tilde{H}_3$.

The procedure outlined for plates 1 and 2 is repeated for successive plates to the point where the feed is added. If the feed is to be added at the optimum location, it will usually be admitted to the column at some point where it has approximately the same composition as some stream in the column (this matter will be discussed later). At the feed plate the contributions of the feed stream must be considered in the material, enthalpy, and component balances. When the calculations apply to plates beneath the feed, they proceed just as they did for the column above the feed plate, except that if Eq. (41-13) is used, it must contain a term to account for the feed stream.

The calculations continue for successive plates until a vapor stream is found which has a composition that indicates that it is in equilibrium with the bottom product $\tilde{x}_B$. This vapor stream will be the vapor from the reboiler and marks the end of the calculations. The principal object, of course, has been to determine the number of stages required to give a specified separation of a certain feed into overhead and bottom products of predetermined compositions $\tilde{x}_D$ and $\tilde{x}_B$. In the course of making the calculations, the compositions and enthalpies of all streams have been determined, so the determination of the heat-transfer rate in the condenser and reboiler is a matter simply of making enthalpy balances on the fluid streams entering and leaving these auxiliary pieces of equipment. In addition, the feed plate has been located and the rates of all streams have been determined. The temperatures will have been found (or can readily be found from a knowledge of total pressure and stream composition), so that the volumetric flow rates of all streams can be found directly. This information is necessary so that the tower diameter and the dimensions of such mechanical equipment in the column as the downcomers and bubble caps can be determined.

The McCabe-Thiele Method of Analysis

In the Sorel analysis the principal difficulty was in the trial-and-error determinations of the enthalpies of the vapor streams $\tilde{H}_2$, $\tilde{H}_3$, etc. As a first approximation, it was suggested that these enthalpies might be considered equal. This assumption made it possible to solve for the vapor compositions and then to calculate the vapor enthalpies. Lewis[1] made a similar assumption when he suggested that the vapor rates $\tilde{V}_1$, $\tilde{V}_2$, $\tilde{V}_3$, etc., might be considered to be equal. In sections of the column where no feed is added or side streams withdrawn, the assumption of equal vapor rates implies equal liquid rates, as can be seen from Eq. (41-8).

For many systems in which the components have similar molecular structures, the assumption of Lewis is sufficiently accurate so that the trial-and-error part of the Sorel solution is eliminated. The over-all material and enthalpy balances [Eqs. (41-8) and (41-9)] become superfluous, and only the balance on the more volatile component [Eq. (41-12)] is needed. If all vapor streams in the column above the feed are flowing at the same rate, we can designate this rate by a common symbol $\tilde{V}$; similarly, we designate the rate of all liquid streams as $\tilde{O}$. Thus Eq. (41-12) is written as

$$\tilde{y}_2 = \frac{\tilde{O}}{\tilde{V}} \, \tilde{x}_1 + \frac{\tilde{D}\tilde{x}_D}{\tilde{V}} \tag{41-14}$$

This equation applies equally well as a relation between $\tilde{y}_3$ and $\tilde{x}_2$, or, for that matter, between any pair of passing streams in Fig. 41-3. Thus the Lewis modification reduces the Sorel method to a series of alternate equilibrium and component-balance calculations without trial and error.

With reference to Fig. 41-3, the first calculation would be to find $\tilde{x}_1$ knowing $\tilde{y}_1$ and the equilibrium data. Then $\tilde{y}_2$ would be found from Eq.

---

[1] W. K. Lewis, *Ind. Eng. Chem.*, **14**:492 (1922).

(41-14). Next $\tilde{x}_2$ would be found as the composition of a stream in equilibrium with $\tilde{y}_2$. After this, $\tilde{y}_3$ would be found by substituting $\tilde{y}_3$ and $\tilde{x}_2$ in Eq. (41-14) for $\tilde{y}_2$ and $\tilde{x}_1$. In this manner the calculations would proceed down the column. At and below the feed plate, the addition of the feed would have to be considered in the material-balance equation; otherwise the method of calculation would be unaltered.

The method of McCabe and Thiele[1] is simply a graphical solution of the Sorel equations, with the simplification of constant vapor and liquid rates as suggested by Lewis. The advantage of the McCabe-Thiele method depends on the linearity of Eq. (41-14). McCabe and Thiele suggested that this function be plotted as an operating line on the same graph as the equilibrium curve of $\tilde{y}$ versus $\tilde{x}$, so that the number of equilibrium stages can be determined by a graphical construction. The stages are counted between the equilibrium and operating lines just as in Chaps. 39 and 40.

Before proceeding with the details of the McCabe-Thiele method we shall examine the assumption of constant vapor and liquid rates (often called constant molal overflow). The principal source of enthalpy on a bubble-cap plate is the saturated vapor approaching the plate from below. This enthalpy, some of which is given up by condensation in the liquid on the plate, causes the vaporization of some of the liquid on the plate. The vapor produced joins the uncondensed vapor rising from the plate and represents the principal enthalpy stream leaving the plate. In addition, there may be a heat loss through the walls of the column, though this is usually slight, and there is also a small difference in the enthalpies of the liquid stream arriving at the plate and the liquid stream leaving. It can be seen, therefore, that the two vapor streams are the principal "carriers" of enthalpy. If the two components have similar molecular structure and behavior, the molal latent heat of vaporization divided by the absolute temperature is approximately constant. This generalization is known as Trouton's rule. Since the streams of vapor leaving adjacent plates are at nearly the same temperature, the molal latent heats are nearly the same if the system follows Trouton's rule. Thus, if heat losses are negligible, a mole of vapor condensing in the liquid on a plate will cause the generation of another mole of vapor from the liquid. In these circumstances, therefore, the condition of equal molal vapor rates between plates is achieved. It is important to note that Trouton's rule refers only to molal latent heats. The latent heats written as Btu/lb are far from constant. Hence an equation similar to Eq. (41-14) in which the liquid and vapor rates are expressed in lb/hr would not be linear because the rates O and V would not be constant.

[1] W. L. McCabe and E. W. Thiele, *Ind. Eng. Chem.*, **17**:605 (1925).

Fig. 41-4. *Operation of a rectifying column with constant molal overflow.*

Rectifying Columns. Fractionating columns in which the feed enters the bottom of the column as a vapor are known as rectifying, or enriching, columns. An overhead product is produced in the same manner as in a complete fractionating column; this product may be quite rich in the more volatile component. The bottom product, however, which is the stream of liquid from the bottom plate, is seldom much leaner than the feed, so that only one of the two product streams can be said to be a fairly pure product. In the sense that the less volatile component is preferentially removed from the vapor ascending the column, the operation of a rectifying column can be considered somewhat analogous to that of a gas-absorption tower. It also resembles the enriching section of the extraction system with reflux, described in Chap. 40.

The rectifying column is somewhat simpler to analyze than a complete fractionating column, so we shall consider the rectifying column first. We shall refer to Fig. 41-4, in which the system is supplied with a saturated vapor feed at the rate of $\tilde{F}$ lb moles/hr and produces saturated-liquid products at the rate of $\tilde{D}$ and $\tilde{B}$ lb moles/hr. The condenser at the top produces a saturated liquid of composition $\tilde{x}_D$, part of which is removed as the overhead product. The remainder of the condensate is returned to the column on the top plate as a saturated-liquid reflux.

A material balance is written for the more volatile component for the portion of the column above plate $n + 1$, as shown in Fig. 41-4.

$$\tilde{V}\tilde{y}_{n+1} = \tilde{O}\tilde{x}_n + \tilde{D}\tilde{x}_D \tag{41-15}$$

Fig. 41-5.   *McCabe-Thiele diagram for a rectifying column (Example 41-2).*

a.   **Equilibrium line.**
b.   **Enriching line, slope** $\tilde{O}/\tilde{V} = 0.80$.

This may be written explicitly for $\tilde{y}_{n+1}$ as

$$\tilde{y}_{n+1} = \frac{\tilde{O}}{\tilde{V}} \tilde{x}_n + \frac{\tilde{D}\tilde{x}_D}{\tilde{V}} \tag{41-16}$$

Equation (41-16) is a linear relation if $\tilde{O}$ and $\tilde{V}$ are constant. When plotted on a graph of $\tilde{y}$ versus $\tilde{x}$, it gives a straight line with a slope $\tilde{O}/\tilde{V}$. The intercept if extended to the y axis is $\tilde{D}\tilde{x}_D/\tilde{V}$. The line is shown on Fig. 41-5, which also shows the equilibrium curve and a line drawn at 45° from the origin. The line representing Eq. (41-16) is an operating line, or more specifically, an enriching line. It can be located in a variety of ways. Points on the line represent passing streams; because $\tilde{y}_1$, $\tilde{x}_D$, and $\tilde{x}_R$ are identical and $\tilde{y}_1$ and $\tilde{x}_R$ are passing streams, a point on the 45° line at $\tilde{x}_D$ represents these three streams and is a point on the operating line. Another point can be found on the operating line at any section where the compositions of the passing streams are known. For example, the balance which gave Eqs. (41-15) and (41-16) could have been written to include all the plates in the column. Thus $\tilde{y}_{N+1}$ would be $\tilde{y}_F$ and $\tilde{x}_N$ would be $\tilde{x}_B$. If we know the feed and bottom-product compositions, we can plot this point on the operating line as representing passing streams at the lowest point in the column. This is also the lowest point on the enriching line and is shown in Fig. 41-5.

For a rectifying column $\tilde{O} = \tilde{B}$ and $\tilde{V} = \tilde{F}$, so that if the flow rates of these external streams are known, $\tilde{O}/\tilde{V}$ is readily determined. Alternatively, $\tilde{O}/\tilde{V}$ can be found from the reflux ratio $\tilde{O}/\tilde{D}$ by writing

$$\frac{\tilde{O}}{\tilde{V}} = \frac{\tilde{O}}{\tilde{O} + \tilde{D}} \tag{41-17}$$

Both numerator and denominator of the right side are divided by $\tilde{D}$ to give

$$\frac{\tilde{O}}{\tilde{V}} = \frac{\tilde{O}/\tilde{D}}{\tilde{O}/\tilde{D} + 1} \tag{41-18}$$

Hence, if $\tilde{O}/\tilde{D}$ is specified, the slope of the operating line $\tilde{O}/\tilde{V}$ can be found. Sometimes $\tilde{O}/\tilde{V}$ is referred to as the internal reflux ratio and $\tilde{O}/\tilde{D}$ as the external reflux ratio.

The number of equilibrium stages required to give a specified separation is found as in previous chapters. By successive horizontal and vertical steps between the equilibrium and operating lines, we find the number of stages required to give the specified separation between the overhead and bottom streams. Each stage is represented by an intersection, or step, which touches the equilibrium curve.

Example 41-2

A rectifying column is supplied with a saturated-vapor feed containing 30 mole per cent A and 70 mole per cent B and is to produce a saturated-liquid distillate containing 90 mole per cent A and 10 mole per cent B. The reflux ratio $\tilde{O}_R/\tilde{D}$ is 4. Find the number of theoretical stages required to give the separation, assuming constant molal overflow. Vapor-liquid equilibrium data are given on a plot of $\tilde{y}$ versus $\tilde{x}$ shown in Fig. 41-5. Component A is more volatile than component B.

The slope of the operating line $\tilde{O}/\tilde{V}$ is found from Eq. (41-18) to be 0.80. The line starts at the 45° line at $\tilde{x}_D = \tilde{x}_R = \tilde{y}_1 = 0.90$ and is drawn with a slope of 0.80. The line terminates at the lower end at $\tilde{y}_F = 0.30$. The value on the $\tilde{x}$ axis at this point represents the bottom-product composition $\tilde{x}_B$.

Equilibrium stages are stepped off as described above. It is seen that 4.4 stages are required to give the desired separation.

Stripping. A stripping column is usually characterized by having the feed supplied to the top of the column, as shown in Fig. 41-6. In this way it resembles the portion of a complete fractionating column from the feed plate to the reboiler. The feed is usually supplied as a saturated liquid, and the overhead product is the vapor rising from the top plate. This vapor is somewhat richer in terms of the more volatile component than is the feed. However, it is usually not a stream of very great purity. The only stream leaving the stripping column that has a very high concentration is the saturated-liquid bottom product from the reboiler. This stream can be quite rich with respect to the less volatile component. In this sense the stripping column in distillation is analogous to the stripping column in gas absorption in which a liquid stream passing down the column is stripped of a volatile component by a stream of vapor passing upward.

The stripping column shown in Fig. 41-6 is analyzed by the McCabe-Thiele method in Fig. 41-7. Constant molal rates of $\tilde{O}'$ and $\tilde{V}'$ are assumed for all streams in the column. A material balance is written for the more volatile component around that section of the column below plate $m + 1$.

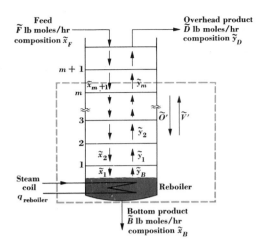

Fig. 41-6.   Operation of a stripping column with constant molal overflow.

$$\tilde{O}' \tilde{x}_{m+1} = \tilde{V}' \tilde{y}_m + \tilde{B} \tilde{x}_B \tag{41-19}$$

which is rearranged to give

$$\tilde{y}_m = \frac{\tilde{O}'}{\tilde{V}'} \tilde{x}_{m+1} - \frac{\tilde{B} \tilde{x}_B}{\tilde{V}'} \tag{41-20}$$

If $\tilde{O}'$ and $\tilde{V}'$ are constant, then Eq. (41-20) is linear. On Fig. 41-7 the function is designated as the stripping, or operating, line and represents compositions of passing streams at any horizontal cross section in the column. The stripping line can be found by a variety of methods. At the top of the column we may know the compositions of the feed entering and the vapor leaving. If the feed is a saturated liquid, the point $\tilde{x}_F, \tilde{y}_D$ represents the upper end of the line. The lower end can be found by determining the intersection with the 45° line. At the 45° line $\tilde{y} = \tilde{x}$, and making this substitution in Eq. (41-19), we get

$$\tilde{O}' \tilde{x} = \tilde{V}' \tilde{x} + \tilde{B} \tilde{x}_B$$

which gives the $\tilde{x}$ value at the intersection as

$$\tilde{x} = \frac{\tilde{B} \tilde{x}_B}{\tilde{O}' - \tilde{V}'}$$

$$= \tilde{x}_B \tag{41-21}$$

An additional device for locating the line is to use the slope. If the feed is a saturated liquid, $\tilde{O}' = \tilde{F}$ and $\tilde{V}' = \tilde{D}$, so that $\tilde{O}'/\tilde{V}'$ can be found merely by knowing the flow rates of the terminal streams.

The determination of the number of equilibrium stages in a stripping

$\tilde{y}_D = 0.805$

Fig. 41-7. *McCabe-Thiele diagram for a stripping column (Example 41-3).*
  a. Equilibrium curve.
  b. Stripping-line slope = $^{100}\!\!/_{85}$.

column is similar to the procedure used for an enriching column. We can start at either end of the operating line; we arbitrarily choose the bottom. The composition of the vapor leaving the reboiler $\tilde{y}_B$ is found on the equilibrium curve at $\tilde{x}_B$. This is a vertical step from the 45° line at $\tilde{x}_B$. The composition of the liquid flowing down from the plate to the reboiler $\tilde{x}_1$ is found by solving Eq. (41-20) graphically. This requires the construction of a horizontal step at $\tilde{y}_B$ to the operating line, giving $\tilde{x}_1$ at the intersection. Composition $\tilde{y}_1$ is found by a vertical step at $\tilde{x}_1$ to the equilibrium line, and composition $\tilde{x}_2$ by a horizontal step to the operating line. This procedure is continued until the upper end of the operating line is reached or passed. The number of equilibrium stages is found by counting the intersections on the equilibrium curve. Each intersection represents a pair of streams in equilibrium: a vapor rising from a stage and a liquid descending from the same stage. Hence each intersection represents an equilibrium stage.

Example 41-3

A stripping column is supplied with 100 lb moles/hr of saturated-liquid feed containing 70 mole per cent A and 30 mole per cent B. It is to produce a bottom product containing 10 mole per cent A and 90 mole per cent B at the rate of 15 lb moles/hr. Find the number of theoretical stages required to give this separation, assuming constant molal overflow. Vapor-liquid equilibrium data are plotted on Fig. 41-7 in terms of the mole fraction of component A, which is the more volatile of the two components.

By an over-all material balance we see that the overhead product is produced at the rate of 85 lb moles/hr. A material balance for component A gives

$$(100)(0.70) = (15)(0.10) + (85)\tilde{y}_D$$

from which we find

$$\tilde{y}_D = 0.805$$

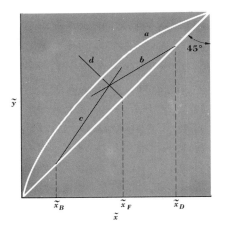

$\tilde{y}$

$\tilde{x}_B$ $\tilde{x}_F$ $\tilde{x}_D$

$\tilde{x}$

Fig. 41-8.   Operating lines for a complete fractionating column with a feed consisting of a mixture of vapor and liquid.

a.   **Equilibrium curve.**

b.   **Enriching line.**

c.   **Stripping line.**

d.   *q* **line.**

The upper end of the operating line is located at $\tilde{y}_D = 0.805$, $\tilde{x}_F = 0.70$, and the lower end at $\tilde{x}_B = 0.10$ on the 45° line. Thus the position of the operating line is determined. The slope is $^{100}\!/_{85}$, though this piece of information need not be used.

The number of stages may be seen on Fig. 41-7 to be 4.3, including the stage which is the reboiler.

Complete Fractionating Columns. When a column contains bubble-cap plates both above and below the feed injection point, a possibility exists of producing both rich overhead and bottom products. In this sense, as well as in schematic appearance, the complete fractionating column combines the properties of both enriching and stripping columns. The complete column has both a reflux condenser and a reboiler, as shown in Fig. 41-2.

The operating lines in the McCabe-Thiele analysis of a complete column are illustrated in Fig. 41-8. Two operating lines are shown; they are described by the same equations, (41-16) and (41-20), as the enriching and stripping lines of the respective columns. Furthermore, the lines may be located by some of the same techniques as were used for the separate columns.

One minor change which applies to the analysis of complete fractionating columns is in the treatment of the feed stream. A number of possibilities exist, depending on the condition of the feed. The feed may be a subcooled liquid (below its saturation temperature), a saturated liquid, a mixture of saturated liquid and saturated vapor, a saturated vapor, or a superheated vapor. The quantitative relations between the streams $\tilde{V}$, $\tilde{V}'$, $\tilde{O}$, and $\tilde{O}'$ depend on which of the above conditions describes the feed. For convenience, we shall introduce a quantity designated q, which is defined as the number of moles of saturated liquid produced on the feed plate by each mole of feed added to the column. With this definition we write the follow-

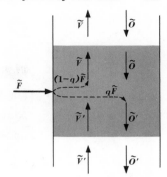

Fig. 41-9.   *Schematic diagram showing effect of feed quality when feed is a saturated liquid or a saturated vapor.*

ing relationships between the streams above and below the feed plate:

$$\tilde{O}' = \tilde{O} + q\tilde{F} \tag{41-22}$$

$$\tilde{V}'_{\bullet} = \tilde{V} + (q - 1)\tilde{F} \tag{41-23}$$

These operating conditions are represented in Fig. 41-9 for a feed containing saturated liquid, saturated vapor, or a mixture of the two.

Because the amount and quality of the feed affect the relative amounts of the vapor and liquid streams in the column, it can be seen that the feed condition also affects the slopes of the two operating lines $\tilde{O}/\tilde{V}$ and $\tilde{O}'/\tilde{V}'$. On the McCabe-Thiele diagram, the quantity of the feed determines the locus of intersection of the two operating lines. At the point of intersection, the material balances, Eqs. (41-15) and (41-19), which are represented graphically by the operating lines, can be subtracted to give a locus of intersection on the plot of $\tilde{y}$ versus $\tilde{x}$:

$$\tilde{y}(\tilde{V}' - \tilde{V}) = \tilde{x}(\tilde{O}' - \tilde{O}) - \tilde{B}\tilde{x}_B - \tilde{D}\tilde{x}_D \tag{41-24}$$

In this equation we substitute for $\tilde{V}' - \tilde{V}$ from Eq. (41-23) and for $\tilde{O}' - \tilde{O}$ from Eq. (41-22). In addition, the sum of the last two terms on the right-hand side of Eq. (41-24) is equal to $\tilde{F}\tilde{x}_F$, in which $\tilde{x}_F$ represents the over-all composition of the feed, regardless of quality. Making these substitutions, the locus of intersection of the two operating lines becomes

$$\tilde{y}(q - 1)\tilde{F} = \tilde{x}q\tilde{F} - \tilde{F}\tilde{x}_F \tag{41-25}$$

which is rearranged to give

$$\tilde{y} = \frac{q}{q - 1}\,\tilde{x} - \frac{\tilde{x}_F}{q - 1} \tag{41-26}$$

The straight line described by Eq. (41-26) is known as the *q* line. The intersection of the *q* line and the 45° line is found by equating $\tilde{y}$ and $\tilde{x}$ in Eq. (41-26). In this circumstance Eq. (41-26) reduces to $\tilde{x} = \tilde{x}_F$, in which $\tilde{x}_F$ designates the over-all composition of the feed rather than just the composition of the liquid phase. The other piece of information used to

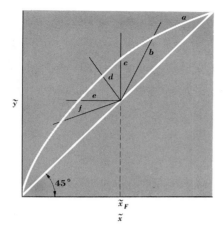

Fig. 41-10.   Location of q line as a function of feed quality. ($\bar{x}_F$ is over-all feed composition regardless of quality.)

    a. **Equilibrium line.**
    b. **Subcooled liquid *q* line.**
    c. **Saturated liquid *q* line.**
    d. **Liquid and vapor *q* line.**
    e. **Saturated vapor *q* line.**
    f. **Superheated vapor *q* line.**

locate the q line is its slope.   The relation between slope and feed quality is indicated in Table 41-1.

The possible locations of the q line are shown in Fig. 41-10.   For feed which contains a mixture of saturated liquid and saturated vapor it can be shown that the q line intersects the equilibrium curve at values of $\tilde{y}$ and $\tilde{x}$ which are identical with the compositions of the vapor and liquid phases in the feed.   That this is true for a feed which is all saturated vapor or all saturated liquid may be seen in Fig. 41-10.   For subcooled liquid or superheated vapor feed, the intersection of the q line and equilibrium curve has no such significance.

Table 41-1.   Effect of Feed Quality on Slope of q Line

Feed quality	q	Slope of q line, $q/(q-1)$
Subcooled liquid................	>1	>1
Saturated liquid................	1	∞
Liquid and vapor................	$0–1$	Negative
Saturated vapor................	0	0
Superheated vapor..............	<0	$0–1$

The determination of stream compositions in a complete fractionating column is very similar to the procedure used for stripping and rectifying columns.   A situation for which the feed is added at the optimum plate is illustrated in Fig. 41-11a.   It can be seen that passing-stream compositions are found on the top operating line above the point of intersection of the two operating lines; below this intersection, passing-stream compositions are found using the bottom operating line.

For the system illustrated in Fig. 41-11a, the second plate is the optimum

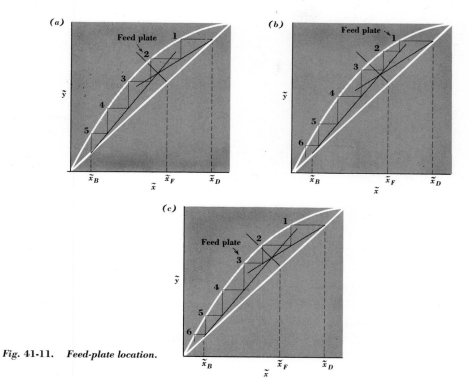

Fig. 41-11.   Feed-plate location.

feed plate.   This means that if the feed is a saturated or a subcooled liquid, it is added to the liquid flowing onto plate 2 from the plate above.   If the feed is a saturated or superheated vapor, the construction of Fig. 41-11*a* implies that the feed is added beneath plate 2 and joins the vapor rising from the plate below.   The final possibility is that the feed is a mixture of vapor and liquid.[1]   The construction of Fig. 41-11*a* implies that the vapor and the liquid of the feed are separated and the liquid is added directly above the feed plate while the vapor is injected underneath the feed plate. Although this may not be done in practice, such procedure, nevertheless, is the implication of the commonly used analysis shown in Fig. 41-11*a*.

The feed plate shown in Fig. 41-11*a* is the optimum feed plate, but not the only possible choice.   The feed plate for the same operating lines may be the first plate as shown in Fig. 41-11*b* or the third plate as in Fig. 41-11*c*. It can be seen on the diagrams that, for these latter possibilities, a greater number of plates are required to give the same specified separation between

[1] From the slope of the q line in Fig. 41-11*a*, we see that this is the situation actually represented here.

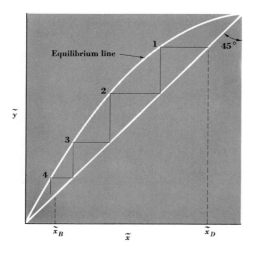

Fig. 41-12.   McCabe-Thiele analysis for total reflux and minimum plates.

overhead and bottom products.   Thus the location of the feed plate at the intersection of the operating lines is the optimum choice.   From the constructions of Fig. 41-11, it is evident that the feed plate may be located anywhere between the points where the two operating lines intersect the equilibrium curve.

If a column operates with more than one feed stream, each feed is represented by its own q line, which is found by locating a point on the 45° line representing the over-all composition of that feed and drawing a line with a slope of $q/(q-1)$, as shown by Eq. (41-26).   Each q line is the locus of intersection of the operating lines representing passing streams immediately above and below the feed in question.   For example, a column with two feeds would have three operating lines, one for each section of the column in which molal liquid and vapor rates are assumed to be constant.   For a given set of operating lines, each feed stream would have an optimum injection point, which would give the specified separation with a minimum number of equilibrium stages.

Limiting Reflux Conditions.   In Chap. 40 we considered for extraction two limiting reflux conditions which are also of interest in distillation. One is the condition of total reflux.   This means that all vapor from the top plate is condensed and returned as liquid reflux.   Thus $\tilde{O} = \tilde{V}$, and the slope of the top operating line is unity.   If the feed stream and bottom-product stream are also shut off, then the liquid and vapor rates $\tilde{O}'$ and $\tilde{V}'$ beneath the feed are also equal and are equal to the rates above the feed plate.   Thus both operating lines have slopes of unity and coincide

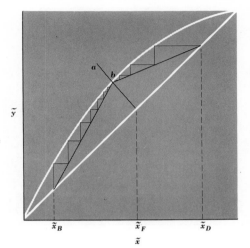

Fig. 41-13. *McCabe-Thiele analysis for minimum reflux and an infinite number of plates.*

    a.   q line.
    b.   Pinch zone.

with the 45° line. The situation is illustrated in Fig. 41-12, in which the equilibrium stages are stepped off. It can be seen that for this system the number of stages for a separation between specified values of $\tilde{x}_B$ and $\tilde{x}_D$ is a minimum.

A second limiting reflux condition is minimum reflux. If the overhead-product composition $\tilde{x}_D$ is specified, the location of the top operating line is dependent on the slope $\tilde{O}/\tilde{V}$. For a given vapor rate $\tilde{V}$, any increase in the rate of product withdrawal $\tilde{D}$ means a decrease in the rate of reflux being returned to the column, and hence a decrease in the liquid rate $\tilde{O}$. As $\tilde{O}/\tilde{V}$ decreases, the intersection between the top and bottom operating lines at the q line moves farther from the 45° line in the direction of the equilibrium curve. This is accompanied by an increase in the number of stages necessary to give a fixed product separation $\tilde{x}_B$ and $\tilde{x}_D$. At the point where the intersection of the operating lines touches the equilibrium curve, an infinite number of stages will be required. This is illustrated in Fig. 41-13, in which the zone of zero separation (the pinch zone) occurs on both sides of the feed plate. If a still lower value is chosen for $\tilde{O}/\tilde{V}$, the intersection of the operating lines would occur outside the equilibrium curve and two zones of infinite plates would occur. By definition, however, we shall restrict the term minimum reflux to apply to the maximum reflux rate at which infinite plates occur.

For an azeotropic system the zone of infinite plates does not necessarily occur at the feed plate. This is shown in Fig. 41-14, in which the zone of infinite plates is located by drawing the operating line tangent to the equilibrium curve. The reflux rate which would give this operating line is the minimum reflux rate. For the system shown in Fig. 41-14, the choice

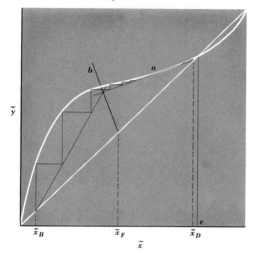

Fig. 41-14. *McCabe-Thiele analysis for minimum reflux and an infinite number of plates for an azeotropic system.*
  a.   **Pinch zone.**
  b.   **q line.**
  c.   **Azeotropic composition.**

of a sufficiently low value for $\tilde{x}_D$ would mean that the zone of infinite plates would occur just at the feed, as it does in nonazeotropic systems.

Partial Condensers.   The overhead product may be produced as a saturated vapor if the vapor from the top plate is only partially condensed. The liquid condensate is returned to the column as reflux.   The reason for this method of operation may be that an excessive column pressure would be required to cause total condensation with cooling water at atmospheric temperature.   Alternatively, total condensation might be achieved with a lower column pressure, but with some form of refrigeration to remove heat from the condenser.   Both these methods of operation are expensive, however, and if the overhead product is to be used as fuel or as a gaseous reactant in some other part of the process, it will usually be taken as a vapor from the overhead condenser.

In some partial condensers the vapor and liquid phases are in equilibrium.   For this case the McCabe-Thiele analysis, shown in Fig. 41-15, is the same as for a total condenser.   The equation for the enriching line is the same as Eq. (41-16); $\tilde{x}_D$ represents the composition of the gaseous product, and $\tilde{D}$ is the rate at which it is produced in pound moles per hour. The enriching line still crosses the 45° line at $\tilde{x} = \tilde{x}_D$, as may be shown by substituting $\tilde{x} = \tilde{x}_n = \tilde{y}_{n+1}$ in Eq. (41-16).   The first step on the McCabe-Thiele diagram represents conditions in the condenser, so that the condenser provides one of the theoretical stages required for the separation.

Other possible methods of condenser operation were discussed in Chap. 27.   A portion of the vapor may be completely condensed, and the remainder unchanged, so that both the gaseous overhead product and the liquid reflux have the same composition, and no separation is achieved in

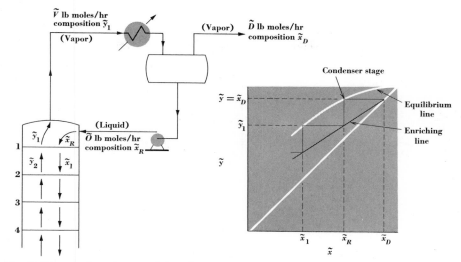

Fig. 41-15. *Analysis for a partial condenser from which the vapor and liquid phases leave in equilibrium.*

the condenser.   Alternatively, a separation equivalent to several theoretical stages may be achieved in condensers with vertical tubes in which the vapor and liquid flow countercurrently to each other.   Such condensers often subcool the liquid.   Subcooled reflux when added to the top plate returns to the saturation temperature and produces an amount of internal reflux, $\tilde{O}$, greater than the amount of external reflux added, $\tilde{O}_R$.

Steam Injection.   It is sometimes convenient to supply heat by injecting steam directly into a distillation apparatus instead of having the steam condense in a closed coil.   When the liquid being distilled is immiscible with water, the technique is known as steam distillation.   The presence of the steam in the vapor phase reduces the partial pressure of the other components at a fixed total pressure and thus lowers the saturation temperature of the liquid to be distilled.   Steam distillation is commonly used to distill organic liquids which might decompose if heated to temperatures high enough to cause them to boil without the presence of the steam.   Gases other than steam may also be used, but steam is usually preferred because of its inertness and availability.

Steam is also injected into binary-distillation systems in which water is the less volatile of two components being separated.   In this case the closed steam coil in the reboiler is replaced by a sparger, from which the steam is injected as small bubbles into the liquid in the reboiler.   Mass transfer occurs between the liquid and the bubbles, and if sufficient contact time is

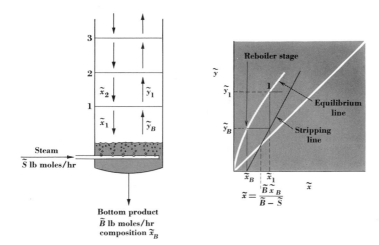

Fig. 41-16.   *McCabe-Thiele analysis for a miscible binary system with open steam.*

available, the bubbles are in equilibrium with the liquid when they leave the reboiler.

The analysis of a system in which open steam is added to the reboiler may be carried out using the customary stripping-line equation [Eq. (41-20)]. This expression is valid because it represents a mass balance for the more volatile component, none of which has been added in the steam. The stripping line no longer crosses the 45° line at $\tilde{x} = \tilde{x}_B$, however. In the analysis which leads to Eq. (41-21), we now substitute $\tilde{B} - \tilde{S}$ for $\tilde{O}' - \tilde{V}'$, so that the intersection with the 45° line occurs at $\tilde{x} = \tilde{B}\tilde{x}_B/(\tilde{B} - \tilde{S})$, in which $\tilde{S}$ is the rate of steam addition in pound moles per hour. A more useful piece of information is the intersection of the stripping line with the $\tilde{x}$ axis. When $\tilde{y}_m$ in Eq. (41-19) is zero, we get

$$\tilde{x}_{m+1} = \frac{\tilde{B}\tilde{x}_B}{\tilde{O}} \tag{41-27}$$

If constant molal overflow exists, $\tilde{S} = \tilde{V}'$, so that $\tilde{B} = \tilde{O}'$ and we see that $\tilde{x}_{m+1} = \tilde{x}_B$. The analysis is illustrated in Fig. 41-16. The counting of steps begins at $\tilde{x}_B$ as usual.

For systems identical in all other respects, the use of open rather than closed steam dilutes the bottom product. In addition, an extra fraction of a stage is required, as may be seen in Fig. 41-16. The advantage of open steam lies in the simpler construction of the heating coil.

In binary systems in which water is the more volatile of the two components, the use of open steam in the reboiler would not be suitable. In such systems the overhead product is the water-rich stream; pure water

Fig. 41-17.   McCabe-Thiele analysis for a system with a side stream.

may be used as reflux to increase the concentration of the more volatile component on the plates at the top of the column.   As in the use of open steam, this causes the useful portion of the operating line (this time the enriching line) to extend below the 45° line.

Side Streams.   Product streams are occasionally taken from sections of the column between the top and bottom; these are known as side streams. The side stream may be either vapor or liquid.   Occasionally a vapor side stream is withdrawn, condensed, and returned to the column as liquid. The purpose is to reduce the vapor velocity in the tower and provide higher plate efficiency.   Side streams may be withdrawn, however, merely because a product of that composition is desired.

The McCabe-Thiele analysis for a column with a liquid side stream is illustrated in Fig. 41-17.   The principal effect of a side stream on the analysis is to alter either the vapor or the liquid rate, so that a third operating line must be introduced to describe passing streams in the column.   The top and bottom operating lines are found in the usual way, and the analysis which gives the q line is unaffected by the side stream.   The operating line for the middle portion of the column is found by writing a material balance around either the top or bottom of the column, including the plate from which the side stream is taken.   In Eq. (41-28) a material balance is written for the more volatile component around the top:

$$\tilde{y}_4 \tilde{V}' = \tilde{x}_3 \tilde{O}' + \tilde{S}\tilde{x}_s + \tilde{D}\tilde{x}_D \tag{41-28}$$

which is solved for $\tilde{y}_4$ to give

$$\tilde{y}_4 = \frac{\tilde{O}'}{\tilde{V}'} \tilde{x}_3 + \frac{\tilde{S}\tilde{x}_s + \tilde{D}\tilde{x}_D}{\tilde{V}'} \tag{41-29}$$

This is the equation for the middle operating line. Like the other operating lines, it has a slope equal to the mole ratio of the liquid and vapor rates. This operating line may be located by the q line which determines the intersection of the operating lines immediately above and below the feed, or it may be fixed by the arbitrary specification of the side-stream composition $\tilde{x}_s$. The point representing the side stream is on both the upper and middle operating lines, because the withdrawal of a side stream changes only the amount of the stream from which it is taken and not its composition. If a step on the McCabe-Thiele diagram does not actually land at the intersection, this indicates that, for the conditions chosen, an impossible side-stream composition has been specified. This is usually remedied by changing the reflux ratio slightly so that the composition on all stages is altered.

Dilute Solutions. For dilute solutions the graphical analysis of McCabe and Thiele may best be carried out on log-log graph paper. The equilibrium curve reduces to a straight line with a slope of 1, because in the dilute range Henry's law usually applies. The operating line, however, is curved and must be plotted by calculating a number of points, using the operating-line equation and locating these on the graph. The steps representing equilibrium stages are marked off with vertical and horizontal lines, just as they would be on rectangular-coordinate graph paper.

The Ponchon-Savarit Method of Analysis

The analysis of binary-distillation systems by the method of Ponchon[1] and Savarit[2] represents a graphical solution of the equations of Sorel. The principal difference from the McCabe-Thiele method is that the liquid and vapor rates in moles per hour are not assumed to be constant for flows between adjacent plates. The only assumption we make in the Ponchon-Savarit method is that there are no heat losses through the walls of the column.

The Ponchon-Savarit solution is usually performed on an enthalpy-composition diagram similar to Fig. 41-18. The units used in this figure are Btu/lb mole and mole fraction. Some writers use diagrams in which the

[1] M. Ponchon, *Tech. moderne*, **13**:20 (1921).
[2] R. Savarit, *Arts et métiers*, pp. 65, 142, 178, 241, 266, 307 (1922).

Fig. 41-18. *Enthalpy-composition diagram for ethanol-water system at 1 atm.; equilibrium diagram (ỹ versus x̄) superimposed.*

units are Btu/lb and mass fraction. The method is valid for any consistent set of units.

The enthalpy-composition diagram represents data at a fixed total pressure. The upper line represents the enthalpy of saturated vapor, and the lower line the enthalpy of saturated liquid. Superimposed on the diagram in Fig. 41-18 is a $\tilde{y}$-$\bar{x}$ diagram as used in a McCabe-Thiele analysis. The $\tilde{y}$ scale is on the right-hand vertical axis, while the $\bar{x}$ scale is the same horizontal composition scale used for values of both $\bar{x}$ and $\tilde{y}$ on the enthalpy-composition diagram. The $\tilde{y}$-$\bar{x}$ diagram is used to locate tie lines on the enthalpy-composition diagram. The technique is illustrated in the examples shown in Fig. 41-19.

Lever-arm Principle. The Ponchon-Savarit method of analysis depends upon the graphical addition and subtraction of properties of streams of fluid by the lever-arm principle. This has already been considered in Chap. 40; it will be reviewed here briefly with reference to some of the special problems encountered in distillation.

In the system shown in Fig. 41-20 a stream of fluid (a binary mixture) expands continuously through a valve into a separator at a pressure such that the fluid forms an equilibrium mixture of vapor and liquid. The rates $\tilde{F}$, $\tilde{D}$, and $\tilde{B}$ lb moles/hr are constant. The separator is insulated,

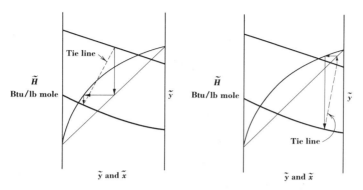

Fig. 41-19.   *Use of $\tilde{y}$ versus $\tilde{x}$ diagram in locating tie lines on an enthalpy-composition diagram.*

so there are no heat leaks.   An over-all mass balance and a mass balance on the more volatile component may be written as follows:

$$\tilde{F} = \tilde{D} + \tilde{B} \tag{41-30}$$

$$\tilde{x}_F \tilde{F} = \tilde{y}_D \tilde{D} + \tilde{x}_B \tilde{B} \tag{41-31}$$

If we substitute for $\tilde{F}$ from Eq. (41-30) in Eq. (41-31) and rearrange, we obtain

$$\frac{\tilde{D}}{\tilde{B}} = \frac{\tilde{x}_F - \tilde{x}_B}{\tilde{y}_D - \tilde{x}_F} \tag{41-32}$$

This equation provides a relation between the rates of $\tilde{D}$ and $\tilde{B}$ and the compositions of the three streams.

We now write an enthalpy balance for the separator.

$$\tilde{H}_F \tilde{F} = \tilde{H}_D \tilde{D} + \tilde{H}_B \tilde{B} \tag{41-33}$$

If we substitute for $\tilde{F}$ from Eq. (41-30) in Eq. (41-33) and rearrange, we get

$$\frac{\tilde{D}}{\tilde{B}} = \frac{\tilde{H}_F - \tilde{H}_B}{\tilde{H}_D - \tilde{H}_F} \tag{41-34}$$

We combine Eqs. (41-32) and (41-34) to obtain a relation between rates, compositions, and enthalpies.

$$\frac{\tilde{D}}{\tilde{B}} = \frac{\tilde{x}_F - \tilde{x}_B}{\tilde{y}_D - \tilde{x}_F} = \frac{\tilde{H}_F - \tilde{H}_B}{\tilde{H}_D - \tilde{H}_F} \tag{41-35}$$

The proportionality between enthalpies and compositions expressed in this equation can also be rearranged to give

$$\frac{\tilde{y}_D - \tilde{x}_F}{\tilde{H}_D - \tilde{H}_F} = \frac{\tilde{x}_F - \tilde{x}_B}{\tilde{H}_F - \tilde{H}_B}$$

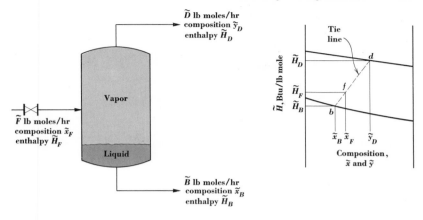

Fig. 41-20. *Example showing use of lever-arm principle.*

which indicates that points on the enthalpy-composition diagram representing streams B, F, and D must be on a straight line. Streams B and D are in equilibrium and must be represented at the ends of a tie line, so stream F must be on the tie line.

If we know the composition and enthalpy of the feed, $\tilde{x}_F$ and $\tilde{H}_F$, the point on the enthalpy-composition diagram which represents the feed can be located immediately (point f on Fig. 41-20). Since only one tie line passes through this point, it is located by trial and error and fixes the locations of points d and b at the ends of the tie line.

The rates $\tilde{D}$ and $\tilde{B}$ are fixed by the ratios of composition differences and enthalpy differences as expressed in Eq. (41-35). If $\overline{bd}$ is considered to be the hypotenuse of a right triangle, it is seen by using the properties of similar triangles that the proportionalities expressed in Eq. (41-35) can be extended to include the ratio

$$\frac{\tilde{D}}{\tilde{B}} = \frac{\overline{bf}}{\overline{fd}} \tag{41-36}$$

The foregoing derivation of the lever-arm principle is similar to the development given in Chap. 40. The three mass balances, Eqs. (40-1) to (40-3), were written for the total streams, for component A, and for component B. For the enthalpy-composition diagram the three balances are written for the over-all streams, for component A, and for the enthalpies of the streams.

If we had substituted for $\tilde{D}$ from Eq. (41-30) in Eqs. (41-31) and (41-33), we should have obtained

$$\frac{\tilde{B}}{\tilde{F}} = \frac{\tilde{x}_D - \tilde{x}_F}{\tilde{y}_D - \tilde{x}_B} = \frac{\tilde{H}_D - \tilde{H}_F}{\tilde{H}_D - \tilde{H}_B} \tag{41-37}$$

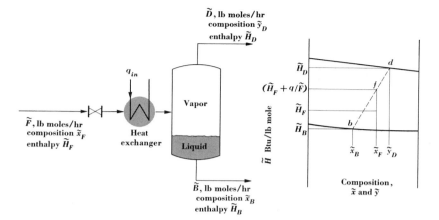

Fig. 41-21.   Example showing use of lever-arm principle for streams of mass and enthalpy.

Thus we see that the mass rates $\tilde{B}$ and $\tilde{F}$ can be expressed by the proportionality

$$\frac{\tilde{B}}{\tilde{F}} = \frac{\overline{fd}}{\overline{bd}} \tag{41-38}$$

By a similar procedure we can derive the expression

$$\frac{\tilde{D}}{\tilde{F}} = \frac{\overline{fb}}{\overline{bd}} \tag{41-39}$$

In addition to relating graphically streams containing both mass and enthalpy, we can include the effect of a stream of enthalpy, i.e., a heat input. In Fig. 41-21 we have a system in which heat is added to the feed stream at the rate q Btu/hr. Otherwise it is similar to the system shown in Fig. 41-20.

The over-all material balance and the balance on the more volatile component are represented by Eqs. (41-30) and (41-31) of the previous discussion. The enthalpy balance, however, has become

$$\tilde{H}_F \tilde{F} + q = \tilde{H}_D \tilde{D} + \tilde{H}_B \tilde{B} \tag{41-40}$$

A stream of enthalpy cannot be represented on an enthalpy-composition diagram by itself, but must be associated with a stream of mass. Therefore we write Eq. (41-40) as

$$\left(\tilde{H}_F + \frac{q}{\tilde{F}}\right)\tilde{F} = \tilde{H}_D \tilde{D} + \tilde{H}_B \tilde{B} \tag{41-41}$$

If we now substitute for $\tilde{F}$, as was done to obtain Eq. (41-35), we get

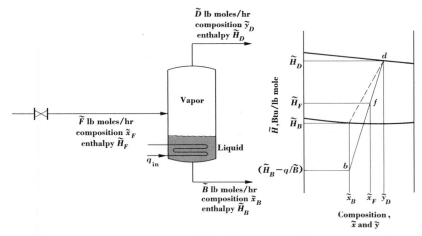

Fig. 41-22. *Example showing subtraction of enthalpy from a stream of mass.*

$$\frac{\tilde{D}}{\tilde{B}} = \frac{\tilde{x}_F - \tilde{x}_B}{\tilde{y}_D - \tilde{x}_F} = \frac{(\tilde{H}_F + q/\tilde{F}) - \tilde{H}_B}{\tilde{H}_D - (\tilde{H}_F + q/\tilde{F})} \tag{41-42}$$

This result is similar to Eq. (41-35) except for the enthalpy of the feed. If the point f is located at composition $\tilde{x}_F$ and enthalpy $\tilde{H}_F + q/\tilde{F}$, the analogy is exact, and we see that for the line $\overline{bfd}$ in Fig. 41-21 we can write

$$\frac{\tilde{D}}{\tilde{B}} = \frac{\overline{bf}}{\overline{fd}} \qquad \frac{\tilde{B}}{\tilde{F}} = \frac{\overline{fd}}{\overline{bd}} \qquad \frac{\tilde{D}}{\tilde{F}} = \frac{\overline{fb}}{\overline{bd}} \tag{41-43}$$

just as we did with the corresponding line in Fig. 41-20.

To complete the picture we recognize that the enthalpy of the fluid leaving the heat exchanger is actually $\tilde{H}_F + q/\tilde{F}$. If the properties of the feed stream had been considered at this point rather than before the exchanger, the entire analysis would have been identical with that in Fig. 41-20.

As an alternative to the addition of enthalpy to the feed stream in Fig. 41-21, we shall consider the subtraction of enthalpy from one of the product streams, say the bottom product. This is done for the system shown in Fig. 41-22. We write an over-all enthalpy balance just as we did in Eq. (41-41), except that we arbitrarily place q on the right-hand side of the equation.

$$\tilde{H}_F \tilde{F} = \tilde{H}_D \tilde{D} + \left(\tilde{H}_B - \frac{q}{\tilde{B}}\right)\tilde{B} \tag{41-44}$$

If we substitute for $\tilde{F}$ from the material and component balances, we get

$$\frac{\tilde{D}}{\tilde{B}} = \frac{\tilde{x}_F - \tilde{x}_B}{\tilde{y}_D - \tilde{x}_F} = \frac{\tilde{H}_F - (\tilde{H}_B - q/\tilde{B})}{\tilde{H}_D - \tilde{H}_F} \tag{41-45}$$

Thus, if we locate point b at composition $\tilde{x}_B$ and enthalpy $\tilde{H}_B - q/\tilde{B}$, we have a proportionality much as before, and the lever-arm principle [as represented in Eqs. (41-43)] applies as usual.

The reasoning associated with Fig. 41-22 is somewhat more abstract than that for Fig. 41-21. In the former problem the addition of enthalpy occurred and produced a stream (the fluid leaving the heat exchanger) which actually had an enthalpy equal to $\tilde{H}_F + q/\tilde{F}$. In the latter case, however, the stream with enthalpy $\tilde{H}_B - q/\tilde{B}$ is purely imaginary. No such stream exists in the system. The concept is, nevertheless, of great value, as will be shown in our subsequent analysis.

The enthalpy stream q could just as well have been subtracted from the overhead-product stream $\tilde{D}$ as from $\tilde{B}$. In fact, the point $(\tilde{y}_D, \tilde{H}_D - q/\tilde{D})$ can be found quite readily on Fig. 41-22 by drawing a straight line from $(\tilde{x}_B, \tilde{H}_B)$ through $(\tilde{x}_F, \tilde{H}_F)$ to a vertical line through $\tilde{y}_D$. This line would represent the material and enthalpy balances just as completely as the line $\overline{dfb}$ shown.

Analysis of Distillation Columns. The use of the lever-arm principle in the analysis of a section of a distillation column is shown in Fig. 41-23. The bubble-cap plates are assumed to be equilibrium stages, and we shall assume that we know the amounts, compositions, and enthalpies of streams O_3 and V_4. The points representing these streams are shown in the enthalpy-composition diagrams in Fig. 41-23.

The composition of stream O_4 is found from vapor-liquid equilibrium data and plotted at the opposite end of the tie line from V_4, with which it is in equilibrium. This is shown in Fig. 41-23a. To find the point representing V_5, we write a material balance around plate 4,

$$\tilde{O}_3 + \tilde{V}_5 = \tilde{O}_4 + \tilde{V}_4 \tag{41-46}$$

and rearrange this to provide an equation expressing the difference between passing streams,

$$\tilde{V}_4 - \tilde{O}_3 = \tilde{V}_5 - \tilde{O}_4 \tag{41-47}$$

If $\tilde{V}_4 - O_3$ is treated as a single hypothetical stream of mole rate $\tilde{\Delta}$, we can write

$$\tilde{V}_4 - \tilde{O}_3 = \tilde{\Delta} = \tilde{V}_5 - \tilde{O}_4 \tag{41-48}$$

The point representing stream Δ on the diagram can be found readily since we know the amounts of V_4 and O_3. If $\tilde{V}_4 > \tilde{O}_3$, a straight line is drawn from point O_3 through V_4 and extrapolated a distance such that the following ratio applies. This extrapolation is shown in Fig. 41-23b.

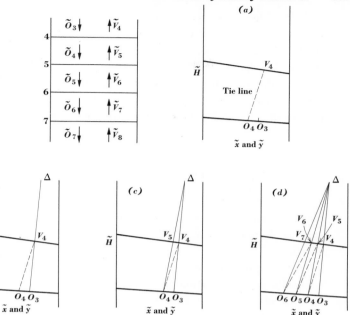

Fig. 41-23.   *Use of an enthalpy-composition diagram for finding passing streams in a distillation column.*

$$\frac{\tilde{V}_4}{\tilde{O}_3} = \frac{\overline{\Delta O_3}}{\overline{\Delta V_4}} \tag{41-49}$$

This basis of this step is perhaps more apparent if we write the first equality of Eq. (41-48) as

$$\tilde{V}_4 = \tilde{O}_3 + \tilde{\Delta} \tag{41-50}$$

and apply the lever-arm rule to streams O_3 and Δ.   From this equation it is seen that the following additional proportionalities between mole rates and the lengths of line segments on Fig. 41-23 apply.

$$\frac{\tilde{V}_4}{\tilde{\Delta}} = \frac{\overline{\Delta O_3}}{\overline{V_4 O_3}} \qquad \frac{\tilde{\Delta}}{\tilde{O}_3} = \frac{\overline{V_4 O_3}}{\overline{\Delta V_4}} \tag{41-51}$$

Either of these equations would be easier to use in finding the point Δ than Eq. (41-49), because each contains only one segment of unknown length. The rate $\tilde{\Delta}$ is, of course, simply an arithmetic difference as defined in Eq. (41-48).

Having found the point Δ, the rest of the analysis follows directly.   A relation between $\tilde{O}_4$, $\tilde{V}_5$, and $\tilde{\Delta}$ is given in Eq. (41-48).   We have already found the point O_4, and Eq. (41-48) tells us that

$$\tilde{V}_5 = \tilde{O}_4 + \tilde{\Delta} \tag{41-52}$$

Thus we know that point V_5 lies on a straight line joining points O_4 and Δ. In addition, V_5 is a saturated vapor, so we find point V_5 at the intersection of the saturated-vapor line and the line joining Δ to O_4.   This is illustrated in Fig. 41-23c.

To find the points representing the rest of the streams we repeat the above procedures.   For example, O_5 is found on a tie line at the opposite end from V_5.   Point V_6 is found by writing a material balance around plate 5,

$$\tilde{O}_4 + \tilde{V}_6 = \tilde{O}_5 + \tilde{V}_5 \qquad\qquad (41\text{-}53)$$

which may be rearranged to give

$$\tilde{V}_5 - \tilde{O}_4 = \tilde{V}_6 - \tilde{O}_5 = \tilde{\Delta} \qquad\qquad (41\text{-}54)$$

Since we know points O_5 and Δ, we locate V_6 at the intersection of the saturated-vapor line with the line joining O_5 and Δ.   This is shown in Fig. 41-23d.

The procedure we have followed is the graphical equivalent of a series of equilibrium calculations alternating with material and enthalpy balances. The use of a tie line is similar to an equilibrium calculation, and the use of the Δ point in finding a vapor stream is equivalent to writing equations for material and enthalpy balances around a plate and solving for the properties of the one unknown stream.   The value of $\tilde{\Delta}$ between all plates is identical if there is no heat loss, no feed stream added, and no side stream taken off; it is a difference which can be considered as a hypothetical stream.   This hypothetical stream has a finite rate ($\tilde{V} - \tilde{O}$ for the case shown), a finite composition, and a finite enthalpy.   If $\tilde{O}$ had been greater than $\tilde{V}$, the point Δ would have been below the saturated-liquid line and, in fact, could have a large negative enthalpy.   In some systems, such as columns with two feed streams, the point Δ can lie outside the composition range of 0 to 1.   The only place it does not appear is between the saturated-vapor and saturated-liquid lines.   In this region it would represent the addition of a vapor and a liquid stream rather than the difference between them.

Rectifying Columns.   The general principles of operation of rectifying columns have already been discussed in the section on the McCabe-Thiele method of analysis.   We shall show here the analysis according to the Ponchon-Savarit method.

The operation of a typical rectifying column is shown in Fig. 41-4. For the present discussion we shall assume that we know the compositions and enthalpies of streams F, B, and D.   Each plate will be assumed to be an equilibrium stage, but constant molal overflow will not be assumed. As the first step, an enthalpy balance is written for the entire column.

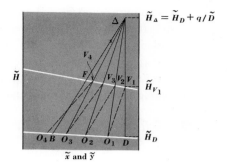

Fig. 41-24. *Ponchon-Savarit analysis of a rectifying column.*

$$\tilde{F}\tilde{H}_F = \tilde{B}\tilde{H}_B + \tilde{D}\tilde{H}_D + q \tag{41-55}$$

As seen earlier, q cannot be represented on an enthalpy-concentration diagram unless it is expressed in terms of its effect on a stream of mass. Therefore we rewrite Eq. (41-55) as

$$\tilde{F}\tilde{H}_F = \tilde{B}\tilde{H}_B + \tilde{D}\left(\tilde{H}_D + \frac{q}{\tilde{D}}\right) \tag{41-56}$$

In this equation we have simply an addition of three streams, two with their actual enthalpies and the third, D, with a hypothetical enthalpy $\tilde{H}_D + q/\tilde{D}$. If the points F, B, and D are given (as on Fig. 41-24), a line through F and B extrapolated to a composition $\tilde{x}_D$ (a vertical line through D) terminates at the point $(\tilde{x}_D, \tilde{H}_D + q/\tilde{D})$. This point, as we shall see presently, also represents a difference between passing streams, so it will be designated Δ on Fig. 41-24. From Eq. (41-56) we see that the rate $\tilde{\Delta}$ equals the rate $\tilde{D}$. The stream of overhead vapor V_1 has the same composition as the product stream D but lies on the saturated-vapor line. The reflux stream O_R is identical in all properties with the product stream D but differs in amount.

The liquid overflow from the first plate O_1 is in equilibrium with V_1, so O_1 lies on a tie line at the opposite end from V_1. To find V_2 we write a balance on a volume which encloses the condenser and the top plate. In terms of enthalpy we get

$$\tilde{V}_2\tilde{H}_2 = \tilde{O}_1\tilde{H}_1 + \tilde{D}\tilde{H}_D + q \tag{41-57}$$

which may also be written

$$\tilde{V}_2\tilde{H}_2 - \tilde{O}_1\tilde{H}_1 = \tilde{D}\left(\tilde{H}_D + \frac{q}{\tilde{D}}\right) \tag{41-58}$$

We recognize the right-hand side of Eq. (41-58) as designating the stream represented by the point Δ on Fig. 41-24. We have previously found the location of O_1, so the point representing stream V_2 can be found on a line joining points Δ and O_1. We also know that stream V_2 is a saturated vapor, so that it must lie at the intersection of the saturated-vapor locus with the line joining Δ to O_1.

The analysis continues with the location of O_2 on a tie line opposite V_2. The vapor stream V_3 which is passing O_2 is found by an enthalpy balance including the condenser and the first two plates.

$$\tilde{V}_3 \tilde{H}_3 - \tilde{O}_2 \tilde{H}_2 = \tilde{D}\left(\tilde{H}_D + \frac{q}{\tilde{D}}\right) \tag{41-59}$$

We join the point O_2 and the point Δ [which represents the right-hand side of Eq. (41-59)] and get V_3 at the intersection with the saturated-vapor line.

Further steps are similar to those indicated above. Liquid compositions are found by drawing tie lines from the vapor points, whereas vapor points are found using Δ, which represents the difference between passing streams in both amount and enthalpy. When a tie line hits point B (or passes it on the left), then the correct number of steps will have been taken. Each tie line represents an equilibrium stage. As in the McCabe-Thiele analysis, it is seldom that a whole number of stages will give the specified bottom-product composition.

The reflux ratio $\tilde{O}_R/\tilde{D}$ is equal to the ratio of the segments $\overline{\Delta V_1}/\overline{V_1 D}$ on Fig. 41-24. This may be proved as follows: The line segment $\overline{\Delta D}$ represents an enthalpy difference $\tilde{H}_\Delta - \tilde{H}_D$, which is equal to $q/\tilde{D}$. The line segment $\overline{V_1 D}$ represents an enthalpy difference $\tilde{H}_{V1} - \tilde{H}_D$ equal to $q/\tilde{V}_1$. If we take the difference between these quantities, we see that the segment $\overline{\Delta V_1}$ must be represented by the difference in enthalpies $\tilde{H}_\Delta - \tilde{H}_{V1}$ or $q(1/\tilde{D} - 1/\tilde{V}_1)$. We then write the following proportionality:

$$\frac{\overline{\Delta V_1}}{\overline{V_1 D}} = \frac{q(1/\tilde{D} - 1/\tilde{V}_1)}{q/\tilde{V}_1}$$

$$= \frac{\tilde{V}_1}{\tilde{D}} - 1$$

$$= \frac{\tilde{O}_R}{\tilde{D}} \tag{41-60}$$

At total reflux, $\tilde{D}$ is zero, so the ratio $\overline{\Delta V_1}/\overline{V_1 D}$ is infinite. To represent this, the point Δ must be an infinite distance above the diagram. Thus vertical lines are drawn from the liquid locus when the Δ point is used for finding the passing vapor streams at total reflux.

Minimum reflux occurs when the tie lines and the difference lines (those

Fig. 41-25.   *Ponchon-Savarit analysis of a stripping column.*

drawn to Δ) coincide at any stage.   Starting from V_1, the difference lines decrease in slope as we move to the left on the diagram.   The difference line with the lowest slope would be one passing from B through F.   If Δ is sufficiently low, the line from B through F to Δ will coincide with a tie line. This condition indicates that even if an infinite number of steps were taken, at this point the composition on succeeding plates would not change. Thus we have the zone of infinite plates at the feed point, which we discussed earlier in the section on the McCabe-Thiele analysis.   The value of $\overline{\Delta V_1/V_1 D}$ when this occurs is the minimum reflux ratio and is analogous to the situation shown for a complete column in Fig. 41-13.

If the equilibrium behavior of the mixture is such that an inflection point occurs in the $\tilde{y}$-$\tilde{x}$ diagram (as in Fig. 41-14), the minimum reflux ratio is found by the procedure of extrapolating a number of tie lines to the vertical line from D and V_1.   The highest intersection of tie lines (considering only those to the right of F) locates the Δ point which corresponds to the minimum reflux ratio.

Stripping Columns.   The operation of a stripping column is shown in Fig. 41-6, and the Ponchon-Savarit analysis in Fig. 41-25.   We shall assume that we know the compositions and enthalpies of streams F, D, and B.   First, an enthalpy balance around the entire column is written.

$$\tilde{F}\tilde{H}_F + q = \tilde{D}\tilde{H}_D + \tilde{B}\tilde{H}_B \tag{41-61}$$

The heat q which enters the system from the steam coils in the reboiler is combined mathematically with the bottom product, and Eq. (41-61) is written as

$$\tilde{F}\tilde{H}_F = \tilde{D}\tilde{H}_D + \tilde{B}\left(\tilde{H}_B - \frac{q}{\tilde{B}}\right) \qquad (41\text{-}62)$$

By the usual method of adding streams graphically, we see that the point $(\tilde{x}_F, \tilde{H}_F)$ must lie on a line joining point $(\tilde{y}_D, \tilde{H}_D)$ to point $(\tilde{x}_B, \tilde{H}_B - q/\tilde{B})$. Thus we find this latter point on Fig. 41-25 by the intersection of a vertical line through B with the extrapolation of the straight line through D and F.

The point $(\tilde{x}_B, \tilde{H}_B - q/\tilde{B})$ is designated as Δ because it represents a difference between passing streams, just as the Δ point did in Fig. 41-24 for a rectifying column. From the considerations which led to its location, we see that the Δ point represents the material and enthalpy difference between streams F and D. By writing an over-all balance for any section of the stripping column (as shown by the dashed line in Fig. 41-6), we see also that the Δ point represents the material and enthalpy difference between any pair of passing streams. This difference is equal in amount to the amount of bottom product withdrawn per unit of time, and the difference in enthalpy is equal to $\tilde{B}\tilde{H}_B - q$. Hence, if we know the location of Δ and also the point on the enthalpy-concentration diagram representing any vapor or liquid stream in the column, we can find the point representing the passing stream at that section.

The procedure for locating the streams in the stripping column is shown on Fig. 41-25. First we find the point representing the vapor V_B from the reboiler on a tie line with B. The point representing O_1' is found by joining V_B to Δ. The vapor stream V_1' is found on a tie line from O_1', and the liquid O_2' on a line joining V_1' with Δ. The construction proceeds in this fashion until a tie line reaches or passes to the right of point D. Each tie line represents an equilibrium stage.

Complete Fractionating Columns. The Ponchon-Savarit analysis of a complete fractionating column is illustrated in Fig. 41-26. The column shown in Fig. 41-2 is the column we analyze here.

From the McCabe-Thiele analysis it will be recalled that for a complete fractionating column there are two operating-line equations. In the Ponchon-Savarit analysis these relations are expressed as Δ points. One Δ point will describe the difference between passing streams in the column above the feed plate, and the other below the feed plate. The analysis is first directed to finding these two Δ points. The information specified will be the composition and enthalpy of the feed, overhead distillate and bottom product, and the reflux ratio. Thus we can fix the points F, B, D, and Δ_1 on Fig. 41-26. The location of Δ_2 is found at the intersection of a vertical line through B with a line extrapolated from Δ_1 through F. The basis for this procedure may be shown by writing an enthalpy balance for the entire column.

Fig. 41-26. *Ponchon-Savarit analysis of a complete fractionating column.*

$$\tilde{F}\tilde{H}_F + q_{\text{reb}} = \tilde{B}\tilde{H}_B + \tilde{D}\tilde{H}_D + q_{\text{cond}} \tag{41-63}$$

This is rearranged in the following form:

$$\tilde{F}\tilde{H}_F = \tilde{B}\left(\tilde{H}_B - \frac{q_{\text{reb}}}{\tilde{B}}\right) + \tilde{D}\left(\tilde{H}_D + \frac{q_{\text{cond}}}{\tilde{D}}\right) \tag{41-64}$$

The two terms on the right-hand side of Eq. (41-64) represent Δ_2 and Δ_1, respectively, and because of the additive relation between F, Δ_2, and Δ_1 shown in the equation, the three points are on the same straight line.

The equilibrium stages may be constructed starting from either B or V_1. The first step is to construct a tie line; this represents an equilibrium calculation. A line is then drawn to the appropriate Δ point to determine the point representing the passing stream; this represents a material and enthalpy balance. Successive tie lines and difference lines are constructed until the desired range of composition is covered. The choice of which difference point to use is usually based on the desire to achieve a maximum separation with each stage. With this criterion, point Δ_1 is used for all difference lines constructed to the right of $\overline{\Delta_1 F \Delta_2}$, and Δ_2 is used for all difference lines to the left of $\overline{\Delta_1 F \Delta_2}$. If the criterion of maximum separation is not used, then either Δ point can be used within certain limits. The significance of switching from one Δ point to the other is that this step indicates the feed-plate location. Since each tie line is an equilibrium stage, the tie line which touches difference lines going to separate Δ points

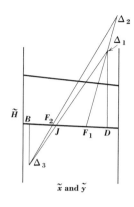

Fig. 41-27. *Ponchon-Savarit analysis of a column with two feeds.*

is the tie line representing the feed plate. The situation illustrated in Fig. 41-26 is one in which the optimum feed-plate location is used. If Δ_1 is used for the first difference line to the left of $\overline{\Delta_1 F \Delta_2}$, a smaller separation would be achieved than by using Δ_2. Similarly, if Δ_2 were used for difference lines to the right of $\overline{\Delta_1 F \Delta_2}$, a poorer separation would result than that shown.

Other Systems. A number of special situations exist which illustrate the versatility of the Ponchon-Savarit method. A column with two feeds is analyzed in Fig. 41-27. As usual, the Δ points are located first. It is assumed that B, F_1, F_2, and D are defined and can be located immediately and that the reflux ratio is known. This enables us to find Δ_1. There will be three Δ points for the column (just as there would be three operating lines in a McCabe-Thiele analysis), and we first find the Δ point for the portion of the column beneath the lower feed stream F_2. This point we call Δ_3. The procedure is to add streams F_1 and F_2 graphically by joining them with a straight line and locating the addition point J on the basis of the lever-arm principle.

$$\frac{\tilde{F}_1}{\tilde{F}_2} = \frac{\overline{JF_2}}{\overline{JF_1}} \tag{41-65}$$

The over-all enthalpy and material balances are the same for a system with separate feeds F_1 and F_2 as for a system in which F_1 and F_2 are physically combined as stream J before being added to the column. The point Δ_3 is found by drawing a line from Δ_1 through J and extrapolating this to the intersection of a vertical line through B.

We next find Δ_2, which represents the difference between passing streams in that section of the column between the injection points for F_1 and F_2.

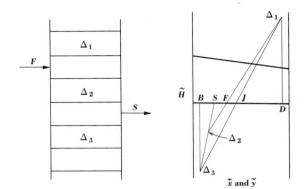

Fig. 41-28.   *Ponchon-Savarit
analysis of a column with a side
stream.*

We do this by recognizing that material and enthalpy balances can be
written for streams F_2, Δ_2, and Δ_3.   Thus these three points must be on a
single straight line.   Likewise, a material and enthalpy balance can be
written containing only terms for streams F_1, Δ_1, and Δ_2, so that these
three points must also be on a single straight line.   Thus we find Δ_2 at the
intersection of one line from Δ_3 through F_2 with another line from F_1 through
Δ_1.   The equilibrium stages are marked off in the customary fashion by
alternately drawing tie lines and difference lines.   The criterion for each
feed-plate location is usually that the difference lines be drawn to the Δ
point which will give the maximum separation for that step.

Side streams can be treated in a similar fashion.   The procedure is
illustrated in Fig. 41-28.   The feed stream and the side stream are subtracted because they flow in opposite directions relative to the column.
The subtraction is done graphically using the lever-arm rule

$$\frac{\tilde{F}}{\tilde{S}} = \frac{\overline{JS}}{\overline{JF}} \tag{41-66}$$

or more conveniently as

$$\frac{\tilde{F} - \tilde{S}}{\tilde{S}} = \frac{\tilde{J}}{\tilde{S}} = \frac{\overline{SF}}{\overline{JF}} \tag{41-67}$$

Stream J, which is the equivalent of the feed stream minus the side stream,
is used in the same manner as the combined feeds in a two-feed column.
A line is drawn from Δ_1 through J to the intersection of a vertical line
through B.   This locates the Δ point for the lowest portion of the column,
Δ_3.   The intermediate Δ point, Δ_2, is found at the intersection of a line
through Δ_3 and S with another line through Δ_1 and F.   The location of
the equilibrium stages is done by methods similar to those already shown.

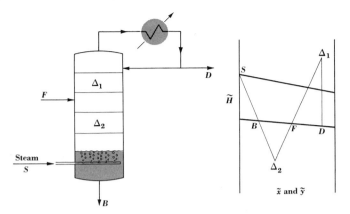

Fig. 41-29.   Ponchon-Savarit analysis of a column with open stream.

In this case, however, a tie line must pass through S, and different Δ points *must* be used on either side of this tie line.

The injection of saturated steam into the reboiler is illustrated in Fig. 41-29.   The only unusual thing about this system is that the lower Δ point represents the difference between the bottom product withdrawn and the steam added, as can be shown by writing the appropriate material and enthalpy balances.   Consequently, Δ_2 lies on a line through S and B. As usual, it also lies on a line from Δ_1 through F, so that the intersection determines Δ_2.   Equilibrium stages are marked off in the usual fashion.

One other system of interest is the partial condenser.   This is shown in Fig. 41-30, which is self-explanatory.   The reflux ratio $\tilde{O}_R/\tilde{D}$ is the ratio of lengths $\overline{\Delta_1 V_1}/\overline{V_1 O_R}$.

Comparison of Ponchon-Savarit and McCabe-Thiele Methods of Analysis. The Ponchon-Savarit method, as we have said, is more rigorous than the McCabe-Thiele method.   However, in many systems the difference is not great.   It can be seen from an enthalpy-composition diagram that when the saturated vapor and liquid loci are parallel, straight lines, the ratio of liquid to vapor rates represented by the following equation will be constant.

$$\frac{\tilde{O}}{\tilde{V}} = \frac{\overline{\Delta_1 V}}{\overline{\Delta_1 O}} \tag{41-68}$$

If the ratio $\tilde{O}/\tilde{V}$ is constant, then the operating-line equations for the McCabe-Thiele analysis will be straight lines, and the two methods of analysis will give identical results.   The extent of deviation of the vapor and liquid loci from being straight, parallel lines is therefore a measure of

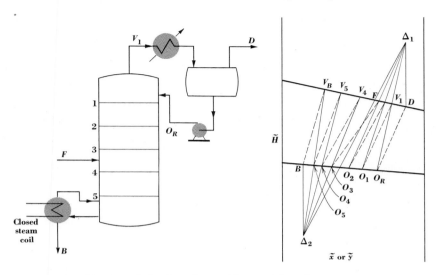

Fig. 41-30.   Ponchon-Savarit analysis of a column with a partial condenser.

the inaccuracy of the McCabe-Thiele method.   It is important to note that the loci must be straight and parallel on a plot of enthalpy per unit mole versus mole fraction.   Ponchon-Savarit analyses are frequently made (with perfect rigor) on diagrams of enthalpy per unit mass versus mass fraction.   The deviation of the vapor and liquid loci from being straight, parallel lines is usually much greater on this type of diagram than on a diagram using mole units.   This kind of diagram, however, does not give any direct indication of the accuracy of the McCabe-Thiele analysis for the system represented.

One criticism often made of the usefulness of the Ponchon-Savarit method is that enthalpy-composition data are available for only a very few systems.   The enthalpy-composition diagram can be constructed approximately, however, if data on the latent heats of vaporization of the pure substances are available.   The procedure is simply to join the points representing enthalpies of the pure substances with straight lines.   This will usually be quite accurate for the gas phase but less accurate for the liquid phase.   Nevertheless, the use of an enthalpy-composition diagram constructed in this way will generally give more accurate results than the McCabe-Thiele analysis.

Example 41-4

A fractionating column operating at 1 atm pressure is supplied at the optimum location with a saturated-liquid feed containing 40 mole per cent ethanol and 60 mole per

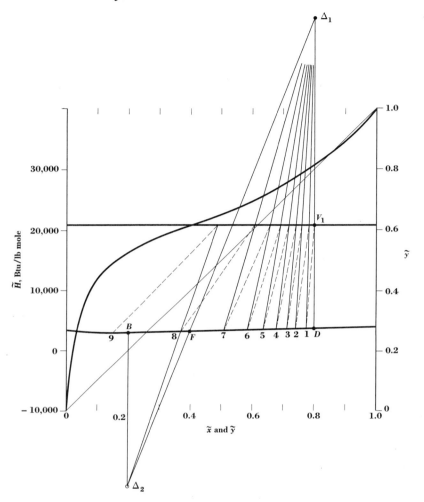

Fig. 41-31.   Ponchon-Savarit analysis of the problem in Example 41-4.

cent water.   The column produces a saturated-liquid overhead product containing 80
mole per cent ethanol and a saturated-liquid bottom product containing 20 per cent
cent ethanol.   The reflux ratio is 2.0.   Find:
  (a) The number of theoretical stages required to give the separation
  (b) The optimum feed-plate location assuming 100 per cent plate efficiency
  (c) The heat load in the reboiler in Btu/lb mole of bottom product
  (d) The heat load in the condenser in Btu/lb mole of overhead product
  The solution is illustrated in Fig. 41-31.   Points F, D, and B can be plotted immediately.   The upper difference point Δ_1 is plotted using Eq. (41-60).   The lower difference point Δ_2 is found at the intersection of a line extrapolated from Δ_1 through F
with a vertical line through B.   The equilibrium stages are marked off starting at V_1
and ending with the ninth stage, which would give a liquid composition leaner than

that specified for B.   Thus the number of stages required for the specified separation is 8.8.   The feed plate is the eighth plate because the tie line representing this plate crosses the $\Delta_1 F \Delta_2$ line.   It can be seen that a line extrapolated from Δ_2 through the lower end of this tie line gives a leaner vapor composition than is obtained with a line joining the bottom of the tie line with Δ_1.   Since the feed is a saturated liquid, it is added to the liquid flowing onto the eighth plate.

The heat load in the reboiler is represented by the vertical distance between B and Δ_2, since the bottom product and the hypothetical stream Δ_2 differ only by the heat added to the reboiler.   This heat load is 25,500 Btu/lb mole of B.

The heat load in the condenser is represented by the vertical distance between Δ_1 and D, since Δ_1 can be regarded as the equivalent of stream D plus the heat removed in the condenser.   This heat load can be seen on the diagram to be 51,300 Btu/lb mole of D.

PROBLEMS

41-1. A rectifying column operating at 1 atm is supplied with a saturated-vapor feed containing 40 mole per cent ethanol and 60 mole per cent water.   The bottom product and the overhead product are saturated liquids containing 15 mole per cent and 76 mole per cent ethanol, respectively.   Assuming constant-molal-flow rates in the column, find the internal reflux ratio $\tilde{O}/\tilde{V}$ and the external reflux ratio $\tilde{O}_R/\tilde{D}$.   In addition, find the number of equilibrium stages required to give the specified separation.

41-2. A fractionating column operating at 1 atm pressure is supplied with 100 lb moles/hr of a feed stream which is 25 mole per cent saturated vapor and 75 mole per cent saturated liquid.   This feed has an over-all composition of 40 mole per cent ethanol and 60 mole per cent water and is added at the optimum location.   The overhead product leaves the condenser as a saturated liquid containing 80 mole per cent ethanol. The bottom product is also a saturated liquid and contains 5 mole per cent ethanol. The column operates with constant molal overflow and at a reflux ratio $\tilde{O}_R/\tilde{D}$ equal to $1.5(\tilde{O}_R/\tilde{D})_{\min}$.   Find:

(*a*) The minimum reflux ratio

(*b*) The vapor and liquid rates both above and below the feed plate at the specified operating reflux ratio

(*c*) The heat loads on the reboiler and condenser in Btu/hr

(*d*) The number of equilibrium stages required to perform the separation

(*e*) The minimum number of equilibrium stages required to perform the separation

41-3. A feedstock containing 32.1 mole per cent *n*-butane and 67.9 mole per cent *n*-pentane is supplied as a saturated liquid at the optimum location of a fractionating column operating at 50 psia.   The feed rate is 100 lb moles/hr, and a distillate product containing 88.5 mole per cent *n*-butane is removed at the rate of 30 lb moles/hr.   The condenser at the top of the column removes 1 million Btu/hr of heat and produces saturated-liquid product and reflux streams.   Assuming constant molal overflow, determine:

(*a*) The reflux ratio

(*b*) The vapor and liquid rates in lb moles/hr both above and below the feed plate

(*c*) The number of theoretical stages required to produce the separation

(*d*) The composition of the bottom product

The following equilibrium data are available, expressed as mole fraction of *n*-butane:

$\tilde{x}$	1	0.725	0.568	0.439	0.321	0.207	0.108	0
$\tilde{y}$	1	0.885	0.785	0.681	0.553	0.397	0.232	0

The latent heat of vaporization of the feed may be taken as 8500 Btu/lb mole.

41-4. A rectifying column containing 16 actual plates (over-all efficiency 50 per cent) is fed a saturated vapor containing 38 mole per cent A and 62 mole per cent B. The saturated-liquid distillate produced from the column contains 80 mole per cent A, and the bottom product contains 30 mole per cent A. A liquid side stream is also taken off the column. If the external reflux ratio $\tilde{O}_R/\tilde{D}$ is 10.9 and the column is achieving a maximum separation under the conditions, find:

(a) The composition of the side stream
(b) The internal reflux ratio above the side-stream plate
(c) The internal reflux ratio beneath the side-stream plate
(d) The actual plate from which the side stream is taken

The equilibrium relationship between vapor and liquid mixtures of A and B may be satisfactorily represented by a relative volatility of 1.50. Assume constant molal overflow.

41-5. A stream of 1000 lb moles/hr of saturated liquid containing 30 mole per cent methanol in water is fed at the optimum location of a distillation column. The column operates with constant molal overflow at a reflux ratio $\tilde{O}_R/\tilde{D}$, which is twice the theoretical minimum reflux ratio. A saturated-liquid distillate which contains 90 mole per cent methanol is produced from the overhead condenser. The bottom product from the reboiler contains 10 mole per cent methanol.

(a) Find the number of theoretical stages provided by the column and the vapor and liquid rates above and below the feed plate.

(b) After several months of successful operation in the manner described above, a water leak develops in the overhead condenser so that 900 lb/hr of water is leaking into the condensate. The condenser is operated in such a manner that the reflux and product streams are still saturated liquids and the reflux ratio $\tilde{O}_R/\tilde{D}$ is the same as it was in part (a). Furthermore, the boil-up rate from the reboiler remains the same as before. However, internal reflux ratios and terminal compositions will obviously be changed. Find the new values for the internal vapor and liquid rates and the overhead- and bottom-product compositions.

Equilibrium data (mole fraction methanol):

$\tilde{x}$	0.046	0.094	0.157	0.217	0.321	0.425	0.534	0.632	0.727
$\tilde{y}$	0.267	0.402	0.533	0.602	0.680	0.745	0.791	0.829	0.883

41-6. A rectifying column is fed a saturated vapor containing 20 mole per cent A and 80 mole per cent B. An overhead distillate is produced at the rate of 200 lb moles/hr containing 90 mole per cent A. The bottom product contains 15 mole per cent A.

To prevent an excessive vapor rate in the column, a vapor stream is taken off between the third and fourth plates from the bottom of the column and completely condensed. It comes off at the rate of 400 lb moles/hr. After condensation it returns to the column as a saturated liquid and is fed onto the fifth plate from the bottom of the column. Assuming 100 per cent plate efficiency and constant molal overflow, calculate:

(a) The feed and bottom-product rates
(b) The vapor and liquid rates in all sections of the column
(c) The side-stream composition
(d) The number of plates required to perform the separation

Equilibrium data (mole fraction A):

$\tilde{x}$	0.1	0.2	0.3	0.4	0.5	0.6	0.7	0.8	0.9
$\tilde{y}$	0.163	0.305	0.428	0.538	0.636	0.723	0.803	0.875	0.940

41-7. A stripping column operating at 1 atm pressure is fed a saturated liquid containing 38 mole per cent ethanol. The bottom product is a saturated liquid containing 5 mole per cent ethanol. The heat added to the reboiler is 30,000 Btu/lb mole of bottom product. Using an enthalpy-composition diagram, find by graphical construction:

(a) The number of theoretical stages required to perform the separation

(b) The heat input to the reboiler per pound mole of feed

(c) The heat input to the reboiler per pound mole of overhead product

41-8. A fractionating column is supplied with a saturated-liquid feed containing 21 mole per cent ethanol and 79 mole per cent water. The overhead distillate product is a saturated liquid which contains 83 mole per cent ethanol; the bottom product is a saturated liquid which contains 5 mole per cent ethanol. The column operates at 1 atm pressure with a reflux ratio twice the minimum value. Use the Ponchon-Savarit method to find:

(a) The number of theoretical stages required

(b) The optimum feed-plate location

(c) The heat load in the reboiler (Btu/lb mole of bottom product)

(d) The heat load in the condenser (Btu/lb mole of distillate product)

41-9. A conventional fractionating column, operating continuously at 1 atm pressure, is equipped with a reboiler and an overhead partial condenser, both of which act as equilibrium stages, and six bubble plates. The feed, which is added at the optimum location, contains 30 mole per cent ethanol and 70 mole per cent water and has an enthalpy of 10,000 Btu/lb mole. The partial condenser produces a saturated liquid and a saturated vapor at equal mole rates. All the liquid from the condenser is returned to the column as reflux, and all the vapor is taken off as a product. The bottom product is a saturated liquid containing 5 mole per cent ethanol and 95 mole per cent water. The heat added to the reboiler amounts to 10,000 Btu/lb mole bottom product leaving the reboiler. Find the over-all plate efficiency.

MULTICOMPONENT SEPARATIONS

   The separation operations which we have studied in the preceding chapters have been restricted to systems of two or three components. In the discussion of gas absorption in Chaps. 37 to 39, the solute transferred from the gas to the liquid was a single component. In distillation (Chap. 41), a binary system was considered in which the aim of the operation was to alter the proportions of the two constituents. In the study of extraction in Chap. 37, we considered the transfer of one component between a pair of insoluble liquids. Later in Chap. 40 we examined extraction operations for systems in which the liquid solvents were partially miscible, but we were interested in the transfer of only one component. In all these operations, the possibility exists that a multitude of components may be present and transferred between phases.

   Whether in nature or industry, systems reacting chemically usually produce a number of products. One aim of the engineer in industry is, of course, to diminish the number of side reactions by choosing the most favorable conditions for a reaction. It is often not possible, however, to eliminate the production of by-products. Hence the engineer must frequently design equipment to separate the desired product, not only from the remainder of the unreacted feed, but also from the by-products of the reaction. A good example from nature is crude petroleum, in which mixtures of hundreds of chemical compounds have been produced by naturally occurring processes. The principal efforts of the petroleum-refining industry in the past have been to separate the crude petroleum into fractions, each consisting of a mixture of closely related compounds of similar properties. These fractions we know as gasoline, kerosene, lubricating oil, etc.

   The methods of analyzing the separation of the binary and ternary systems discussed in the previous chapters can be extended to multicomponent systems rather simply for some operations, such as gas absorption with dilute solutions. For other operations, such as multicomponent dis-

656

tillation, the analysis becomes rather complex.   The difference can be attributed to the effects of the additional components on the two basic steps of any mass-transfer analysis: the equilibrium and the material-balance calculations.   If these are affected significantly for any one solute by the presence of the other solutes, then the interactions must be considered in the analysis.   If, however, the transfer of any one component is unaffected by the simultaneous transfer of the other components, the analysis with respect to each component can be considered independently, except for the restriction of common solvent rates, temperature, pressure, and tower height or number of stages.

Absorption of a Dilute Multicomponent Mixture

To illustrate the remarks made above we consider the absorption by a liquid solvent of several solutes present in small amounts in a gas.   The operation may be done either in a packed tower or in a tower containing a number of bubble plates.   Because the initial gas concentration is low, the removal of some or all of any solute does not affect the gas rate significantly.   Likewise the absorption of some or all of any solute into the liquid phase does not increase the liquid rate significantly.   Thus it is apparent that a mass balance may be solved for the mole fraction of each component in the gas and liquid phases at any cross section of the tower from a knowledge of the gas and liquid rates and the terminal compositions at one end of the tower.   Such equations were presented in Chaps. 37 and 39 and are referred to as operating-line equations.

The other important point to consider is the effect of the additional solutes on the equilibrium relations.   If the solutions behave as ideal solutions, the equilibrium concentrations are not affected by the presence of the other components, whether solutes or solvent.   For dilute solutions this condition is often achieved, so that the Henry's law constant for each solute is unaffected by the presence of additional solutes.

As a consequence we see that the design of a gas-absorption system for treating lean multicomponent mixtures is performed exactly as outlined in previous chapters for a single solute.   Since only a single set of gas and liquid rates and one tower height exist for each system, we are not free to specify all terminal compositions independently.   Rather, a specified separation may be chosen for one solute and the required tower dimensions and flow rates determined which best give this separation.   The separations obtained for the other components with these tower dimensions and flow rates can then be calculated.

In the specific case of a packed tower, the first calculation might be a determination of the number of transfer units [using Eq. (37-25), (37-27), or (37-28)] and the height of a transfer unit for one solute. These would then be multiplied to give the height of the tower. Then, for a second solute, the height of the tower would be divided by the height of a transfer unit for that component to get the number of transfer units. The equation for the number of transfer units would then be solved for the terminal composition of the second solute. This procedure could be repeated for any number of solutes.

The situation described above is often encountered in gas absorption, stripping, and extraction processes and is so straightforward that the methods and equations given for the systems with only one solute will not be rewritten here.

If the analysis were for the purpose of designing a stage contactor, as described in Chap. 39, similar procedures would be employed. The operating lines such as the one relating $\tilde{Y}_{An+1}$ to $\tilde{X}_{An}$ would remain straight and parallel regardless of concentration, because their slopes are merely the molal ratio of inert liquid to insoluble gas. For dilute mixtures the equilibrium lines would also be straight, so that the determination of the number of theoretical plates could be performed for each component independently.

The operation of a plate column for the absorption of a gas containing three components is illustrated in Fig. 42-1. The three components differ in volatility, A being most volatile and C least volatile. They are present in equal amounts in the inlet gas; hence all operating lines terminate at the same ordinate value ($\tilde{Y}_{N+1} = \tilde{Y}_A = \tilde{Y}_B = \tilde{Y}_C$). The solvent is pure, so the lower ends of all operating lines terminate at the same value of the abscissa ($\tilde{X}_{Ao} = \tilde{X}_{Bo} = \tilde{X}_{Co} = 0$). The ratio of the solvent rate $\tilde{L}_s$ to the insoluble-gas rate $\tilde{G}_I$ is the common slope of all operating lines.

If the exit concentration of one component is specified, the number of plates is fixed, so that all other exit concentrations are likewise fixed. To illustrate this assertion let us arbitrarily say that half of component B is to be absorbed in the column. This choice of $\tilde{Y}_{B1}$ enables us to locate the lower end of the operating line for B. We also know the slope $\tilde{L}_s/\tilde{G}_I$, so we draw the operating line to end at the specified value of $\tilde{Y}_B$, which is designated simply as $\tilde{Y}_{N+1}$ in Fig. 42-1. We can immediately determine the number of stages in the column either by the graphical construction of steps, as was shown in Chap. 39, or by solving Eq. (39-21).

Because the number of stages has now been fixed, we cannot arbitrarily specify the exit-gas concentration for any other component. This quantity must be determined either by graphical trial-and-error procedures or by solving Eq. (39-24) for the terminal concentration. The graphical

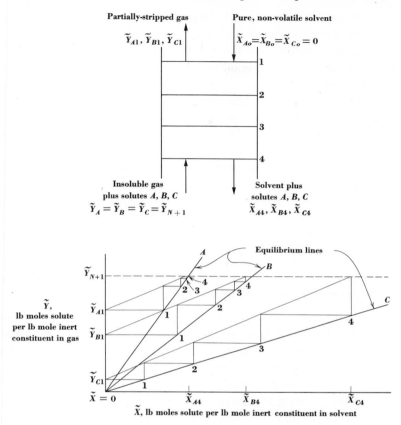

Fig. 42-1. *Gas absorption of a multicomponent mixture in a plate column.*

procedure can be illustrated with reference to Fig. 42-1. Considering for the moment component A, we draw above the equilibrium line for A a straight line which we intend to test as a possible operating line for A. It has the same slope as the operating line for B and ends at $\tilde{X} = 0$ and $\tilde{Y} = \tilde{Y}_{N+1}$ just as the line for B does. The steps representing plates are then constructed. If the number coincides with the number already found for the specified separation of component B, we have chosen the correct location for the operating line for A. We locate the operating line for C by an identical procedure.

Examination of Fig. 42-1 shows that, in spite of the fact that the concentrations of all components in the inlet gas are the same, the concentration in the exit gas of the most volatile component (A) is the highest, since it is least absorbed. Component C, which is least volatile, has the lowest concentration in the exit gas because it is the component most absorbed. The solvent becomes almost saturated with A shortly after entering the column and leaves in this state of near saturation with respect to A at the bottom. Large quantities of C are absorbed by the solvent near the bottom, and the closest approach to equilibrium with respect to C occurs at the top, where the gas is almost stripped of C. The behavior of any additional soluble components in the gas can be analyzed in exactly the same manner.

The absorption of a multicomponent mixture in a packed tower proceeds in a manner similar to that described in Fig. 42-1 for absorption in a plate column. In a packed column the driving force for transfer of component A decreases quickly as the concentration of A in the solvent increases. Thus the greatest driving force occurs at the top, where the solvent is pure. Conversely, for the least volatile component C, the greatest driving force occurs at the bottom, where the concentration of C in the gas is greatest. The driving force diminishes only at the top, where the concentration of C in the gas phase is greatly diminished.

Absorption of a Rich Multicomponent Mixture

The design of an absorption tower for a rich multicomponent mixture may be a fairly complex and tedious task. One of the difficulties is obtaining equilibrium data. Where the compounds are of similar molecular structure (as in many hydrocarbon systems), it may be permissible to assume that ideal solutions are formed, even though the concentrations of the diffusing components are appreciable. Even in this case, however, the equilibrium lines if plotted as $\tilde{Y}$ versus $\tilde{X}$ are curved, so that analytical solutions assuming linear equilibrium behavior are ruled out for this type of representation. In general, ideal-solution behavior cannot be assumed, and experimental data or some empirical correlation derived from experimental data on similar systems are essential.

The second major difficulty in analyzing the absorption of rich mixtures is in determining the location of the operating line for each component. As mentioned earlier, the operating line, if dependent on total gas and liquid rates, will not be straight because the absorption of substantial amounts of solute will change the gas and liquid rates in the column. This is a major difficulty when analyzing multicomponent systems because, as we have already seen, the various solutes are absorbed at different rates in each section of the column. Since the rates of absorption depend on the gas and liquid flow rates and the flow rates depend on the absorption rates, we have a problem which can be solved only by a trial-and-error procedure.

The problems encountered in the design of packed towers and plate towers differ somewhat because of the nature of the information sought.

We shall first consider the design of a packed tower. A system is chosen arbitrarily in which three solutes A, B, and C of known concentration are carried into the tower by an insoluble carrier gas I and absorbed by a non-volatile liquid S. The problem is to find the height of packing necessary to give a specified exit-gas composition $\tilde{y}_{A1}$. For each of the three solutes we can write a mass balance around a section of the tower extending from some arbitrarily chosen cross section to the bottom, where all compositions are known. These equations are similar to Eq. (37-8). We can also write similar but simpler material-balance equations for the insoluble carrier gas I and the nonvolatile component S in the solvent stream. These five equations contain 10 variables, $\tilde{y}_A$, $\tilde{y}_B$, $\tilde{y}_C$, $\tilde{y}_I$, $\tilde{x}_A$, $\tilde{x}_B$, $\tilde{x}_C$, $\tilde{x}_S$, $\tilde{L}$, and $\tilde{G}$. Two additional equations which can be written are $\Sigma\tilde{y} = 1$ and $\Sigma\tilde{x} = 1$, so that three more equations are needed to provide the total of 10 necessary to solve for the 10 variables. These three equations are the integrated rate equations for the three diffusing components:

$$z = (H_G n_G)_A = (H_G n_G)_B = (H_G n_G)_C \tag{42-1}$$

We have, however, introduced an eleventh variable, z, the height of packing from the bottom of the tower to the cross section being considered. Thus we have 11 variables and 10 equations, and one variable can be chosen arbitrarily. If this is one of the composition variables at the cross section within the tower, say $\tilde{y}_A$, the 10 equations can be solved for all 10 remaining variables, including $\tilde{x}_A$. Thus a point $(\tilde{x}_A, \tilde{y}_A)$ can be established on the operating line. The procedure is repeated for values of $\tilde{y}_A$, ranging from $\tilde{y}_{Ao}$ to $\tilde{y}_{A1}$. In this way the complete operating line can be established for component A (and for B and C also, in the course of these calculations).

One major difficulty in this technique is that analytical expressions are not available for the numbers of transfer units n_{GA}, n_{GB}, or n_{GC} for concentrated solutions. These must be found by graphical integration [Eq. (37-17)], and the possibility of a direct algebraic solution of the 10 simultaneous equations is thus eliminated. Hence the solution must be found by some stepwise procedure. One which is fairly straightforward and can be made as accurate as desired is to analyze the column as a series of short sections. Over each section, gas and liquid rates are assumed to be constant and the methods described earlier for dilute solutions applied. The fact that the solutions are not dilute is of little consequence. The significant thing is that only small changes of composition occur over each segment of the column being analyzed. As a result, the operating lines for any one segment can be assumed to be straight and the analysis proposed earlier for dilute solutions applied to that segment. The repetition of this procedure makes it possible ultimately to determine all exit-gas compositions and the tower height if only one exit-gas composition is specified.

As the size of the segments is reduced, we approach a differential segment as a limit. The differential equations for the mass and energy balances and for interphase transfer for a point in a tower have been written as Eqs. (38-27) *et seq.* In Chap. 38 the only solute considered was the component A; if the other solutes, say D and E, are present, we merely add to the list of differential equations expressions such as Eqs. (38-28) and (38-30) written for D, E, etc. The set of differential equations must be solved simultaneously by a numerical method such as the Euler or Runge-Kutta procedure. Such calculations are now rarely done by hand, but are easily solved by an electronic computer.

We next examine the absorption of a rich mixture using a plate tower. If $\tilde{Y}$ is plotted against $\tilde{X}$, the operating lines remain straight, just as for a dilute solution. The slopes of the operating lines represent the ratio of solute-free liquid to solute-free gas, which is constant regardless of the amount of solute present in either phase. The difficulties in locating the equilibrium line are, however, considerable. Even when ideal solutions are assumed, the equilibrium values of $\tilde{Y}$ and $\tilde{X}$, by virtue of their definition, depend on the concentrations of all solutes in each phase. Therefore, before any point $(\tilde{X}_A, \tilde{Y}_A)$ can be plotted on the equilibrium line, the concentrations of B and C in the solvent and in the gas phase must be known. This requirement is shown by writing the definitions of $\tilde{Y}_A$ and $\tilde{X}_A$:

$$\tilde{y}_A = \frac{\tilde{Y}_A}{1 + \tilde{Y}_A + \tilde{Y}_B + \tilde{Y}_C} \tag{42-2}$$

and

$$\tilde{x}_A = \frac{\tilde{X}_A}{1 + \tilde{X}_A + \tilde{X}_B + \tilde{X}_C} \tag{42-3}$$

Thus, even if the equilibrium relation between $\tilde{y}_A$ and $\tilde{x}_A$ is known, it is also necessary to know $\tilde{Y}_B$, $\tilde{Y}_C$, $\tilde{X}_B$, and $\tilde{X}_C$ for each point where $\tilde{Y}_A$ and $\tilde{X}_A$ are to be calculated from $\tilde{y}_A$ and $\tilde{x}_A$. Trial-and-error procedures can be used by guessing the rates of separation and then using this information to locate the equilibrium curves. If several solutes of widely differing volatilities are present in large amounts, this procedure can become tedious. A simpler method is probably that of constructing a diagram in which both equilibrium and operating lines are plotted in terms of $\tilde{y}_A$ versus $\tilde{x}_A$, as described earlier for the analysis of packed towers. The equilibrium stages can be counted on this diagram just as well as on a $\tilde{Y}_A$ versus $\tilde{X}_A$ diagram. Another trial-and-error procedure is that proposed by Sherwood and

Pigford,[1] involving a modified gas-composition variable differing from both $\tilde{Y}_A$ and $\tilde{y}_A$.

Absorption calculations for multicomponent mixtures are done by hand as described above only for preliminary estimates. For a reliable design, plate-to-plate energy and mass balances are performed by a computer according to the method of Sorel, as described below for multicomponent distillation. This method applies even when there is no insoluble vapor-phase component or nonvolatile liquid-phase component. The actual heat effects are also considered, and these may be far from negligible.

Multicomponent Distillation[2]

The analysis of multicomponent distillation offers many of the same problems encountered in the analysis of gas-absorption systems. Distillation is seldom done in packed towers, so we need consider only plate columns. Several new problems, however, are added. First, in distillation we usually are not dealing with systems in which there is a nonsoluble constituent in the gas and a nonvolatile constituent in the liquid, so we must be concerned with the transfer of all components in both phases. Second, the magnitude of the change in composition for most constituents in a distillation column is so great that we are concerned with "rich mixtures" in most problems.

Other problems primarily associated with distillation systems include thermal effects, the use of reflux, the withdrawal of side streams, and the introduction of feed into the column at some point other than the top or bottom. Because of these complications we seldom attempt graphical or analytical solutions for problems of multicomponent distillation. Instead we perform plate-to-plate calculations similar to those already described for binary systems in Chap. 41. All methods involve a succession of equilibrium calculations alternating with material-balance calculations. The methods differ chiefly in the assumptions used in making these calculations.

We shall first apply the Sorel method. If we consider a system containing only the top plate and the condenser of a distillation column (as shown in Fig. 41-3), we see that the first step is to obtain the composition of the liquid leaving the plate (assuming a total condenser and saturated reflux).

[1] T. K. Sherwood and R. L. Pigford, "Absorption and Extraction," 2d ed., McGraw-Hill Book Company, Inc., New York, 1952.

[2] C. S. Robinson and E. R. Gilliland, in "Elements of Fractional Distillation," 4th ed., chap. 9, McGraw-Hill Book Company, Inc., New York, 1950, present a general discussion of multicomponent distillation with a number of illustrative examples.

If the composition of the vapor leaving the top plate is known (that is, the composition of the product stream) and the pressure in the column is fixed, according to the phase rule the composition and temperature of the liquid leaving the plate are fixed, regardless of the number of components present.

To obtain the composition of the vapor arriving at the top plate from the plate below, we write mass balances around the top plate for all components. These are of the same form as Eq. (41-12), derived for the more volatile component of a binary system. Writing Eq. (41-12) for component A, we have

$$\tilde{y}_{A2} = \frac{\tilde{O}_1}{\tilde{V}_2}\, \bar{x}_{A1} + \frac{\tilde{D}\tilde{x}_{AD}}{\tilde{V}_2} \tag{42-4}$$

The liquid composition $\bar{x}_{A1}$ has been found by the equilibrium calculation, so Eq. (42-4) contains only three unknowns, $\tilde{y}_{A2}$, $\tilde{O}_1$, and $\tilde{V}_2$. The product rate $\tilde{D}$ is usually specified in advance. Similar equations are written for all components, so for a system of i components we obtain i equations containing $i + 2$ unknowns.

Two additional equations which may be written are the total mass and enthalpy balances.

$$\tilde{O}_R + \tilde{V}_2 = \tilde{O}_1 + \tilde{V}_1 \tag{41-8}$$

$$\tilde{O}_R \tilde{h}_R + \tilde{V}_2 \tilde{H}_2 = \tilde{O}_1 \tilde{h}_1 + \tilde{V}_1 \tilde{H}_1 \tag{41-9}$$

The rates $\tilde{O}_R$ and $\tilde{V}_1$ are fixed by the product rate $\tilde{D}$ and the reflux ratio $\tilde{O}_R/\tilde{D}$, so that if all the enthalpies were known, we should now have $i + 2$ equations and $i + 2$ unknowns and the equations could be solved simultaneously. Three of the enthalpies, $\tilde{h}_R$, $\tilde{h}_1$, and $\tilde{H}_1$, are known (that is, they can be computed from the known compositions and temperatures of their respective saturated streams). The fourth enthalpy, $\tilde{H}_2$, is not known, however, and cannot be calculated until the unknown stream compositions ($\tilde{y}_{A2}$, $\tilde{y}_{B2}$, etc.) are determined.

The solution is obtained by assuming a value for one of the unknown variables, say $\tilde{H}_2$. The rates $\tilde{O}_1$ and $\tilde{V}_2$ are found from Eqs. (41-8) and (41-9), and then the mole fractions of all components in stream V_2 are determined, using component balances like Eq. (42-4). From the compositions obtained and the appropriate enthalpy data on the components, we calculate $\tilde{H}_2$ to check the initial assumption.

When the calculations have been repeated a sufficient number of times to provide a satisfactory check on $\tilde{H}_2$, we proceed to the calculations for the next plate. The first step is an equilibrium calculation to determine the composition of stream O_2. Next we write the mass and enthalpy balances around plate 2, which are similar to the balances around plate 1. The solution of these balances is done by a trial-and-error procedure, similar to that employed for the top plate.

For a rectifying column the plate-to-plate calculations are continued downward until the vapor composition obtained by the trial-and-error calculation matches the specified feed composition. This is not likely to occur at any one plate for all components because the initial choice of the overhead-product composition, product rate, and reflux ratio will have been made arbitrarily. To obtain a vapor composition beneath the bottom plate which matches the feed composition, alterations must be made in the variables assumed for the top of the column. Thus the entire set of plate-to-plate calculations must be repeated until the compositions check at the bottom with the desired accuracy.

For a stripping column, calculations are made starting with the streams entering and leaving the reboiler. The rate and composition of the bottom product and the rate of vapor production are arbitrarily chosen and plate-to-plate calculations made in an upward direction in the manner described for the rectifying column. When the liquid composition matches that of the feed stream, calculations are discontinued. As in the design of the rectifying column, the bottom conditions chosen arbitrarily are altered and the calculations repeated until the liquid composition at the top of the stripping column checks that of the feed.

The design of a complete fractionating column containing both rectifying and stripping sections requires that both sets of calculations be made in such a way that stream compositions match at the feed section. In view of the large amount of work required and the repetitive nature of the calculations, it is not surprising that plate-to-plate calculations are now done largely by digital computers. If the calculations are done manually, it is customary to use some short-cut procedure.[1]

In Chap. 41 we saw that the plate-to-plate calculations for binary distillation were greatly simplified when it was assumed that constant-molal-flow rates existed for each stream; that is, $\tilde{O}_R = \tilde{O}_1 = \tilde{O}_2$, etc., and $\tilde{V}_1 = \tilde{V}_2 = \tilde{V}_3$, etc. This eliminated the need for over-all mass and enthalpy balances. If we use this assumption in analyzing multicomponent systems, Eq. (42-4) can be solved for the mole fraction of any component in stream V_2 without the necessity of making trial-and-error calculations. This simplification greatly reduces the total labor required, but does not affect the

---

[1] An analysis of multicomponent distillation and a review of various design procedures for use with digital computers are presented by B. D. Smith in "Equilibrium Stage Processes," McGraw-Hill Book Company, Inc., New York, to be published.

trial-and-error equilibrium calculations which must still be made at each plate. The assumption of constant-molal-flow rates can be made only for systems obeying Trouton's rule. Now that digital computers are available for the design of equipment for multicomponent separations, the necessity for making this assumption has greatly diminished.

Even more simplified procedures may be applied to the determination of the number of stages required for multicomponent distillation if only a preliminary design is required. Perry, p. 622, presents an empirical method which involves:

1. The calculation of the number of stages at total reflux, N_{min}
2. The calculation of the minimum reflux ratio $(\tilde{O}/\tilde{D})_{min}$
3. The use of an empirical correlation relating N_{min} and $(\tilde{O}/\tilde{D})_{min}$ to the actual number of theoretical stages N required at a finite reflux ratio $(\tilde{O}/\tilde{D})$

This method is useful when making calculations to determine the economic optimum reflux ratio for a tower. The final design, however, is better made by plate-to-plate calculations.

Example 42-1

Ethylene is being manufactured by passing a saturated hydrocarbon feed, such as ethane, through a heater in which the gas is cracked at about 1500°F. The mixture leaving the cracking tubes is rapidly cooled and then separated into a number of streams in a series of fractionating towers. After the lightest and heaviest components have been removed, the remaining mixture is fed to a tower called a deethanizer. Ethane and ethylene are removed from the top, and the bottoms consist of almost pure propylene. The feed to such a tower is as given in the following table.

Component	Lb moles/hr	Mole fraction
CH_4	0.09	0.0002
C_2H_4	302.29	0.5300
C_2H_6	122.18	0.2140
C_3H_6	141.96	0.2482
C_3H_8	4.28	0.0075
C_4H_{10}	0.08	0.0001
Total..........	570.88	1.000

It is required to find the number of theoretical stages necessary in a tower in which the propylene mole fraction in the distillate is reduced to 0.0054 and the ethane mole fraction in the bottoms to 0.0002. The ethane and the propylene are the key, or distributed, components. Lighter components appear in the bottoms only as traces; these are the nondistributed components. A material balance over the tower can now be built up as shown in the following table. The tower operates at about 200 psia; the distillate is produced as a vapor from a partial condenser.

	Flow, lb moles/hr		
Component	Feed	Distillate	Bottoms
CH_4	0.09	0.09	
C_2H_4	302.29	302.29	
C_2H_6	122.18	122.15	0.03
C_3H_6	141.96	2.31	139.65
C_3H_8	4.28	. . . . . .	4.28
C_4H_{10}	0.08	. . . . . .	0.08
Total.	570.88	426.84	144.04

Since the total quantity of the bottoms stream is little affected by the ethane in this stream, the mole fraction ethane can be used to estimate the quantity of ethane in the bottoms as 0.03 mole/hr. The total bottoms are now subtracted from the feed to find the total distillate, and the amount of propylene in the distillate is found by difference.

It is helpful to do some approximate calculations before starting the plate-to-plate procedure. We begin by using the Fenske-Underwood equation to find the minimum plates required to obtain the desired distribution of the key components. This minimum occurs at total reflux, so the operating-line equation for a component reduces to $\bar{y}_{An+1} = \bar{x}_{An}$.

The Fenske-Underwood equation can be derived by the following analysis. At the top of the tower we have

$$\bar{y}_{A1} = K_{A1}\bar{x}_{A1} \tag{1}$$

$$\bar{y}_{B1} = K_{B1}\bar{x}_{B1} \tag{2}$$

and a similar equation for each component. We let A be the light key and B the heavy key, and we define the relative volatility α_{AB} by

$$\alpha_{AB} = \frac{K_A}{K_B} \tag{3}$$

so that we have

$$\frac{\bar{y}_{A1}}{\bar{y}_{B1}} = \alpha_{AB}\frac{\bar{x}_{A1}}{\bar{x}_{B1}} \tag{4}$$

The operating-line equation at total reflux then permits us to write

$$\frac{\bar{y}_{A1}}{\bar{y}_{B1}} = \alpha_{AB}\frac{\bar{y}_{A2}}{\bar{y}_{B2}} \tag{5}$$

Similarly, at the second plate down, we find

$$\frac{\bar{y}_{A2}}{\bar{y}_{B2}} = \alpha_{AB}\frac{\bar{y}_{A3}}{\bar{y}_{B3}} \tag{6}$$

An assumption of the method is to take α_{AB} as constant at a suitable average value in the tower; note that α_{AB} varies much less than K_A or K_B.

Equations (5) and (6) are combined to give

$$\frac{\bar{y}_{A1}}{\bar{y}_{B1}} = \alpha_{AB}{}^2\frac{\bar{y}_{A3}}{\bar{y}_{B3}} \tag{7}$$

For all N stages we have

$$\frac{\tilde{y}_{A1}}{\tilde{y}_{B1}} = \alpha_{AB}{}^{N-1}\frac{\tilde{y}_{AN}}{\tilde{y}_{BN}} \tag{8}$$

or

$$\frac{\tilde{y}_{AD}}{\tilde{y}_{BD}} = \alpha_{AB}{}^{N}\frac{\tilde{x}_{AB}}{\tilde{x}_{BB}} \tag{9}$$

where N includes the reboiler and partial condenser, if any. A similar equation holds for any other component; for example,

$$\frac{\tilde{y}_{CD}}{\tilde{y}_{BD}} = \alpha_{CB}{}^{N}\frac{\tilde{x}_{CB}}{\tilde{x}_{BB}} \tag{10}$$

When the terminal compositions for the light and heavy keys are substituted in Eq. (9), with α_{AB} corresponding to an average tower temperature of 2.2°F, it is found that $N_{\min}$ is 8.8 stages. The estimation of the average temperature is based on empirical procedures and is not given here.

The next step in the work is to find the approximate value of the minimum reflux ratio. The method of Underwood (Perry, p. 624), which assumes a constant α, gives $(\tilde{O}/\tilde{D})_{\min}$ equal to 0.447. The number of stages at intermediate reflux ratios is then found by Gilliland's correlation (Perry, p. 622), which gives N as a function of $N_{\min}$, $(\tilde{O}/\tilde{D})_{\min}$, and $\tilde{O}/\tilde{D}$. The calculations described up to this point can be programmed for a digital computer; the results of such a computation are as given in the following table.

$\tilde{O}/\tilde{D}$	N
0.447	∞
0.492	25.4
0.655	20.2
0.792	17.8
1.055	15.2
1.544	12.8
2.055	11.7
3.010	10.7
∞	8.8

From these data it is possible to make an economic analysis of operating and capital costs. It is found that the optimum $\tilde{O}/\tilde{D}$ is about 1.5 times the minimum, or about 0.66. We are now ready to perform the plate-to-plate calculations to find the temperature and composition profiles in the tower and the exact number of theoretical stages.

The method of Sorel is used, and the first step is the calculation of the temperature, quantity, and composition of the liquid leaving the first stage (the partial condenser) based on the vapor quantity and composition leaving the stage, that is, $\tilde{V}_1$, $\tilde{y}_{AD}$, $\tilde{y}_{BD}$, $\tilde{y}_{CD}$, etc. However, the distillate composition given in the table lacks values for the heavy nondistributed components. These substances must actually be present in trace quantities, so that they will appear on the lower trays of the column. We estimate the necessary compositions by using Eq. (10) with N equal to 8.8; all the mole fractions except $\tilde{y}_{CD}$ are known. For butane, for instance, the computation gives $\tilde{y}_{\text{butane } D} = 1.68 \times 10^{-12}$. From the complete composition of stream V_1 (or D) thus estimated, the temperature and composition of the dew-point liquid are calculated by the trial-and-error calculation described in the text. From this composition and temperature and the known reflux ratio, the values of $\tilde{V}_2$, $\tilde{y}_{A2}$, $\tilde{y}_{B2}$, $\tilde{y}_{C2}$, etc., are calculated by trial and error from the mass and energy balances around the first stage in the manner already described in the text.

The plate-to-plate calculations are best done on an automatic computing machine. One of the simplest procedures is to calculate downward until the liquid leaving a stage is about what is expected at the feed tray. Then a similar set of calculations is started from the bottom of the tower and continued upward until the liquid leaving a tray is as close as possible in composition to that found on the last tray calculated from the top of the tower. The lack of matching of compositions at the middle of the tower requires the adjustment of the compositions at the ends of the tower; the over-all material balance and the mole fraction of the key components must of course be respected. A suitable computer program for making the adjustments necessary to obtain a match at the feed tray can be devised, and iterations are performed on the tray-to-tray calculations until the match is good enough. Usually two or three iterations will suffice.

The plate-to-plate calculations described above have been programmed for a digital computer, and the results for the problem given are shown in Fig. 42-2. The temperature and composition profiles are shown; 24 theoretical stages are required. The vapor rate varies from $\tilde{V}_1 = 708.6$ lb moles/hr to $\tilde{V}_8 = 644.1$ lb moles/hr in the top section, so that the importance of not assuming a constant molal overflow is evident.

Azeotropic and Extractive Distillation

The separation by distillation of components in a binary system is sometimes hindered by the formation of a constant boiling mixture known as an azeotrope. A system containing an azeotrope is shown in Fig. 42-3. If a mixture rich in component B is distilled in a fractionating column, the limiting product compositions, regardless of the number of stages, are pure B and a mixture of azeotropic composition. Because the stream approaching pure B in composition has the higher boiling point, it is produced as a bottom product. The overhead product, or lower-boiling stream, approaches the composition of the azeotrope. If the feed composition is to the right of the azeotrope in Fig. 42-3, a different situation exists. The overhead product still approaches the azeotrope in composition, but the bottom product approaches pure A in composition.

The separation of a mixture of A and B into two streams, each of which is nearly pure, cannot be done by a single binary distillation at the pressure for which the data in Fig. 42-3 are shown. A number of alternatives exist, however. One is that the pressure in the column be altered to some value at which an azeotrope is no longer formed. An example of this behavior is provided by the ethanol-water system, which forms azeotropes containing 7.88 mass per cent water at 14,500 mm Hg pressure, 4.4 mass per cent water at 760 mm Hg pressure, and no azeotrope at 70 mm Hg pressure.

A second method of performing the separation is to use two distillation columns which operate at different pressures. For the ethanol-water system, one column operating at atmospheric pressure might produce a bottom product rich in water and an overhead product of nearly azeotropic composition. If this overhead product contained less than 7.88 mass per cent

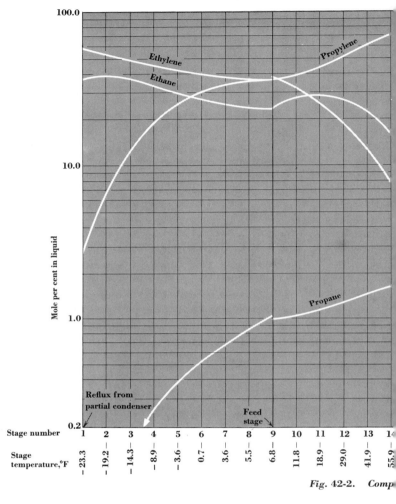

Fig. 42-2.   *Comp*

water, it could be fractionated in a column operating at 14,500 mm Hg pressure to produce nearly pure ethanol as the bottom product.

A third method of separating the two components is to add another component, which alters the relative volatility of the two original components. If the proper additive is chosen, the formation of an azeotrope may be entirely eliminated and the original components separated to any desired extent. This method of altering the relative volatility has also been used in systems in which no azeotrope exists but in which the closeness of the relative volatility to unity makes a separation very difficult. Because additional devices must be supplied to remove the additive from the product streams, an economic analysis does not always justify the use

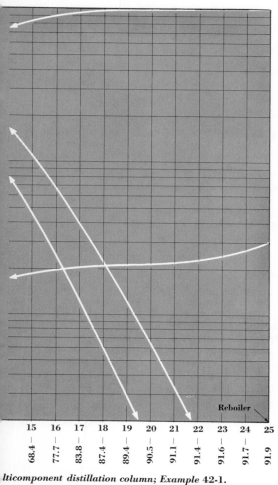

15	16	17	18	19	20	21	22	23	24	25
68.4	77.7	83.8	87.4	89.4	90.5	91.1	91.4	91.6	91.7	91.9

lticomponent distillation column; Example 42-1.

of the additive with its recovery system in place of the straightforward, but difficult, binary separation.

The technique of adding a third component to alter the relative volatility is successful mainly for binary mixtures which do not obey Raoult's law. For example, the original mixture may consist of two substances of nearly the same volatility but of greatly different polarity. If the added constituent has a greater polarity than either of the original two components, it generally increases the volatility of the less polar constituent relative to the more polar constituent. An example of this behavior is shown in Table 42-1, in which phenol is added to toluene and a mixture of paraffin hydrocarbons which have boiling points in the vicinity of the

Fig. 42-3.   *Phase behavior at constant pressure of a binary system containing a homogeneous azeotrope.*

toluene boiling point.   Another example would be the addition of water to a mixture of acetone and methanol.   Water is more polar than methanol, and methanol is more polar than acetone.   The addition of water increases the volatility of acetone relative to the methanol.   If an additive less polar than either of the original pair were added, it would increase the

Table 42-1.   Effect of Phenol on the Relative Volatility of Paraffin-Toluene Mixtures

Composition, mole per cent			Relative volatility (paraffin-toluene)
Paraffin	Toluene	Phenol	
50	50	0	1
30	30	40	1.5
20	20	60	2.0
0	0	100	3.7 (as a limit)

volatility of the more polar substance.   As an example, the addition of a hydrocarbon to acetone-methanol mixtures would make the methanol more volatile than the acetone.   The thermodynamic effects of additives are discussed by Robinson and Gilliland.[1]

The terms "extractive" and "azeotropic" distinguish the classes of compounds used as additives.   Extractive distillation usually refers to systems in which the added compound has a substantially lower vapor pressure than either compound in the original binary mixture.   An example of extractive distillation is the use of acetone in the separation of a mixture of *n*-butane and 2-butene.   As would be expected, the volatility of *n*-butane

[1] *Op. cit.*, chap. 10.

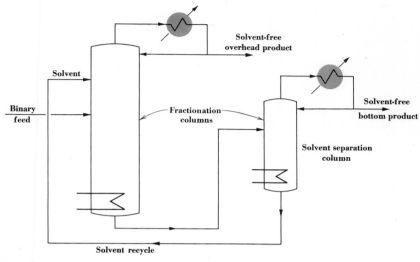

Fig. 42-4.   Typical flow sheet for an extractive distillation process.

is increased relative to that of the 2-butene.   Acetone boils at a temperature 60°C greater than either component, so that it does not appear in substantial amounts in the vapor phase.   For this reason it must be added near the top of the column as a liquid.

A typical extractive-distillation process is shown in Fig. 42-4.   One of the advantages of extractive distillation is that the separation of the additive from both components of the binary mixture is generally quite easy. Only a few plates are needed above the solvent injection plate to fractionate the solvent out of the vapor stream.   In addition, a simple auxiliary distillation column serves to remove the additive from the bottom product. An example of the design of an extractive-distillation system is shown in Perry, sec. 9.   The principal difference from the design of an ordinary ternary distillation column is in the nonideality of the liquid solution. Reliable equilibrium data are often difficult to find for new systems.

Azeotropic distillation is the term descriptive of processes in which the additive has a boiling point of approximately the same magnitude as those of the original components in the binary mixture being separated.   As a result, the additive appears in significant concentrations on all plates in the system.   This would ordinarily mean that separation of the additive from each of the original components would be difficult.   Usually, however, the additive is chosen so that it forms a heterogeneous azeotrope with one or both of the original components.   A heterogeneous azeotrope is one from which two liquid phases are formed when vapor of azeotropic com-

Fig. 42-5. *Phase behavior at constant pressure of a binary system containing a heterogeneous azeotrope.*

position is condensed. This behavior is shown in Fig. 42-5. A vapor at a temperature above the azeotropic temperature can produce either a liquid in the α region or a liquid in the β region or both. All vapors of composition between the α and β regions alter in composition as the condensing temperature is decreased until the azeotropic composition is reached. At this point, further condensation occurs at constant temperature and α and β liquids are formed simultaneously. This property may be of considerable assistance in the separation of the additive from the overhead or bottom

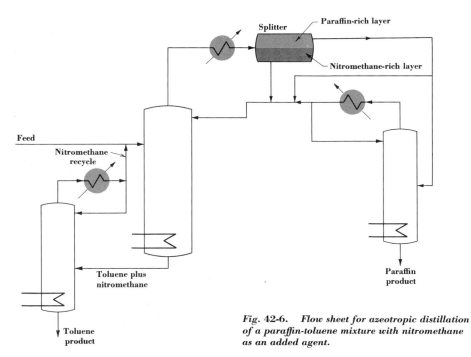

Fig. 42-6. *Flow sheet for azeotropic distillation of a paraffin-toluene mixture with nitromethane as an added agent.*

product. Usually, however, some additional provision must be made for solvent separation. This may be auxiliary distillation equipment or a liquid-liquid extraction unit.

An example of azeotropic distillation is the paraffin-toluene system with nitromethane as the additive. A flow sheet is shown in Fig. 42-6. The paraffin-toluene mixture boils at 110°C at atmospheric pressure and is treated with nitromethane, which boils at 101°C. The overhead product from the main tower consists of a paraffin-nitromethane mixture which, when condensed, forms two liquid phases. The nitromethane-rich phase is returned directly to the top plate of the tower, and the paraffin layer is sent to an auxiliary fractionating column which separates the remaining nitromethane from the paraffin. The bottom product from the main fractionating tower must also be fractionated to produce the toluene product and an additive stream which is returned to the tower.

PROBLEMS

42-1. A vapor-liquid separator operating adiabatically at 215 psia produces a vapor stream containing 35 mole per cent methane, 23 mole per cent ethane, 24 mole per cent propane, 12 mole per cent *n*-butane, 4 mole per cent *n*-pentane, and 2 mole per cent *n*-hexane. The vapor stream leaving the separator constitutes 60 mole per cent of the feed entering. Find the composition of the feed stream and the liquid-product stream.

42-2. A natural gas stream contains 88 mole per cent methane, 6 mole per cent ethane, 4 mole per cent propane, and 2 mole per cent *n*-butane. The gas is to be treated in a bubble-plate tower with a nonvolatile absorber oil flowing at the rate of 4 moles absorber oil/mole inlet gas. Determine the number of theoretical stages required to recover 80 per cent of the propane, and find the fractional recovery of the other components under these conditions. The tower operates at 3 atm pressure and 60°F. Assume that Raoult's law applies for all solutes except methane, which can be considered insoluble.

42-3. A fractionating column is supplied with 500 moles/hr of a feed which is a saturated liquid at 65 psia. The feed contains 1.2 mole per cent propane, 23.0 mole per cent *n*-butane, and 75.8 mole per cent *i*-butane. The column is equipped with a total condenser which produces a saturated-liquid reflux at a pressure of 65 psia. The overhead-product composition is to be 5 mole per cent propane, 5 mole per cent *n*-butane, and 90 mole per cent *i*-butane. The bottom-product composition is not specified, but it is apparent that only a negligible amount of propane will be present.

(*a*) Find the overhead- and bottom-product rates and the bottom-product composition.

(*b*) Find by plate-to-plate calculations the minimum number of plates required to perform the specified separation. Check this with the results of the Fenske-Underwood equation (Perry, p. 623, eq. 82).

42-4. A hydrocarbon stream containing 37 mole per cent *n*-butane, 32 mole per cent *i*-pentane, 21 mole per cent *n*-pentane, and 10 mole per cent *n*-hexane is fed as a saturated liquid at column pressure to a debutanizing column at the rate of 4750 lb moles/day. The debutanizer is to produce a feedstock for an isomerization process at the rate of 1250 lb moles/day with a minimum of 95 mole per cent *n*-butane and the remainder chiefly *i*-pentane. The column has a total condenser and is to produce a saturated-liquid overhead product at 100°F. The pressure drop in the column will be neglected. Find:

(a) The pressure in the column

(b) The temperature of the feed

(c) The temperature of the bottom product

(d) The number of plates required to give the specified separation at a reflux ratio $(\tilde{O}_R/\tilde{D})$ of 2

42-5. In extractive distillation the added component has a much lower vapor pressure than the components in the original mixture. In azeotropic distillation the added component has about the same vapor pressure as the original mixture. Discuss the possible advantages and disadvantages of a type of distillation in which the third component has a much higher vapor pressure than the original mixture.

MASS TRANSFER WITH CHEMICAL REACTION 43

The height of a contacting device for a mass-transfer operation can often be significantly reduced by causing a chemical reaction to occur with the solute in the absorbing phase. For example, carbon dioxide can be absorbed from air simply by using water as the solvent in a packed tower. However, the solubility of carbon dioxide in water at atmospheric pressure is rather low, and as we saw in Chaps. 33 and 37, the solubility often has an appreciable effect on the mass-transfer rate. Hence, if the water phase contains an additive such as potassium carbonate, sodium carbonate, sodium hydroxide, or monoethanolamine, which reacts chemically with the carbon dioxide, the height of the packed tower and the amount of absorbing liquid required can be substantially reduced.

The effect of the chemical reaction occurs in two ways. If the reaction goes to completion, the solvent phase can absorb a total amount of carbon dioxide equal to the stoichiometric amount necessary to react with the additive, plus the amount of carbon dioxide capable of being physically absorbed by the solvent. The quantity of solvent needed is thus decreased. As a second effect, the reaction of carbon dioxide with the additive reduces the concentration of carbon dioxide along the diffusion path within the solvent. Hence the resistance to mass transfer at any cross section within the column is decreased.

The absorption of carbon dioxide with simultaneous chemical reaction is an operation of industrial importance. Two other examples of systems which illustrate simultaneous mass transfer and chemical reaction are the absorption of hydrogen sulfide with an aqueous sodium carbonate solution and the absorption of sulfur dioxide from air with milk-of-lime solution.

If the object of the operation is to recover the solute, the reaction must be readily reversible so that the solute can be released from the solvent after leaving the tower.   In the absorption of carbon dioxide by sodium carbonate solution the following chemical reaction occurs:

$$Na_2CO_3 + CO_2 + H_2O \rightleftharpoons 2NaHCO_3$$

At ambient temperatures the equilibrium vapor pressure of carbon dioxide is only a few millimeters of mercury for a solution which is 1 N with respect to Na.   At temperatures above 200°F, however, the equilibrium vapor pressure of carbon dioxide is increased manyfold.   Consequently, the method of operation is to absorb carbon dioxide in a solution at low temperatures and strip the concentrated solution of CO_2 at high temperatures.

Other kinds of operations may use simultaneous mass transfer with chemical reaction to produce a desired product, as in the absorption of sulfur trioxide to produce sulfuric acid and in the absorption of oxides of nitrogen to produce nitric acid.   Other possible uses include selective removal processes.   As noted in the previous chapter, the relative separation of solutes absorbed from a multicomponent mixture cannot be altered completely arbitrarily.   If a gas-absorption column is designed to produce a given separation for one solute, the separations obtained for the other solutes are fixed.   If, however, a substance is added to the solvent phase which reacts with the various solutes at different rates, then the selectivity of absorption can to some extent be controlled.   An illustration of this is the treatment of gaseous hydrocarbon mixtures with aqueous solutions containing cuprous salts.   Unsaturated hydrocarbons in the gas phase are absorbed by the liquid phase, in which they react with the cuprous salts to form nonvolatile compounds.   The saturated hydrocarbons, however, do not react chemically and undergo only a slight amount of physical absorption.

One aspect of mass transfer with chemical reaction that is sometimes overlooked is that the absorption of certain gases in water may cause ionization or other reactions to occur without the addition of any reagent to the water.   These reactions occur, for example, when such gases as chlorine, carbon dioxide, and ammonia are absorbed in water.   In the absorption of carbon dioxide the ionization reaction proceeds slowly and is of no consequence.   On the other hand, chlorine hydrolyzes at an appreciable rate when dissolved in water, and the driving force for diffusion of chlorine should be based on the absorbed but unreacted chlorine rather than on total chlorine content.

It should be clear from the previous discussion that the occurrence of a reaction with the solute in the solvent phase does not automatically make the mass-transfer resistance in that phase negligible.   If the solvent itself reacts with the solute and the reaction is rapid, the mass-transfer resistance may be negligible. The same effect is obtained if the reagent is not the solvent but is an additive present in large concentrations. The correctness of neglecting the liquid-phase resistance will, however, depend on the magnitude of the gas-phase resistance. If the gas-phase resistance is small and the reaction in the liquid phase does not approach completion, or proceeds at a low rate, the solute may encounter a significant resistance to mass transfer in the liquid phase. The design of mass-transfer systems involving chemical reactions must be studied carefully to ensure that the chemical reaction actually increases the transfer rate. The limited knowledge of reaction mechanisms and rates makes prediction of the rates so uncertain that experimental data are often a necessity. If, on the other hand, a safe-side design is satisfactory, the beneficial effects of the chemical reaction on mass transfer can usually be ignored and the design based purely on a mechanism of physical absorption.

The analysis of a mass-transfer system in which a chemical reaction occurs will be discussed in subsequent pages. We shall not consider all the systems which have been analyzed to date, but shall restrict our discussions to certain systems which are both typical and useful. Much work is currently being done on these problems, and it is likely that in the next decade major advances will be made.

We shall not consider any systems in which mass is transferred to a fluid-solid interface at which a reaction occurs. Although the mass transfer and the chemical reaction in these systems are coupled steps, both presumably can be analyzed independently and are related only by boundary conditions. Instead, we shall limit our discussions to homogeneous chemical-reaction systems in which mass is being transferred within the same phase in which the reaction is occurring.

Analytical Solutions for Rapid, Irreversible Reactions

A number of analytical solutions to problems of simultaneous diffusion and chemical reaction are available in the literature on mass transfer. The approaches are those which we have already encountered in preceding chapters on mass transfer. One has for a basis the film theory in which the resistance to mass transfer is considered as limited to a thin, stagnant film of negligible solute capacity. Another approach is to consider the mass-transfer process as one of unsteady-state diffusion into fresh fluid elements which periodically appear at an interface. As a third alternative, we shall consider the analysis of a chemical reaction in a laminar boundary layer.

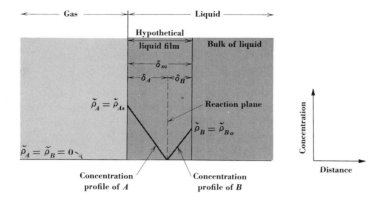

Although solutions are available for various types of reactions, we shall consider only the following extremely rapid, irreversible reaction:

$$A + B \rightarrow AB$$

Component A is the diffusing solute which is absorbed from a gas into a liquid. The liquid phase contains nonvolatile reagent B dissolved in a nonvolatile solvent C. The results can also be applied to systems in which mass transfer occurs from the liquid to the gas with reaction in the gas phase and to systems in which transfer occurs between two liquids. Since the reaction goes to completion at very high rates, the separate existence of molecules of both A and B at any one plane normal to the diffusion path is not possible.

Diffusion and Reaction in a Stagnant Film.[1] If the diffusion rates in a stagnant film reach a steady state, reactant A, which is present at the vapor-liquid interface in the constant concentration $\tilde{\rho}_{As}$, diffuses into the liquid film to a reaction plane where the concentration $\tilde{\rho}_A$ is zero. At the same time component B, which has a concentration $\tilde{\rho}_{Bo}$ in the main body of liquid, diffuses in the opposite direction through the film to the reaction plane where the concentration $\tilde{\rho}_B$ is also zero. This situation is illustrated in Fig. 43-1.

The location of the reaction plane is dependent on the concentrations $\tilde{\rho}_{As}$ and $\tilde{\rho}_{Bo}$ and on the relative diffusion rates of A and B. If the solvent were pure B or if the diffusivity D_{AC} of A in the liquid were small, the reaction would occur at the gas-liquid interface and A would be present in the liquid phase only as part of the compound AB. On the other hand,

---

[1] The analysis in this section was first proposed by S. Hatta, *Tech. Repts. Tôhoku Imp. Univ.*, **8**:1 (1928–1929).

if the bulk concentration of reactant B in the liquid phase $\tilde{\rho}_{Bo}$ were very small, or if the diffusivity D_{BC} of B in the liquid were small, the reaction plane would be a substantial distance inside the liquid. Finally, if the reaction did not proceed at a high rate or did not go to completion, the plane of reaction would be, instead, a zone of reaction of finite thickness which would contain finite concentrations of both A and B.

The rate of diffusion of A from the interface at steady state is

$$\tilde{N}_A = \frac{D_{AC}}{\delta_A} (\tilde{\rho}_{As} - 0) \tag{43-1}$$

It is assumed that the rate of diffusion of A is small, so that no important bulk transport occurs and the presence of the compound AB has no effect on the diffusion rate of A. Similar assumptions are made in writing an equation for the rate of diffusion of B.

$$-\tilde{N}_B = \frac{D_{BC}}{\delta_B} (\tilde{\rho}_{Bo} - 0) \tag{43-2}$$

Because the moles of A and B entering the reaction are the same, the rates $\tilde{N}_A$ and $-\tilde{N}_B$ are equal at steady state. If we substitute $\delta_m - \delta_A$ for δ_B in Eq. (43-2) and combine this equation with Eq. (43-1), we can solve for the thickness of the region containing A as

$$\delta_A = \delta_m \frac{D_{AC}\tilde{\rho}_{As}}{D_{AC}\tilde{\rho}_{As} + D_{BC}\tilde{\rho}_{Bo}} \tag{43-3}$$

This expression is substituted in Eq. (43-1) to give the rate of diffusion of A as

$$\tilde{N}_A = \frac{D_{AC}\tilde{\rho}_{As}}{\delta_m} \left(1 + \frac{D_{BC}\tilde{\rho}_{Bo}}{D_{AC}\tilde{\rho}_{As}}\right) \tag{43-4}$$

which can be compared with the definition of the liquid-phase mass-transfer coefficient for this system,

$$\tilde{N}_A = k_\rho''(\tilde{\rho}_{As} - 0) \tag{43-5}$$

to give the following expression for k_ρ'':

$$k_\rho'' = \frac{D_{AC}}{\delta_m} \left(1 + \frac{D_{BC}\tilde{\rho}_{Bo}}{D_{AC}\tilde{\rho}_{As}}\right) \tag{43-6}$$

The mass-transfer coefficient k_ρ with no chemical reaction, as derived using the stagnant-film theory in Chap. 33, is D_{AC}/δ_m. Hence the effect of the chemical reaction on mass transfer may be expressed as the ratio of k_ρ'' to k_ρ by the equation

$$\frac{k_\rho''}{k_\rho} = 1 + \frac{D_{BC}\tilde{\rho}_{Bo}}{D_{AC}\tilde{\rho}_{As}} \tag{43-7}$$

Low bulk concentration $\tilde{\rho}_{Bo}$ or low diffusivity D_{BC} tends to decrease the

Fig. 43-2. *Calculated concentration profiles for a rapid reaction in a liquid film ($D_{AC} = 3.9 \times 10^{-5}$ sq ft/hr, $D_{BC} = 1.95 \times 10^{-5}$ sq ft/hr). (From T. K. Sherwood and R. L. Pigford, "Absorption and Extraction," 2d ed., p. 336, McGraw-Hill Book Company, Inc., New York, 1952.)*

advantage resulting from the chemical reaction and make the process one approaching pure physical absorption. On the other hand, high values of these quantities tend to give high values of the mass-transfer coefficient k_ρ''.

Equation (43-7) is the result of an oversimplified model. Nevertheless, the model appears to be qualitatively correct, and it expresses the effect of the chemical reaction in a simple form. The mass-transfer coefficient in Eq. (43-7) is, however, dependent on the two concentration terms $\tilde{\rho}_{As}$ and $\tilde{\rho}_{Bo}$, and in the design of an absorption column these must be known at every cross section before k_ρ'' can be determined. On the other hand, the interfacial concentration $\tilde{\rho}_{As}$ is dependent on the ratio of the mass-transfer coefficients for the two phases, as we saw in Chap. 33. Thus the determination of the driving force for mass transfer at each section of the column requires a trial-and-error solution.

The Penetration Theory and Chemical Reaction. The penetration theory discussed in Chap. 35 can also serve as the basis of a model for analyzing mass transfer with chemical reaction.[1] We consider the same chemical system as in the previous section. Solute A is transferred from a gas to a liquid, where it undergoes a rapid, irreversible reaction with reactant B. The liquid initially contains a uniform concentration $\tilde{\rho}_{Bo}$ of reactant B and is brought by an eddy to a gas-liquid interface where the concentration

[1] P. V. Danckwerts, *Trans. Faraday Soc.*, **46**:300 (1950); T. K. Sherwood and R. L. Pigford, "Absorption and Extraction," 2d ed., chap. 9, McGraw-Hill Book Company, Inc., New York, 1952.

of solute A is constant at $\tilde{\rho}_{As}$. The reaction between A and B occurs first at the surface of the liquid, and as B is consumed, the plane of reaction moves into the liquid. The rate of transfer of A diminishes with time as the length of the diffusion path for A increases. The concentration of B is assumed to be constant at $\tilde{\rho}_{Bo}$ at a great distance from the reaction plane.

The situation described above is illustrated in Fig. 43-2. The concentration profiles for both $\tilde{\rho}_A$ and $\tilde{\rho}_B$ move to the right with time. The profiles can be calculated by solving the unsteady-state diffusion equations

$$\frac{\partial \tilde{\rho}_A}{\partial \theta} = D_{AC} \frac{\partial^2 \tilde{\rho}_A}{\partial y^2} \qquad 0 < y < y_R \tag{43-8}$$

and

$$\frac{\partial \tilde{\rho}_B}{\partial \theta} = D_{BC} \frac{\partial^2 \tilde{\rho}_B}{\partial y^2} \qquad y_R < y < \infty \tag{43-9}$$

The boundary conditions which apply to the liquid phase are

$$\begin{aligned}
\tilde{\rho}_A &= \tilde{\rho}_{As} && \text{at } y = 0 \\
\tilde{\rho}_B &= \tilde{\rho}_{Bo} && \text{at } \theta = 0 \\
\tilde{\rho}_B &= \tilde{\rho}_{Bo} && \text{at } y = \infty \\
\tilde{\rho}_A &= \tilde{\rho}_B = 0 && \text{at } y = y_R
\end{aligned}$$

$$D_{AC} \frac{\partial \tilde{\rho}_A}{\partial y} = -D_{BC} \frac{\partial \tilde{\rho}_B}{\partial y} \qquad \text{at } y = y_R$$

The problem is similar to the ordinary unsteady-state diffusion problem which served as a basis for the penetration theory in Chap. 35. Here, however, there is an additional variable y_R, which represents the distance of the reaction plane from the gas-liquid interface at any instant.

The partial differential equations (43-8) and (43-9), when solved simultaneously, give solutions in terms of the error function, just as Eq. (35-29) did. For the special case in which $D_{BC} = D_{AC}$, the solution for $\tilde{\rho}_A$ is

$$\frac{\tilde{\rho}_{As} - \tilde{\rho}_A}{\tilde{\rho}_{As} + \tilde{\rho}_{Bo}} = \text{erf} \frac{y}{2\sqrt{D_{AC}\theta}} \tag{43-10}$$

The instantaneous rate of absorption is

$$\tilde{N}_A = -D_{AC} \left(\frac{\partial \tilde{\rho}_A}{\partial y} \right)_{y=0} \tag{43-11}$$

When $\tilde{\rho}_A$ in Eq. (43-10) is differentiated with respect to y and substituted in Eq. (43-11), we obtain

$$\tilde{N}_A = (\tilde{\rho}_{As} + \tilde{\rho}_{Bo}) \sqrt{\frac{D_{AC}}{\pi\theta}} \tag{43-12}$$

The average absorption rate for a time of exposure θ_C of the surface is

$$\tilde{N}_{A,\mathrm{av}} = \frac{1}{\theta_C} \int_0^{\theta_C} \tilde{N}_A \, d\theta \tag{43-13}$$

Equation (43-12) is substituted in Eq. (43-13), and the integration performed to give

$$\tilde{N}_A = 2(\tilde{\rho}_{As} + \tilde{\rho}_{Bo}) \sqrt{\frac{D_{AC}}{\pi \theta_C}} \tag{43-14}$$

This may be compared with the equation giving the average mass-transfer rate in terms of a mass-transfer coefficient k_ρ''.

$$\tilde{N}_A = k_\rho''(\tilde{\rho}_{As} - 0) \tag{43-5}$$

Equations (43-14) and (43-5) are equated, giving the following expression for k_ρ'':

$$k_\rho'' = 2 \left(1 + \frac{\tilde{\rho}_{Bo}}{\tilde{\rho}_{As}}\right) \sqrt{\frac{D_{AC}}{\pi \theta_C}} \tag{43-15}$$

If this equation is compared with Eq. (35-35), in which the mass-transfer coefficient for purely physical absorption was derived from the penetration theory, we see that the following ratio is obtained:

$$\frac{k_\rho''}{k_\rho} = 1 + \frac{\tilde{\rho}_{Bo}}{\tilde{\rho}_{As}} \tag{43-16}$$

Thus, for the special case $D_{AC} = D_{BC}$, the film theory and the penetration theory give identical results. If the diffusivities are not equal, the relation for k_ρ''/k_ρ found by the application of the penetration theory is not equal to the relation obtained using the film theory but is considerably more complicated. Details of the solution are given by Sherwood and Pigford.[1]

Chemical Reaction in a Laminar Boundary Layer. Recent work by Friedlander and Litt[2] has provided an analytical solution for the problem of diffusion with a rapid chemical reaction in a laminar boundary layer on a flat plate. Their solution is limited to situations where the mass-transfer rate is low, so that the normal velocity component at the plate is negligible. In this situation the Blasius solution of the flow equations, discussed in Chap. 12, describes the velocity profiles in the boundary layer.

The diffusion pattern is much the same as that described in the preceding examples. Component A is provided at the plate either by the dissolution or vaporization of some soluble substance or by flow through the pores of the plate. The concentration of A in the fluid at the plate is fixed at $\tilde{\rho}_{As}$. Component B is present in the free stream at the uniform concentration $\tilde{\rho}_{Bo}$ and diffuses toward the plate through a concentration boundary layer. At some plane within the boundary layer the reactants meet and

---

[1] *Ibid.*

[2] S. K. Friedlander and M. Litt, *Chem. Eng. Sci.*, **7**:229 (1958).

the reaction occurs.   Since the reaction goes to completion instantaneously, the concentrations of both components at this reaction plane will be zero.

In the boundary layer between the plate and the reaction plane the simplified form of the differential equation describing diffusion is

$$u_x \frac{\partial \tilde{\rho}_A}{\partial x} + u_y \frac{\partial \tilde{\rho}_A}{\partial y} = D_{AC} \frac{\partial^2 \tilde{\rho}_A}{\partial y^2} \tag{43-17}$$

which can be reduced to an ordinary differential equation by the usual similarity transformation, $\eta = y\sqrt{u_o/\nu x}$ and $f(\eta) = \psi/\sqrt{x\nu u_o}$. The concentration variable is also made dimensionless, so that the differential equation may be written

$$\frac{d^2(\tilde{\rho}_A/\tilde{\rho}_{As})}{d\eta^2} + \frac{\mathsf{Sc}_A \, f(\eta)}{2} \frac{d(\tilde{\rho}_A/\tilde{\rho}_{As})}{d\eta} = 0 \tag{43-18}$$

A partial differential equation similar to Eq. (43-17) can be written for component B in the region between the reaction plane and the edge of the concentration boundary layer.   If the same transformations which give Eq. (43-18) are performed, we obtain

$$\frac{d^2(\tilde{\rho}_B/\tilde{\rho}_{Bo})}{d\eta^2} + \frac{\mathsf{Sc}_B \, f(\eta)}{2} \frac{d(\tilde{\rho}_B/\tilde{\rho}_{Bo})}{d\eta} = 0 \tag{43-19}$$

The boundary conditions for Eqs. (43-18) and (43-19) are

$$\frac{\tilde{\rho}_A}{\tilde{\rho}_{As}} = 1 \qquad\qquad \eta = 0$$

$$\frac{\tilde{\rho}_B}{\tilde{\rho}_{Bo}} = 1 \qquad\qquad \eta = \infty$$

$$\frac{\tilde{\rho}_A}{\tilde{\rho}_{As}} = \frac{\tilde{\rho}_B}{\tilde{\rho}_{Bo}} = 0 \qquad\qquad \eta = \eta_R$$

$$D_{AC} \frac{\partial \tilde{\rho}_A}{\partial y} = -D_{BC} \frac{\partial \tilde{\rho}_B}{\partial y} \qquad \eta = \eta_R$$

Equations (43-18) and (43-19) are solved for $\tilde{\rho}_A$ and $\tilde{\rho}_B$, and the mass-transfer rate found from the concentration gradient at $y = 0$, as in Eq. (43-11). The rate thus found may be compared with the rate equation containing the mass-transfer coefficient, Eq. (43-5), to give an expression for k_ρ''. If the expression for k_ρ'' is multiplied by x/D_{AC} to give the local Sherwood number, we obtain the following relation among dimensionless groups:

$$\mathsf{Sh}_x = \frac{0.332 \, (\mathsf{Sc}_A)^{1/3} \, (\mathsf{Re}_x)^{1/2}}{1 - \theta_{1AR}} \tag{43-20}$$

The local Sherwood number is $k_\rho'' x/D_{AC}$, and the group $1/(1 - \theta_{1AR})$ represents the factor applied to the purely physical absorption system to take into account the effects of the chemical reaction.   For the special case where $Sc_A = Sc_B$, the factor $1/(1 - \theta_{1AR})$ is shown to be equal to $1 + \tilde{\rho}_{Bo}/\tilde{\rho}_{As}$, which is identical with the correction factor found by both the film and penetration theories. In the limiting case where $\tilde{\rho}_{Bo}/\tilde{\rho}_{As}$ is large, the factor $1/(1 - \theta_{1AR})$ is represented by $\dfrac{\tilde{\rho}_{Bo}}{\tilde{\rho}_{As}}\left(\dfrac{Sc_A}{Sc_B}\right)^{\frac{2}{3}}$. For intermediate conditions the reaction factor may be calculated by methods shown in the original paper.

A more recent paper by Acrivos[1] shows that the reaction factor developed by Friedlander and Litt is valid for shapes other than flat plates. The extension to other geometries is most accurate for values of the Schmidt number greater than 1, but is considered reasonably accurate for $Sc \cong 1$.

The von Kármán integral method used in previous chapters to obtain solutions for both laminar- and turbulent-boundary-layer flows has been adapted by Potter[2] to the problem discussed in this section. For laminar systems in which $\tilde{\rho}_{Bo}/\tilde{\rho}_{As}$ is greater than 2, the following correction factor was found to apply:

$$\frac{k_\rho''}{k_\rho} = \left(\frac{D_{AC}}{D_{BC}}\right)^{\frac{1}{3}} + \left(\frac{D_{BC}}{D_{AC}}\right)^{\frac{2}{3}} \frac{\tilde{\rho}_{Bo}}{\tilde{\rho}_{As}} \tag{43-21}$$

Other Systems

Sherwood and Ryan[3] have studied mass transfer with rapid, irreversible chemical reaction in turbulent systems. The integration of the rate equation for combined molecular and turbulent transfer,

$$\tilde{N}_A = -(D_{AC} + D_{ACe})\frac{d\tilde{\rho}_A}{dy} \tag{43-22}$$

is the basis for comparing mass-transfer coefficients for systems with and without chemical reaction. The results do not differ greatly from those of the film theory of Hatta presented earlier. Experimental data on the dissolution of benzoic acid into aqueous sodium hydroxide solutions match the theoretical results of Sherwood and Ryan within 50 per cent. The film theory fits the data somewhat better.

All the methods of analysis considered in this chapter have been concerned with rapid, irreversible reactions. Several other possible systems have been reported in the literature, including those with conditions such as rapid, reversible reactions, first-order reactions, and second-order re-

[1] A. Acrivos, *Chem. Eng. Sci.*, **13**(2):57 (1960).
[2] O. E. Potter, *Trans. Inst. Chem. Engrs. London*, **36**:415 (1958).
[3] T. K. Sherwood and J. M. Ryan, *Chem. Eng. Sci.*, **11**(2):81 (1959).

actions. References to many of them are given by Olander,[1] who analyzes the effects of rapid, reversible reactions.

We shall not consider further aspects of the problem of chemical reaction with mass transfer. Some of the qualitative results of these new variables can be discerned from the discussions already presented in this chapter. For quantitative results the reader is referred to the original works in the references quoted above.

PROBLEMS

43-1. Solid spheres of benzoic acid are suspended in a 1 N solution of sodium hydroxide moving at a velocity of 10 ft/sec. Find the rate of dissolution in pound moles per hour at the instant when the spheres have a diameter of ½ in. The solution may be assumed to be at uniform temperature of 25°C. The Schmidt numbers for aqueous solutions of benzoic acid and 1 N sodium hydroxide may be taken as 900 and 524, respectively, at 25°C.

43-2. Using the data given in Prob. 43-1, find the rate of dissolution of a flat plate consisting of benzoic acid. Sodium hydroxide solution (1 N) is assumed to be flowing over the plate at a temperature of 25°C with a velocity of 10 ft/sec. The plate is 1 ft square and consists of benzoic acid on both upper and lower surfaces.

43-3. A gas stream containing 3 mole per cent carbon dioxide and the remainder air in the usual atmospheric proportions is scrubbed with a 1 N sodium hydroxide solution in a packed tower. The gas mass velocity is 400 lb/(hr)(sq ft), and the liquid-mass velocity is equal to the minimum liquid rate necessary if pure water is used. The tower is packed with 1-in. Raschig rings and operates at a uniform temperature of 25°C. Find the height of packing necessary if 90 per cent of the carbon dioxide is to be removed from the gas stream. The Schmidt number for carbon dioxide in water at 25°C is 0.94

[1] D. R. Olander, *AIChE Journal,* **6**:233 (1960).

INDEX

INDEX